Dear Don —
Hope this book helps
guest. I know you will do well @
U of W.

Paul John Port
10-18-04

HVAC DESIGN MANUAL
FOR
HOSPITALS AND CLINICS

This publication was prepared under ASHRAE Special Project SP-91 in cooperation with the cognizant ASHRAE group, TC 9.8, Large Building Air-Conditioning Applications.

LIST OF CONTRIBUTORS

Final Voting Committee Members

Robert Cox, P.E.
Farnsworth Group
Paul J. DuPont, P.E.
DuPont Engineering
Douglas Erickson
American Society for Health Care Engineering
Kimball Ferguson, P.E.
Duke University Health System
Milton Goldman, M.D., P.E.
Mann Mechanical Co.
Jeffrey Hardin, P.E.
U.S. Army Corps of Engineers
Richard D. Hermans, P.E.
Center for Energy and Environment
Carl N. Lawson
Duke University Medical Center
John Lewis, P.E.
P2S Engineers, Inc.

Farhad Memarzadeh, Ph.D., P.E.
National Institutes of Health
Frank A. Mills, C.Eng.
Environmental Design Consultants Ltd., U.K.
Vince Mortimer
NIOSH
Paul T. Ninomura, P.E.
Indian Health Service
Mary Jane Phillips
*U.S. Navy Bureau
of Medicine and Surgery (Ret.)*
Anand K. Seth, P.E.
Partners HealthCare System, Inc.
Andrew Streifel
University of Minnesota

Other Major Contributors and Reviewers

*Original members who are no longer active
**Active Corresponding Members
(Only major reviewers and contributors are listed. The committee is very thankful to numerous individuals who freely gave their time to review several parts of this manual.)

Joseph Bonanno, Senior Engineer (Multiple Chapters)
Richard D. Kimball Company, Inc.
Cris Copley, P.E. (Chapter 12)
BR+A
Jason D'Antona, P.E. (Appendix G)
Partners HealthCare System, Inc.
Richard DiRinzio (Appendix H)
Engineered Solutions
Alexandra Dragan, Ph.D., P.E.*
Department of Public Work
Kenneth E. Gill, P.E.*
Aguirre Corp.
William Goode, P.E. (All Chapters)
W.J. Goode Corp.
Ray Grill, P.E. (Chapter 11)
RJA Group
Darold Hanson* (Chapter 10)
Formerly with Honeywell, now retired
George Hardisty, P.E. (Appendix G)
BR+A
Joe Howard*
Formerly with BJC Health Systems
Leon Kloostra (Chapter 10)
Titus Corp.
Paul Konz, P.E. (Appendix G)
TRO
Mitsu Koshima, Senior Engineer (Multiple Chapters)
Richard D. Kimball Company, Inc.
John Kramer, P.E. (Chapter 10)
Staff Engineer, Duke Medical Center

Mark Lentz, P.E.*
Lentz Engineering & Associates
Olga Leon, P.E.** (All Chapters)
Partners HealthCare System, Inc.
C. Glen Mayhall, M.D. (Chapter 2)
University of Texas Medical Branch
Howard J. Mckew, P.E., CPE (Multiple Chapters)
Richard D. Kimball Company, Inc.
Andrew Nolfo, P.E.** (Multiple Chapters)
NEBB
Andrew Persily, Ph.D. (Chapter 2)
National Institute of Standards and Technology
Chris Rousseau, P.E.*
Newcomb & Boyd
Anesha Morton Rumble
*Formerly with NIOSH; Currently with
MCAQ (Mecklenburg County Air Quality)*
Teerachai Srisirikul (Appendix H)
Partners HealthCare System, Inc.
Esmail Torkashvan, P.E.** (Multiple Chapters)
NIH, NCRR
Marjorie Underwood (Chapter 2)
Mt. Diablo Medical Center, Concord, Calif.
James E. Woods, Ph.D., P.E. (Chapter 2)
Building Dianostic Research Institute
Mark Yankich, P.E. (Chapter 9)
Rogers, Lovelock, and Fritz

Walter Grondzik, Technical Editor (All Chapters)
Florida A&M University

HVAC DESIGN MANUAL
FOR
HOSPITALS AND CLINICS

 American Society of Heating, Refrigerating and Air-Conditioning Engineers, Inc.

ISBN 1-931862-26-5

ASHRAE STAFF

SPECIAL PUBLICATIONS

Mildred Geshwiler
Editor

Erin S. Howard
Assistant Editor

Christina Helms
Assistant Editor

Michshell Phillips
Secretary

PUBLISHING SERVICES

Barry Kurian
Manager

Jayne Jackson
Production Assistant

PUBLISHER

W. Stephen Comstock

DEDICATION

This design manual is dedicated to our friend and colleague, John Lewis. While the manual was being prepared, John suffered a stroke. During the final months of its preparation, we missed his keen engineering insight, insistence on technical accuracy, and clear and understandable writing. Above all, we missed his humor and friendly presence at our meetings. We look forward to his continuing contribution to health care engineering and HVAC design. The ASHRAE SP 91 Committee is grateful for extraordinary effort by John Lewis in creating this document.

CONTENTS

FOREWORD xiii

CHAPTER 1—INTRODUCTION 1

    1.1   Preface 1

    1.2   Purpose 2

    1.3   Intended Audience 2

    1.4   Overview. 2

CHAPTER 2—TERMINOLOGY 5

    2.1   Introduction 5

    2.2   Terms 5

CHAPTER 3—FACILITY DESCRIPTIONS. 15

    3.1   Introduction—Health Care Facilities 15

    3.2   Patient Care Units. 16

    3.3   Diagnostic and Treatment Centers 17

    3.4   Surgery Suites. 21

    3.5   Administrative Areas 21

    3.6   Support Services. 23

CHAPTER 4—OVERVIEW OF HEALTH CARE HVAC 27

    4.1   Introduction 27

    4.2   Infection and Safety Hazards 28

    4.3   Infection Control. 29

    4.4   Criteria 31

    4.5   Energy Efficiency and Operating Cost. 32

    4.6   Equipment Sizing for Heating and Cooling Loads. 32

    4.7   Ventilation and Outside Air Quality. 40

    4.8   Environmental Control 41

    4.9   HVAC "System Hygiene". 42

    4.10 Flexibility for Future Changes 43

    4.11 Integrated Design 43

CHAPTER 5—HVAC SYSTEMS 47

    5.1   Introduction 47

    5.2   HVAC Systems. 47

    5.3   All-Air Systems 48

5.4   Air and Water Systems 53
5.5   All-Water Systems 54
5.6   Unitary Refrigerant-Based Systems for Air Conditioning 55

CHAPTER 6—DESIGN CONSIDERATIONS FOR EXISTING FACILITIES 57
6.1   General Considerations for Existing Facilities 57
6.2   Infection Control During Construction 58

CHAPTER 7—COOLING PLANTS 61
7.1   Introduction 61
7.2   Design Considerations 61
7.3   Optimizing Energy Efficiency 66
7.4   Chilled Water Distribution Systems 67
7.5   Chiller Plant Controls and Instrumentation 69
7.6   Start-Up and Commissioning Activities 70
7.7   Cooling Plants for Clinics 70

CHAPTER 8—SPACE AND PROCESS HEATING SYSTEMS 71
8.1   General 71
8.2   Heating Plant Considerations 71
8.3   Features of Heating Equipment 74
8.4   Terminal Heating Equipment 76
8.5   Piping Systems 76
8.6   Domestic Water Systems 78
8.7   Sterilization and Humidification 79

CHAPTER 9—AIR-HANDLING AND DISTRIBUTION SYSTEMS 87
9.1   Introduction 87
9.2   Concept Design 87
9.3   Basic Air-Handling Unit Design Considerations 87
9.4   Air-Handling System Alternatives 94
9.5   Ductwork 96
9.6   Terminal Units 98
9.7   Room Air Distribution 99
9.8   Acoustical Considerations 101
9.9   General Considerations for Handling Saturated Air 103
9.10   Desiccant Systems 103
9.11   Packaged Units 104

CHAPTER 10—CONTROLS AND INSTRUMENTATION 105
10.1   Introduction 105
10.2   Characteristics and Attributes of Control Methods 105
10.3   Pressurization, Outside Air Ventilation, and Outside Air Economizer Controls 106
10.4   Isolation Rooms and Similar Rooms with RDP Criteria 109
10.5   Operating Room Controls 110
10.6   Laboratory Controls 111
10.7   General Control Sequences Used in Hospitals and Clinics 111
10.8   Control "Safeties" 112
10.9   DX System Controls 113

CHAPTER 11—SMOKE CONTROL AND LIFE SAFETY 115
11.1   Introduction 115
11.2   Smoke Compartments and Barriers 117

11.3   Passive Smoke Control..120

11.4   Active Smoke Control...120

11.5   Stairwell Pressurization..122

11.6   Elevators...123

11.7   Controls and Sequencing...123

11.8   Energy Management and Smoke Control 124

11.9   Testing and Commissioning...124

11.10   Health and Life Safety...125

11.11   Atrium Smoke Control...126

11.12   Engineered Fire Safety Design..127

11.13   Climatic Effects on Building Systems...127

CHAPTER 12—ROOM DESIGN 129

12.1   General Information..129

12.2   Role of Ventilation in Infection Control and Comfort..............................129

12.3   Health Care Room Design Criteria 133

CHAPTER 13—CLINICS AND OTHER HEALTH CARE FACILITIES 143

13.1   Occupancy Classifications..143

13.2   Clinic Spaces 145

CHAPTER 14—OPERATION AND MAINTENANCE 147

14.1   Introduction 147

14.2   Maintenance...147

14.3   Modern Maintenance Tools 149

14.4   Operation 153

14.5   Complying with Joint Commission Requirements 153

14.6   Construction...155

14.7   Special Maintenance Considerations for HVAC Systems/Equipment..............160

14.8   Building Commissioning 160

14.9   Capital Investment Planning 160

CHAPTER 15—COMMISSIONING 161

15.1   Introduction 161

15.2   Commissioning Authority 161

15.3   The Commissioning Process 162

15.4   Documentation..165

15.5   Construction Process and Commissioning Interface 167

15.6   Retro-Commissioning 168

15.7   Costs, Offsets, and Benefits 170

15.8   Summary 172

CHAPTER 16—ENERGY EFFICIENT DESIGN AND
CONSERVATION OF ENERGY RESOURCES..173

16.1   Introduction 173

16.2   Health Care Constraints...173

16.3   Energy Usage in Health Care Facilities...174

16.4   Design of Energy Efficient HVAC Systems.......................................181

16.5   Air-to-Air Heat Recovery Strategies 187

16.6   Design of Energy Efficient Chilled Water and Condenser Water Systems 189

16.7   Energy Conservation Design of Central Heating Systems..........................192

16.8   Design of Energy Efficient Building Envelopes 195

16.9 Operations and Maintenance 195
16.10 Commissioning/Recommissioning 195
16.11 Financing an Energy Efficiency Program 195

APPENDIX A—MANAGING CONSTRUCTION AND RENOVATION
TO REDUCE RISK IN HEALTH CARE FACILITIES............................... 197
   A.1   Introduction 197
   A.2   Risk Assessment.. 197
   A.3   Planning 198
   A.4   Environmental Assessment 198
   A.5   Ventilation Control.. 199
   A.6   Project Implementation 199
   A.7   Communication 200
   A.8   Commissioning 201
   A.9   Legal Issues 201

APPENDIX B—DISASTER MANAGEMENT.. 203
   B.1   Introduction 203
   B.2   Terrorism 203
   B.3   Disaster Classification 204
   B.4   Space Definitions.. 206
   B.5   Required Services in Emergency and Disaster 207
   B.6   Summary 208

APPENDIX C—LOAD CALCULATIONS AND EQUIPMENT HEAT GAINS 213
   C.1   Introduction 213
   C.2   Outdoor and Indoor Design Conditions................................. 213
   C.3   Design Loads 213
   C.4   Diversity Factors and Schedule of Operations........................ 214
   C.5   Supply Air 215
   C.6   Air Balance.. 215
   C.7   HVAC Equipment Sizing 215

APPENDIX D—INFECTION CONTROL ISSUES 217
   D.1   Introduction 217
   D.2   Context for Infection Control.. 217
   D.3   Nonsocomial Infection Costs and Morbidity........................... 217
   D.4   Isolation 218
   D.5   Anterooms 218
   D.6   Infection 219
         Airborne Respiratory Diseases and Mechanical Systems
         for Control of Microbes, W.J. Kowalski and William Bahnfleth 220

APPENDIX E—LIFE-CYCLE COST ANALYSIS.. 231
   E.1   Life-Cycle Cost Analysis... 231

APPENDIX F—VENTILATION STANDARDS AND CURRENT TRENDS....................... 233
   F.1   Introduction 233
   F.2   Ventilation Codes and Standards 233
   F.3   Ventilation Background and Details................................... 234
   F.4   Air Diffusion Criteria... 237
   F.5   New Trend in Ventilation System Design 244
   F.6   Conclusions 246

APPENDIX G—POWER QUALITY ISSUES. 247

    G.1   Emergency Power. 247

    G.2   Variable Frequency Drives 248

APPENDIX H—SAMPLE CONTROL STRATEGIES. 253

    H.1   Sequence of Operation of 100% Outside Air-Handling Unit
with Two Supply Fans, a Common Exhaust Fan, and a Hot Water
Run-Around Loop Heat Recovery System. 253

    H.2   Sequence of Operation of 100% Outside Air-Handling Unit
with Exhaust Fan and Hot Water Run-Around Loop Heat Recovery System 255

    H.3   Sequence of Operation of 100% Outside Air-Handling Unit
with Face and Bypass and Exhaust Fan 257

    H.4   Sequence of Operation of Air-Handling Unit with Return Air Fan and Air-Side Economizer . . . 258

    H.5   Sequence of Operation of Hot Deck and Cold Deck Air-Handling Unit
with Return Air Fan and Air-Side Economizer
(Dehumidification and Cooling of All Supply Air with Reheat for Hot Stream) 260

APPENDIX I—OPERATING ROOM AIR DISTRIBUTION. 263

    *Comparisons of Operating Room Ventilation Systems in the
Protection of the Surgical Site*, Farhad Memarzadeh and Andrew P. Manning 265

REFERENCES 279

BIBLIOGRAPHY 287

INDEX 291

FOREWORD

First and foremost, this document is *not* a standard or a guideline. It is a *design manual*. It provides design strategies known to meet applicable standards and guidelines, whatever they may be.

The concept of the Health Care Facility Design Manual (*Design Manual*) was approved in 1996 at the ASHRAE Annual Meeting in Boston. At the January Winter Meeting in San Francisco, a forum was held to explain the project and ask the ASHRAE membership what they wanted to see in the manual. We had our first short committee meeting in San Francisco in January 1997, after which our work began. The committee met four times a year, twice at the national meetings and twice at other locations.

Even though we were working on a design manual, the committee identified a need for research. Some of this research was conducted by one of the committee members and published by ASHRAE. Dr. Farhad Memarzadeh, from the National Institutes of Health, conducted extensive research on patient room, isolation room, and operating room air distribution. The research used both numerical and experimental techniques. Numerical technique included computational fluid dynamics and particle tracking model. The performance of the numerical approach was successfully verified by comparison with an extensive set of experimental measurements. The patient room findings helped change the ventilation rates in the *Guidelines for Health Care Facilities*, published by AIA. The operating room results will be incorporated in the next edition of the *ASHRAE Handbook*.

As discussed in the *Design Manual*, temperature, humidity, and ventilation play important roles in the survival of airborne microorganisms. Most codes that are applicable to HVAC construction, however, do not currently address HVAC design criteria relevant to the effectiveness of ventilation, temperature, or humidity in controlling airborne microorganisms. The problem appears to be less prevalent in North American jurisdictions but is a real and serious problem in many parts of the world. The intent of this statement is only to point out an existing problem, which must be corrected through other channels. We hope that the *Design Manual* will be adopted widely and used as a tool for education. We also hope that it will start an open dialog with code officials, the Authority Having Jurisdiction (AHJ), clinicians, and HVAC designers, which will lead to the adoption of reasonable standards.

I want to thank ASHRAE for giving me the opportunity and privilege to contribute in a major way to a definitive document associated with one's profession. I also wish to thank two individuals in particular: Mark Lentz, past chair of ASHRAE TC 9.8 (Large Building Air-Conditioning Applications), who took the lead in starting this project and recruiting me. The other is William Seaton, who, in his position of Manager of Research for ASHRAE, provided us with all of the needed support. I also want to thank ASHRAE and Michael Vaughn, Manager of Research and Technical Services, for continued support and confidence.

It has been my privilege to work with a group of highly talented individuals who freely and voluntarily gave their time and incurred expenses to work on this manual. To all of them, I extend a hearty personal and ASHRAE thank you. I have included a list of current committee members and other contributors. During the past four years while this manual was being compiled, several committee members were forced, due to time constraints or health, to relinquish their involvement in this work. I do not want to minimize their contribution because it was very significant. Those contributors who were former committee members are so marked.

I thank the SP 91 committee and the many other contributors for their time and hard work.

Respectfully submitted,
Anand K. Seth, P.E.
Chair, SP 91
May 2003

CHAPTER 1
INTRODUCTION

1.1 PREFACE

The design of heating, ventilating, and air-conditioning (HVAC) systems for hospitals, outpatient clinics, and other health care facilities is a specialized field of engineering. The higher filtration requirements for operating rooms and the pressure relationships between adjacent spaces are a few of the many design issues that are especially critical to the proper design and functioning of an HVAC system in a health care facility.

Health care facilities have special design criteria. Knowledge of, and insight into, these criteria are needed to develop a design that will satisfy the owner and operators of the facility. Knowledge of regulatory requirements will minimize compliance problems.

There are special considerations for the design of operating rooms. The HVAC requirements for operating rooms include regulating temperature and humidity, as well as space pressurization, filtration of the supplied air, allowable recirculation of the air, and the effectiveness of air delivery system options.

Health care facilities are environments of controlled hazards. Exposure to aerosolized pharmaceuticals, airborne contagions, and strong cleaning chemicals are examples of these hazards.

Building-related illness, especially associated with airborne infectious agents, continues to be a challenge for health care organizations that treat infectious patients and those extremely susceptible to environmental microbes such as *Legionella* and *Aspergillus*. This manual will help delineate best practices for design and maintenance to optimize the safety of occupants.

A fundamental premise of this manual is that a well-designed HVAC system augments the other facets of the built environment to offer a "healing environment;" minimizes the airborne transmission of viruses, bacteria, fungal spores, and other bioaerosols; and minimizes the impact of the building and its processes on the environment. This premise, if followed, will help to establish a safe environment in modern health care facilities.

This manual was prepared by members of ASHRAE Special Projects Committee SP-91, under the sponsorship of ASHRAE Technical Committee (TC) 9.8, Large Building Air-Conditioning Applications, which believed there was a need for a manual on this subject. The SP-91 committee began work on this manual in 1997. This interdisciplinary committee included design engineers, environmental health specialists, researchers, past and present chairpersons of the ASHRAE Handbook chapter on health care facilities, representatives from the revision task force for the American Institute of Architects' *Guidelines for the Design and Construction of Hospitals and Health Care Facilities*, and the American Society of Hospital Engineers. Contributors also included members of the American College of Surgeons.

Knowledge and experience with basic HVAC systems are presumed as prerequisites for users of this manual. We assume that the reader is familiar with the theory and analysis of HVAC systems and refrigeration equipment and processes.

This manual will refer the reader to other standard HVAC design publications (for example, the *ASHRAE Handbook* series and ASHRAE special publications) for basic HVAC system design information.

1.2 PURPOSE

The purpose of this manual is to provide a comprehensive source for the design, installation, and commissioning of HVAC systems for hospitals and clinics, including:

- Environmental comfort,
- Infection control,
- Energy conservation,
- Life safety, and
- Operation and maintenance.

This manual is intended to serve as a guide to the selection of HVAC systems for hospitals, clinics, and other health care facilities and to fill a gap left by current resources related to HVAC design for health care facilities. (These include the AIA *Guidelines for Design and Construction of Hospitals and Health Care Facilities, ASHRAE Handbook—HVAC Applications*, and *ANSI/ASHRAE Standard 62, Ventilation for Acceptable Indoor Air Quality* [AIA 2001; ASHRAE 1999a, 2001c].)

This manual is also intended to guide the design of HVAC systems to facilitate the operation and maintenance of hospitals and health care facilities.

1.3 INTENDED AUDIENCE

The intended audience for this manual includes:

- Engineers
    - Experienced hospital designers who will use it as a reference
    - Established firms for training personnel in-house

- Facility managers
- Infection control personnel
- Facility maintenance staff
- Contractors
- Owners
- Building officials
- Accreditation officials
- Licensure officials

Contractors, building officials, and owners can use this manual to familiarize themselves with the scope of technical issues and criteria for mechanical systems in medical facilities.

1.4 OVERVIEW

HVAC systems for hospitals and health care facilities have special requirements because of the inherent nature of their functions and the unique susceptibility of patients. The design must provide a ventilation system that minimizes exposure hazards for health care providers and provides a comfortable working environment. HVAC systems must also provide ventilation that minimizes the hazard exposure of visitors.

Hospitals, skilled nursing facilities, and outpatient surgical centers (ambulatory surgical centers) are the primary types of facilities addressed in this book. A more detailed list of targeted facilities is provided in Chapter 3.

Chapter 2, "Terminology," provides definitions for the nomenclature that one needs to understand in order to work in this field. Many of these terms are unique to health care facilities. The chapter is intended to promote uniformity of usage and consistency in communication relating to the mechanical design of hospitals and the major technical issues. The terms are consistent with the *ASHRAE Terminology of HVAC&R.*

Chapter 3, "Facility Descriptions," briefly describes the various types of patient-related health care facilities covered in this manual and the major units that make up these health care facilities.

Chapter 4, "Overview of Health Care HVAC," describes the design approach from planning and design criteria through commissioning. This chapter introduces and summarizes HVAC design considerations and methodologies that are particularly significant in designing systems for hospitals. The design concepts introduced in Chapter 4 are developed fully in other chapters of this manual. The topics introduced in Chapter 4 include infection control, noninfectious airborne contaminants, air quality, outside air ventilation, rates of total air change, room pressure relationships, dry-bulb temperature and humidity, filtration, codes, phases of design, equipment and system reliability and redundancy considerations, energy conservation, sound and vibration, life-cycle costing, value engineering, quality assurance of engineering design, peer review, construction management, and system commissioning.

Chapter 5, "HVAC Systems," discusses HVAC systems and their applications. Hospitals require central systems to meet filtration and humidity requirements. Constant volume systems are common. Chapters in the *ASHRAE HVAC Systems and Equipment* volume should be read in conjunction with this chapter because a conscious effort was made to not duplicate material from the Handbook except where necessary for continuity.

Chapter 6, "Design Considerations for Existing Facilities," covers unique requirements for health care facilities including a description of facility condition assessment and infection control during construction.

Chapter 7, "Cooling Plants," provides a broad overview of issues of which designers should be aware when designing cooling plant equipment and systems for hospital service. It describes the types of systems encountered in hospitals, configuration considerations, and the need for equipment redundancy and dependability. It also covers alternative cooling plant and heat rejection methods and the integration of thermal storage systems.

Chapter 8, "Space and Process Heating Systems," provides a broad overview of issues of which designers should be aware when designing heating plant equipment and systems for hospital service. It describes the types of systems encountered in hospitals, configuration considerations, and the need for equipment redundancy and dependability. The chapter also provides a fairly in-depth treatment of the use of steam for humidification and sterilization, including a discussion of corrosion and system treatment chemicals related to system performance and human health.

Chapter 9, "Air-Handling and Distribution Systems," discusses design considerations for air-handling systems and distribution equipment and emphasizes features necessary for proper installation, operation, maintainability, noise control, and minimization of microbial contamination.

Chapter 10, "Controls and Instrumentation," provides a background on controls and describes specific issues unique to hospitals and clinics.

Chapter 11, "Smoke Control and Life Safety," describes the delicate yet demanding relationship of HVAC systems to engineered smoke evacuation units, smoke management systems, and passive management of smoke. Also covered are the special design requirements for managing the movement of smoke in health care facilities to permit continuous occupancy of these buildings.

Chapter 12, "Room Design," provides information regarding individual rooms in hospitals. This chapter describes ventilation designs for various spaces in hospitals that have been used in practice to restrict air movement between spaces, dilute and remove airborne microorganisms and odors, and maintain required temperature and humidity levels. Information includes diffuser types, layout suggestions, typical loads, airflow rates, and typical system applications for environmental control, infection control, and process cooling.

Information regarding the physical sizes and shapes of the rooms, the typical processes they hold, potential equipment, people, lighting, and specific infection control needs can be found in Chapter 3, "Facility Descriptions."

Chapter 13, "Clinics and Other Health Care Facilities," discusses the requirements for clinics and other health care facilities.

Chapter 14, "Operation and Maintenance," discusses operation and maintenance in hospitals and clinics—which is more extensive and critical than in most other types of occupancies. The maintenance function in health care facilities can be provided in many different ways; some owners use in-house staff for sophisticated and sensitive maintenance services, whereas other owners perform a minimum of work in house and contract out all other needed services. All repair work, training, systems changes, and upgrades provided by the maintenance staff in patient care facilities must be carefully documented. This chapter discusses many issues facing facilities managers and explains how to design for reduced maintenance costs.

Chapter 15, "Commissioning," provides guidance on commissioning and testing. Commissioning and accurate testing are especially crucial for hospitals and clinics to ensure proper operation of HVAC systems, which are typically complex and work in close concert with the health care services provided.

Chapter 16, "Energy Efficient Design and Conservation of Resources." Hospitals consume large quantities of energy. Energy-conscious HVAC systems can make a dramatic difference in the ongoing cost of facility operation. Health care facilities also consume large amounts of other resources—such as water and consumable materials—and produce large volumes of waste, much of which requires special removal and storage techniques. This section provides an overview of the principles and approaches for achieving energy-efficient operation and the effective use of resources to reduce operating costs, conserve valuable resources, and reduce the environmental impact of the building (including reducing harmful emissions and controlling wastes). Information is included to guide building owners and operators and their designers toward HVAC design solutions that embody energy-efficient principles and achieve occupancy comfort, safety, and well-being.

Appendices

A. Managing Construction and Renovation to Reduce Risk in Health Care Facilities

This appendix describes management of construction risk to patients, health care workers, and visitors due to almost continuous construction and renovation activities as health care organizations upgrade utilities, communications, and diagnostic/ therapeutic equipment.

B. Disaster Management

Appendix B addresses the concerns of hospitals when subjected to either internal or external disasters that might affect the institutions' mechanical systems to the point of disrupting services. Disasters such as an earthquake, train wreck, chemical spill, bioterrorism, or infectious epidemic present an *added* set of considerations, primarily the designation of emergency spaces for serving larger than usual numbers of victims. Provision of care can be greatly aided if spaces such as lobbies and meeting rooms have mechanical capabilities already in place that allow them to function as emergency treatment areas.

C. Load Calculations and Equipment Heat Gains

This appendix is not intended to duplicate any of the chapters in the *ASHRAE Handbook–Fundamentals* on air-conditioning load calculations but rather to highlight the specific aspects of cooling and heating load calculations for health care facilities.

D. Infection Control Issues

This appendix describes the infection control issues in health care facilities, which are the only places where nosocomial infections can be acquired. Patients who have the worst infections wind up at a hospital. The appendix contains a paper entitled "Airborne Respiratory Diseases and Mechanical Systems for Control of Microbes," published by HPAC (Kowalski and Bahnfleth 1998).

E. Life-Cycle Cost Analysis

Life-cycle cost analysis (LCCA) is a method of evaluating the economic value of design alternatives on a life-in-use basis, taking account of manufacture, supply, delivery to site, energy consumption, maintenance, and final disposal. This appendix shows how LCCA can provide a best value approach to HVAC design.

F. Ventilation Standards and Current Trends

There is currently a range of design solutions to the ventilation of hospitals and clinics and differing air change rates proposed by authoritative sources such as the AIA Guidelines and ASHRAE Handbook (AIA 2001; ASHRAE 1999a). European design guidance shows further differences. This appendix comments upon and compares these differences and includes a table that summarizes "best practices" ventilation rates and temperature and humidity requirements for each functional area. The appendix provides historical background on ventilation systems for comfort and quality of the environment. It also gives insight into ongoing research into ventilation rates and air distribution that may result in changes in the future.

G. Power Quality Issues

Appendix G provides an overview of guidelines for selecting areas and systems that should be served from an emergency power source. It also describes the hospital as a critical facility that must continue to operate during utility power outages. The main electrical service to the hospital building should be as reliable as possible.

H. Sample Control Strategies

This appendix includes guidelines that describe different strategies that could be used in the operation of 100% outside air-handling units with two supply fans, a common exhaust fan, and a hot water run-around loop heat recovery system.

I. Operating Room Air Distribution

This appendix contains a paper entitled "Comparison of Operating Room Ventilation Systems in the Protection of the Surgical Site," published by ASHRAE (Memarzadeh and Manning 2002). The paper compares the risk of contaminant deposition on an operating room (OR) surgical site and back table for different ventilation systems.

CHAPTER 2
TERMINOLOGY

2.1 INTRODUCTION

Today, technical issues once primarily of interest to ASHRAE members impact interdisciplinary applications outside the HVAC&R industry. This chapter on terminology is intended to promote uniform usage of terms and consistency in communications relating to mechanical design of hospitals and health care facilities and the major technical issues. Some terms that are widely accepted in general HVAC&R usage have different meanings in the medical and health care fields.

2.2 TERMS

age of air the time that has elapsed after the air enters a space (at any given point).

Background: The air entering any part of the room is a mixture of recirculated and "fresh" air. The "freshness" of the air and its dilution capability at a particular point are characterized by its "age."

air change rate airflow in volume units per hour divided by the building space volume in identical volume units (normally expressed in air changes per hour [ACH or ACPH]).[1]

Background: Mean air change rate for a specified period can be measured using *ASTM E 741-83, Test Method for Determining Air Leakage Rate by Tracer Dilution.*

air-conditioning general building supply supply air from an air-conditioning system whose service area includes exclusively spaces that are not unique to health care settings.

Background: Example spaces include offices, mechanical and electrical spaces, workshops, restrooms, kitchens, restaurants, cafeterias, gift shops, lobbies, waiting rooms, and janitors' closets.

air-cleaning system a device or combination of devices used to reduce the concentration of airborne contaminants, such as microorganisms, dusts, fumes, respirable particles, other particulate matter, gases and/or vapors in air.[2]

Background: Some examples of air-cleaning devices are filters in air-handling units or ducts and fixed or freestanding portable devices that remove airborne contaminants by recirculating air (through a HEPA filter).

Related term: *HEPA filter.*

air-conditioning process in enclosed spaces, a combined treatment of the air to control (as specified) temperature, relative humidity, velocity of motion, and radiant heat energy level, including consideration of the need to remove airborne particles and contaminant gases. Some partial air conditioners, which may not accomplish all of these controls, are sometimes selected for their capability to control specific phases of air treatment.[3]

air-conditioning system assembly of equipment for air treatment to control simultaneously its temperature, humidity, cleanliness, and distribution to meet the requirements of a conditioned space.[4]

---

1. ASHRAE. 1991. *Terminology of HVAC&R.* Atlanta: American Society of Heating, Refrigerating and Air-Conditioning Engineers, Inc.

2. ASHRAE. 2001. *ANSI/ASHRAE Standard 62-2001, Ventilation for Acceptable Indoor Air Quality.* Atlanta: American Society of Heating, Refrigerating and Air-Conditioning Engineers, Inc.
3. *ASHRAE Terminology.*
4. Ibid.

air irritant a particle or volatile chemical in air that causes a physiological response when in contact with mucosa in the eye, nose, or throat.

air volume migration the volume of air that is exchanged during room entry/exit (through a doorway between a room and the area beyond its door).[5]

air, exhaust air removed from a space and discharged outside the building by mechanical or natural ventilation systems.[6]

air, makeup any combination of outdoor and transfer air intended to replace exhaust air and exfiltration.[7]

air, outdoor (1) air outside a building or taken from the outdoors and not previously circulated through the system;[8] (2) ambient air that enters a building through a ventilation system, through intentional openings for natural ventilation, or by infiltration.[9]

Related term: *ventilation effectiveness.*

air, recirculated air removed from a space and reused as supply air.[10]

air, supply air delivered by mechanical or natural ventilation to a space that is composed of any combination of outdoor air, recirculated air, or transfer air.[11]

air, transfer air moved from one indoor space to another.[12]

airborne droplet nuclei small-particle residue (5 μm or smaller) of evaporated droplets containing microorganisms that remain suspended in air and can be dispersed widely by air currents within a room or over a long distance.[13,14]

5. Hayden, C.S., et al. 1998. Air volume migration from negative pressure isolation rooms during entry/exit. *Applied Occupational and Environmental Hygiene* 13(7): 518-527. Ohio.
6. ASHRAE. 2001. *ANSI/ASHRAE Standard 62-2001, Ventilation for Acceptable Indoor Air Quality.* Atlanta: American Society of Heating, Refrigerating and Air-Conditioning Engineers, Inc.
7. Ibid.
8. Ibid.
9. Ibid.
10. Ibid.
11. Ibid.
12. Ibid.
13. AIA. 2001. *Guidelines for Design and Construction of Hospital and Health Care Facilities.* Washington, D.C.: American Institute of Architects.

Background: Airborne droplet nuclei—viable or nonviable—are caused by the evaporation of moisture in which a particle is embedded. Generally such a residual particle is smaller than 5 μm after evaporation of an original particle up to 150 μm in diameter. Some of these particles can be infectious, depending on the origin of the droplet.

Related term: *airborne infectious agent.*

airborne infection isolation room a room designed with negative pressurization to protect patients and people outside the room from the spread of microorganisms (transmitted by airborne droplet nuclei) that infect the patient inside the room.

Background: Common airborne infectious agents include measles, tuberculosis, and chicken pox. Patients who have suspected or diagnosed airborne infections are placed in specially ventilated rooms to help contain patient-released infectious particles.

Related terms: *airborne droplet nuclei*; *pressurization.*

airborne infectious agent an airborne particle that can cause an infection.

Background: Airborne transmission occurs by dissemination of either airborne droplet nuclei or dust particles that contain the infectious agent. Microorganisms carried in this manner can be dispersed widely by air currents and may become inhaled by a susceptible host within the same room or at a distance from the source patient, depending on environmental factors. Special air handling and ventilation are required to prevent airborne infectious agent transmission.[15]

Related term: *airborne droplet nuclei.*

airborne pathogen an airborne particle that can cause disease.

Background: Airborne pathogens are infectious organisms or chemicals that can produce disease in a susceptible host. This term may also apply to any microscopic agent that is a respiratory irritant and includes allergens and toxigenic fungi. Viruses, bacteria, fungi, and asbestos are examples of respiratory pathogens. The fungi and some bacteria, most notably actinomycetes, form spores. Spores can become airborne and are resistant to factors that destroy viruses and bacteria. Spores are the most important cause of noncommunicable diseases.

14. Garner, J.S. 1996. Guideline for isolation precautions in hospitals. *Infection Control & Hospital Epidemiology* 17(1):53-80.
15. Ibid.

anteroom a room separating an isolation room from a corridor.

Background: An isolation room setting is for patients who are both infectious and immunosuppressed. The anteroom would have ventilation control to minimize the effects of airborne spread of disease by manipulating door closure and ventilation while protecting the patient from common airborne disease. Sometimes these rooms are used for gowning, washing hands, and transfer of meal trays.

Related terms: *airborne infection isolation room*; *immunocompromised infectious host*.

aspergillosis a fungal disease that may be present with a variety of clinical symptoms; produced by several of the *Aspergillus* species.

Background: Individuals who are immunosuppressed or immunocompromised are most at risk for aspergillosis. *A. fumigatus* and *A. flavus* are the most common causes of aspergillosis in human beings.

Related term: *airborne pathogen*.

asepsis a condition of being free from microbes; free from infection, sterile, free from any form of life.[16]

Background: From the same root: *sepsis*, an infected condition, and *antisepsis*, action to eliminate microbes and infection.

bioaerosol particles or droplets suspended in air that consist of or contain biological matter such as bacteria, pollens, fungi, skin flakes, and viruses.

Background: Bioaerosols include microorganisms (culturable, nonculturable, and dead microorganisms) and fragments, toxins, and particulate waste products from all varieties of living things. Bioaerosols are ubiquitous in nature and may be modified by human activities. All persons are repeatedly exposed, day after day, to a wide variety of such materials. Individual bioaerosols range in size from submicroscopic particles (<0.01 μm) to particles larger than 100 μm in diameter.[17]

birthing rooms (also **LDR, LDRP**) birthing rooms in today's hospital are a specialized version of a single-patient room.

Background: These areas are also called LDRs (labor/delivery/recovery). If the patient stays in the same room until discharge, the space is identified as an LDRP (labor/delivery/recovery/postpartum). These areas are for normal, uncomplicated births. If something should happen during the labor phase, the patient is transferred to a true delivery room.

Related term: *delivery room.*

building air infiltration uncontrolled inward leakage of air (that may contain entrained water vapor) through cracks and interstices in any building element and around windows and doors of a building, caused by the pressure effects of wind or the effect of differences in the indoor and outdoor air density.[18]

Background: This air may contain airborne contaminants.

Related terms: *exfiltration, infiltration, sealed room.*

CT scan (computed tomographic scan) Visualizes a (body) cross-sectional single plane by computer analysis of multidirectional X rays.

Background: "Tomography" is a procedure, usually X ray, that focuses on a single plane of an item rather than its full thickness.

community acquired infection an infection present or incubating in a patient upon admission to a hospital.

Related terms: *nosocomial infection*; *occupationally acquired infection.*

clean steam steam for humidification and/or sterilization that is generated in a system without chemical additives.

Related term: *steam autoclave.*

contaminant (also sometimes **pollutant**) any impurity, any material of an extraneous nature, associated with a chemical, a pharmaceutical preparation, a physiologic principle, or an infectious agent.[19]

Related terms: *airborne infectious agent; airborne pathogen; local ventilation exhaust; pollutant; pollution; ventilation efficiency.*

contaminant, airborne an unwanted airborne constituent that may reduce the acceptability of air.[20]

Related terms: *airborne infectious agent; airborne pathogen; local ventilation exhaust; pollutant; pollution; ventilation efficiency.*

contamination the act of contaminating, especially the introduction of disease germs or infectious material into or on normally sterile objects.

---

16. *Taber's Cyclopedic Medical Dictionary (12th ed.)*. Philadelphia: F.A. Davis Company.
17. ACGIH. 2001.
18. *ASHRAE Terminology.*
19. *Stedman's Medical Dictionary (27th ed.)*. 2000. Baltimore: Williams & Wilkins.
20. ANSI/ASHRAE Standard 62-2001.

Background: Contamination is the second step of the disease process relationship,

[Infection] $\approx$ [Dose] $\times$ [virulence] $\times$ [time/level of host defenses].

Concentration of contaminants (in the air) leads to contamination of living tissue, which leads to colonization, which leads to infection, which leads to disease.[21]

Related terms: *airborne infectious agent; contaminant*; *pollutant*.

control (HVAC&R)   (1) a device for regulating a system or component in normal operation, manually or automatically; (2) broadly, methods and means of governing the performance of any apparatus, machine, or system.[22]

Background: If "automatic," the implication is that the control is responsive to changes in pressure, temperature, or another variable whose magnitude is being regulated.

control (industrial hygiene)   method(s) to isolate or remove hazards from the workplace.

Background: In removing contaminants and/or pollutants, the industrial hygiene term "control" is used to describe methods that can be employed, for example, to isolate or remove pathogen hazards from the workplace. Three strategies of control are customarily used alone or in combination:

1. Administrative controls (example: schedules to minimize risk).

2. Engineering controls (example: ventilation design).

3. Personal protective equipment (example: face masks for workers).

control (medical)   method to eradicate or ameliorate a disease process (treatment and/or public health measures).

corridor   (1) walkway interior within a building; (2) *public corridor*: corridor not intended for use by in-house patients; (3) *patient corridor*: corridor to patient rooms that would be used by patients.

critical HVAC equipment   equipment essential for HVAC operation that is connected to the emergency power system.

cystoscopy   examination of the bladder by an instrument (cystoscope) inserted via the urethra.

---

21. *Taber's Cyclopedic Medical Dictionary (12th ed.)*.
22. *ASHRAE Terminology*.

Background: Irrigating fluid is conducted via the sheath (of the instrument) into the bladder. The cystoscopic procedure can be performed in an Operating Room, Cystoscopy Room, or at the patient's bed.

delivery room   a room identical to a general operating room.

Background: Delivery rooms are now used primarily for C-sections, breech births, or other complicated deliveries.

Related terms: *birthing room*; *operating room*.

design conditions   the values of ventilation, temperature, and humidity within which a system is designed to operate to provide conditioned air. Filtering levels also may be required.

diagnosis   activities, including history taking, physical examination, and laboratory evaluation, that determine the nature of a patient's illness and its origin.

Related terms: *diagnostic clinic*; *treatment*.

diagnostic clinic   a diagnostic clinic is a facility where patients are regularly seen on an ambulatory basis for diagnostic services or minor treatment but where major treatment requiring general anesthesia or surgery is not performed.

dialysis   an external method of adjusting the levels of ions and chemicals in the blood (a process normally performed by the kidneys).

Background: During dialysis, the patient's blood is diverted to the dialysis equipment, osmotically filtered, and then returned to the patient.

dedicated equipment connection (utilities)   water, waste, steam, medical gases, chilled water, and electricity.

Background: Some medical and hospital equipment (such as radiation therapy) requires a dedicated (not shared with other loads) supply main utility connection, separate from utilities supplied to the general area.

Related term: *equipment, medical*.

endoscopy   a general term meaning the visualization of body cavities and structures through an inserted optical instrument.

endoscopy area   an environment for endoscopy.

Background: Some specific endoscopic procedures require anesthesia and are performed in an operating room or an endoscopy room equipped for anesthesia

epidemiology study of the distribution and determinants of disease.

Background: Not limited to infectious diseases; includes all human illnesses, for example, cancer and metabolic diseases.

equipment, medical equipment specific to a medical procedure or activity.

Background: Examples are specialized equipment in departments such as Diagnostic Radiology, Therapeutic Radiology, Clinical Laboratory, Pharmacy, Administration, Central Sterile Processing, Surgery, Emergency, and Laser Surgery.

(emergency) exam rooms exam rooms (or treatment rooms) are spaces used for emergency treatment of broken bones, lacerations, foreign objects, concussions, etc.

Background: Exam rooms provide services to treat the injury or illness and then to discharge the patient, or to stabilize the patient for further observation or treatment as a hospitalized patient.

Related term: *treatment room.*

exhaust air see *air, exhaust.*

exfiltration air leakage outward through cracks and interstices and through ceilings, floors, and walls of a space or building.[23]

Related terms: *building air infiltration; infiltration; sealed room.*

filter see *air cleaning system.*

freestanding emergency clinic an emergency facility that is separated from a hospital.

Background: A freestanding emergency clinic; includes provisions for temporary observation of patients until release or transfer. This type of unit requires special transportation planning to accommodate the transfer of patients.

hematology the study of blood and blood forming tissues and the disorders associated with them.

HEPA filter (absolute filter) high efficiency particulate air filter.[24]

Background: HEPA filter is filtration with removal efficiencies of 99.97% or higher of particu-

lates larger than 0.30 microns. See Chapter 4, Section 4.3.2, High Efficiency Filtration.

Related term: *air cleaning system.*

hospital (institution) an institution for treating the sick, suitably located, constructed, organized, managed, and staffed to provide scientifically, economically, efficiently, and unhindered, all or any recognized part of the complex diagnostics and treatment modalities for physical and mental illnesses (adapted from *Dorland's Illustrated Medical Dictionary*[25]).

Background: A hospital is a 24-hour facility, equipped to perform critical and emergency surgical procedures and has all of the necessary support laboratories and services within the building to accomplish this, including in-bed patient care.

Related term: *treatment clinic.*

immunocompromised host (sometimes **immunosuppressed host**) an individual whose immune system has been weakened by disease (such as AIDS) or medical treatment (such as chemotherapy).

immunocompromised infectious host a patient who is both an immunocompromised host and a potential transmitter of infection.

Related terms*: airborne infection isolation rooms; anteroom.*

indoor air quality the composition and characteristics of the air in an enclosed space that affect the occupants of that space.[26]

Background: The indoor air quality of a space is determined by the level of indoor air pollution and other characteristics of the air, including those that impact thermal comfort, such as air temperature, relative humidity, and air speed. Indoor air quality is of considerable interest and relevance in health care occupancies. Indoor air quality in health care settings must incorporate considerations for infectious and other airborne contaminants.

The HVAC or ventilation system should

1. provide outdoor air ventilation to provide dilution ventilation,

2. reduce airborne particulates in the recirculated portion of the ventilation air via filtration and have filtration capabilities suitable for the contaminants of concern,

---

23. ANSI/ASHRAE Standard 62-2001.
24. *ASHRAE Terminology.*

25. *Dorland's Illustrated Medical Dictionary (29th ed.).* 2000. Philadelphia: W.B. Saunders Co.
26. ASTM. 2000. D1356-00a: *Standard Terminology Relating to Sampling and Analysis of Atmospheres.* West Conshohocken, Pa.: ASTM International.

3. provide special airflows such as for operating rooms.

Related terms: contaminant; pollutant; pollution; ventilation effectiveness; ventilation efficiency.

industrial hygiene the science and art devoted to anticipating, recognizing, evaluating, and controlling those environmental factors or stresses that arise in or from the workplace and may cause sickness, impaired health and well-being, or significant discomfort and inefficiency among workers or among the citizens of the community.[27]

Related term: control (industrial hygiene).

infiltration air leakage inward through cracks and interstices and through ceilings, floors, and walls of a space of a building.[28]

Related term: building air infiltration

intensive care rooms rooms in which the level of patient care and electronic monitoring of patients are greatly increased over conventional patient rooms.

Background: ICU spaces today are specialized. Common uses are as follows: Surgical Intensive Care Unit (SICU), Medical Intensive Care Unit (MICU), Cardiac Care Unit (CCU), and Post-Anesthesia Care Unit (PACU).

invasive procedure for the purpose of this manual, insertion of an instrument or device into the body through the skin or body orifice for diagnosis or treatment.

Related term: procedure.

laboratory a location equipped to perform tests and experiments and to investigative procedures and for preparing reagents, therapeutic chemicals, and radiation.[29]

Background: Major laboratories include Chemistry, Hematology, Microbiology, and Tissue (Pathology). There are many specialty (sub) laboratories that are suited to particular procedures. See Chapter 3, Section 3.3.6.

local exhaust (local ventilation exhaust) local exhausts operate on the principle of capturing an airborne contaminant or heat at or near the source.

Related terms: Control (industrial hygiene); ventilation efficiency.

makeup air see air, makeup.

medical gas oxygen, nitrogen, nitrous oxide, vacuum and medical compressed air, and vacuum and anesthetic gas are typical medical gases used throughout hospitals.

minor operating room for the purpose of this manual, a Class A Operating Room as defined by the American College of Surgeons.[30]

Related term: operating room.

minor surgery the classical surgical definition of minor surgery is an operation in which a body cavity is not entered or in which a permanent device is not inserted by incision.

MRI (magnetic resonance imaging) body imaging by measuring changes in energy resonance in a large magnetic field.

Background: Located within an MRI room are the magnet, the housing, and the patient table. For specific space, utility, and power requirements, see Chapter 12, Section 12.3.7.

mycosis any disease caused by fungi.

nosocomial infection (hospital-acquired infection) an infection that is acquired in a hospital and that was not present or incubating upon admission. Also known as "hospital-acquired infection."

Related terms: community acquired infection; occupationally acquired infection.

nursing 24-hour-care units, acute medical/surgical patients units of patient care rooms that contain the majority of patient beds in today's health care facility.

Background: Rooms are limited to two patient beds (called semiprivate rooms); however, the current trend is for these rooms to have only one bed (called private rooms). A patient room must have a toilet directly accessible from within the room. In most states, a patient room must have a hand washing facility within the room proper. In semiprivate rooms, a cubicle curtain provides privacy between beds. All rooms must be provided with an outside window, and, in many states, this window needs to be operable by a tool or key. The latest fire codes are permitting patient room windows fixed in place,

27. NSC. 1988. Fundamentals of Industrial Hygiene. Chicago: National Safety Council.
28. ANSI/ASHRAE Standard 62-2001.
29. Stedman's Medical Dictionary (27th ed.).

30. American College of Surgeons. 1976. Definition of surgical microbiologic clean air. Bulletin of American College of Surgeons 61:19-21.

eliminating the need for operable sashes. A standard patient unit consists of approximately 30 beds.

nursing 24-hour-care units, *critical patients* **(ICUs)** critical care nursing units housing seriously ill patients receiving the maximum of care.

Background: This patient care unit is the best the hospital has to offer in terms of personnel and technology. Critical care nursing units require special space and equipment considerations. Not all hospitals provide all types of critical care. Some may have a small combined unit; others may have separate, highly specialized units. Following are examples of specialized critical care units: Neurological Intensive, Burn/Wound Intensive, Cardiopulmonary, Surgical Intensive, Medical Intensive, Step-Down, Geriatric Intensive, Pediatric Intensive, Neonatal Intensive, Coronary.

Related term: *step-down units.*

nursing 24-hour-care, *specialty care patients* whether a freestanding specialty hospital or a unit within a hospital, specialty care units are nursing units that have a specific clinical function.

Background: Most of these units are similar to a standard nursing unit, but special design considerations are required for the specific patient population receiving treatment. For example, in a geriatric nursing unit, lighting levels may need to be increased, physical barriers removed and spaces enlarged to permit additional wheelchair use, additional handrails installed to assist in mobility, and ventilation rates increased to remove odors. Following is a partial list of specialty units: Rehabilitation, Geriatric, Dementia, Subacute Care Hospice, AIDs Units, Psychiatric, and Detoxification.

occupiable space an enclosed space intended for human activities, excluding those spaces intended primarily for other purposes (such as storage rooms and equipment rooms that are occupied occasionally for short periods of time).[31]

occupationally acquired infection an infection acquired while working in a medical care setting.

Related terms: *community acquired infection; nosocomial infection.*

operating room a room specifically designed for surgical procedures. In common understanding, this means most types of surgical procedures, especially those that involve the administration of anesthesia,

multiple personnel, recovery room access, and a fully controlled environment.[32]

Related terms: *invasive procedure; procedure; minor operating room.*

operating rooms, *cardiac transplant operating rooms* an operating room for open heart bypass surgery and heart transplant surgery.

Background: These are similar to general operating rooms but normally require larger room space.

operating rooms, *neurosurgery* an operating room for brain and/or spinal surgery.

Background: This room typically has ceiling-mounted microscope equipment and viewing equipment. These fixture requirements (location) should not conflict with good air distribution practices.

opportunistic microorganism an ordinarily non-infectious agent that becomes infectious in an immunocompromised host.

Related term: *immunocompromised host.*

outdoor air see *air, outdoor.*

outpatient surgical facility a facility for surgery (may include outpatient dental surgery) where overnight patient care is not anticipated.

Background: The functional program for an outpatient surgical facility describes in detail the staffing, patient types, hours of operation, function and space relationships, transfer provisions, and availability of offsite services. If the outpatient surgical facility is part of an acute care hospital or other medical facility, services may be shared to minimize special requirements.

patient care units patient care units are those areas of health care facilities where 24-hour around-the-clock nursing care is provided to patients.

Background: There are three typical categories of patient care units (see related terms). Each of these categories has unique care delivery strategies and consists of the patient care room or area and all of the necessary administrative and clinical support space to serve the specialized needs of the patient population.

Related terms: *nursing 24-hour care units, acute medical/surgical; nursing 24-hour care units, critical nursing care;* and *nursing 24-hour care units, specialty nursing care.*

---

31. ANSI/ASHRAE Standard 62-2001.

32. AIA *Guidelines for Design and Construction of Hospital and Health Care Facilities.*

patient rooms   patient rooms are normally semiprivate (two patients) or private (for individual patients).

Background: Each patient room is provided with a private toilet/shower. Patient care is provided for recuperation from a procedure, patient observation, and diagnosis. Rooms are normally contained within a department and supervised by an individual or by multiple nursing stations. A medicine preparation/dispensing area, clean and soiled linen and holding areas, housekeeping support, and staff facilities complement each department.

pneumonia   inflammation of lung tissue.

Background: The cause of pneumonia is generally bacterial or viral, but on occasion pneumonia may be caused by an opportunistic airborne fungi (especially in immunocompromised hosts). There are also noninfectious causes such as chemical or radiation exposure.

pollutant   an undesired contaminant that results in pollution.

Background: A pollutant may or may not be an infectious agent.

Related terms: *contaminant; pollution.*

pollution   rendered unclean or unsuitable by contact or mixture with an undesired contaminant.[33]

Related terms: *contaminant; pollutant.*

pressurization   a difference in pressure between a space and a reference pressure.

Background: Pressurization is important for infection control. Positive pressurization produces a net flow of room air out of a space toward the reference space through any opening between the two spaces. Negative pressurization produces a net flow of air into a space from the reference space through any opening between the two spaces.

1. *Volumetric flow rate (VFR) criteria.* This difference in pressure between the room and the adjacent architectural space(s) is accomplished under most codes by providing differentials in volumetric flow rates (VFR) of supply, return, and exhaust air and door(s) closure.

2. *Room differential pressure (RDP) criteria.* Most hospital rooms can be designed using only VFR criteria for pressurization. For areas of high-risk assessment, RDP criteria (where used) require a sealed room (with significant differentials) for pressurization (see Appendix A.5.2) so that the room remains (an indica-

---

33. *Stedman's Medical Dictionary* (27th ed.).

tor is required) positively or negatively pressured (determined by the design). AIA Guideline 2001 requires (in certain rooms) an RDP of 0.01 in. w.g. (2.5 Pa).

Related terms: *airborne infection isolation room, building air infiltration; exfiltration; infiltration; protective environment room; sealed room.*

procedure   treatment of a patient.

Background: There are many diagnostic and treatment procedures. Invasive and minimally invasive procedures are performed in operating rooms.

Related terms: *invasive procedure; operating room; treatment.*

protective environment rooms   a patient care setting that requires positive pressurization to protect the patient from human and environmental airborne diseases.

Background: This protection is needed for patients who are immunocompromised either from treatment or from disease.

Related terms: *airborne infection isolation room; pressurization.*

process cooling   the use of chilled water in health care settings that is not seasonal but related to a process.

Background: Examples of process cooling include modular cooling units (MCU), linear accelerators, magnetic resonance imaging, PET (Positron Emission Tomographic) scanners, data centers, and refrigeration condensers.

radiology   the scientific (medical in this case) discipline of dealing with X rays and other forms of radiant energy for imaging and treating internal body structures.

radiology rooms   areas for patient X rays, conventional and digital, and image processing.

Background: These rooms are normally heavily used, and the electronic equipment produces a varying amount of heat in the space.

recirculated air   see *air, recirculated.*

room air distribution effectiveness   a measure of how effectively the ventilation system provides supply air to the room to maintain acceptable air quality in the occupied zone.

Related term: *ventilation effectiveness.*

sealed room   a room that has minimal leakage--to prevent air from being pulled through cracks around windows, utility connections, ceilings, or other wall penetrations.

Related terms: *building air infiltration*; e*xfiltration*; *infiltration*.

skilled nursing facility   a facility that houses persons who need intermittent nursing services.

skin squame   a small flake of epidermal skin tissue.

Background: Skin flakes carry bacteria and are of concern in the sterile field of an operating room.

Related terms: *operating room*; *sterile field*.

steam autoclave   a sealed vessel that can hold items in an environment of pressurized (15 pounds per square inch [103 kPa]) steam at 250°F (121°C) for an extended period of time (20 minutes or more) to kill all microorganisms, including bacterial spores.[34]

step-down units   a group of beds used for transition from the Critical Care Unit to the Nursing Unit.

Related term: *nursing 24-hour units, critical patients*.

sterile   condition of being free from all living microorganisms and their spores.[35]

sterile field   a designated sterile surface in and around an invasive procedure site. The following are considered boundaries of the sterile field in surgery:

1.   The surface of the sterile drapes down to the level of the operating room table. The arms and gloves are considered to be in the sterile field.

2.   The fronts of the gowns of the operating personnel from the neck lines to the level of the table.

3.   Equipment that is properly draped, such as the Mayo stand and the horizontal surfaces of the back table(s).

4.   Portions of properly draped equipment, such as properly draped microscopes and X-ray machines.

5.   The light handles but not the lights.

6.   The anesthesia screen from the level of the table up to the top of the screen.

Related term: *operating room*.

supply air   see *air, supply*.

swing beds   a group of beds used for different nursing purposes, depending on current needs.

thermal surgical plume   a convection current (of air) rising from the wound site due to the body heat of the patient, operating room personnel, and radiant heat from the surgical light.[36]

transfer air   see *air, transfer*.

trauma room   trauma rooms are areas that are used to care for patients whose injuries or illnesses are more severe than can be adequately treated in conventional exam rooms.

Background: Trauma rooms are also frequently referred to as "crisis rooms" or "shock rooms." The main purpose of the trauma room is to stabilize a seriously injured patient for additional treatment, usually in an operating room.

treatment   activities taken to eradicate or ameliorate a patient's disease.

Related terms: *procedure*; *treatment clinic*.

treatment clinic   a facility totally detached from a hospital that serves patients, as outpatients, without provision for overnight stays.

Background: The facility has its own dedicated HVAC systems. A treatment clinic is a facility that provides, on an outpatient basis, major or minor treatment for patients that would render them incapable of taking action for self-preservation under emergency conditions without assistance from others.[37] (see NFPA Standard 99 1999). This facility is a new and emerging form of outpatient center that can provide a wide array of outpatient diagnostic services and minimally invasive procedures.

Related term: *hospital*.

treatment rooms   "treatment rooms" is a general category for rooms where medical procedures are performed.

Background: Procedures include bronchoscopy, cryosurgery, etc.

triage   the act of determining the severity of illness/injury of patients so that those who have the most emergent illnesses/injuries can be treated immedi-

---

34.   *McGraw-Hill Encyclopedia of Science and Technology*. 1997. New York: McGraw Hill.

35.   *Taber's Cyclopedic Medical Dictionary* (12th ed.).

36.   Woods, J.E., D.T. Braymen, R.W. Rasmussen, P.E. Reynolds, and G.M. Montag. 1986. Ventilation requirements in hospital operating rooms—Part I: Control of airborne particles. *ASHRAE Transactions* 92(2A):396-426. Atlanta: American Society of Heating, Refrigerating and Air-Conditioning Engineers, Inc.

37.   NFPA. 1999. *Standard 99: Health Care Facilities Standard*. Quincy, Mass.: National Fire Protection Association.

ately and those less severely injured can be treated later or in another area (see Appendix B.4.1).

UV ultraviolet irradiation.

Background: Ultraviolet radiation is that portion of the electromagnetic spectrum described by wavelengths from 100 to 400 nm.

Related term: *UVGI.*

UVGI ultraviolet germicidal irradiation.

Background: Ultraviolet germicidal irradiation is that portion of the electromagnetic spectrum described by wavelengths from 200 to 270 nm. Ultraviolet germicidal irradiation is a use of UV radiation to kill or inactivate microorganisms. UVGI lamps can be used in ceiling or wall fixtures or within air ducts of ventilation systems.[38]

Related term: *UV.*

ventilation rate see *air change rate.*

ventilation a process of supplying air to or removing air from a space for the purpose of controlling air contaminant levels, humidity, or temperature within the space.[39] Such air may not have been conditioned.

Mechanical ventilation is ventilation provided by mechanically powered equipment such as motor-driven fans and blowers, not by devices such as wind-driven turbine ventilators and mechanically operated windows.

Natural ventilation is ventilation provided by thermal, wind, or diffusion effects through doors,

windows, or other intentional openings in the building.[40]

Background: The fundamental functions of ventilation may also incorporate smoke control requirements or removal of contaminants from known specific sources in a space.

Related term: *pressurization.*

ventilation effectiveness (E_v) the ability of a ventilation system to deliver air to the breathing (or occupied) zone of a space or the workspace in such a zone.

Related terms: *air, outdoor*; *room air distribution effectiveness.*

ventilation efficiency the ability of a system to remove contaminants generated by a source in a room.

Related term: *local exhaust.*

waiting room(s) in patient areas, these are spaces where nonpatients (i.e., family members) wait. In clinics and in emergency departments, these are spaces where patients who are seeking diagnosis and treatment wait.

Background: There may be a requirement to isolate airborne infectious disease patients and/or receive a contaminated individual exposed to hazardous materials.

waste anesthetic gas anesthetic gases that have been delivered to the patient and are exhaled or are in excess of the amount consumed by the patient.

water activity water activity is an indicator of the amount of water in a material that is available to support microbial growth.

---

38. CDC. 1994. Guidelines for preventing the transmission of mycobacterium tuberculosis in healthcare facilities. *MMWR Recommendations and Reports*: 43(RR-13): October 28. U.S. Department of Health and Human Services, Public Health Service, Centers for Disease Control and Prevention, Atlanta.
39. ASHRAE Standard 62-2001.

40. Ibid.

CHAPTER 3
FACILITY DESCRIPTIONS

3.1 INTRODUCTION—HEALTH CARE FACILITIES

A hospital is an institution for treating and caring for four or more persons who need medical attention 24 hours a day, every day. Hospitals can be classified in three ways: (1) by length of stay, (2) by the diseases of its patients, and (3) by the type of ownership.

- Short-term hospitals are those where patients stay less than 30 days.
- Specialty hospitals, such as cancer centers, centers for women and children, or mental health centers, define themselves by the type of services provided.
- Ownership can be of three types:
  - Community owned
  - Proprietary (either nonprofit or for-profit)
  - Government owned, as by the Department of Defense or the Veterans Administration.

3.1.1 Acute Care Hospital

An acute care hospital provides all types of medical care and is where the length of a patient's stay is more than one day and less than thirty days. Many hospitals also have associated outpatient care on the same campus.

3.1.2 Mental Health Hospital

A mental health hospital is a specialty hospital that provides psychiatric care to patients for more than one day.

3.1.3 Primary Care Outpatient Center

A primary care center serves as the patient's first point of entry into the health care system and as the continuing focal point for all needed health care services. Primary care practices provide patients with ready access to their own personal physician or to an established backup physician when the primary physician is not available.

Primary care practices provide health promotion, disease prevention, health maintenance, counseling, patient education, and diagnosis and treatment of acute and chronic illnesses in a variety of health care settings (e.g., office, inpatient, critical care, long-term care, home care, and day care).

Primary care practices are organized to meet the needs of patients who have undifferentiated problems and where the vast majority of patient concerns and needs are met in the primary care practice itself. Primary care practices are generally located in the patient's community, thereby facilitating access to health care while maintaining a wide variety of specialty and institutional consultative and referral relationships for specific care needs. The structure of the primary care practice may include a team of physicians and non-physician health professionals.

3.1.4 Small Primary (Neighborhood) Outpatient Facilities

A small primary outpatient facility is typically a neighborhood clinic or doctors' office building. These facilities will have anywhere from one to as many as ten different doctors' offices. They are usually under 5,000 square feet (465 square meters) in area.

3.1.5 Outpatient Surgical Facilities

There are a number of surgical procedures that can be performed as outpatient surgery. Discharge from the facility is expected within a reasonably short period of time.

Classes of surgical facilities (American College of Surgeons 1996) include:

- *Class A*: Provides minor surgical procedures performed under topical, local, or regional anesthesia without preoperative sedation. Excluded are intravenous, spinal, and epidural routes; these methods are appropriate in Class B and C facilities.
- *Class B*: Provides minor or major surgical procedures performed in conjunction with oral, parenteral, or intravenous sedation or under analgesic or dissociative drugs.
- *Class C*: Provides major surgical procedures that require general or regional block anesthesia and support of vital bodily functions.

Outpatient surgical facilities usually are Class A facilities and may, under certain circumstances, be Class B facilities.

3.1.6 Assisted Living

Assisted living is senior housing that provides individual apartments, which may or may not have a kitchenette. Facilities offer 24-hour on-site staff, congregate dining, and activity programs. Nursing services are provided for an additional fee.

3.2 PATIENT CARE UNITS

3.2.1 General Medical and Surgical Nursing Units

The term *medical and surgical nursing unit* is used to identify all general acute-care nursing services. Units may have either medical, surgical, orthopedic, pediatric, gynecologic, or a combination of patients. The term is also sometimes used to identify all noncritical care units. A distinction may also be made with respect to licensing because many units used for specialized services fall under this generic classification. For specific temperature, humidity, and airflow requirements refer to Table 4.1.

3.2.2 Airborne Infectious Isolation Rooms (AII)

This is a patient room that demonstrates, through periodic or continuous testing, inward air flow through all six surfaces and sustained negative air pressure with respect to all adjoining interior rooms, which has specific ventilation design features, including 100% exhaust, well-mixed air distri-

bution throughout the room, and a general flow of air from clean to less clean areas. An airborne infectious isolation room may or may not have an anteroom. It may or may not have an electronic pressure monitoring and control system; a mechanical means of measuring the pressure relationship, however, is required for all new rooms.

3.2.3 Protective Environment Room

A protective environment room is a patient room that demonstrates, by continuous or periodic testing, outward air flow through all six surfaces and sustained positive air pressure with respect to all six surfaces, including the outside wall. It has specific ventilation design features, including HEPA filtered supply air, from nonaspirating unidirectional flow air diffusers placed approximately over the bed, return air registers placed low on the wall near the room entrance, and a general air flow pattern from the patient toward the door.

3.2.4 Critical Care Nursing Units.

Critical care nursing units provide intensive, specialized services to extremely ill patients. These may be specialized for cardiac, medical, coronary, neurological, or other diagnostic groupings or may, as in many smaller institutions, be generalized. Critical care beds are licensed separately from other patient bed categories. Whether specialized or generalized, programming considerations for the units are similar, except for neonatal intensive care units.

These units are also commonly referred to as "Intensive Care Units," a term that connotes the degree of service rendered as opposed to "critical care," which denotes the condition of the patient. The distinction, while interesting, is not considered important for the purposes of this manual.

Critical care nursing is a relatively new phenomenon that is rapidly growing in importance. Advances in medical technology have made treatments possible in cases once considered incurable. The use of general medical and surgical beds may decrease, but the need for critical care beds has increased.

Another class of unit is emerging as a bridge between Critical Care Units and general or specialized medical and surgical units. The characteristics of this class include relatively small numbers of beds (3–20), higher staffing ratios, monitoring of some or all patients, and coordination of patient care with Critical Care Unit staff. Often referred to as Special Care Units or Step-Down Units, these are customarily beds licensed under the medical and surgical umbrella.

3.2.5 Newborn Nurseries

A nursery provides care to newborn infants as an adjunct to postpartum nursing units. Three levels of service are generally recognized: Level I for normal newborns, Level II for intermediate care, and Level III for critically ill infants. The functional components of a Level I nursery include an admissions area, a well baby nursery, and a suspect nursery.

Level III Neonatal Intensive Care Units (NICU) are highly specialized, tertiary care facilities generally regulated under a state or regional plan for such centers. Level II NICUs are also regulated in most areas; however, their frequency is much greater, and many hospitals that offer obstetric service have at least a few Level II beds.

Normal and intensive nursing operations for infant care are much more focused at the patient's bedside than other types of nursing units. For that reason, support areas for staff, including supply storage, must be located closer to the patient's bedside than in other types of units.

3.2.6 Labor, Delivery, and Recovery Units (Birthing Centers)

Labor and Delivery (L&D) Units provide services to expectant mothers before admission for delivery, provide care to mother and infant during labor and delivery, and provide recovery for mothers immediately after delivery.

Prenatal care is generally provided to "high risk" mothers and may occur at intervals for days or even weeks before delivery. Hospitals of all sizes may experience an increase in the numbers of these patients due to increases in drug addiction and AIDS and decreases in the numbers who seek routine prenatal care.

A hospital may also offer classes for expectant parents in alternative birthing techniques. After admission, the department is responsible for labor and for delivery. Some hospitals may perform cesarean deliveries in their Surgery Department. After delivery, the infant is transported to the nursery and the mother is "recovered" from the effects of any anesthesia that may have been administered, then transported to a postpartum nursing unit.

With respect to the facilities required, there are three classes of deliveries: traditional, cesarean section (C-Section), and alternative. Traditional deliveries use separate spaces for labor, delivery, and recovery. C-Section delivery also uses three spaces, but the delivery room is larger and has full surgical capabilities and equipment. Alternative delivery utilizes one of two concepts. The first, labor/delivery/recovery, uses a single room for all the functions provided in the traditional concept. The second, labor/delivery/recovery/postpartum, uses a single room as in L/D/R but extends its use to include care of the mother and infant for the duration of their hospital stay.

3.2.7 Bone Marrow Transplant (BMT) Units

Bone Marrow Transplant units comprise a suite of protective environment rooms set apart from the normal traffic patterns of the hospital and are pressurized positively with respect to other patient wards adjacent, above, and below the BMT unit. The unit may have HEPA filtered air supplied to the corridors and patient day rooms.

3.2.8 Physical Therapy

Physical therapy provides rehabilitative services for restoring musculoskeletal function. Services include evaluation and treatment and are provided to inpatients and outpatients.

The scope of services offered varies widely. Departments located in hospitals that have specialty orthopedic or cardiac services may have quite extensive capabilities. In the former, speech and occupational therapy may be created as separate administrative units. In the latter, a cardiac rehabilitation department may be created.

Treatments for inpatients take place both in the department and at bedside. Outpatient treatments take place in the department, although some hospitals may have a separate outpatient PT unit. Patient visits are scheduled, and their duration is reasonably predictable. The department operates five or six days per week.

3.2.9 Subacute Care Units

A Subacute Care Unit is a portion of a general hospital or long-term care facility set aside for the care of patients who have non-acute conditions and who continue to require some observation after discharge from an inpatient service.

3.3 DIAGNOSTIC AND TREATMENT CENTERS

3.3.1 Surgical Suites

Surgical Departments may be organized to provide service to inpatients, outpatients, or both. Most hospitals provide some facilities dedicated to outpatient surgery. These may range from scheduling/reception/registration only to a completely separate outpatient Surgical Department attached to or free-standing from the hospital complex.

Typical components of a Surgical Department include a suite of operating rooms, anesthesia work areas, recovery, and staff support. Central Sterile Services (which may serve Obstetrics and Emergency as well) is a closely related function.

3.3.2 Cardiac Catherization Suites

Cardiac catheterization provides diagnostic and therapeutic procedures such as coronary angiograms, electrophysiology, angioplasty, pacemaker insertion, and heart catheterizations. The equipment used includes a sophisticated fluoroscopic imaging system that can operate in either a single or biplanar mode. Catheterization labs are normally associated with open-heart surgery programs. Some procedures require reserving an open-heart surgical team and room for emergency surgery.

In addition to the procedure room, associated spaces house electrical generators, transformers and switchgear, system controls, computers, image-recording devices, film processors, catheter storage, and administrative staff and support functions.

Cardiac catheterization is a relatively new procedure characterized by rapid development of equipment, routines, and associated services. Labs established for five or more years may be upgraded, usually with an attendant need for greatly increased space and improved room environmental features.

3.3.3 Obstetrical Suites

Obstetrical suites are a suite of rooms including a delivery room for surgical deliveries, an antepartum room, a labor room, a recovery room, postpartum rooms, support areas, and possibly rooms that serve more than one function such as labor/delivery/recovery and labor/delivery/recovery/postpartum.

3.3.4 Emergency/Trauma Center

Emergency/Trauma Centers provide care to ameliorate the effects of trauma or sudden illness. They may also be the providers of "only resort" for primary care during evenings and on weekends and holidays. They may serve as a clinic or office for physicians to see patients during non-office hours, and they may serve as part of the admitting route for obstetric (labor and delivery) units. Emergency services were formerly categorized into three levels based on the services available. The lowest level of service generally uses on-call physicians, whereas the highest, Level I, provides full-time specially trained physicians, availability of a surgical suite and team, and other specialty services.

The provision of emergency services, and therefore the Emergency Department, is an institutional option. The operation of an Emergency Department follows a fairly standard pattern. The patient is presented either by EMS ambulance/helicopter, by private motor vehicle, or by self-ambulation at one of two portals. One of the two portals is a public entrance, and the other is an "ambulance"/staff-only entrance. Arrival may be anticipated by prior notification or may be unannounced and unexpected. The condition of the patient is assessed by a triage nurse in some departments and by a less formal method in others. If the patient's condition appears to warrant immediate attention, the patient is taken to an appropriate treatment room or cubicle in the medical service area of the department, provided that space is available. If the patient's condition is not critical, the patient is generally asked to register and complete other payment/medical history forms and then is seated in a waiting area to be treated as staff and space are available.

Some patients may be transported to Diagnostic Imaging or a portable radiographic unit brought to the Emergency Department. A lab technician may be called to take specimens. Patients may be moved from one treatment area to another or to holding stations, so-called because they are reserved for longer-term observation or for maintaining a patient in the Emergency Department until the patient can be admitted to an inpatient unit. In the case of serious trauma or medical condition, the patient may be transported to the Surgical Department.

3.3.5 Imaging Suite

Diagnostic imaging includes ultrasonic, radiographic, and electromagnetic examination of tissue and anatomic chemistry. It is a service characterized by rapid technological change, increasing specialization, and significant capital investment. Services of the department may be provided to inpatients, emergency patients, and outpatients, although in some cases separate outpatient departments are established.

Typically, Diagnostic Imaging departments are organized around types of equipment. Radiographic, tomographic, and fluoroscopic equipment composes one section, nuclear medicine a second, computerized tomography ("CAT scan") a third, ultrasonography a fourth, and mammography a fifth. In hospitals of 100 to 250 beds, it is not unusual for all diagnostic imaging equipment to be arranged as a single administrative and space-planning unit. In hospitals that have more than 250 beds, specialization becomes more frequent, and separate areas are planned for each of several equipment groupings.

Larger hospitals may also combine certain types of diagnostic imaging equipment into functional service units. For example, a radiographic unit and CAT scan system might be located in the Emergency Department, mammography and ultrasound systems located in a Women's Center, and so forth.

Typical components of the Diagnostic Imaging Department include procedure rooms, procedure room direct-support spaces, other direct-support spaces, departmental support spaces, and miscellaneous support spaces.

3.3.6 Laboratory Suite

A laboratory in a health care facility performs chemical and physical tests and visual analysis of specimens of patient body fluids and tissue. It may also be responsible for postmortem examinations or for testing and preparation of blood and its by-products prior to their use in treatment of patients.

Tests are performed by machine or by technicians using bench apparatus. The results of tests are recorded manually on paper forms or electronically and are transmitted on paper forms, by electronic means, or by voice communication.

Lab technicians at bedside obtain patient specimens from emergency and/or from surgery or from outpatient "drawing stations" in the lab itself. Tests are performed on the specimens according to the specific orders of physicians or according to standing orders. Tests may be performed on a scheduled basis or on an immediate ("stat") basis.

Laboratories are customarily organized in functional sections. In some hospitals, an outpatient lab may perform certain routine, commonly ordered outpatient tests, and the central lab performs all inpatient tests and the less routine outpatient tests. Examples of major lab types are:

Laboratory, Acute Care (emergency laboratory): The Acute Care Laboratory in a health care facility is operated 24 hours a day, 7 days a week for emergency and "stat" (immediate) laboratory work.

Laboratory, Blood Transfusion: The Blood Transfusion Laboratory is responsible for the storage and dispensing of blood components, for patient sample testing, and the preparation of frozen red cells and other specialized components.

Laboratory, Chemistry: Tests conducted in a Chemistry Laboratory include general chemistries, blood gas analysis, therapeutic drug testing, endocrine testing, and comprehensive emergency toxicology and psychotropic drug testing services.

Laboratory, Gastrointestinal. The Gastrointestinal Laboratory usually performs diagnostic hepatitis virology tests other than those used for routine screening of blood donors.

Laboratory, Neurochemistry/Amino Acid: The Neurochemistry /Amino Acid Laboratory diagnoses and treats disorders associated with abnormal metabolism of amino acids, organic acids, and carnitine and their derivatives. The laboratory offers diagnostic testing for patients suspected of having an inborn error of metabolism. *(This laboratory work would be done in a chemistry or similar laboratory.)*

Laboratory, Thyroid/Endocrine The Thyroid/Endocrine Laboratory provides full diagnostic testing, test interpretation, and management consultation for patients with endocrine and metabolic disorder and state-of-the-art metabolic assays for the diagnosis of endocrine disorders including thyroid, pituitary, adrenal, and bone disease. (*This laboratory work would be done in a chemistry or similar laboratory*).

Laboratory, Clinical Immunology. The Clinical Immunology Laboratory performs agarose gel electrophoresis, immunoelectrophoresis, and immunofixation to detect monoclonal antibodies in serum, urine, and cerebrospinal fluid.

Laboratory, Hematology. The Hematology Laboratory performs cell counts on blood and other body fluids.

Laboratory, Special Clotting Section. The Special Clotting Section laboratory provides tests for evaluation of coagulopathy. (*This laboratory work would be done in a Hematology or similar laboratory*).

Laboratory, Microbiology. The Microbiology Laboratory provides tests in bacteriology, virology, parasitology, mycobacteriology, mycology, and infectious diseases serology.

Laboratory, Tissue Typing. The Tissue Typing Laboratory performs tests required for bone marrow and solid organ transplantation.

3.3.7 Renal Dialysis Suite

A suite of rooms for renal dialysis may include equipment rooms for producing pure water, treatment rooms that contain stations for patients, waiting, administration, equipment cleaning, and other support functions.

3.3.8 Endoscopy Suites and Rooms

Endoscopy rooms are characterized by the particular body cavity being visualized and manipulated by the insertion of optical instruments. Endoscopes can be fitted with video cameras that allow visualization by more than one person, teaching, and recording of images and procedures. The video equipment often involves dual monitors and requires added space.

Lower Gastrointestinal Tract Endoscopy:

Anoscopy, proctoscopy, and sigmoidoscopy can be undertaken with rigid instruments and are performed in ordinary treatment rooms or doctors' offices. There is little danger of infecting the patient; the instruments, however, have been inserted into "dirty" areas and require ready access to cleaning facilities and equipment. Odor is a problem, particularly if internal bleeding is encountered.

Colonoscopy became possible with the advent of flexible fiberoptic instruments. Although performed via the same dirty orifice, the procedure is often not tolerated without sedation and/or anesthesia, and there is a small potential of perforating the colon, necessitating location within, proximity to, or quick access to hospital facilities. Biopsy, tumor excision, and cauterization are procedures that can be performed through the colonoscope. The advisability of anesthesia becomes greater as the magnitude or complexity of the procedure increases.

Flexible/fiberoptic instruments have components and seals that can be destroyed in high-pressure/high-temperature environments (autoclaves). Sterilization of these instruments is done by gas sterilization (ethylene oxide) or by soaking in germicidal solutions.

Upper Gastrointestinal Tract Endoscopy:

Gastroscopy (endoscopy of the stomach) was previously done with rigid scopes but now is more easily done with flexible instruments. Specimens of stomach and duodenal fluids are obtained for laboratory analysis. Tissue samples are taken for histological (tissue) examination, and fluid and washings are taken for cytological (cells) examination. Local anesthetic spray may be used to suppress the gag reflex, which facilitates instrumentation. Transmission of infection to the patient from the environment is usually not a problem. Contents of the stomach are usually sterile because of the hydrochloric acid content.

Esophagoscopy is similar to gastroscopy. Perforation of the esophagus is possible, particularly if esophageal stricture or cancer is present. This complication would require immediate hospitalization and possibly would require surgery; therefore, hospital access is required.

Bronchoscopy involves instrumentation of the lungs with either a rigid or a flexible instrument. Coughing is induced by the insertion of the instrument and by the procedures involved. The cough droplets can contain highly infectious and resistant organisms as well as *M. tuberculosis*. The operating personnel, as well as the hospital environment, have to be protected from the droplets and from possible aerosolization of highly infectious organisms.

Urinary Tract and Other Endoscopy

Cystoscopy (endoscopy of the urinary bladder) can be done in a doctor's office or at the bedside. Infection can be introduced by the instruments; therefore, sterilization of equipment, skin preparation, and draping are important. The bladder is usually sterile; however, it can harbor highly resistant microorganisms that can spread by contact. Cystoscopic surgery and cystoscopic x-rays often require anesthesia and are performed on a special urologic table. Because sterility of the air is not as important in cystoscopic surgery as it is in open surgery (surgery through an incision) and because a special table is required, cystospy is ordinarily performed in a dedicated cystoscopy room, a room often much smaller than an open-surgery room. As newer procedures become available, such as cystoscopic surgery using camera and monitors, laser cystoscopic surgery, cryoscopic (freezing) surgery, cystoscopic lithotripsy (ultrasonic, electrostatic, or laser stone crushing), and extracorporeal lithotripsy, more and more equipment is crowded into the cystoscopy room.

Ureteroscopic surgery requires a yet different table, a table that allows cystoscopy and is radiolucent, allowing real-time fluoroscopy of the patient's abdomen using a C-arm X-ray machine. Ureteroscopic surgery can be performed in the cystoscopy room if the room is large enough to contain the special table, the C-arm, the monitors, and a large cart of ureteroscopic equipment; otherwise, it is performed in an open-surgery room.

Nephroscopic surgery (endoscopic surgery of the kidney) is performed either in an open-surgery room equipped with a C-arm or in a C-arm room (Radiology Department) equipped for surgery. The video equipment, X-ray equipment, and the surgical equipment require ample space.

Arthroscopy and arthroscopic surgery (endoscopy of joints) is done in an operating room under full sterile conditions. The joint cavity is highly susceptible to infection. Infections of the joint cavity are difficult to eradicate and can be devastating to the patient.

Abdominal endoscopic surgery, the performance of major abdominal surgery, such as gall bladder removal through endoscopic instruments, is done in an open operating room under full sterile conditions. Generally, four monitors are used, two on either side of the table so that the operators do not have to twist around to view the monitors. Of the two monitors, one is for real time and the other is used for freezing an image or for image retrieval from a recording device. Lighting intensity in the room is usually lowered. The room is equipped and prepared to go immediately into open surgery if necessary.

Note: The above procedures are discussed in detail because they require differing environments. Other forms of "endoscopy" (such as fundoscopy, cavernoscopy, sinoscopy, etc.) require similar space and equipment as those noted above and can be performed in rooms already constructed for the more common procedures.

3.4 SURGERY SUITES

3.4.1 Outpatient Surgery Suites

Outpatient surgery, also known as "day surgery" or "ambulatory surgery," provides surgical service to outpatients. The configuration of this service relative to the Surgery Department ranges from completely freestanding to fully integrated. Freestanding facilities include a suite of operating rooms, recovery, instrument preparation, patient registration and billing spaces, and all other necessary support services. Integrated facilities may share some or most of those functions with the inpatient surgical service.

Some hospitals may process patients scheduled for postoperative admission to an inpatient nursing unit through the Outpatient Surgery area. These patients may be referred to as "AM admissions."

Unique functions in Outpatient Surgery include registration, dressing and preparation, postrecovery, and, in some arrangements, third-stage recovery. Registration includes check-in upon arrival, verification that tests are complete, and coordination with billing and business services. Dressing and preparation include changing into a surgical gown, preoperative preparation, and holding before transport to an

Operating Room. Postoperative functions may include recovery from general anesthesia in a separate recovery room and usually includes one or more additional stages of recovery and "postrecovery" before the patient is discharged.

3.4.2 Inpatient Surgery Suites

Surgery performed to inpatients is performed in inpatient surgery suites. These suites may be designed differently for different types of surgery performed.

3.5 ADMINISTRATIVE AREAS

3.5.1 General Offices

Administration provides executive management for all aspects of a hospital. The administrator generally supervises a second-level tier of managers responsible for patient services, ancillary services, logistical, and other support services. Directors or managers for marketing and planning, medical staff relations, and public relations may also report to the senior executive.

Larger institutions may have an umbrella organization under which there are subsidiary for-profit or not-for-profit components. Each of these may fall under the direction of an executive director, president, or senior vice-president, who, in essence, "wears two hats." For the purposes of this section, Administration includes the workspaces for those managers and their administrative support staff who manage the hospital component.

3.5.2 Accounting

Accounting and Finance provides executive management for all aspects of a hospital's financial performance. Accounting and Finance may have administrative responsibility for functions such as a business office, data processing, and admitting. In some organizations, Accounting and Finance may be combined with Business or with Administration. If that is the case, the number of staff (and space requirements) is usually small and can be calculated as a part of either department.

3.5.3 Business Office

The Business Office provides record keeping and operating services related to inpatient and outpatient accounts and charges and hospital operating expenses. With regard to financial affairs, it can be considered a hub through which information flows. The sophistication of business office activities is increasing as the complexity and number of reimbursement schemes increase. In some organizations, Accounting and Finance and Admitting may be combined with the Business Office.

3.5.4 Patient Records

Patient Records receives patient treatment information, transcribes and records the information in a predetermined format, assists in classifying information, and assists in retrieving records and portions of records for various users. A record is maintained for each inpatient and for certain outpatients, such as those who visit the Emergency or Outpatient Surgery departments.

Information is received in written form or through electronic media (such as dictation systems) from all patient contact departments and from physicians. The record is maintained as a single file for each patient or for each patient visit. Records of outpatient visits to diagnostic departments, such as radiology and the lab, may be maintained by those departments.

Patient Records may also be responsible for maintaining a reference library for physicians and/or staff. This department communicates frequently with physicians and, to facilitate interaction, is often located adjacent to the main hospital's physician lounge.

The implementation of Diagnostic Related Groups as a reimbursement methodology and increasing regulatory agency and consumer interest in the use and quality of care and patient outcomes have expanded the workload of this department. Some aspects of this increase come under the purview of separate quality assurance or utilization review functions that must work with the information maintained in patient records.

3.5.5 Patient Information Systems

Accurate and prompt patient information is vital for modern patient treatment. This field is currently seeing revolutionary change. Some of the important issues in patient information systems include

- distribution and expansion capability,
- use of telecommunications,
- use of paperless technology,
- use of electronic medical records,
- a need for specialized service closets.

3.5.6 Main Lobby, Admitting, and Waiting Spaces

The Admitting Department schedules and registers patients and coordinates the initiation of their financial and medical records. Service may be provided to both inpatients and outpatients, or a separate department may be responsible for outpatients. Emergency Department (ED) patients are generally registered within the ED; however, Admitting Department, Business Office, or other personnel may operate the function. Inpatients arriving "after hours" may be admitted at the Emergency Department's registration area.

As outpatient services have increased in volume and hospitals have worked to retain or capture a larger share of this workload, there has been a trend to create a physically (and sometimes administratively) separate outpatient admitting/processing area.

The basic planning unit for Admitting is designated as a workstation. A workstation may include a registration booth, a room (office), a cubicle, or other designated station in which the admitting process for an individual inpatient takes place. In addition, the Admitting department generally has workstations for personnel who verify insurance coverage, assist in scheduling, or supervise. All of these areas are included within the definition of a workstation for this section.

It is important to realize that the medical conditions of the patient population and visitors in public waiting areas are not controlled. Unless the clinical staff screens patients initially upon arrival, those who need airborne isolation may be waiting in these open areas unmasked and nonsegregated for hours. Special HVAC treatment of such spaces may be necessary.

3.5.7 Outpatient Services

Outpatient services, those delivered to patients who are not admitted and who do not occupy an inpatient bed for 24 hours or more, may include a range of functions and services. At one end of the range are functions related to reception, registration, scheduling, and billing for medical services provided in other departments. At the other end are departments that have a full complement of medical and diagnostic services including limited examination, consultation, and specimen-taking functions. Departments that operate as clinics would occupy the middle ground.

3.5.8 Education Department

The Education Department provides in-service, patient, and community education programs. It is usually associated closely with Nursing Administration because of its in-service training role. In some institutions, patient and community education are provided by medical service departments according to their specialties.

There is a wide variation in the arrangement of Education Department classroom areas. Some institutions use departmental conference rooms, dining areas, and other spaces as classrooms, whereas others provide some or all classrooms seats in "dedicated" rooms. These variations may result from local factors, such as marketing, or the areas of medical service that are specialties at the hospital, such as obstetrics. Hospitals may also have established programs for seniors or cardiac rehabilitation that require large meeting areas.

3.6 SUPPORT SERVICES

3.6.1 Dietary Department
(Cafeteria, Kitchen, and Storage)

The Dietary Department provides meals for inpatients and employees. Inpatient meals are generally prepared for consumption in the patient's room, although units such as psychiatric and rehabilitation may have satellite dining areas. Cafeteria service may also be provided for visitors, physicians, and the public. Some hospitals also operate snack bars or specialty food service shops and vending areas.

The fixed equipment used for cooking, processing, and storage is served by electricity, gas, water, and drain lines. This makes adjustments to this department, once constructed, difficult and expensive. The kitchen area may also be classified by building and fire codes as a "hazardous location," which requires special construction features.

A variety of systems are used to prepare, deliver, and service inpatient meals and for cafeteria operation. In large facilities, food may be prepared well in advance of its use and "blast" frozen either in serving portions or bulk. At the time of delivery and service, the food is thawed, heated, and portioned in the main kitchen or in satellite kitchens at nursing units. An alternative system involves preparation and cooking of food immediately before delivery and service. The hot/cold food is portioned to individual trays or plates and delivered to patients. Beverages may accompany the tray or may be placed on the tray at a nourishment kitchen at the nursing unit. The food may also be delivered in bulk to the nursing unit and portioned to trays in a satellite kitchen for service to patients.

Cafeteria service usually has either a serving line or a "scramble" system. In the latter type, main courses, salads, desserts, beverages, fast food, etc.,

are grouped in separate sections of the serving area. Patrons go directly to the section that contains the item they desire rather than progress through a single line. In either arrangement, a short order service may be provided.

Current trends in food service are to increase the number of food selection options, improve quality, and give the cafeteria component of the department a more appealing environment.

3.6.2 Central Sterile Services

Central Sterile Services cleans and prepares instruments and equipment for use in surgical procedures, delivery, emergency care, and related areas. In some hospitals, the function of the department includes distribution of certain clean supplies.

The following functions are included under Central Sterile Services:

- Cleanup of surgical and obstetric case carts; separation of trash, linens, and instruments.
- Decontamination of instruments and washing of carts.
- Cleaning of instruments including ultrasonic cleaning and soaking and processing through a washer/sterilizer.
- Assembly of instrument sets and supplies for surgical packs and packaging.
- Sterilization of packs, labeling, and storage.
- Preparation of case carts or sets of packs for scheduled and emergency procedures.
- Delivery of case carts or sets of packs to served departments.
- Receipt and stocking of supplies and linens to be used in packs.
- Inventory control and administration.

3.6.3 Materials Management

Materials Management purchases, receives, stocks, distributes, and inventories chargeable and nonchargeable supplies. It may also be responsible for purchasing equipment and building materials used by maintenance.

In some hospitals, the stocking and distribution of chargeable supplies (mostly patient-use items) is under a function known as Central Sterile Services.

The materials storage function has several components. Receiving checks in supplies delivered from the carrier and uncrates the boxes. Bulk items are taken to a bulk storage area and boxed items to a storage section. Further unpacking may occur, and some items may be placed in a storage section designed for unit-of-issue fulfilling.

Supply orders from departments are picked from the storage shelving or bins on either a scheduled or as-called-for basis. Supply areas in departments may be restocked by using exchange carts or a par (minimal) level resupply cart.

3.6.4 Pharmacy

Pharmacy orders, controls, prepares for dispensing, and dispenses medications for inpatients and emergency patients. It may also provide the same functions for outpatients and/or employees. Certain bulk items, such as IV solutions, may be ordered, stored, and/or distributed by the materials management function; however, all solutions that are pre-mixed must generally be kept under the control of the hospital pharmacist even if they are stored elsewhere.

Record keeping is an integral component of the department's activities, and this has encouraged a trend toward computer systems for that purpose and for billing and checking prescriptions for contraindications.

With respect to departmental space configuration, there are three prevalent systems: traditional, unit dose, and satellite. The traditional system distributes medications to nursing units and patient care departments in quantities that are used until exhausted. For nursing units, the medication is separated into doses and administered by staff according to the order of the prescribing physician. A "bench stock" may also be maintained on the unit.

The unit dose system uses presorted, individually packaged doses for each patient. These may be delivered in a cassette system on a scheduled basis. Nursing staff opens and administers the dose at the prescribed time. There are variants of this delivery system including labeled zip-lock bags. Each bag contains the medication(s) to be administered to the patient at a given time. The empty bags are returned as verification of administration and for billing. Under this system, a "bench stock" may also be maintained on the unit.

The satellite system includes small pharmacy units at inpatient nursing units and in certain ancillary departments, such as Emergency and Surgery. These are staffed full- or part-time by a registered pharmacist. These satellites stock a supply of the medications most frequently used by the departments they serve. In this arrangement, the central

pharmacy functions as an area to prepare special items such as IV additive solutions and as a bulk receiving, control, administrative, and storage area.

3.6.5 Environmental and Linen Services

Environmental Services includes housekeeping and linen service. Housekeeping provides routine and on-call cleaning and removal of trash from interior building areas with the usual exception of mechanical and electrical service rooms. Housekeeping service may be extended to include adjacent hospital-operated office buildings and outpatient facilities.

Linen service involves changing bed linens; collecting bed linens and other soiled items such as towels, blankets, pillows, and scrub suits; receiving and controlling clean linens; stocking and distributing linen carts; and maintaining a backup stock of linens. The hospital may operate a full service laundry on or off campus or have small capacity washers and dryers for miscellaneous items.

Linen service operates from a central area to sort linens and restock linen carts. Linen supplies for operational areas are maintained in designated linen storage rooms or on wire carts or exchange carts in clean utility rooms. Soiled linens are placed in local collection rooms and then collected in larger carts for removal to a central soiled linen holding area before they are picked up by the laundry service.

Housekeeping operates both from a central staging/supply/equipment storage area and from satellite areas (janitor closets). Supplies and equipment for housekeeping activities for a designated section of the building are maintained in the janitor closet, and the assigned housekeepers operate from this base during most of their shift. Personnel return to the main area at shift change or to receive new assignments. Trash collected by the housekeeper is emptied into large carts and taken to a dumpster, compactor, or incinerator.

3.6.6 Engineering and Maintenance Shops

Engineering Services operates and maintains the hospital physical plant. Operations include start-up and control of environmental systems for cooling, heating, ventilation, domestic water, steam, normal and emergency power, lighting, and other building utilities. Operations also include minor construction with in-house personnel and coordination with construction contractors, designers, and hospital staff for larger projects.

Maintenance includes identifying building assets, performing routine maintenance and operator tests, and ensuring that contract maintenance services are properly performed. Engineering is also responsible for grounds maintenance including mowing, snow removal, placing directional signs, and care of pavements.

A separate unit, which usually falls within the administrative purview of Engineering Services, inspects, tests, and repairs certain types of medical equipment. This section is usually known as Biomedical Engineering.

The Director of Engineering may also have collateral duties including safety and security.

Engineering Services requires space for maintenance shops, for storage of maintenance materials, and for administrative support. Maintenance shops, such as woodworking, painting, and welding, may have environmental control problems as serious as those of medical operations spaces.

Outbuildings may be employed for storing hazardous liquids, vehicles, and fuel-driven equipment.

3.6.7 Autopsy/Morgue

The morgue facility is a group of spaces for the preparation, storage, and dissection of human cadavers or portions thereof, for the purpose of determining cause of death or for teaching and research purposes. Patients who die in the hospital must be transported using corridors or elevators used by others. It is recommended that special care be taken to shield the public from this activity. Autopsy/morgue spaces are usually located away from general traffic in the hospital and have requirements for receiving dead human bodies, storage, viewing, and ultimate pick up by undertakers

Several aspects of the autopsy room require mechanical attention. The greatest danger dealing with autopsy is that the deceased patient might harbor infective organisms that can be introduced into the environment by manipulation of tissues. *M. tuberculosis* is of particular concern. These organisms may or may not have been known to be present prior to section (autopsy). Viable organisms persist after death.

Noxious chemicals, such as formaldehyde or phenol, may be used for tissue preservation. Such chemicals may be heavier than air, necessitating low or local exhaust.

3.6.8 Trash and Compactor Area

Health care facilities generate a lot of solid waste. Some of the waste is Medical Waste, which must be treated in strict accordance to regulations. Many hospitals install local treatment systems, which render this waste harmless so it then can be mixed with the regular solid waste. Multiple compactors are usually provided to handle this waste in an efficient manner. The compactor area must be accessible to roads and large trucks.

CHAPTER 4
OVERVIEW OF HEALTH CARE HVAC

4.1 INTRODUCTION

Health care facility HVAC systems are required to meet a variety of demands and applications, at a high standard of performance, in many ways unique to the buildings they serve. In perhaps no other application is the HVAC system a more important, and integral, component of the building's *process*—or that process more vital to human safety and health. The variety and level of demands placed on the HVAC systems, the nature of loads and design conditions, requirements for dependability and system hygiene, and—not least—the necessity to interface with a variety of other complex building systems, all make the HVAC system design uniquely challenging. It is the intent of this chapter to provide an introduction to the demands and services required of health care HVAC systems, as well as a brief discussion of the more salient design considerations.

4.1.1 Required HVAC Services

As in other types of buildings, health care facility HVAC systems are required to establish comfortable environmental conditions through the control of temperature, air movement, relative humidity, noise, and objectionable odors. Environmental control is important, not merely in providing personal comfort, but in facilitating the healing process: simply stated, a comfortable patient heals faster. In addition, health care facility HVAC systems are called upon to support a variety of medical functions, practices, and systems critical to health and safety, including the following:

- *Infection Control.* Medical facilities are places where relatively high levels of pathogenic (disease-causing) microorganisms are generated and therefore require stringent practices and controls

to safeguard the staff and patient population. The HVAC system is one of several tools and processes used in the control of infection.

- *Environmental Control for Specific Medical Functions.* Certain medical functions, treatments, or healing processes demand controlled environmental temperature and/or relative humidity conditions that exceed the requirements of mere personal comfort.

- *Hazard Control.* Many medical facilities include functions where chemicals, fumes, or aerosols are generated that pose health or safety hazards. HVAC equipment is used in such applications to remove, contain, or dilute the environmental concentration of such contaminants to safe levels.

- *Life Safety.* HVAC systems contribute to the detection and containment of fire and smoke and may be called upon to evacuate or exclude smoke from atria or exit enclosures. Engineered smoke control systems may be called for to provide complex zoned pressurization control.

Depending upon the type of medical facility, the characteristics of its patient population, and the nature of medical procedures performed, the range and criticality of services required in the above-listed categories will vary. Similarly, the complexity of the HVAC system design and the need for close coordination with the design of other major building systems will vary by facility.

4.1.2 Basic Classification of Health Care Facilities

Health care facilities range widely in the nature and complexity of services they provide and (generally speaking) in the relative degree of illness or injury of the patients treated—from a neighborhood general practitioner's office to large regional or university medical centers and specialty hospitals. As a rule, environmental control requirements and the relative role of the HVAC system in life safety and infection control become more important with increasing complexity of the medical services provided and the degree of illness of the patient population. A description of the several classifications of health care facility and departmental functions is provided in Chapter 3 of this manual.

4.2 INFECTION AND SAFETY HAZARDS

Health care facilities include by their nature populations and processes that produce biological, chemical, and radiation hazards to human safety and health. Additional chemical or biological hazards can enter from the natural environment or be generated within building materials and equipment as a result of poor design or maintenance. Examples of potential chemical hazards include highly volatile substances and solutions used in laboratory and disinfection processes, leaking anesthesia gas, and carbon monoxide or other combustion gases entering outside air intakes. Radiation hazards can result from improperly handled nuclear medicines or poorly shielded X-ray processes. This chapter will deal largely with the control of the biological hazards represented by the microorganisms that cause nosocomial (acquired in the hospital) infections. The term "contaminant," however, will often be used to refer to the airborne hazards from any sources.

4.2.1 Sources of Infectious Organisms

A primary source of pathogenic microorganisms in the health care environment is the patient suffering from contagious disease. In addition, several other significant and potentially deadly sources of infection include the microbes carried on the person of every human being, contaminated outside air or water supplies, and microbe "amplification" or growth sites within the building itself. Due to these factors, the health care environment will often have relatively larger concentrations of microorganisms than are found in conventional buildings. Exposed to these are those persons—the patient population—most susceptible to acquiring life-threatening infection via several potential pathways.

- Patients with open wounds from trauma, burns, or surgery present an opportunity for microbes to bypass the body's protective outer covering, the skin.

- In some patients, the body's natural immune system is weakened by disease, injury, or medical treatment, resulting in decreased ability to fight off infection. In the most severe such "immune-compromised" patient cases (such as bone marrow transplant patients), the body's immune system may be completely dysfunctional.

- Contagious diseases not considered dangerous to the general public, such as measles and chicken pox, pose grave health risk to the fetuses of pregnant mothers who may acquire the infection through, for example, exposure to other patients in a waiting room.

The risk of infection is not limited to patients. Visitors, and more particularly health care workers, are easily exposed to contagious disease through a variety of circumstances and means.

4.2.2 Modes of Transmission: Direct Contact and Airborne

Disease may be transmitted through two primary means: direct contact (including ingestion) and airborne. The means of transmission is determined by the nature of the infectious organism and/or how it enters or exists within the building environment.

Direct contact transmission results when the pathogen enters the body through a wound, open sore, or vulnerable body location (mouth, eyes, etc.) via contact with unwashed hands, infectious body fluids, droplets from sneezes or coughs, or other infected objects or material. Examples of direct contact infection opportunities include:

- *Hand contact*, as when unwashed hands have had contact with an infection source (an ill patient, a contaminated equipment surface, etc.) and in turn transfer the organism by touching a vulnerable part of one's own or another's body.
- *Contact of a vulnerable body part with an infected body fluid*, such as might occur in an accidental splash of contaminated blood droplets from a laboratory specimen.
- *Needle stick*, whereby a health care provider accidentally sticks a contaminated syringe needle into his or herself.
- *Insect transmission*, by bite or by direct transfer of pathogens from a contaminated substance (trash, animal droppings, etc.) to human food or food preparation surfaces.
- *Contact with infected liquid droplets produced by a sneeze, cough, or talking by a person with*

contagious disease. Many of these droplets are of a mass and size (>5 microns) that cause them to settle out of the air quickly, limiting "infectivity" to a radius of several feet. A single sneeze can produce 100,000 aerosolized particles; coughing can produce on the order of 10,000 particles per minute.

Studies indicate that the great majority of nosocomial infections result from direct contact, the greatest single cause being the unwashed hands of health care providers.

Airborne transmission is usually distinguished as resulting from respiration of particles or aerosols of low mass and size (1.0-5.0 microns) that can remain indefinitely suspended in air. Infectious bacteria, fungi, and viruses normally are transmitted into the air in forms larger than the individual microbe, such as via attachment to organic or inorganic dusts and particles such as soot, skin cells, or the "droplet nuclei" that are the residual of aerosolized liquid droplets. Particles of this size are easily respirated deeply into the lungs, where in a suitably vulnerable host or in high enough concentration, they can overcome the body's immune system and cause disease. Typical means of airborne transmission include the following:

- *Sneezing, coughing, and talking by an infected person* produce many particles light enough to remain suspended in air. These activities can therefore spread infection by both the direct and airborne infection routes.
- *Resuspension into air of in-situ microbes*, settled or trapped in building dust or debris, furnishing materials (including bed coverings), equipment, and room finishes and released by disturbing activities such as bed-making, maintenance, and construction work.
- *Aerosolization of contaminated water droplets* via shower heads, spray humidifiers, or evaporative cooling equipment (including cooling towers). Aerosolization of infectious particles or droplets also can occur via surgical and autopsy procedures, particularly those involving powered cutting or abrasion tools.
- *Carriage on human skin flakes* (squames), which the average person sheds into the environment at a rate of about 1,000 squames per hour (Hambraeus 1988).
- *Amplification (reproduction) within HVAC airflow equipment*, especially areas where moisture and dirt can accumulate, such as cooling coil drain pans, wet filters, and porous duct linings exposed to direct moisture.

It is the airborne route of infection over which the HVAC system is most effective as part of the health care facility's overall infection control effort.

4.2.3 Exposure Classifications

Health care authorities have established exposure levels for a number of pathogens, representing the number of infectious organisms, or the number per unit volume of air, which pose significant threats of disease in healthy individuals. The CDC Action Level is one such indicator of relative infection potential or "infectivity." For example, the CDC Action Level for the Tuberculosis bacillus or the Ebola virus is 1.0 infectious unit (a single microorganism), detectable in any sampled volume of air; these particular microorganisms are considered among the most deadly. The Infectious Dose is another such indicator and varies from a single microbe to thousands, depending upon the species of microorganism.

4.3 INFECTION CONTROL

4.3.1 An Overall Approach

Health care professionals utilize a wide range of specialty equipment and engineering controls and observe rigid operational disciplines, practices, and techniques, to control infection. Infection control equipment and practices are regulated by federal and state government authorities, which also set standards for engineering controls. In addition, civilian agencies such as the Joint Commission for the Accreditation of Healthcare Organizations (JCAHO), as well as in-house infection control committees, act as safety and infection control "watch dogs."

Some common infection control approaches include the following.

- Surgical, medical treatment, and invasive diagnostic instruments, appliances, and materials undergo sterilization or high-level disinfecting processes and are protected from contamination until used by enclosure in sterile packaging.
- Hand washing and surgical scrub stations are provided to sanitize the hands of health care providers before they touch a patient.
- "Gowning" and other sterile garments, including masks, hair and foot coverings, and gloves, cover the person of surgical personnel.
- "Sterile Technique" and "Aseptic Technique" are practiced during surgical and other invasive procedures.

- Government- and industry-regulated practices control the handling, storage, and disposal of potentially infectious materials, such as used dressings and syringe needles, pathology specimens, and blood products. Regulations also define personal protective equipment requirements for health care workers.

- Room and fixed equipment surfaces in surgical and other invasive treatment or diagnostic rooms are sanitized prior to use. Other cleaning, sanitizing, laundering, disinfection, and general good housekeeping practices are observed throughout the health care facility.

- Facility floor and circulation plans are normally designed to minimize "clean" and "dirty" cross traffic and provide for separate storage of contaminated and clean materials.

- Diagnosed or suspected cases of contagious disease are isolated in disease isolation spaces specially designed to prevent the spread of infection.

- Patients with severely suppressed immune systems are housed or treated in protective isolation spaces designed to exclude airborne pathogens.

- Directional airflow control, filtration, exhaust, and dilution ventilation are applied as engineering controls to minimize exposure to airborne contaminants.

- Environmental temperature and relative humidity in surgical and other critical spaces are kept within ranges that help support bodily immune functions and/or inhibit pathogen viability.

This list is not complete but is intended to convey the fact that the HVAC system is but one element, albeit an important one, of an overall infection control program. In addition to providing "active" infection controls, such as apply in the final four infection control approaches listed above, a properly designed HVAC system can be an important contributor to overall building sanitation by helping to prevent envelope condensation and other building conditions conducive to microbe growth. Conversely, a poorly designed HVAC system can provide numerous opportunities not only within the building, but within the system itself, for the generation of pathogenic organisms.

4.3.2 The HVAC System's Role in Infection and Hazard Control

The HVAC system contributes to infection and hazard control through "engineering control" functions including dilution ventilation, contaminant exhaust, directional airflow control, and filtration, as well as by controlling environmental temperature and relative humidity. In many applications, all or most of these functions are performed simultaneously.

Dilution ventilation, combined with contaminant exhaust, is the process of lowering the concentration of airborne contaminants in a space by **exhausting contaminated air** and supplying the space with contaminant-free makeup air. Effectiveness is generally proportional to the space air change rate and the relative efficiency of the air delivery system in mixing the clean air throughout the space. According to the specific medical application and nature of the contaminants, the makeup air may consist totally of fresh (outside) air or be a combination of fresh and recirculated (properly filtered) air.

Directional airflow is the control of airflow into or out of a room, or unidirectionally through a defined "clean" area of a room, according to the specific functional requirement. Directional airflow has three major applications:

- Establishment of directional airflow into or out of one space from the space or spaces adjoining. The directional control of the airflow is achieved by the establishment of a relative differential pressure between the spaces. Directional airflow out of a space (positive relative pressurization) is utilized when there is a need to protect room occupants or materials from airborne contaminants outside the space. Airflow into a space (negative pressurization) is utilized when it is desired to prevent contaminants released in the space from spreading to adjoining areas. The actual achievement of a specific room pressure differential, relative to surrounding spaces, is dependent not only upon the room's relative supply-return/exhaust airflow configuration but also upon the airtightness of the room's construction. A generally accepted practice to ensure the achievement of directional airflow between spaces is the establishment of a minimum 75 cfm (35 L/s) flow differential and/or a 0.01 in. w.g. (2.5 Pa) pressure differential.

- Within rooms, directional flow, sometimes referred to as "plug" or laminar flow, may be achieved to a limited extent with special low-velocity, nonaspirating supply diffusers that project unidirectional airflow for a distance into the space. In concept, this arrangement provides a "wash" of clean air to remove or exclude contaminants from the "clean" zone of influence, to be exhausted at strategically located exhaust or return registers; in actuality, the location of the exhaust or return opening has a minimal effect on room airflow pattern.

• Directional airflow control is also the principle utilized in laboratory fume hoods, biosafety cabinets, and other specially manufactured protective ventilation equipment. The equipment is normally designed to establish a relatively high (usually about 100 fpm [0.5 m/s]) flow velocity over the working surface, sufficient to transport and remove volatized or aerosolized contaminants from the worker's breathing zone. More detailed information for such medical specialty exhaust equipment may be obtained from publications of the National Council of Government Industrial Hygienists.

High efficiency filtration is used to remove the majority of microorganisms from the air supply.

• Filters rated 90%-95% efficiency (using the ASHRAE Dust Spot Test Method) may be expected to remove 99.9% of all bacteria and similarly sized particles. Such filters are required by some codes and standards to be installed in all patient treatment, examination, and bedroom spaces.

• The HEPA filter shall exhibit a minimum efficiency of 99.97% when tested at an aerosol of 0.3 micrometer diameter and is mandated by some codes for protective environments and specialty operating rooms. In addition to being very effective at bacteria and mold filtration, HEPA filters are also effective in filtering viable viruses, which, although occurring in sizes as small as 0.01 micron, are normally attached to a particle (such as a droplet) much larger in size.

Combination HEPA filter/fan recirculation air units, including portable models, are employed in some protective environment and disease isolation applications, particularly for existing buildings with limited ventilation upgrade capability. These units supplement central ventilation systems to (in effect) achieve a greater number of air changes in the space. The effectiveness of all filters can be compromised by leakage at filter gaskets and frames.

Filter rating using Minimum Efficiency Reporting Value (MERV) is discussed in Chapter 9.

Ultraviolet germicidal irradiation (UVGI) is being seen increasingly in microbiocidal HVAC applications. Airborne microorganisms are destroyed by exposure to direct UVGI in the wavelength range of 200-270 nanometers, given suitable exposure conditions, duration, and intensity. Air-handling unit and duct-mounted and packaged UV-fan recirculation units are available that help eliminate viable microorganisms from the air supply or prevent their growth on irradiated equipment. Upper-level room UVGI arrangements are available that continuously irradiate the upper areas of a room but avoid direct radiation of the lower, occupied levels, where the radiation could be harmful. As only part of the space is radiated, many authorities question the effectiveness of upper-level UVGI. In general, all UVGI equipment must be adequately maintained to be effective; dust can reduce lamp output, and burned-out lamps are normally not readily evident. In addition, UVGI is less effective when air relative humidity exceeds about 70%. For these and possibly other reasons, most codes and authorities will accept UVGI only as "supplemental" protection (to HEPA filtration systems) for disease and protective isolation applications. Refer to Chapter 12 for additional information.

Space temperature and relative humidity influence the potential for infection in several different ways.

• Several studies indicate that the survival rates of airborne microorganisms in the indoor environment are greatest in very low, or very high, ranges of relative humidity (RH), depending upon the nature (bacteria, virus, fungi) and species of the organism. Evidence seems to indicate that most microorganisms are less viable, and therefore less infectious, in a middle-range RH of 40-70%.

• Moderately humidified environments are believed to increase the settling rate of infectious aerosols; a possible reason for this is that in more humid surroundings relatively heavy aerosol droplets are less likely to dry, lose mass, and remain suspended in the air.

• Excessively dry conditions can lead to drying of the mucous coatings on special tissues in the upper and lower respiratory tracts, which have the function of capturing respirated particles before they can be breathed deeply into the lungs.

• High temperatures in an operating room, or RH levels greater than 60%, can lead to patient sweating, which in turn can increase the risk of infection from microorganisms carried on the patient's own skin.

4.4 CRITERIA

Among the HVAC designer's first tasks is to establish the design criteria for a project. Most state and federal government agencies, and many local governments, establish criteria for the design of health care facilities within their jurisdictions. The jurisdiction may utilize its own criteria and codes or cite model, national, or international building codes or design standards. Some private health care institutions and corporations also establish design requirements. Frequently adopted or cited codes, standards, and design guidelines relating to health care facility HVAC systems include:

- The American Institute of Architect's *Guidelines for Design and Construction of Hospital and Health Care Facilities* (AIA Guidelines).
- Standards and handbooks of the American Society of Heating, Refrigerating and Air-Conditioning Engineers (ASHRAE).
- National Fire Protection Association (NFPA) standards.
- The Joint Commission on Accreditation of Healthcare Organizations' "Environment of Care" standards.
- The American Conference of Governmental Industrial Hygienists' publication *Industrial Ventilation*.
- Centers for Disease Control and Prevention (CDC) guidelines and recommended practices.
- Model mechanical codes, including the Standard, BOCA, ICBO, and Uniform Mechanical Codes.

Typical criteria for HVAC design include indoor and outdoor environmental design conditions, outside and total air change requirements, economic considerations for equipment selection, requirements for redundancy or backup equipment capacity, solar characteristics, room pressure relationships, filtration, and other criteria needed for systems and equipment selection and sizing. Other factors and data that influence the HVAC design, such as envelope and equipment insulation, glazing characteristics, occupancy schedules, and ventilation or conditioning requirements for special equipment or processes, may be provided by specific project documentation or may require investigation by the designer.

In addition to basic design criteria, the designer is responsible for acquainting him/herself with applicable government regulations and should establish in the project's Scope of Work who has responsibility for any permits required by the jurisdiction.

Table 4-1 provides a summary of "best practice" recommendations. These specifically address room conditions, including space pressurization, minimum outdoor and total air, exhaust, recirculation, relative humidity, temperature, and supplemental guidance for many typical hospital and clinic rooms. Table 4-1 illustrates the selected "best practice" requirements from both the *1999 ASHRAE Handbook—HVAC Applications* and the 2001 AIA Guidelines. Notes from both references regarding individual rooms are summarized with Table 4-1. These criteria should be used when not superseded by criteria from the owner or local jurisdiction.

These "best practice" criteria are based upon committee experience in design application of existing criteria (Appendix F, Table F-1). Rationale for design is discussed in more detail in relevant chapters and appendices in this manual.

4.5 ENERGY EFFICIENCY AND OPERATING COST

Health care facilities continuously face the challenge, and pressure, of being cost-effective. The annual operating costs of HVAC systems, including both energy consumption and maintenance materials and manpower, constitute a significant portion of overall building costs. Subject to compatibility with the health care functions of the facility, including considerations of redundancy and dependability of service, operational cost should be a primary consideration in the selection of major HVAC systems and equipment.

Systems and equipment should be designed with overall energy efficiency in mind, and consideration given to the application of such potential energy-cost-saving features as heat recovery, airside economizers, electric demand shifting, hybrid cooling, solar energy, and heat pumps. To determine the relative cost-effectiveness of two or more project alternatives, the most comprehensive and straightforward economic method is a life-cycle cost analysis (LCCA). This analysis takes into consideration all cost elements associated with a capital investment during the life cycle of use of the system or equipment purchase. Additional information on economic analyses is provided in Appendix E of this manual.

4.6 EQUIPMENT SIZING FOR HEATING AND COOLING LOADS

4.6.1 Design Capacity

Design criteria for health care facilities include temperature, relative humidity, and ventilation requirements affecting equipment capacity and cooling/heating load. In some cases it may be necessary to establish and maintain a range of room conditions, with different setpoints for summer or winter operation. The HVAC design must ensure that the required

Table 4-1.

Function Space	Pressure Relationship to Adjacent Areas (a)	Minimum Air Changes of Outdoor Air per Hour (b)	Minimum Total Air Changes per Hour (c)	All Air Exhausted Directly to Outdoors (m)	Air Recirculated Within Room Units (d)	Relative Humidity (n)(%)	Design Temperature (o) °F [°C]
SURGERY AND CRITICAL CARE							
Operating room (recirculating air system) (e) (r)	P	5	25	-	No	30-60	68-75 [20-23.9]
Operating/surgical cystoscopic rooms (e), (p), (q) (r)	P	5	25		No	30-60	68-75 [20-23.9]
Delivery room (p) (r)	P	5	25	-	No	30-60	68-75 [20-23.9]
Recovery room (p)	-	2	6	-	No	30-60	70-75 [21.1-23.9]
Critical and intensive care	-	2	6	-	No	30-60	70-75 [21.1-23.9]
Newborn intensive care	-	2	6	-	No	30-60	72-78 [22.2-25.6]
Treatment room (s)	-	-	6	-	-	30-60	70-75 [21.1-23.9]
Nursery suite	P	5	12	-	No	30-60	75-80 [23.9-26.7]
Trauma room (crisis or shock) (f) (s)	-	3	15	-	No	30-60	70-75 [21.1-23.9]
Trauma room (conventional ED or treatment) (f) (s)	P	2	6	-	No	30-60	70-75 [21.1-23.9]
Anesthesia gas storage	N	-	8	Yes	-	-	-
Endoscopy	N	2	6	-	No	30-60	68-73 [20-22.8]
Bronchoscopy (q)	N	2	12	Yes	No	30-60	68-73 [20-22.8]
ER waiting rooms	N	2	12	Yes	-	30-60	70-75 [21.1-23.9]
Triage	N	2	12	Yes	-	-	70-75 [21.1-23.9]
Radiology waiting rooms	N	2	12	Yes (t) (u)	-	-	70-75 [21.1-23.9]
Class A Operating (procedure) room (e) (r)	N	3	15	-	No	30-60	70-75 [21.1-23.9]

Table 4-1. (Continued)

Function Space	Pressure Relationship to Adjacent Areas (a)	Minimum Air Changes of Outdoor Air per Hour (b)	Minimum Total Air Changes per Hour (c)	All Air Exhausted Directly to Outdoors (m)	Air Recirculated Within Room Units (d)	Relative Humidity (n)(%)	Design Temperature (o) °F (°C)
NURSING							
Patient room	-	2	6(v)	-	-	30-60	70-75 [21.1-23.9]
Toilet room (g)	N	Optional	10	Yes	No	-	-
Newborn nursery suite	-	2	6	-	No	30-60	72-78 [22.2-25.6]
Protective environment room (i), (q), (w)	P	2	12	-	No	-	70-75 [21.1-23.9]
Airborne infection isolation room (h),(q), (x)	N	2	12	Yes (u)	No	-	70-75 [21.1-23.9]
Isolation alcove or anteroom (w) (x)	P/N	2	10	Yes	No	-	-
Labor/delivery/recovery/postpartum (LDRP)	-	2	6(v)	-	-	30-60	70-75 [21.1-23.9]
Public Corridor	N	2	2	-	-		
Patient corridor	-	2	4	-	-		
ANCILLARY							
RADIOLOGY (y) X-ray (diagnostic and treatment)	-	2	6	-	-	30-60	72-78 [22.2-25.6]
X-ray (surgery/critical care and catheterization)	P	3	15	-	No	30-60	70-75 [21.1-23.9]
Darkroom	N	2	10	Yes (j)	No	-	-
Laboratory, general (y)	N	2	6	Yes	No	30-60	70-75 [21.1-23.9]
Laboratory, bacteriology	N	2	6	Yes	No	30-60	70-75 [21.1-23.9]
Laboratory, biochemistry (y)	P	2	6	-	No	30-60	70-75 [21.1-23.9]
Laboratory, cytology	N	2	6	Yes	No	30-60	70-75 [21.1-23.9]
Laboratory, glasswashing	N	Optional	10	Yes	-	-	-
Laboratory, histology	N	2	6	Yes	No	30-60	70-75 [21.1-23.9]

Table 4-1. (Continued)

Function Space	Pressure Relationship to Adjacent Areas (a)	Minimum Air Changes of Outdoor Air per Hour (b)	Minimum Total Air Changes per Hour (c)	All Air Exhausted Directly to Outdoors (m)	Air Recirculated Within Room Units (d)	Relative Humidity (n)(%)	Design Temperature (o) °F [°C]
Microbiology (y)	N	-	6	Yes	No	30-60	70-75 [21.1-23.9]
Laboratory, nuclear medicine	N	2	6	Yes	No	30-60	70-75 [21.1-23.9]
Laboratory, pathology	N	2	6	Yes	No	30-60	70-75 [21.1-23.9]
Laboratory, serology	P	2	6	Yes	No	30-60	70-75 [21.1-23.9]
Laboratory, sterilizing	N	Optional	10	Yes	No	30-60	70-75 [21.1-23.9]
Laboratory, media transfer	P	2	4	-	No	30-60	70-75 [21.1-23.9]
Autopsy room (q)	N	2	12	Yes	No	-	-
Nonrefrigerated body-holding room (k)	N	Optional	10	Yes	No	-	70 [21.1]
Pharmacy	P	2	4	-	-	30-60	70-75 [21.1-23.9]
ADMINISTRATION							
Admitting and waiting rooms	N	2	6	Yes	-	30-60	70-75 [21.1-23.9]
DIAGNOSTIC AND TREATMENT							
Bronchoscopy, sputum collection, and pentamidine administration	N	2	12	Yes	-	30-60	70-75 [21.1-23.9]
Examination room	-	2	6	-	-	30-60	70-75 [21.1-23.9]
Medication room	P	2	4	-	-	30-60	70-75 [21.1-23.9]
Treatment room	-	2	6	-	-	30-60	70-75 [21.1-23.9]
Physical therapy and hydrotherapy	N	2	6	-	-	30-60	72-80 [22.2-26.7]
Soiled workroom or soiled holding	N	2	10	Yes	No	30-60	72-78 [22.2-25.6]
Clean workroom or clean holding	P	2	4	-	-	30-60	72-78 [22.2-25.6]

Table 4-1. (Continued)

Function Space	Pressure Relationship to Adjacent Areas (a)	Minimum Air Changes of Outdoor Air per Hour (b)	Minimum Total Air Changes per Hour (c)	All Air Exhausted Directly to Outdoors (m)	Air Recirculated Within Room Units (d)	Relative Humidity (n)(%)	Design Temperature (o) °F (°C)
STERILIZING AND SUPPLY							
ETO-sterilizer room	N	-	10	Yes	No		
Sterilizer equipment room	N	-	10	Yes	No		
Central medical and surgical supply							
Soiled or decontamination room	N	2	6	Yes	No	30-60	72-78 [22.2-25.6]
Clean workroom	P	2	4	-	No	30-60	72-78 [22.2-25.6]
Sterile storage	P	2	4	-	-	30-60	72-78 [22.2-25.6]
SERVICE							
Food preparation center (l)	-	2	10	Yes	No		
Warewashing	N	Optional	10	Yes	No		
Dietary day storage	-	Optional	2	-	No		
Laundry, general	N	2	10	Yes	No		
Soiled linen sorting and storage	N	Optional	10	Yes	No		
Clean linen storage	P	2 (Optional)	2	-	-		
Linen and trash chute room	N	Optional	10	Yes	No		
Bedpan room	N	Optional	10	Yes	No		
Bathroom	N	Optional	10	Yes	No		72-78 [22.2-25.6]
Janitor's closet	N	Optional	10	Yes	No		

Table 4-1. (Continued)

Notes:

P = Positive N = Negative ± = Continuous directional control not required

(a) Where continuous directional control is not required, variations should be minimized, and in no case should a lack of directional control allow the spread of infection from one area to another. Boundaries between functional areas (wards or departments) should have directional control. Lewis (1988) describes methods for maintaining directional control by applying air-tracking controls. Design of the ventilation system shall provide air movement, which is generally from clean to less clean areas. If any form of variable air volume or load shedding system is used for energy conservation, it must not compromise the pressure balancing relationships or the minimum air changes required by the table. See note z for additional information.

(b) The ventilation rates in this table cover ventilation for comfort, as well as for asepsis and odor control in areas of acute care hospitals that directly affect patient care. Ventilation rates in accordance with ASHRAE *Standard 62, Ventilation for Acceptable Indoor Air Quality*, should be used for areas for which specific ventilation rates are not given. Where a higher outdoor air requirement is called for in Standard 62 than in Table 4-1, the higher value should be used.

(c) Total air changes indicated should be either supplied or, where required, exhausted. Number of air changes can be reduced when the room is unoccupied if pressure relationship is maintained and the number of air changes indicated is reestablished any time the space is being utilized. Air changes shown are minimum values. Higher values should be used when required to maintain room temperature and humidity conditions based upon the cooling load of the space (lights, equipment, people, exterior walls and windows, etc.).

(d) Recirculating HEPA filter units used for infection control (without heating or cooling coils) are acceptable. Gravity-type heating or cooling units such as radiators or convectors shall not be used in operating rooms and other special care areas.

(e) For operating rooms, 100% outside air should be used only when codes require it and only if heat recovery devices are used.

(f) The term "trauma room" as used herein is a first aid room and/or emergency room used for general initial treatment of accident victims. The operating room within the trauma center that is routinely used for emergency surgery should be treated as an operating room.

(g) See section on patient rooms in *ASHRAE Handbook—HVAC Applications* for a discussion of design of central toilet exhaust systems.

(h) The airborne infectious isolation rooms described in this table are those that might be used for infectious patients in the average community hospital. The rooms are negatively pressurized. Some isolation rooms may have a separate anteroom. Refer to the discussion in the chapter for more detailed information.

(i) Protective environment rooms are those used for immunosuppressed patients. Such rooms are positively pressurized to protect the patient. Anterooms are generally required and should be negatively pressurized with respect to the patient room.

(j) All air need not be exhausted if darkroom equipment has scavenging exhaust duct attached and meets ventilation standards regarding NIOSH, OSHA, and local employee exposure limits.

(k) A nonrefrigerated body-holding room is only applicable to facilities that do not perform autopsies on-site and use the space for short periods while waiting for the body to be transferred.

(l) Food preparation centers should have an excess of air supply for positive pressurization when hoods are not in use. The number of air changes may be reduced or varied for odor control when the space is not in use. Minimum total air changes per hour should be that required to provide proper makeup air to kitchen exhaust systems. See Chapter 30, "Kitchen Ventilation," *1999 ASHRAE Handbook—HVAC Applications*. In addition care must be taken to ensure that exfiltration or infiltration to or from exit corridors does not compromise the exit corridor restrictions of NFPA 90A, the pressure requirements of NFPA 96, or the maximum defined in the table. The number of air changes may be reduced or varied to any extent required for odor control when the space is not in use. See Section 7.31.D1.p. (2001 AIA Guidelines).

(m) Areas with contamination and/or odor problems shall be exhausted to the outside and not recirculated to other areas. Individual circumstances may require special consideration for air exhaust to the outside; intensive care units in which patients with pulmonary infection are treated and rooms for burn patients are examples. To satisfy exhaust needs, replacement air from the outside is necessary. Minimum outside air quantities should remain constant while the system is in operation.

(n) The relative humidity ranges listed are the minimum and maximum limits where control is specifically needed. These limits are not intended to be independent of a space temperature. For example, the relative humidity is expected to be at the higher end of the range when the temperature is also at the higher end, and vice versa.

(o) For indicated temperature ranges, the systems shall be capable of maintaining the rooms at any point within the range during normal operation. A single figure indicates a heating or cooling capacity to at least meet the indicated temperature. This is usually applicable when patients may be undressed and require a warmer environment. Use of lower temperature is acceptable when patients' comfort and medical conditions require those conditions.

(p) National Institute for Occupational Safety and Health (NIOSH) Criteria Documents regarding "Occupational Exposure to Waste Anesthetic Gases and Vapors" and "Control of Occupational Exposure to Nitrous Oxide" indicate a need for both local exhaust (scavenging) systems and general ventilation of the areas in which the respective gases are utilized.

Table 4-1. (Continued)

(q) Differential pressure between space and corridors shall be a minimum of 0.01 inch water gauge (2.5 Pa). If monitoring device alarms are installed, allowances shall be made to prevent nuisance alarms.

(r) Because some surgeons or surgical procedures may require room temperatures that are outside of the indicated range, operating room design conditions should be developed in consort with all users, surgeons, anesthesiologists, and nursing staff. The required total air change rates are also a function of space temperature setpoint, supply air temperature, sensible and latent load in the space. For recent research refer to Appendix I.

(s) The first aid room and/or "emergency room" used for initial treatment of accident victims can be ventilated as noted for the "treatment room." Treatment rooms used for bronchoscopy shall be treated as bronchoscopy rooms. Treatment rooms used for cryosurgery procedures with nitrous oxide shall contain provisions for exhausting waste gases.

(t) In a recirculating ventilation system, HEPA filters can be used in lieu of exhausting the air from these spaces to the outside. In this application, the return air shall be passed through the HEPA filters before it is introduced into any other spaces.

(u) If exhausting the air from an airborne infection isolation room to the outside is not practical, the air may be returned through HEPA filters to an air-handling system exclusively serving the isolation room.

(v) Total air changes per room for patient rooms and labor/delivery/recovery/postpartum rooms may be reduced to 4 when supplemental heating and/or cooling systems (radiant heating and cooling, baseboard heating, etc.) are used.

(w) The protective environment airflow design specifications protect the patient from common environmental airborne infectious microbes (i.e., *Aspergillus* spores). These special ventilation areas shall be designed to provide directed airflow from the cleanest patient area to less clean areas. These rooms shall be protected with HEPA filters at 99.97 percent efficiency for 0.3 micron-sized particles in the supply airstream. These interrupting filters protect patient rooms from maintenance-derived release of environmental microbes from the ventilation system components. Recirculation HEPA filters can be used to increase the equivalent room air exchanges. Constant volume airflow is required for consistent ventilation for the protected environment. If the design criteria indicate that airborne infection isolation is necessary for protective environment patients, an anteroom should be provided. Rooms with reversible airflow provisions for the purpose of switching between protective environment and airborne infection isolation functions are not acceptable (2001 AIA Guidelines).

(x) The infectious disease isolation room described in these guidelines is to be used for isolating the airborne spread of infectious diseases, such as measles, varicella, or tuberculosis. The design of airborne infection isolation (AII) rooms should include the provision for normal patient care during periods not requiring isolation precautions. Supplemental recirculating devices may be used in the patient room to increase the equivalent room air exchanges; however, such recirculating devices do not provide the outside air requirements. Air may be recirculated within individual isolation rooms if HEPA filters are used. Rooms with reversible airflow provisions for the purpose of switching between protective environment and AII functions are not acceptable (2001 AIA Guidelines).

(y) When required, appropriate hoods and exhaust devices for the removal of noxious gases or chemical vapors shall be provided (see Section 7.31.D14 and 7.31.D15 2001 AIA Guidelines and NFPA 99).

(z) A simple visual method such as smoke trail, ball-in-tube, or flutterstrip can be used for verification of airflow direction. These devices will require a minimum differential air pressure to indicate airflow direction. In accordance with AIA 2001 Guidelines, recirculating devices with HEPA filters may have potential uses in existing facilities as interim, supplemental environmental controls to meet requirements for the control of airborne infectious agents. Limitations in design must be recognized. The design of either portable or fixed systems should prevent stagnation and short circuiting of airflow. The supply and exhaust locations should direct clean air to areas where health care workers are likely to work, across the infectious source, and then to the exhaust, so that the health care worker is not positioned between the infectious source and the exhaust location. The design of such systems should also allow for easy access for scheduled preventative maintenance and cleaning.

As with the data presented in Table 4-1, these notes have been extracted from the *ASHRAE Handbook—HVAC Applications* and the 2001 AIA Guidelines for Design and Construction of Health Care Facilities. *Material from the AIA 2001 Guidelines is used with permission.*

room conditions can be established under the most stringent operational or outside weather conditions defined by applicable design criteria.

4.6.2 Outside Design Conditions

Outdoor air temperature and relative humidity, as well as other climatic information (wind speed, sky clearness, ground reflectance, etc.), must be well defined to enable accurate cooling and heating load calculations. Outside design temperatures are normally provided by governing criteria, which either provide specific temperature values to be used or else cite a published weather standard (such as the *ASHRAE Handbook—Fundamentals*) and design severity (0.4% DB, etc.).

Many criteria call for use of the ASHRAE 0.4% dry-bulb (DB) and mean coincident wet-bulb (MWB) temperatures for cooling applications and the 99.6% dry-bulb temperature for heating, for inpatient and some outpatient (normally surgical) facilities where environmental conditions are relatively more critical to patient well being. Typical criteria for outpatient clinics call for using the ASHRAE 1% and 99% design temperatures for cooling and heating loads, respectively. Maximum cooling load can occur at peak WB conditions when outside air demands are high; for this reason, and for sizing evaporative and dehumidification equipment, designers should consider peak total load (latent plus sensible) climatic conditions for each project. ASHRAE has several design weather publications and products to aid the designer, including a *Design Weather Sequence Viewer* CD, WYEC2 data, and ASHRAE *EXTREMES*. Refer to the ASHRAE web site (www.ashrae.org) for further information.

For any project, the designer must be careful to use climatic data for the site closest to the actual project location. The designer must also carefully consider characteristic features of the building or surroundings that can affect heating and cooling loads. As an example, ventilation air drawn into a building from a location near a dark-colored roof may be at significantly higher temperature than the design dry-bulb for the project location.

4.6.3 Equipment Loads

Designers new to health care facility design often have difficulty in estimating the cooling loads contributed by medical equipment. Like other equipment, the heat released to the surroundings by an item of medical equipment is often much less than its full-load electrical rating. Heat release will also vary according to how frequently the equipment is used and for how long each "use cycle" lasts.

Appendix C of this manual provides some basic guidance for estimating medical equipment loads, but medical technology—and equipment—changes quickly; designers should attempt to obtain the most up-to-date information for the actual medical equipment to be provided. Heat release information is often available from equipment manufacturers, and information on the frequency of usage may come from the eventual equipment user. Another typically good source of information is the medical equipment planner for each project. Manufacturers of some high-convective-heat release equipment (such as sterilizers and cooking equipment) offer guidance on the design of exhaust hoods for heat removal at the source. Designers should also become aware of the heat release and environmental conditioning requirements for electronic communications and data equipment spaces that support various medical functions.

4.6.4 Equipment Redundancy and Service Continuity

The fundamental importance of maintaining reasonable interior conditions in critical patient applications often dictates that some degree of backup heating, and in many cases cooling and/or ventilation, capacity should be available in the event of major HVAC equipment failure. According to the applicable codes or criteria, inpatient and many outpatient surgical facilities may be required to have up to 100% backup capability for equipment essential to system operation. It should be recognized that even where loss of a major HVAC service does not jeopardize life or health, it may lead to inability to continue medical functions and unacceptable economic impact to the building owner. Designers should also recognize that routine maintenance requirements will, at least on an annual or seasonal basis, require major plant equipment to be taken off line for extended periods. Even where 100% redundancy is not required, it is often prudent to size and configure plant equipment for "off season" operation to enable extended maintenance of individual units.

Emergency power (EP) is mandated by several codes and standards for HVAC equipment considered essential for safety and health. Facility heating, particularly for critical and patient room spaces, is normally required to be connected to the EP system, as is the cooling system in some jurisdictions. Federal government regulations and/or guidelines require that ventilation equipment serving disease isolation and protective isolation rooms be connected to the emergency power system. As emergency power generation and distribution equipment is expensive, these requirements can impact the configuration and sizing of HVAC plant and air-handling equipment.

Depending upon facility type, location, system characteristics, applicable criteria, and owner desires, the following services and equipment may be required to be connected to the emergency power system. Refer to Appendix G for more details.

• Ventilation: supply, return, and exhaust fans to maintain critical pressure relationships or to control hazards or contaminant levels.

• Heating and steam generation equipment: boilers, pumps, fuel supply, air-handling units, and other equipment needed to support heating of inpatient areas, freeze protection, and supply of steam to sterilization or other critical processes.

• Domestic water pumps.

• Domestic hot water generation and recirculation for patient care and dietary areas.

• Cooling generators, pumps, and air-handling and other equipment necessary to continue cooling for critical inpatient or sensitive equipment areas.

• Controls needed to support the above equipment.

In developing commissioning requirements, designers should ensure that equipment to be connected to the EP system is tested in both normal and emergency power modes of operation.

4.7 VENTILATION AND OUTSIDE AIR QUALITY

Health care facilities require large amounts of fresh, clean, outside air for breathing and for control of hazards and odors through dilution ventilation and exhaust makeup. Under normal circumstances, outside air contains much lower concentrations of microorganisms, dust, soot, and gaseous contaminants than indoor air. When filtered by high efficiency filtration, such as is mandated by many codes, outside air can be virtually free of microorganisms and particulates. When outside air is not at an acceptable quality level, as may occur in heavily industrialized areas, special gas adsorption filtration may be required on air intakes. In addition to a good source of outside air, adequate ventilation requires the careful location of intakes to avoid contamination, exhaust of contaminants, an adequate and controlled quantity of makeup air, and good distribution and mixing of the clean air throughout the spaces served. *ASHRAE Standard 62-2001, Ventilation for Acceptable Indoor Air Quality* should be utilized as a minimum standard for ventilation design.

4.7.1 Ventilation Air Quantity

Many codes and standards provide minimum outside airflow rates for individual health care facility spaces, based either on a flow rate per person or room air change rate basis. Standard 62-2001 is often cited as a minimum standard for determining outside air quantity for individual spaces and in addition provides guidance for calculating minimum outside air rates for central systems. Minimum total room airflow rates (combined outside air and recirculation) are also often mandated by codes or criteria, based upon the cumulative dilution effect of central systems serving large numbers of spaces, the air-cleaning effectiveness of high efficiency filtration, or the minimum flow required to ensure good air mixing and comfort.

4.7.2 Location of Outside Air Intakes

Outside air intakes must be located an adequate distance away from potential contamination sources to avoid intake of contaminants. Typical minimum separation requirements are 25 feet (7.6 meters), established by the *AIA Guidelines*, and 30 feet (9.1 meters), according to the *ASHRAE Handbook— HVAC Applications*. These distances should only be considered as preliminary guides: greater separation may be required depending upon the nature of the contaminant, the direction of prevailing winds, and the relative locations of the intake and contaminant sources. The *ASHRAE Handbook—Fundamentals* provides further design guidance and calculation methods to help predict airflow characteristics around buildings, stack/exhaust outlet performance, and suitable locations for intakes. General guidance that should be observed for all projects includes the following.

• Do not locate intakes in proximity to combustion equipment stacks, motor vehicle exhausts, building exhausts and stack vents, and cooling towers.

• Keep intakes well above ground level, to avoid contamination from such sources as wet soil or piled leaves and to avoid standing water or snowdrifts. For similar reasons, roof-mounted intakes should terminate well above the roof level (3-4 feet [0.9-1.2 meters] in many codes).

• Provide for adequate access to outside air intake plenums to enable periodic inspection and cleaning. Security considerations may dictate that access be available only via building interiors or via locked equipment room doors.

In the aftermath of the September 11, 2001, terrorist attacks, some jurisdictions are developing requirements for more remote location of outside air intakes and/or other measures to minimize the possibility of access to the intakes by unauthorized persons.

4.7.3 Air Mixing and Ventilation Effectiveness

In most health care applications, it is desirable to introduce fresh air into a space in such a manner as to maximize distribution throughout the space. Doing so maximizes the effectiveness of the ventilation, ensuring that the fresh air is available everywhere it is needed and eliminating stagnant air pockets. As will be further discussed in Chapter 9, good distribution and mixing also contribute to overall room comfort. Good air mixing is achieved by careful selection of diffuser location and performance, with proper attention to room construction features (soffits for example) or perimeter exposures that can affect distribution performance. Additional information is available in Chapter 9.

4.7.4 Exhaust of Contaminants and Odors

Exhaust systems provide for removal of contaminants and odors from the facility, preferably as close to the source of generation as possible. In addition, exhaust systems are used to remove moisture and flammable particles or aerosols. Examples of source exhaust in health care applications include:

- Chemical fume hoods and certain biological safety cabinets are used in laboratories and similar applications where health care workers must handle highly volatile or easily aerosolized materials.
- Special exhaust connections or trunk ducts are used in surgical applications to remove waste anesthesia gases or the aerosolized particles in laser plumes.
- "Wet" X-ray film development machines are normally provided with exhaust duct connections for removal of development chemical fumes.
- Cough inducement booths or hoods are used particularly in the therapy of contagious respiratory disease.

When contaminants or odors cannot practically be captured at the source, the space in which the contaminant is generated should be exhausted. Rooms typically exhausted include laboratories, soiled linen rooms, waste storage rooms, central sterile decontamination (dirty processing), anesthesia storage rooms, and disease isolation rooms. For some potentially very hazardous exhausts, such as from radioisotope chemical fume hoods or disease isolation spaces, codes or regulations may require HEPA filtration of the exhaust discharge, particularly if the discharge is located too close to a pedestrian area or outside air intake.

4.8 ENVIRONMENTAL CONTROL

4.8.1 The Role of Temperature and Relative Humidity

Previous discussions have touched upon the role of temperature and relative humidity in infection control. Temperature and relative humidity are equally important from a patient therapeutic standpoint and in maintaining a reasonable work environment for health care professionals. In an uncomfortable environment, the sick or injured patient is subjected to thermal stress. Thermal stress may cause much more than discomfort: it can render difficult or impossible the patient's ability to properly regulate body heat, it interferes with rest, and it may be psychologically harmful. In addition, poorly controlled conditions can result in such problems as dry skin and mucous membranes, further increasing discomfort and stress. Conditions of temperature and relative humidity that would be considered comfortable for healthy individuals dressed in normal clothing may be very uncomfortable for both patients and health care workers, for a variety of reasons, including the following.

- Patients in both clinical and inpatient facilities may be very scantily clad or, in some instances, unclothed and have little or no control over their clothing.
- In hospital settings, patients are exposed to the environment on a continuous basis, not merely for short periods of time.
- In a variety of cases of disease or injury, patient metabolism, fever, or other conditions can interfere with the body's ability to regulate heat.
- Health care workers often must wear heavy protective coverings, as in surgery and the emergency department, and engage in strenuous, stressful activities.

Table 4-1, previously referenced, provides recommended temperature and relative humidity ranges for typical health care spaces, generally selected in consideration of patients or health care workers. For some special medical conditions, more extreme levels of temperature and relative humidity are sometimes employed in patient therapy, for example:

- Conditions of 90°F (32°C) and 35% RH have been found beneficial in treating certain kinds of arthritis.
- An environment of 90°F (32°C) and 95% RH is sometimes used for burn patients.
- A temperature in the middle 80s (°F) (around 30°C) is sometimes called for in pediatric surgery.

Such high temperatures and/or relative humidities are normally not practically maintainable on a large space (or area) basis and, when called for, would be established in limited environmental enclosures or when using special equipment.

4.8.2 Noise Control

Noise control is of high importance in the health care environment because of the negative impact of high noise levels on patients and staff and because of the need to safeguard patient privacy. The typical health care facility is already full of loud noises from a variety of communications equipment, alarms, noisy operating hardware, and other causes without the noise contribution from poorly designed or installed HVAC equipment. High noise levels hinder patient healing largely through interference with rest and sleep. In addition, like uncomfortable thermal conditions, loud noises degrade the health care provider's working environment, increase stress, and can cause dangerous irritation and distraction during the performance of critical activities. Sources of excessive HVAC noise include:

- Direct transmission of mechanical and/or medical equipment room noise to adjacent spaces.
- Duct-borne noise generated by fans and/or high air velocities in ducts, fittings, terminal equipment, or diffusers and transmitted through ductwork to adjoining occupied spaces.
- Duct breakout noise, when loud noises in ductwork penetrate the walls of the duct and enter occupied spaces.
- Duct rumble, a form of low-frequency breakout noise caused by the acoustical response of ductwork (particularly high-aspect-ratio, poorly braced rectangular duct) to fan noise.

One standard means of quantifying room noise levels is the noise criteria (NC) method, which assigns a single-number noise level to a curve of sound pressure level values (in decibels, dB) estab-

lished for each of the eight audible octave bands. The higher the NC level, the more noisy the space. One characteristic of the NC approach is that it takes into account the subjective perception of noise level by the human ear relative to the frequency of the sound, recognizing that low-frequency noises are better tolerated than high-frequency. Several codes and standards provide maximum NC levels for typical health care facility spaces.

Patient privacy can be compromised when private conversations are intelligibly transmitted between adjoining spaces. Frequent causes of this problem are inadequate acoustical insulation (isolation) properties of the construction elements separating rooms, inadequate sound-dampening provisions in ductwork, and/or inadequate background room sound pressure level. The HVAC ductwork design and diffuser/register selections can greatly influence the latter two causes, by providing a minimum level of background sound contribution from the air distribution system and by ensuring effective attenuation in ductwork. Chapter 9 of this manual provides more detailed information of the causes of, and solutions for, HVAC noise.

4.9 HVAC "SYSTEM HYGIENE"

Although the general topic of nosocomial infection cause and control was discussed above, the designer must be aware of the potential for infection risks that can arise through poor design or maintenance of the HVAC equipment itself. Any location where moisture and nutrient matter collect together can become a reservoir for growth of deadly microorganisms. Generally, hard surfaces (such as sheet metal) require the presence of liquid moisture to support microbe growth, whereas growth in porous materials may require only high (> 50%) relative humidity. Nutrient materials are readily available from such sources as soil, environmental dust, animal droppings, and other organic and inorganic matter. The task of the HVAC designer is to minimize the opportunity for moisture and nutrients to collect in the system, through proper design of equipment, including adequate provisions for inspection and maintenance. Potential high-risk conditions in an HVAC system include:

- Outside air intakes located too close to collected organic debris, such as wet leaves, animal nests, trash, wet soil, grass clippings, or low areas where dust and moisture collect. This is a particular concern with low-level intakes and a primary reason for code-mandated separation requirements between intake and ground, or intake and roof, discussed previously.

- Outside air intakes not properly designed to exclude precipitation. Examples are intakes without intake louvers (or with improperly designed louvers) and intakes located where snow can form drifts or where splashing rain can enter.
- Improperly designed outside air intake opening ledges where the collected droppings of roosting birds carry or support the growth of many dangerous species of pathogens.
- Improperly designed cooling coil drain pans or drainage traps that prevent adequate condensate drainage.
- Air-handling unit or duct-mounted humidifiers not properly designed to ensure complete evaporation before impingement on downstream equipment or fittings.
- Filters and permeable duct linings, which collect dust, located too close to a moisture source, such as a cooling coil or humidifier.
- Improper attention to maintenance during design, resulting in air-handling components that cannot be adequately accessed for inspection or cleaning.

Designers must always bear in mind that even properly designed equipment must be maintainable if it is to remain in clean operating condition. Chapter 9 of this manual provides additional information regarding the proper design of HVAC system components to minimize the potential for microbe growth.

4.10 FLEXIBILITY FOR FUTURE CHANGES

Changes in space utilization are common in health care facilities, and periods of less than ten years between complete remodelings are commonplace. The trend is normally toward more medical equipment and increasing internal cooling loads. The initial design should consider likely future changes, and the design team and owner should consider a rational balance between providing for future contingencies and initial investment costs. Future contingencies may be addressed by such features as:

- Oversizing of ductwork and piping.
- Provision of spare equipment capacity (oversizing) for major plant, air moving, or pumping equipment or provision of plant/floor space for future equipment installation.
- Provision of interstitial utility floors, where maintenance and equipment modification or

replacement can occur with minimal impact on facility operation.

4.11 INTEGRATED DESIGN

4.11.1 General

In order to be successful, the HVAC design must be thoroughly coordinated with the other design disciplines. The HVAC engineer's involvement should begin not later than pre-concept design and continue until design completion. This chapter has addressed some of the design features essential to good air quality, hygienic design, and comfort conditioning, but obtaining these features requires the HVAC designer's early influence on building arrangement and floor plan features that affect equipment location and space availability. Early involvement and design coordination are essential to ensure that:

- Outside air intakes and building exhausts are optimally located to avoid contamination of the building air supply.
- Plant and equipment rooms are well located in relation to the areas they serve, to enable economic sizing of distribution equipment and air and water velocities well within noise limitation guidelines.
- Plant and equipment rooms are so located that equipment noise will not disrupt adjacent occupied spaces.
- HVAC equipment room locations are coordinated with electrical, communications, and plumbing equipment rooms to minimize distribution equipment (duct, piping, cable trays, conduit) congestion and crossover, while providing adequate space for installation and maintenance of these services.
- Sufficient vertical building space is provided for the installation and maintenance of distribution equipment of all trades.
- Sufficient space is provided for plant and equipment rooms, and vertical utility chases, to enable proper installation, operation, and maintenance of the equipment, including provisions for eventual equipment replacement.

4.11.2 Stages of Design Development

The stages of design development, including the number of discrete "submissions," which mark the progress of design and provide an opportunity for owner comment and feedback, vary widely by facility complexity, owner needs, project schedule and budget, and other factors. Whether the design is "conventional" design-bid-build or design-build will also affect the interim stages. For the purpose of emphasizing the need for early and continuous HVAC designer involvement in the overall project design, however, a "typical" five-stage design project is outlined here.

- *Programming and predesign*, wherein the owner and/or his/her agent develops the scope of requirements for the facility. This "program" normally defines the type of services to be provided by the facility and the approximate number and type of spaces to be included in each department. The "program" will normally provide some information regarding the required scope of site and utility development and plant necessary to support the project. Appendix C provides typical load densities that can be used in early evaluation and broad scoping of the HVAC system requirements.
- *Preconcept design*, which typically takes the design to 15-20% development, involves establishing the outline and orientation of the building, preliminary elevations and consideration of envelope materials, department layout including circulation spaces, and in many cases the initial development of the floor plan.
- *Concept design*, completing development of the design to a level approaching 30-35% completion. This level usually includes a fully developed floor plan, an outline of specifications, and concept-level development of all supporting design disciplines.
- *Interim final*, which takes the design to the 60-65% design level, is normally provided to provide an opportunity for owner review and feedback before design finalization.
- *Final design*: complete development of all design documentation.

The HVAC designer should be intimately involved beginning with the Preconcept Design, with some degree of input having been provided for site utility and plant programming/planning. During Preconcept Design, the HVAC engineer's input is necessary for the architect to appreciate the energy and physical plant implications of building orientation, configuration, envelope materials (especially fenestration), and vertical floor height. Involvement enables the HVAC engineer to influence the locations and sizes of plant and equipment rooms and strategies for service distribution, thereby enhancing future maintainability and flexibility for change. Involvement at this stage also enables the HVAC designer to begin to coordinate the design with the

several other major design disciplines with which the HVAC systems must functionally and physically interface.

By the completion of concept design, the floor plan and overall building configuration are normally "locked down," as is the project cost estimate. Later modification or enlargement of equipment space becomes difficult or impossible. Therefore, during concept development the HVAC designer must refine the preliminary load and demand calculations and make final system selections to enable a good estimate of the required equipment cost, capacities, configuration, and dimensional space requirements. The approximate size and distribution arrangement of ductwork and piping mains (especially steam, condensate, or other vertically sloped systems) should be determined, to enable confirmation of the adequacy of building spaces and coordination with other disciplines. Where final equipment or fitting selections are not yet determined, but where these have potential space impact (attenuating equipment, for example), the designer should reserve space on a "worst case" scenario.

For the final design stages, the HVAC designer must refine and complete the design while coordinating with the other design disciplines to stay abreast of design refinements or changes that affect the HVAC system.

4.11.3 Equipment Interface: "Make it Fit"

Because of the many engineering systems that provide service in health care facilities, the need to ensure adequate access for future maintenance, and often because of criteria restrictions on where distribution equipment can be installed (i.e., above circulation spaces), the HVAC designer must carefully coordinate the physical space requirements of his/her equipment. Health care facilities are served by a wide variety of fire protection, electrical power, plumbing, medical gas, and telephone, data, nurse call, and other electronic communication and monitoring systems. All of these must physically fit within allowable distribution spaces along with HVAC ductwork and piping. Often, codes or criteria restrict main utility distribution to circulation spaces in order to minimize the need for maintenance personnel access into occupied spaces and/or to control noise. Codes also restrict certain utilities from passage over electrical and communications spaces, exit enclosures, and certain critical health care spaces, such as operating rooms.

It is the responsibility of design engineers to ensure that the equipment they depict in design drawings can be installed in the spaces indicated with sufficient space for maintenance access, by a prudent contractor using standard construction practices and reasonable judgment in equipment selection, according to the provisions of his/her contract. Where the designer knows that the availability of space is so limited as to require special construction measures or very limited or proprietary equipment selections, it is wise to make this information known in the design documents. A prudent designer depicts and dimensions the equipment on design drawings, including ductwork and piping and showing all major fittings required for coordination (offsets, etc.), balancing, and operation, such that it could reasonably be installed as depicted. These design responsibilities do not detract from the construction contractor's responsibility to properly coordinate the installation work between trades and do not supplant his/her responsibility to execute detailed, coordinated construction shop (installation) drawings.

Most designers check the coordination of their systems with those of other disciplines by a variety of methods that may include multi-dimensional overlays and representative elevational views or sketches. The latter should be provided from at least two perspectives in each congested plant and equipment room and at representative "crowded" locations in distribution areas throughout the facility. Some building owners require submission of such "proof of concept" documents to demonstrate satisfactory interdisciplinary coordination.

4.11.4 Special Considerations for Retrofit/Renovation

Designs for the retrofit or renovation of existing health care facilities, particularly when health care functions must continue during construction in areas surrounding or adjacent to project work, require special attention to factors that can affect patient health and safety. Designs must include provisions to minimize the migration of construction dust and debris into patient areas or the possibility of unplanned interruptions of critical engineering services.

Construction work almost invariably involves the introduction or generation of relatively high levels of airborne dust or debris, which, without appropriate barrier controls, may convey microbial and other contaminants into patient care areas. Demolition activities, the transport of debris, and personnel traffic in and out of the facility can directly introduce contaminants, as can disruption of existing HVAC equipment, removal of barrier walls or partitions, and disturbances of building elements and equipment within occupied areas. Project architects and engineers must work closely with the owner's infection control representative to help assess the potential risks to the patient population during construction activities, and jointly identify the appropriate barrier controls and techniques. Typical barrier precautions can include separation of construction areas by dust-tight temporary partitions, exclusion of construction traffic from occupied areas, and isolation of duct systems connecting construction with occupied spaces. In addition, negative relative pressurization and exhaust of construction areas may be required and, in cases of severe patient vulnerability, the introduction of supplemental HEPA filtration units into patient rooms or other critical spaces may be considered.

Of equal concern, designers must seek to minimize the possibility of unplanned service interruptions during the construction project. Designers should become well acquainted with the existing engineering systems and building conditions to be able to evaluate the impact of new construction. Site investigations should always include inspection of existing equipment plants, rooms, and other equipment and building areas with reasonably available access. Maintenance personnel can often provide information of concealed as-built conditions, and as-built drawings are often available; in many cases, however, the latter are inaccurate or not up to date.

When as-built information is lacking or suspect, designers should attempt to identify existing services that are installed in, or are likely to be affected by, project work, to the extent feasible under the scope of their design contract and the physical or operational limitations of building access. Building owners should recognize the value of accurate as-built information and, when not available from in-house sources, contractually provide for more thorough investigations by the design team. It is the designer's responsibility to identify the nature of alterations of, or extensions to, existing services and equipment, including temporary features, and any required interim or final re-balancing, commissioning, or certification services, necessary to accommodate new building services while minimizing impact to ongoing functions. This will often require the development of a detailed phasing plan, developed in close coordination with the building owner. The goal should be "no surprises"—no interruptions or diminishment of critical services to occupied areas that are not planned and identified to the building owner during the design process. Chapter 6 provides more information on this topic.

CHAPTER 5
HVAC SYSTEMS

5.1 INTRODUCTION

A fundamental difference between conventional HVAC systems design and HVAC systems for hospitals is the need for relative pressurization between rooms/areas within the facility. Generally, airflow is from clean to "less clean" areas. (Refer to Chapter 4, "Overview of Health Care HVAC," and Chapter 12, "Room Design," for additional information.)

The level of air filtration for patient care areas in hospitals is higher than for most other facilities. The *Guidelines for Design and Construction of Hospitals and Health Care Facilities* and the *ASHRAE Handbook—HVAC Applications* provide guidance and recommendations for ventilation and humidity in such areas (AIA 2001; ASHRAE 1999a). Related criteria are provided in Chapter 4, "Overview of Health Care HVAC."

Special considerations for operating rooms impose restrictions on HVAC system selection. The requirements for operating rooms include precise temperature and humidity controls, as well as space pressurization, filtration of the supply air, limits on allowable recirculation of the air, and ventilation effectiveness of the air delivery system (refer to Chapter 12, "Room Design," for details.)

A properly designed HVAC system provides reliable operation, for example, consistent temperature, humidity, and outside air volume and adequate accessibility to facilitate maintenance of the systems. Proper maintenance of the systems will sustain indoor air quality (IAQ) and energy efficiency. Considering future replacement of equipment and accessibility for regular maintenance is an important aspect of design.

Air-based HVAC systems can be divided into two fundamental categories: constant volume and variable air volume (VAV) systems. (Refer to *ASHRAE Handbook—HVAC Systems and Equipment* for further information regarding the general advantages and disadvantages of these systems [ASHRAE 2000].) Constant volume systems are often the choice for patient care areas of hospitals; however, variable volume systems may be used in these areas with proper controls. Constant volume systems offer the simplest design approach where relative pressure differentials between rooms are required—for example, in operating rooms and laboratories. (Refer to Chapter 12 for relative pressure relationships for spaces.) VAV systems are commonly used in areas where relative pressure relationships between rooms need not be controlled, for example, in administrative areas.

ASHRAE Standard 15 and local codes limit the use of direct expansion (DX) refrigerant systems in health care facilities (ASHRAE 2001b). Refer to Chapter 7, "Cooling Plants," for additional information on this important system selection limitation.

5.2 HVAC SYSTEMS

ASHRAE has classified central HVAC systems into three basic categories: all-air systems, all-water systems, and air and water systems (ASHRAE 2000a, 1993). Table 5-1 lists HVAC system types that fall in these basic categories.

All-air systems meet the entire sensible and latent cooling capacity through cold air supplied to the conditioned space. No supplemental heat removal is required at the zone. Heating may be accomplished at the central air handler or at the zone.

Air and water systems condition spaces by distributing air and water supplies to terminal units installed in the spaces. The air and water are cooled or heated by equipment in a central mechanical

Table 5-1. HVAC System Classifications

HVAC System Category	HVAC System
All-air	Constant volume, single duct, terminal reheat Constant volume, double duct Multizone VAV, single duct VAV, dual duct
Air and water	Primary air with induction units Primary air with fan coil (for Type "B" occupancies) Water-source heat pump Fan coil (limited to nonclinical spaces)
All-water	Perimeter Radiation Radiant panels
Unitary (DX)	Packaged terminal air conditioners (PTACs) Packaged split-system air conditioners

room. These systems typically involve air-and-water induction units and fan-coil units.

All-water systems condition spaces by using chilled water circulated from a central refrigeration plant to heat exchangers or terminal units located in or adjacent to the conditioned spaces. Heating water is supplied either through the same piping network or by an independent piping system. Special HVAC systems include thermal storage systems, desiccant systems, and heat recovery systems. Heat recovery systems are often successfully integrated within the HVAC system. Run-around heat recovery systems are commonly used in health care facility designs (refer to Chapter 16, "Energy Efficient Design and Conservation of Resources").

Table 5-2 summarizes HVAC systems typically recommended for the functional areas in health care facilities. Final system selection would depend upon actual layout and design criteria of the facility, redundancy requirements, and life-cycle cost.

5.3 ALL-AIR SYSTEMS

In an all-air system a chiller supplies chilled water to one or more air-handling units. The air-handling units consist of mixing plenums where outdoor air and return air are mixed, filters (medium or high efficiency), cooling and/or heating coils, and fans, all contained in an insulated sheet metal housing. Air is distributed from the air handlers through ductwork (often medium-pressure) to terminal units and then to the space through a low-pressure distribution system. The terminal units regulate heating of the air with hot water, steam, or electric resistance coils in response to space temperature conditions. Air is returned from the space to the unit for recirculation

or exhaust using return or exhaust fans. See Figure 5.1 for general layout of an air-handling system.

5.3.1 Constant or Variable Volume, Single Duct, with Terminal Reheat

Constant volume with reheat systems are currently most commonly used in hospitals. The variable volume with reheat systems are also widely used, provided pressure relationships are maintained. See chapter 16 for further details. The reheat aspect may require justification to some local jurisdictions. See Figure 5-2 for a constant volume reheat system schematic and Figure 5-3 for a variable air volume system schematic.

Advantages

- HVAC equipment is centralized for ease of maintenance
- Central equipment can take advantage of load diversity for optimal sizing
- Can use air-side economizers effectively
- Provides a great deal of flexibility for multiple zones
- Provides good dehumidification control
- Well suited for good control of building pressurization
- Good control of ventilation air quantities
- Opportunity for high levels of filtration.

Disadvantages

- Reheating of cooled air in constant volume systems is not energy-efficient
- First costs can be higher than unitary equipment
- Requires mechanical space for equipment rooms, shafts, etc.

Table 5-2. HVAC System Applicability

Functional Area[a]	HVAC System[b]
Critical care	Constant volume, single duct, terminal reheat Constant volume, double duct, VAV with reheat
Sensitive[c]	Unitary systems (refrigerant-based) [unitary not chilled water]
Clinic	Constant volume, single duct, terminal reheat Constant volume, double duct Multizone VAV with reheat VAV, single duct with fan-powered boxes Including perimeter radiation (if required)[e]
Administrative and general support	Constant volume, single duct, terminal reheat Constant volume, double duct Multizone VAV with reheat VAV, dual duct VAV, single duct with fan-powered boxes Fan-coil (limited to nonclinical spaces) Including perimeter radiation (if required)[e]
Support areas (clinical)[d]	Constant volume, single duct, terminal reheat Constant volume, double duct Multizone VAV with reheat Dual duct Including perimeter radiation (if required)[e]
Patient care areas	Constant volume, single duct, terminal reheat Constant volume, double duct Multizone VAV with reheat Dual duct Including perimeter radiation (if required)[e]
Laboratory	Constant volume, single duct, terminal reheat Constant volume, double duct Multizone VAV with reheat Including perimeter radiation (if required)[e]

a. Refer to Chapter 3.
b. Refer to Chapter 12 for rationale for systems.
c. Sensitive areas require special environmental controls. Examples include computer rooms, communications rooms, MRI, and other ancillary spaces.
d. Support areas (clinical) include sterile processing, central supply, and food services.
e. See 5.5.1.

5.3.2 VAV, Single Duct with Fan-Powered Boxes

The VAV terminal units regulate the volume of air and often heat the air with hot water, steam, or electric resistance coils in response to space temperature conditions. The terminal units are equipped with fans (fan-powered) to recirculate room air for energy conservation and temperature control. The fan-powered boxes may be either constant volume discharge or variable volume. (See Chapter 9 for additional details.)

Advantages

- Plant equipment is centralized for ease of maintenance

- Central equipment can take advantage of load diversity for optimal sizing

- Can use air-side economizers effectively

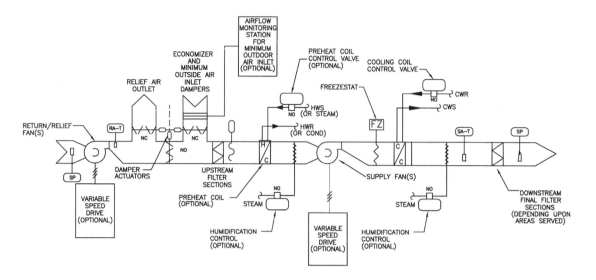

Figure 5-1   General air-handling system schematic.

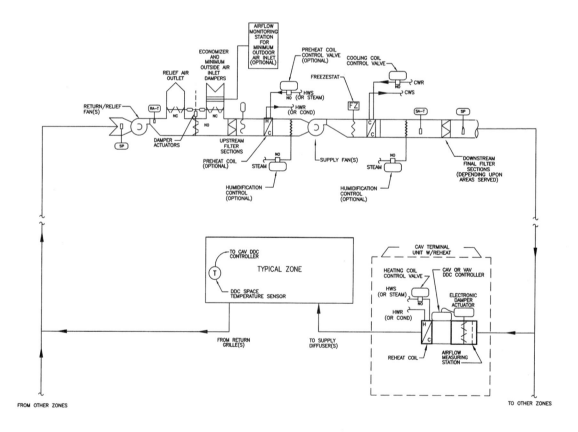

Figure 5-2   Constant volume air-handling system schematic (terminal reheat systems).

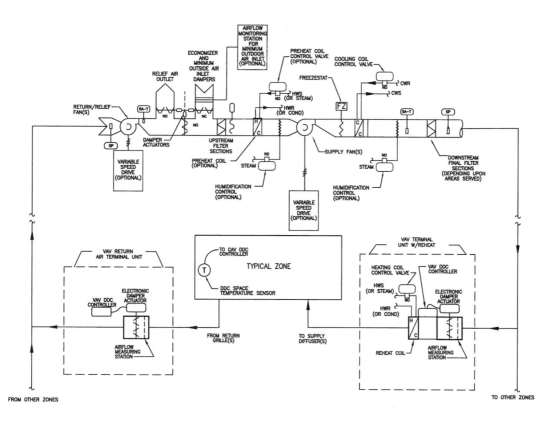

Figure 5-3   Variable air volume air-handling system schematic (terminal reheat systems).

- Variable-speed drives for fan volume control are cost-effective
- Provides a great deal of flexibility for multiple zones
- Provides good dehumidification control
- Good control of ventilation air quantities
- Opportunity for high levels of filtration
- Can use room air as first stage of reheat.

Disadvantages

- First costs can be higher than for unitary equipment.
- Special attention to acoustics is required.

5.3.3 Dual-Duct Systems

Dual-duct systems distribute air from a central apparatus to the conditioned spaces through two parallel ducts. One duct carries cold air and the other warm air, providing air sources for both heating and cooling at all times.

Dual-duct systems represent a good alternative to single-duct systems. Dual-duct systems provide good control of temperature and humidity, the ability to accommodate a variety of zone loads, and ease of adding zones. These systems can be either constant volume or variable volume. See Figure 5-4 for a dual-duct system schematic. Some design variations are described below.

**Dual Fan, Dual Duct
(Constant or Variable Air Volume)**

A dual-fan, dual-duct (DFDD) system blends air from two air-handling units (AHUs) to condition its zones. The cold deck AHU draws outdoor air, mixes it with return air, and cools the supply air if necessary. Economizer control is commonly incorporated.

The neutral (hot deck) AHU filters and recirculates return air. Heat can be added to this airstream.

Single Fan, Dual Duct (Variable Air Volume)

A central hot air (hot deck) and a central cool air (cold deck) supply are ducted to the terminal unit (double duct) where the cold and hot airstreams are mixed and the volume of discharge air is varied to satisfy the room temperature. The terminal units regulate the volume of air in response to space temperature conditions. Air is returned from the space to the air-handling unit for recirculation or exhaust.

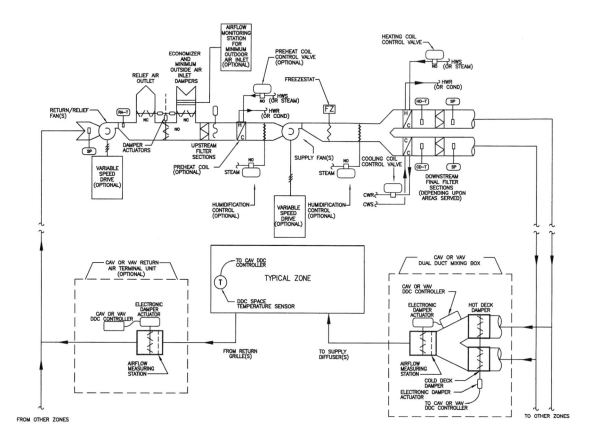

Figure 5-4   Constant volume or variable air volume air-handling system schematic (dual-duct air-handling units).

Advantages

- Plant equipment is centralized for ease of maintenance
- Central equipment can take advantage of load diversity for optimal sizing
- Can use air-side economizers effectively
- Variable-speed drives to control fan volume are cost-effective
- Provides a great deal of flexibility for multiple zones
- Provides good dehumidification control
- Well suited for good control of building pressurization
- Good control of ventilation air quantities
- Opportunity for high levels of filtration.

Disadvantages

- Can be more expensive than unitary equipment
- May require substantial duct space that may increase the building height
- Special attention to acoustics is required.

5.3.4 Multizone Systems

In a multizone system, the requirements of the different building zones are met by mixing cold air and warm air using dampers at the central air handler in response to zone thermostats. The mixed conditioned air is distributed throughout the building by a system of single-zone ducts. A central chiller plant supplies chilled water to the central air-handling unit(s). The air-handling units consist of mixing plenums where outdoor air and return air are mixed, filters (medium or high efficiency), cooling and/or heating coils, and fans, all contained in an insulated sheet metal housing. Air is returned from the space to the air-handling unit for recirculation or exhaust.

Advantages

- Plant equipment is centralized for ease of maintenance
- Central equipment can take advantage of load diversity for optimal sizing

- Can use air-side economizers effectively
- Provides limited flexibility for multiple zones
- Provides good dehumidification control
- Control of building pressurization is possible
- Good control of ventilation air quantities
- Opportunity for high levels of filtration.

Disadvantages

- First costs can be higher than for unitary equipment
- Requires space for mechanical equipment rooms, shafts, etc.
- May require substantial duct space that may increase the building height.

5.4 AIR AND WATER SYSTEMS

5.4.1 Air and Water Induction Units

These systems are not recommended for new construction or renovation. They were popular in the past and engineers may encounter these systems in existing facilities. The description below is for background information only.

The induction system consists of an air supply from a central air handler, which can be either high-pressure or low-pressure, connected to a terminal unit. The supply air is called primary air and is introduced into the terminal via nozzles. A change of pressure induces some of the room air to flow through the unit, hence the name "induction." Space temperature is maintained by coils via a control valve controlled by the room thermostat. Variations on the system, as well as the advantages and disadvantages, are described below.

Low-Pressure Induction Unit: Conditioned air from a central air-handling system is delivered at 0.2 to 0.5 in. w.g. (50 to 125 Pa) pressure to a room induction unit.

High-Pressure Induction Unit: Conditioned air from a central air-handling system is delivered at more than 0.5 in. w.g. (125 Pa) pressure to a room induction unit.

Variable Air Volume Induction Unit

A variable air volume induction unit modulates the amount of primary air to a minimum acceptable value. An induction ratio of one volume of primary air to three volumes of room air provides satisfactory room air motion and distribution. When required, a

reheat coil in the induction unit modulates hot water flow to maintain space temperature.

The following advantages and disadvantages are common to all induction systems:

Advantages

- No rotating parts, less maintenance
- Quiet, no noise problems
- Local control

Disadvantages

- Picks return air at floor level, might pick up unwanted contaminants from floor.
- No local filtration is possible. Manufacturers only offer lint screen as option. Certain patient rooms require local filtration option. Lint screen does not meet hospital filtration standard.
- Requires primary air risers at outside wall. Requires multiple shafts. Usually two units are served from one primary air riser at each level. It is expensive. Each shaft needs to be rated. Fire dampers may be needed at wall penetration.
- No local humidification is possible. Central air system can have humidity control
- Requires year-round reheat system availability.
- Patient room is out of commission during routine maintenance. Unit requires scheduled maintenance. Deposit of particles from return air.

5.4.2 Fan-Coil Units

Fan-coil system units have a finned-tube coil, filter, and fan section. The fan recirculates air continuously from the space through the coil, which contains either hot or chilled water. Some units have electric resistance heaters or steam coils. The filter is usually a cleanable or replaceable low-efficiency (less than 25%) filter that protects the coil from clogging with dirt and lint. (Although it is not recommended, units can be connected to dampered openings in the outside wall to provide some outdoor air for ventilation.) Fan coils are typically installed in a floor-mounted configuration, but horizontal (overhead) models are also available. Fan coils can be ducted to discharge through several outlets, but fan static pressure capacity is usually very limited. Ventilation is usually provided by ducting tempered outside air to the return side of the unit or directly to the space.

The fan-coil piping system can be either a two-pipe or four-pipe configuration. In a four-pipe system, both heating and cooling are available simultaneously, whereas a two-pipe system permits only heating or cooling depending upon the season.

Advantages
- System can economically provide many temperature control zones
- The system conserves space and is useful where ceiling heights are restricted
- Suitable for low-water-temperature heating, such as with heat recovery.

Disadvantages
- Some fans and motors are very inefficient
- Dehumidification can be a problem where high latent loads are present
- Fan coils are maintenance intensive and require regular filter replacement and fan and motor lubrication; condensate drain pans are subject to clogging and overflow and can present infection control problems if located in patient or clinical areas.
- Fans can be noisy
- A two-pipe system can loose temperature control capability in some seasons
- Fan coil systems can have high first cost.

5.5 ALL-WATER SYSTEMS

All-water systems condition spaces by using chilled water circulated from a central refrigeration plant to heat exchangers or terminal units located in or adjacent to the conditioned spaces. Heating water is supplied either through the same piping network or by an independent piping system. All-water systems do not, in themselves, address requirements for ventilation, humidity, etc.

5.5.1 Perimeter Radiation

Baseboard (perimeter) radiation offsets heat loss from building envelopes. Cooler room air near the floor migrates toward the exterior walls and windows where heat loss is occurring. As the air moves to the wall, it is drawn upward into and over the higher temperature finned radiation element. The rate of heat output can be controlled by varying the temperature of the heated media (steam or hot water) inside the tube of the finned element. The flow of heated water being pumped through the tubing can be varied by different control devices, creating a wider range of heat outputs. Baseboard enclosures are available in a wide variety of shapes, sizes and heat outputs. They can be wall mounted, floor mounted or recessed in the wall or floor. Enclosed fin tube radiation is not recommended for patient care areas.

Advantages
- Flexible to meet needs of each room and its specific conditions
- Water can transport more heat per unit volume than air
- Piping can be revised if room layout is redesigned or changed
- Multiple energy sources can be used to heat water or make steam (i.e., gas, oil, electricity, wood, coal, fuel cells, or solar collectors).
- Easy to control for comfort by means of electric or non-electric flow control valves, manual control valves, or even variable speed circuit pumps
- Does not transfer contaminants from room to room
- Does not transfer noise from room to room
- Can be decorated and painted to match the surrounding room finish color or window mullion color.

Disadvantages
- Heating only
- Requires cleaning
- Can present infection control problems
- May require enclosures.

5.5.2 Radiant Panel Systems

Radiant panels heat or cool a space through the emission and absorption of thermal radiation. During heating, the thermal energy emitted by the panels is absorbed by the objects within a space. Conversely, panels absorbing energy emitted by objects in a space accomplish cooling. Both hydronic and electric panels are available for heating applications. Only hydronic panels are available for cooling. Radiant systems are designed to handle the sensible loads within a space; the overall supply air requirements can therefore be limited to the fresh air ventilation requirements. In cooling applications, however, the ventilation air must be sufficiently dehumidified in order to absorb the latent load of the space. Concerns related to condensate formation in cooling applications are addressed by the combined use of dew-point and moisture sensors that regulate the supply water temperature and maintain it above the dew point of the space.

Advantages
- Aesthetically unobtrusive and easy to clean
- Applicable to any ceiling type.
- Can minimize the sensation of drafts.

- Allow full utilization of floor area (i.e., no space required for fan coils)
- Virtually silent
- Individual zone control
- No infection control problems

Disadvantages

- Lower output than finned tube style baseboard
- Requires a separate system for ventilation
- First cost can be higher than for comparable systems
- Condensation can occur in cooling application unless the chilled-water temperature is kept above the dew point.

5.6 UNITARY REFRIGERANT-BASED SYSTEMS FOR AIR CONDITIONING

The model codes place restrictions on refrigerants in health care occupancies. (Refer to Chapter 7, "Cooling Plants," for additional information on this topic.)

5.6.1 Packaged Terminal Air Conditioners

Packaged terminal air conditioners (PTAC) are a class of commercially available equipment usually used to heat and cool a single room. The units are fully self-contained and consist of a fan, filter, direct expansion cooling coil, compressor, air-cooled condenser coil, and condenser fan, all encased in an enclosure made for through-the-wall applications. Heating from PTAC units is usually from electric resistance coils. The units can also be purchased as heat pumps provided with the proper refrigeration accessories. Units can be equipped with ventilation openings of limited size and capacity.

Advantages

- Low initial cost
- Very good for tenant submetering
- Requires only small amount of space at perimeter of building.

Disadvantages

- Poor dehumidification control
- No economizer operation
- Increased maintenance due to multiple units
- Condensate removal during periods of heavy condensation
- Limited ventilation control
- Can be very noisy
- Architectural impact on building envelope
- Can create drafts and have poor air distribution

- Does not handle interior spaces
- Poor filtration
- Less energy efficient than central systems.

5.6.2 Packaged Single-Zone Split System

A packaged single-zone split system uses unitary (factory fabricated) equipment that is fully self-contained to provide heating and cooling. The system consists of an indoor package and an outdoor package that are connected with refrigerant piping and controls. The indoor package has a supply fan, filters, a direct expansion cooling coil, and heating, e.g., hot water, steam, electric resistance, etc. The outdoor unit has compressor(s), condenser coil, and condenser fans. Units can be purchased as heat pumps. Packaged single-zone split systems are typically controlled from a single space thermostat, and one unit is provided for each zone.

Advantages

- Low initial cost, but more than package rooftop systems
- Can be used where there is limited outside space available

Disadvantages

- Requires space inside the building
- Requires separate relief when economizers are used
- Distance between indoor unit and outdoor unit is limited
- Limited zoning capability
- Poor dehumidification control
- Uses more energy than a central system.
- Limited capacity to handle ventilation air.

5.6.3 Packaged Rooftop VAV or Constant Volume Unit

A packaged rooftop variable air volume air-conditioning system uses unitary (factory fabricated) equipment. The unit is fully self-contained and consists of a supply fan; a direct expansion cooling coil; heating (when required) with a gas burner, hot water, steam, or electric resistance; filters; compressors; condenser coils; and condenser fans. Units are usually equipped with outdoor air economizer sections that have no relief, barometric relief, or power relief fans. Units are typically mounted on roof curbs but can also be mounted on structural supports or on grade. Air is distributed from the unit through ductwork (often low-pressure) to terminal units and then to the space through a low-pressure distribution system. The terminal units regulate the volume of air and often heat the air with hot water or electric resistance coils in response to space temperature conditions. Sometimes, the terminal units are equipped with fans (fan-powered) to recirculate room air for energy conservation. Sometimes a separate central hot air (hot deck) system is ducted to the terminal unit (double duct) where the cold and hot airstreams are mixed and the volume of air is varied to satisfy the room temperature. Air is returned from the space to the unit for recirculation or exhaust. Return/exhaust fans can be used for this purpose or the supply fan can be assisted by a power exhaust (spill) fan. VAV systems generally incorporate by-pass air to keep the evaporator coil from freezing during low loads.

A constant volume unit will not contain the above-described VAV components.

Advantages

- Low initial cost for buildings that require multiple zones
- Compact arrangement uses no inside mechanical room space and very little shaft space
- Better dehumidification control than packaged single-zone systems
- Energy efficiency available through variable air volume operation.

Disadvantages

- Can impact building aesthetics
- Higher maintenance than chilled water systems
- Limited capacity to handle ventilation air
- Limited filtration
- Requires structural supports and roof penetrations
- Limited pressurization capability
- May not be able to provide close temperature control.

5.6.4 Summary

System selection is a complicated process that requires input from all affected stakeholders. Refer to Chapters 4, 12, 14, 15, and 16 for related topics.

CHAPTER 6
DESIGN CONSIDERATIONS
FOR EXISTING FACILITIES

6.1 GENERAL CONSIDERATIONS FOR EXISTING FACILITIES

6.1.1 Typical Existing Conditions

After their initial construction, most hospitals go through extensive remodeling, upgrading, and additions. In many cases, the HVAC systems currently installed represented the best technology available at the time. Thus, most hospitals have a wide variety of HVAC system types, ages, and conditions of equipment—and usually physical space limitations. The following are typical conditions and issues encountered in existing health care facilities.

- Air filtration may not be up to current standards.
- Older equipment may not have the capacity to meet new cooling loads or may be at end of its life cycle.
- Controls may be older—in need of upgrade or lacking in performance.
- Ductwork may be dirty, especially return and exhaust ducts.
- Hydronic systems may exhibit deterioration of piping.
- Systems may not be appropriate for changing functions/technology, such as required to change a patient room into a laboratory space.
- There may be a lack of balancing capability, with resulting improper air or water flow.
- Systems are in dire need of retro-commissioning and may not have performed from day one.
- Central chiller plants may contain CFCs and/or need to be upgraded due to age of equipment, lack of flexibility, or capacity.
- Horizontal or vertical space for distribution may not be available to permit addition of new systems or elements.

- Systems may be energy-intensive.
- There may be a lack of sufficient clearance for adequate maintenance.
- There may be significant "deferred" maintenance.

6.1.2 Facilities Condition Assessment (FCA)

To understand the capabilities and limitations of an existing HVAC infrastructure, a comprehensive evaluation and master plan are needed. Such a plan is referred to as a "facilities condition assessment" (FCA). The facilities condition assessment is a process in which a facility's site utilities, architecture, and engineering infrastructure are surveyed and evaluated to identify deficiencies and the capital resources required to correct the deficiencies (Habbas and Martyak 2000). Deficiencies may cover a variety of issues such as:

- Indoor air quality
- Deferred maintenance
- End of life cycle
- Regulatory agency requirements
- Technology-driven obsolescence
- Equipment inefficiency
- Lack of capacity

The following are key elements of a facilities condition assessment:

- Identify each system and the areas and subsystems served. Assess the age, condition, and longevity of major systems and equipment.
- Identify capacities of equipment and major distribution systems. Identify spare capacity and capacity deficiencies.

- Evaluate regulatory compliance issues such as filtration, ventilation quantities, duct lining, life safety, etc.

- Interview staff and develop an understanding of ongoing maintenance problems, lack of access, deferred maintenance, etc.

- Prepare alternatives for upgrading or replacing systems on a priority basis. Determine the phasing of the implementation plan. Plan for horizontal and vertical distribution, continuity of service, and maintaining pressure relationships during and after construction. Integrate architectural, electrical, and structural elements into the plan.

- Estimate costs and time line for implementation.

- Establish priorities based upon (1) serious life safety deficiencies, mandatory regulatory compliance requirements, replacement of failed equipment; (2) improvements in services or attractive rates of return; and (3) long-term improvements to services and infrastructure.

6.1.3 Considerations for Design and Construction of Renovations and Additions

Renovations and additions often require a change or disruption to existing systems and distribution. Continuity of service to areas served by equipment that is not being changed must be considered. The following steps are essential for successful renovations.

- Do a pre-construction air and water balance to determine conditions before the project starts. The idea is to return areas not changed to the same conditions as before the remodeling.

- Ensure that plans for remodeling include strategies to protect areas not under construction from dust (see later discussion).

- Ensure that HVAC systems serving areas other than the construction zone maintain adequate air flows and pressure relationships during construction.

- Ensure that air supplied to the construction zone is not recirculated to other areas.

- Prepare for continuity of service as mentioned in Chapter 4. Plan for temporary HVAC equipment when necessary and for timely and orderly shutdown of equipment when needed.

- Consider if a redesign of the mechanical room is needed for compliance with refrigerant standards. (See section 7.2)

6.2 INFECTION CONTROL DURING CONSTRUCTION

6.2.1 Introduction

Construction and renovation projects in health care facilities require special attention to infection control due to the presence of:

- Susceptible patients, including immunosuppressed patients
- Invasive surgical procedures
- Special hazards for workers and hospital staff such as autopsy rooms, nuclear medicine, etc.

Numerous incidents reinforce the importance of infection control planning. For example, in a midwestern hospital, a small two-room remodeling project resulted in the death of a patient when construction dust contaminated with *Aspergillus* migrated into the patient's room through a toilet room exhaust duct that was common to the patient's room and the room under construction.

Hospital construction and renovation projects can vary in size from major multimillion dollar additions to small one- or two-room renovations. Common sense dictates that any remodeling requires the use of barriers around the work site, including temporary walls and partitions—but the hospital environment requires special care and provisions.

6.2.2 Strategic Planning

The AIA *Guidelines for Design and Construction of Hospitals and Health Care Facilities* states that "design and planning for such [renovation and new construction] projects shall require consultation from infection control and safety personnel. Early involvement in the conceptual phase helps ascertain the risk for susceptible patient(s) and [the risk of] disruption of essential patient services (AIA 2001)." This consultation in the initial stages of planning and design is termed an "infection control risk assessment" (ICRA).

The ICRA should be carried out by a multidisciplinary planning group that involves, at minimum, representatives from the Infection Control/Epidemiology Department, architects, engineers, contractors, facilities, and administration. As a minimum, the group's assessment should address the following:

- Coordination of construction preparation and demolition
- Operating and maintaining facilities during construction
- Postconstruction cleanups

- Monitoring during and after construction
- Contractor accountability in the event of a breach in infection control
- Patient risk
- Health expectations for the contractor's workers
- Traffic patterns during construction
- Transportation and disposal of waste materials
- Emergency preparedness plan

There may be a need to consult environmental experts if the size and complexity of construction will create considerable risk to patients because of location, prolonged time of construction, work conducted in continuous shifts, or continual interruption of air-handling unit operations.

6.2.3 Construction and Renovation Control

Preparations for Demolition

Before construction begins, preparations should focus on isolating the construction/renovation area. Define the type and extent of the project. Projects vary regarding time, number of workers, degree of activity, and proximity to patients who have varying degrees of risk for infection. Patient areas or units that cannot be closed or that are adjacent to a major renovation require special planning. External excavation is ideally conducted during off-hours, so that air-handling units can be shut down and sealed to the extent possible.

Dust and Debris Control

- *Medical Waste Containers*: All medical waste containers should be removed from the construction area before demolition starts.
- *Barrier Systems*: Small projects that generate minimal dust should use fire-rated plastic sheeting, sealed at full ceiling height, and with at least 2-foot overlapping flaps for entry access. Any project that generates moderate to high levels of dust requires rigid, dust-proof, and fire-rated barrier walls with caulked seams. Large, dusty projects need an entry vestibule for clothing changes and tool storage. This entry vestibule barrier should have gasketed doors and tight seals along the entire perimeter of the walls and at all wall penetrations. An interim plastic barrier may need to be installed while the rigid impervious barrier is being constructed.
- *Traffic Control*: Designated entry and exit procedures must be defined.

- *Demolition*: Debris should be removed in carts that have tightly fitted covers, using designated traffic routes. If chutes are used to conduct debris outside, HEPA-filtered fans should maintain negative pressure in the chute, and chute openings should be sealed when not in use. Filters should be bagged and sealed before being transported out of the construction area.
- *Exterior Windows*: Windows should be sealed to minimize infiltration.

Ventilation Control

Air-handling systems that serve areas under construction should be turned off, and all supply and return air openings in the construction area should be sealed. If this is not practical, provide filters over all return openings. Filters should be not less than 95% efficient according to *ANSI/ASHRAE Standard 52.1-1992, Gravimetric and Dust-Spot Procedures for Testing Air-Cleaning Devices Used in General Ventilation for Removing Particulate Matter*. Heavy work in an area may require dampering off or otherwise blocking systems during construction periods if the resulting temporary air imbalance does not affect other areas served by the system(s) (SMACNA 1995).

- *Negative Pressure*: Spaces under construction should be maintained at negative pressures with respect to the adjacent areas not under construction. This should be achieved by using separate construction exhaust fans ducted to the outside, so that recirculation is not possible. If the exhaust cannot be ducted to the outside and must be returned, the exhaust should be filtered to at least 95% before it is recirculated. Adjacent areas should be rebalanced to maintain positive pressure with respect to the construction zone.
- *Source Exhaust*: Some pollution sources can be exhausted directly outdoors using portable fans. These exhausts may require filtration before discharging air to the atmosphere.
- *Vibration*: Core drilling or other sources of vibration should be minimized.
- *Monitoring*: Consider providing airflow sensing devices in construction barriers to signal when negative pressures are not maintained.
- Cleanup should be done by vacuuming with a HEPA-filtered fan device.

Worker Protection

- *Worksite Garb*: Contractor personnel clothing should be free of loose soil and debris before leaving the construction zone. When workers are in invasive procedure areas, they should be provided with disposable jump suits and head and shoe coverings. Workers may need protective gear (for example, respirators) for specific tasks.
- *Facilities Cleaning*: The work site should be cleaned routinely.

Intermittent Operation of Services

Dust and particles are released when fans and other mechanical systems start and stop. Policies should require delaying invasive procedures until sufficient time has elapsed after fans and systems have been restarted following shutdown.

Worker Risk Assessment and Education

Facilities staff should assist the contractor in determining potential environmental risks for workers.

- *Training*: Training must alert workers to the potential for airborne dust containing spores of microorganisms. Duct and piping demolition or modification may involve risks of fungal or other types of contamination. Workers must be trained to work in asbestos-containing areas.

- *Health Protection*: Workers may need health protection, vaccinations, skin tests for tuberculosis, testing for hepatitis, and education before beginning construction.

6.2.4 Post-Construction Cleanup

The contractor should be responsible for cleaning up the project, including work site clearance, cleaning, wiping down, and decontamination. The contractor should minimize dust production while removing partitions around the construction area. All filters should be replaced. The infection control risk assessment should identify all post-construction cleanup requirements for the contractor.

CHAPTER 7
COOLING PLANTS

7.1 INTRODUCTION

Most hospitals have one or more central chilled water plants that represent a major investment in the facility and can also be one of the primary consumers of energy. Most clinics use packaged cooling/ heating equipment.

This chapter describes the components that make up a central chilled water plant. A wide variety of equipment is available on the market. Selecting the correct type is the first step in owning and operating a central chilled water plant. Chilled water plants are systems that meld many different components, including chillers, heat rejection devices, pumps, piping, and controls into a comprehensive entity to provide mechanical cooling to a facility. Also discussed in this chapter are design considerations for formulating an effective plant. The chapter briefly looks at the instrumentation and controls that are so important to a successful plant. Finally, the start-up and commissioning process is reviewed to emphasize how a well-designed and well-constructed plant can ensure delivery of efficiently produced chilled water to air-condition a facility.

7.2 DESIGN CONSIDERATIONS

7.2.1 Use of Refrigerants in a Hospital Environment

In its simplest form, refrigeration is the process of moving heat from one location to another by using refrigerants in a closed cycle. For purposes of this manual, the discussion of refrigeration will be confined to air-conditioning applications—as opposed to refrigeration for food storage, ice making, etc. Hospitals use air-conditioning to remove heat from spaces and ventilation air to maintain comfort and a healthy environment and to assist in treating patients.

A wide variety of refrigerants is used in the air-conditioning process, including halocarbons, ammonia, propane, carbon dioxide, and plain water.

To be useful, refrigerants must have low toxicity, low flammability, and a long atmospheric life. Recently, refrigerants have come under increased scrutiny by scientific, environmental, and regulatory communities because of the environmental impacts attributed to their use.

Refrigerants are classified into groups according to toxicity and flammability. For toxicity, there are two classes based on Permissible Exposure Limits (PEL) greater than 400 ppm (Class A) and less than 400 ppm (Class B). For flammability, there are three classes ranging from Class 1 materials that do not propagate flame to Class 3 materials that are highly flammable. Refrigeration systems are also classified according to the probability that a leakage of refrigerant could enter a normally occupied area. In high-probability systems, leakage from a failed connection, seal, or component could enter an occupied space. Such is the case with direct expansion cooling coils and/or refrigeration components located within the occupied space. Low-probability systems include those whose joints and connections are effectively isolated from occupied spaces. This is the case with chillers, condensers, and other equipment located in refrigeration machine rooms isolated from normally occupied spaces.

ANSI/ASHRAE Standard 15, Safety Standard for Refrigeration Systems, limits the quantity of refrigerant in a high-probability system based upon occupancy group or division and the type of refrigerant (ASHRAE 2001b). The standard further limits the allowable quantity of refrigerant in a high-probability system for institutional occupancies (hospitals) to 50% of the values listed for other types of occupancy. Many code authorities have adopted ASHRAE Standard 15, and some have adopted even more stringent rules for hospital environments. In fact, a number of jurisdictions do not allow high-probability refrigeration systems at all in the hospital environment. Because of these safety concerns, central chilled water systems have been preferred for acute care hospitals.

When applying any type of high-probability refrigerant system, particularly packaged rooftop air conditioners, the designer should verify the quantities of refrigerant in the system (usually within a given circuit) and the acceptability of that volume to the authority having jurisdiction. Calculating the acceptable quantities of refrigerant can be tricky. Refer to ASHRAE Standard 15 for methods and tables of acceptable quantities of refrigerant expressed in lb/1000 ft^3 (equivalent to kilograms/62 m^3) of occupied space.

7.2.2   Machine Room Design

ASHRAE Standard 15 requires that equipment must be located outdoors or within a "machinery room" when the quantity of refrigerant in the system exceeds established limits. Machinery rooms are also required when the aggregate compressor horsepower is 100 hp (75 kW) or more. A machinery room must be designed within strict guidelines, some of which require:

- Continuous and emergency ventilation separate from other building systems
- Continuous monitoring, equipment shutdowns, and remote alarms
- No open flames
- Tight fire-rated room and door construction
- Exit directly to the outdoors
- Special signage
- Restrictions on the location of relief and exhaust outlets and intakes

The chiller plant (machine room) should not be located within the same space as other mechanical or electrical equipment, except that equipment directly related to operating the chillers. The chiller plant should not be located within a boiler room, except when the boiler combustion chamber and air supply are completely isolated from the room. When retrofitting or upgrading an existing chiller plant, care should be taken to include an upgrade of the machinery room where needed. This typically means that, as a minimum, the chiller must be enclosed separately from the boilers and other equipment in accordance with the requirements of Standard 15 and that emergency ventilation systems must be installed.

7.2.3   Siting the Central Plant

Many hospital planners are primarily focused on the relationship of various medical functions and may have a tendency to minimize the importance of the central plant location on the long-term cost and flexibility of a facility. When designing a new project, the location of the central cooling plant relative to other elements in the facility is a critical decision. Numerous factors should be taken into account to determine the best location for this equipment. Some of these factors include:

- Locations relative to other physical elements
- Maintenance considerations
- Location of cooling towers and air-cooled condensers

Centralizing primary mechanical equipment has advantages in operation and maintenance that may be obvious but are worth reviewing here. If the cooling plant is located near and equidistant to the loads served, cost savings are possible due to shorter and smaller distribution piping, and transportation energy for moving fluids to and from the loads being served can be reduced. There are other issues to consider when determining the best location for the central plant. These include:

- Location near shipping/receiving facility
- The aesthetic impact of mechanical equipment on the site
- Ease of access for maintenance personnel
- Future expansion capability
- Acoustical impact of equipment
- Safety in the event of a refrigerant discharge
- Locations of heat rejection devices relative to airflow, noise, and plume abatement

When considering the maintenance aspects of the central plant location in the hospital, one must take into account that hospitals are seldom static in the long term. This means that the central plant must be designed with some consideration to future expansion. Consideration should be given to providing space for additional machinery or replacing cooling equipment with larger capacity machines. This may mean that space is left for future equipment or that the central plant space can be expanded in the future.

Another important consideration when planning a hospital central cooling plant is that machinery will eventually need to be replaced due to age, failure, or changing technology. A plan for removing large equipment must be incorporated into the original design. Wall or roof openings can be built that are easily removable; cranes and other heavy equipment must have access to the machine room; and aisles for moving equipment should be built into the original design. If the mechanical space is located in the upper portions of a building, elevator access to the mechanical space is essential because large equipment, tools, and chemicals need to be brought in regularly. A fully accessible stairway to the roof is the minimum acceptable access for roof-mounted equipment. Ship ladders and roof hatches for access cost less in the short term but are bound to result in additional long-term operating expense.

The central plant must be designed so that maintenance of equipment is the first priority. This means that manufacturers' recommended clearances around and above equipment must be adhered to. Space must be allocated for tube pull clearances, motor removal, and portable (or permanent) gantries for compressor removal. Sufficient space must be allocated for inlet/outlet air for heat rejection equipment. Figure 7-1 illustrates a typical large chilled water plant.

When planning for cooling towers and air-cooled condensers, consideration must be given to their location relative to the site. Heat rejection equipment may have significant acoustical impact. This is especially true when these devices are located near residential property or within easy line-of-sight to patient spaces. Acousticians may need to determine if mitigation is necessary for these devices. Cooling towers have a tendency to create unsightly plumes during conditions of low temperature and high humidity. This may preclude locations adjacent to roadways, for example.

The use of cooling towers has been linked to the outbreak of certain airborne diseases such as Legionellosis. The location of building outdoor air intakes must be carefully considered relative to the possibility of recirculation from a cooling tower plume. Standard code minimum distances for separation are sometimes not adequate to protect the health of occupants. When cooling towers and air-cooled condensers are located close to building elements or in wells or pits, there may be a tendency to recirculate air from the discharge back into the equipment intakes. Such recirculation can severely degrade the performance of the equipment. Even equipment located in the open but adjacent to other similar devices can experience recirculation due to wind

Figure 7-1   Typical chilled water plant.

effects. Considering recirculation phenomena when selecting equipment capacities is good practice.

7.2.4 Sizing the Central Plant

When sizing a central cooling plant, keen understanding of chiller plant cooling loads and how they vary with time is fundamental to proper design. Designers are encouraged to use life-cycle cost analysis as a basis for selecting equipment and optimizing the design. If an existing plant is being modified or expanded, the ability exists to monitor the current cooling load and obtain both an accurate peak load and a cooling load profile. The plant may have a building automation system that has trend logs for monitoring peak loads. Often, a good operator can very accurately report the percentage of full load that a plant experiences during peak weather conditions.

Before a chilled water plant is designed, it is essential to understand how the plant will be operated and what loads it will be expected to handle throughout its service life. Certain key load parameters affect the cooling load profile and, consequently, the nature of the plant design. The following are some of these key parameters:

* The use of outdoor air economizers
* The use of 100% outdoor air units
* Hours of operation
* Constant loads from a process or data center
* Process requirements for a fixed chilled water temperature

The process for estimating peak cooling loads in new construction is explained thoroughly in Chapters 26 through 31 of the *2001 ASHRAE Handbook—Fundamentals* (ASHRAE 2001a). The basic variables for peak-load calculations include weather conditions, building envelope, internal heat gain, ventilation, and, to a lesser extent, infiltration. Less obvious, but nonetheless important, are diversity among the various load elements and the effects of thermal mass. The diversity of loads is a measure of the simultaneous occurrence of varying peak loads. In other words, it is a measure of the likelihood that the occupancy, lighting, and plug loads will each peak at the same time as the envelope load peaks. Recent research by ASHRAE points out that peak cooling conditions do not always occur at maximum design dry-bulb temperatures (and their associated mean coincident wet-bulb conditions) but rather at times of peak wet-bulb temperatures and their associated mean coincident dry-bulb conditions. This can be especially true when ventilation rates are very high – as in health care facilities.

There is inherent uncertainty in the peak load calculation. Any number of the following elements can make the actual load differ from a calculated load:

- Design conditions can vary depending on the building location relative to the weather station from which the data were taken.
- Weather conditions can vary over time, as a result of increasing urbanization and/or changes in land use.
- Building envelope elements are not always what were planned.
- Changes occur in the operation and maintenance of the plant and buildings.
- Ventilation rates can vary.
- Equipment loads can significantly differ from those that were planned for and can vary over time.

For most designers, the perceived risks of understating the peak load condition (undersizing the cooling plant) are much greater than those of overstating the peak load. An undersized cooling plant may not meet the owner's expectations for comfort and may impact the ability to provide essential services. Conversely, oversizing the cooling plant carries an incremental cost penalty that is not always easy to identify. An oversized plant may not be as energy-efficient as a smaller plant. The tendency is for designers to maximize assumptions for peak load and to add safety factors at several levels in the calculation process. Conversely, diversity of loads is not always well understood. One must acknowledge that uncertainties in developing the peak cooling load and the annual load profile are unavoidable.

7.2.5 Fuel Choices

The primary equipment choices for central chilled water plants include electrically driven equipment, fossil-fuel driven equipment, or a combination of the two. Fossil-fuel driven equipment can employ direct-fired or steam absorption chillers, or engine driven chillers. The choice of fuel depends on many factors but is based primarily on life-cycle cost analysis. A life-cycle cost analysis compares different alternatives and takes into account the first cost, annual operation and maintenance costs, future operation and maintenance cost inflation, and the time value of money.

One of the most important elements of the selection process is an accurate estimate of the energy usage of each of the options. The appropriate level of accuracy and detail necessary for energy calculations depends upon the size of the project and the engineering budget. Even for very small projects, chiller plant modeling tools accurately estimate chiller plant performance. For existing projects, measured performance data may be available for use.

The utility rates used in an analysis are very critical because they will vary with time and are difficult to predict. Given this uncertainty, it is often necessary to assume simply that current rates, or something similar, will be in effect during the chiller plant's life cycle. Virtually all utilities charge for energy consumption and for demand. Because chillers are one of the largest energy users in typical buildings, it is essential to take demand charges properly into account. This is particularly true when demand charges are ratcheted, which means that the owner pays some percentage of the maximum peak demand during the year, regardless of the actual monthly demand.

Other factors that enter into fuel choice decision making include the need to operate the chiller plant during prolonged power outages and the availability of waste heat from a cogeneration, solar, or biomass source. In some cases, the availability of a fuel or the cost of bringing a fuel onto the site may determine the best alternative.

With the deregulation of the electric utility industry, more emphasis will be placed on the time of day when peak loads occur. It is likely that incentives for operating a cooling plant during off-peak hours will make thermal storage an attractive alternative. Such cost incentives should be incorporated into the life-cycle cost analysis to make an optimum chiller plant fuel selection.

7.2.6 Chiller Performance and Energy Efficiency Ratings

A number of variables determine the operating characteristics and energy performance of water chillers (DuPont 2000). A chiller is selected to meet a specific requirement for maximum capacity under certain design conditions, to have limited energy consumption at these conditions, and to have specific part-load operating characteristics.

Under peak design conditions, water chiller efficiency is rated by the coefficient of performance (COP). COP is the ratio of the rate of heat removal to the rate of energy input in consistent units for a complete refrigerating system or some specific portion of that system under designated operating conditions. The higher the COP value, the more energy-efficient the machine. ASHRAE Standard 90.1-2001 establishes minimum energy efficiency standards for water chillers (ASHRAE 2001d). Many local jurisdictions have adopted the ASHRAE standard as code-minimum performance.

Another useful energy efficiency rating is the "integrated part-load value" (IPLV). The IPLV is a single-number figure of merit based on part-load COP or kilowatts per ton (kW energy input/ kW cooling output). The part-load efficiency for equipment is based on weighted operation at various load capacities. The equipment COP is derived for 100%, 75%, 50%, and 25% loads and IPLV is based on a weighted number of operating hours (assumed) under each condition—expressed as a single part-load efficiency number.

The "non-standard part-load value" (NPLV) is another useful energy efficiency rating. This is used to customize the IPLV when some value in the standardized IPLV calculation is changed. Efficiencies of electrically driven chillers are also expressed in terms of kilowatts per ton (kW/kW) for peak ratings, IPLV, and NPLV. This is simply another way of describing the COP [COP – 3.516/(kW/ton)]. The lower the kW/ton (kW/kW), the more energy-efficient the machine.

Table 7-1 provides a comparison of typical energy efficiency ratings for various types of water chillers.

7.2.7 Heat Rejection

One of the prime objectives of a chilled water plant is to reject unwanted heat to the outdoors (DuPont 2000). This is accomplished in a number of different ways. Although a number of heat sinks have been used as places to reject heat (including cooling tower ponds, lakes, rivers, groundwater, and city water) the primary means of heat rejection in the HVAC industry are the cooling tower, the air-cooled refrigerant condenser, and the evaporative refrigerant condenser.

Cooling Towers

Simply put, evaporation is a cooling process. More specifically, the conversion of liquid water to the gaseous phase requires the introduction of the latent heat of vaporization. Cooling towers use the heat from condenser water to vaporize water in an adiabatic saturation process. A cooling tower's design exposes as much as possible of the water's surface area to air in order to promote the evaporation of water. The performance of a cooling tower is almost entirely a function of the ambient wet-bulb temperature. The ambient dry-bulb temperature has an insignificant effect on the performance of a cooling tower.

Table 7-1. Energy Efficiency Ratings of Typical Water Chillers

Chiller Type	Capacity Range[a]	COP Range[a]	IPLV Range[b]
Reciprocating	50–230; 400 (176-809; 1407)	4.2–5.5	4.6–5.8
Screw	70–400; 1250 (246-1407; 4396)	4.9–5.8	5.4–6.1
Centrifugal	200–2000; 10,000 (703-7034; 35170)	5.8–7.1	6.5–7.9
Single-effect absorption	100–1700 (352-5979)	0.60–0.70	0.63–0.77
Double-effect absorption	100–1700 (352-5979)	0.92–1.2	1.04–1.30
Gas engine driven	100–3000; 10,000 (352-10551; 35170)	1.5–1.9	1.8–2.3

a. Capacity range is indicated as xx-xxx, followed by the maximum sizes available; units are tons (kW); COP values are for the range of typical capacities indicated.
b. COP units are (Btu per hour output)/(Btu per hour input) (kW output/kW input).

Cooling towers come in a variety of shapes and configurations. A "direct" tower is one in which the fluid being cooled is in direct contact with the air. This is also known as an "open" tower. An "indirect" tower is one in which the fluid being cooled is contained within a heat exchanger or coil and the evaporating water cascades over the outside of the tubes. This is also known as a "closed-circuit fluid cooler." Tower airflow can be driven by a fan (mechanical draft) or can be induced by a high-pressure water spray. Mechanical draft units can blow the air through the tower (forced draft) or can pull the air through the tower (induced draft). The water in a cooling tower invariably flows vertically from the top down, but the air can be moved horizontally through the water (cross-flow) or can be drawn vertically upward against the flow (counterflow).

Chemical Treatment and Cleaning of Cooling Towers

Cooling towers are notorious for requiring high maintenance. Cooling towers have been linked with the outbreak of Legionellosis (Legionnaires' disease). Cooling towers are very good air scrubbers and can accumulate substantial quantities of dirt and debris as they operate. Because they are open to the atmosphere, the water is oxygen-saturated, which can cause corrosion in the tower and associated piping.

Towers evaporate water, leaving behind calcium carbonate (hardness) that can precipitate out on the chiller condenser tubes and decrease heat transfer and energy efficiency. Towers must be cleaned and inspected regularly. Well-maintained and regularly cleaned cooling towers have generally not been associated with outbreaks of Legionellosis. It is best to contract with a cooling tower chemical treatment specialist.

Air-Cooled Refrigerant Condensers

Another method of heat rejection commonly used in chiller plants is the air-cooled refrigerant condenser (ASHRAE 2001b). This can be coupled with the compressor and evaporator in a packaged air-cooled chiller or can be remotely located. Remote air-cooled condensers are usually located outdoors and have propeller fans and finned refrigerant coils housed in a weatherproof casing. Some remote air-cooled condensers have centrifugal fans and finned refrigerant coils and are installed indoors. The maximum size for remote air-cooled refrigerant condensers is about 500 tons (1760 kW), but 250 tons (880 kW) is more common. Remote air-cooled condensers in chilled water plants are seldom used.

Packaged air-cooled chillers are available with capacities up to 400 tons (1410 kW). Air-cooled chillers are used for a number of reasons:

- Water shortages or water quality problems.
- Lower first cost than water-cooled equipment.
- No need for machine rooms with safety monitoring, venting, etc., for packaged air-cooled chillers.
- Less maintenance required than with cooling towers.
- Air-cooled chillers are not as energy-efficient as water-cooled chillers. When comparing the energy efficiency of air-cooled to water-cooled chillers, care must be taken to include the energy consumed in the water-cooled chiller by the condenser water pump and cooling tower. Air-cooled chillers have very good part-load performance; the COP also improves significantly as the air temperature drops.

Evaporative Condensers

Evaporative condensers use a pump that draws water from a sump and sprays it on the outside of a coil. Air is blown (or drawn) across the coil and some of the water evaporates, causing heat transfer. Evaporative condensers are primarily used in the industrial refrigeration sector and have little application in the HVAC industry. Some manufacturers, however, produce small packaged water chillers with evaporative condensers as an integral component.

The effectiveness of the heat transfer process means that for a given load, evaporative condensers can have the smallest footprint of any heat rejection method. An evaporative condenser produces lower condensing temperatures and, consequently, is far more efficient than air-cooled condensing. Maintenance and control requirements for evaporative condensers are similar to those of closed-circuit fluid coolers.

7.3 OPTIMIZING ENERGY EFFICIENCY

Normally, chilled water plants run at peak load for only a few hours a year. During the remainder of the time, a plant operates at part load. The following factors are key to designing a chilled water plant for optimum efficiency:

- Number and size of chillers
- Type and size of heat-rejection devices
- Peak and part-load efficiency of chillers
- Evaporator and condenser water temperatures
- Temperature difference across evaporator and condenser

- Type of chilled water distribution system
- Method of control

7.3.1 Number and Size of Chillers

The number and size of chillers has significant impact on part-load operating performance. The load profile of a building plays a very important role in selecting the number and size of chillers. For example, buildings that operate for long hours at low loads may run more efficiently with multiple chillers, one of which is sized to handle the low load. In this example, the use of a variable-speed drive on the small chiller may also be cost-effective. A single chiller may be most appropriate for small plants.

A life-cycle cost analysis based on a customized load profile is a time-tested way of determining the optimum number and size of chillers. Understanding the first-cost implications and the energy benefits for chillers of various size is beneficial. One way to secure an optimum selection is to establish a procurement process that allows vendors to mix and match their products across a wide range that meets the peak load requirement. This allows pricing to take advantage of a particular "sweet spot" in a vendor's selections. Based upon the equipment selected, the part-load operating characteristics can be evaluated using a computer simulation model to determine the annual energy impact of the selections. This can be put into a life-cycle cost analysis to determine the lowest life-cycle costs for the project.

7.3.2 Type and Size of Heat-Rejection Devices

Heat-rejection devices are not readily adaptable to the chiller procurement method mentioned previously. Water-cooled units are invariably more energy-efficient than air-cooled units, but air-cooled units may have a first-cost advantage. Again, first costs should be analyzed along with annual energy costs to determine the optimum life-cycle costs. When selecting a cooling tower, the incremental first cost for increasing the size of a cooling tower (oversizing the towers) can often be justified by the increased energy efficiency of lower condenser water temperatures or an increase in the number of hours during which the fans run at low speed.

7.3.3 Optimizing Evaporator and Condenser Water Temperatures

The energy efficiency of a water chiller is a direct function of the temperature of the entering condenser water and the leaving evaporator temperature. Raising the evaporator temperature increases the efficiency of the cooling process but also has an impact on the amount of water that needs to be pumped to meet a given load. The greater amount of water pumped may have an impact on the sizing of the piping or pump head and, hence, the first cost of the project. Conversely, lowering the evaporator temperature may have the opposite effect. Likewise, lowering the condenser water temperature increases the chiller efficiency but may require more cooling tower fan energy.

7.4 CHILLED WATER DISTRIBUTION SYSTEMS

The chilled water distribution system melds the chillers, pumps, piping, cooling coils, and controls into a dynamic system that provides mechanical cooling. Because it is one of the most energy-intensive systems used in buildings, understanding how the system components react to varying loads and the interactions among the components is essential for designing a system that has the most effective life-cycle cost.

7.4.1 Constant-Flow Systems

The simplicity of a constant-flow chilled water system is one of the primary attractions of this approach. In constant-flow systems, the flow through the chiller(s), as well as the flow in the distribution piping and at the cooling coil, is constant. Most constant-flow systems use three-way valves at the cooling coils. The following are examples of constant-flow systems.

Single Chiller Serving a Single Cooling Coil

When a single chiller serves a single cooling coil, the simplest approach is to use a constant-volume pump to circulate water between the evaporator and the coil and to eliminate the traditional three-way control valve. One caution when applying this approach is that manufacturers will insist on a sufficient volume of water in the piping system to prevent unstable temperature swings at the chiller. Often, small storage tanks are required when a chiller is closely coupled to a coil.

Single Chiller with Multiple Cooling Coils

When applying a single chiller with multiple cooling coils, using a constant-flow chiller with three-way valves at the cooling coils is a simple time-tested way to achieve a long life-cycle, cost-effective system. An energy-saving control strategy for this approach is to reset the water temperature leaving the chiller based on the position of the coil valves requiring the coldest water temperature.

Multiple Parallel Chillers with Multiple Cooling Coils

On the surface, this approach seems simple, but problems arise during periods of part-load operation. When both (or all) the chillers and pumps operate under a nearly full load, the system works well, but there is little or no opportunity for pumping or cooling tower energy savings. At some point, the load is reduced enough so that one chiller and pump could theoretically handle the load. By turning off one chiller and pump, the reduction in flow from the central plant basically starves all of the coils in the system. This design can still work for many applications, provided that all the loads in the building tend to change together; for example, no one coil demands full flow while others require very little flow.

Multiple Series Chillers with Multiple Coils

One solution to providing multiple chillers in a constant-flow system is to arrange the chillers in series. Then, all of the flow goes through each machine. This method is effective for systems designed with a very high temperature difference. During off- peak periods, the lag machine is turned off, and the lead machine continues to deliver chilled water at the correct temperature. This system works well, although it does not provide chilled water pump energy savings during periods of low load.

7.4.2 Variable-Flow Systems

As can be seen from the discussion of constant-flow systems, the idea of varying the flow in the system has appeal in larger systems that have multiple chillers and multiple loads. The basic advantage is that the plant can effectively be turned down during periods of low load, providing an opportunity for significant energy savings. One of the most popular design concepts for multiple-machine chiller plants is primary/secondary pumping. Systems that use a primary-only, variable-volume design approach are often used because of greater simplicity and cost-effectiveness.

Primary-Only Variable-Flow Design

Primary-only, variable-flow systems consist of single or multiple chillers with system pumps that move water through the chillers and distribution system to the cooling loads (DuPont 2000). The cooling loads are controlled with two-way valves. Typically, a bypass line with a control valve diverts flow from the supply piping to the return piping to maintain either a constant flow through the chiller(s) or to maintain a minimum flow through the chiller(s).

This approach has a simplicity that makes it very attractive (see Figure 7-2).

There are several issues for concern. The bypass valve acts against a relatively high pressure differential, so that it is susceptible to wear, cavitation, and unstable operation at low loads. In some cases, the bypass valves are located at the ends of the distribution loops. This ensures circulation in the main loops and reduces the pressure differential across the control valve. If the by-pass valve maintains constant flow through the chiller(s), there will be no pump energy saved as the loads vary, but pumps can be shut off as chillers are disabled. Variable-speed drives can be added to the primary pumps so that as the demand falls from maximum to minimum, the speed can be adjusted downward, thus saving pump energy.

Primary/Secondary Variable-Flow Design

Primary/secondary variable flow design has become the standard approach for designing large central chilled water plants using multiple chillers with multiple cooling loads (see Figure 7-3). The beauty of the primary/secondary approach is that the piping loop for chillers (primary) is hydraulically independent (decoupled) from the piping loop for the loads (secondary). The key to the design is that two independent piping loops share a small section of piping called the "common pipe." A review of flow patterns in the common pipe reveals that when the two pipe loops have the same flow rate, there is no

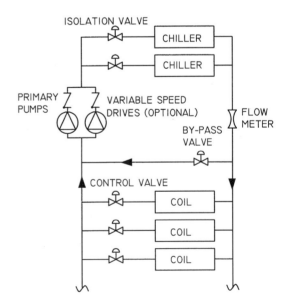

Figure 7-2   Diagram of primary only, variable flow system.

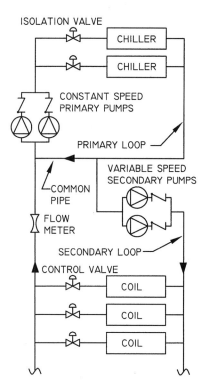

ISOLATION VALVE

CHILLER

CHILLER

CONSTANT SPEED
PRIMARY PUMPS

PRIMARY LOOP

COMMON
PIPE

VARIABLE SPEED
SECONDARY PUMPS

FLOW
METER

SECONDARY LOOP

CONTROL VALVE

COIL

COIL

COIL

Figure 7-3   Diagram of primary/secondary, variable flow system.

flow in the common pipe. Depending upon which loop has the greater flow rate, the flow direction in the common pipe is subject to change. The primary pumps are typically constant-volume, low-head pumps intended to provide constant flow through the chiller's evaporator. The secondary pumps deliver the chilled water from the common pipe to coils that have two-way valves and then return it to the common pipe. These pumps are variable-speed pumps controlled from differential pressure sensors located remotely in the system.

7.5 CHILLER PLANT CONTROLS AND INSTRUMENTATION

7.5.1 Controls

The chilled water plant is one of the most energy-intensive and function-critical spaces within a facility. Special care must therefore be taken to ensure that the plant is operated to conserve energy and provide long-term, reliable service. The automatic control system is at the heart of this effort. Chillers and other plant equipment generate heat and vibration that may adversely affect controls and instrumentation. The control system must be selected to operate in the chiller plant environment.

Microcomputer-based direct digital control (DDC) systems and networks are normally provided in a modern chiller plant. Chiller plant controls incorporate factory-installed instrumentation that can be accessed through network connections. This enables control and monitoring functions to occur across a network. The instrumentation points must be carefully chosen to ensure the proper level of data so that the systems can be optimally controlled. Too much instrumentation can be confusing to the operating staff and difficult for them to maintain. Selection of control and monitoring points should be based on a careful analysis of the chiller plant's control and operating requirements. To justify including a particular control or monitoring point in a chilled water plant, that point must meet at least one of the following criteria:

*   It must be necessary for effective control of the chiller plant as required by the sequence of operations established for the plant.
*   It must be required to gather necessary accounting or administrative information such as energy use, efficiency, or running time.
*   It must be needed by the operating staff to ensure that the plant is operating properly or to notify staff that a potentially serious problem has or may soon occur.

Controllers used in the system must employ a powerful and flexible program language and have the ability to be interfaced with chiller networks, variable-frequency drives, and power-monitoring networks. The most economical method of integrating the instrumentation into the DDC system varies with manufacturer. It is advisable to specify a BACnet gateway between the chiller(s) and the DDC system. If for some reason BACnet is not used as the system protocol, the chiller and controls manufacturers must have an interoperable system so that there is full compatibility without a need for any special gateways or connections.

7.5.2 Performance Monitoring

Performance monitoring can help identify opportunities for energy efficiency (DuPont 2000). Integrating chiller plant monitoring with the control system helps the plant operating staff to determine the most efficient equipment configuration and settings for various load conditions. It also helps the staff to schedule maintenance activities at proper intervals, so that maintenance is frequent enough to ensure the highest levels of efficiency but not so frequent that it incurs unnecessary expense. Most DDC systems that can operate chiller plants effectively are well suited to provide monitoring capabilities. Because chiller plant efficiency is calculated by comparing the chilled water energy output to the energy input (electricity, gas, or other) required to produce the chilled water, efficiency monitoring requires only the following three items.

Chilled Water Output

Because the control instrumentation already includes chilled water supply and return temperatures, only a flow sensor must be added to normal chilled water plant instrumentation.

Energy Input

To obtain the total energy input, it is necessary to install kilowatt-hour sensors on the tower fans, condenser pumps, chillers, and chilled water pumps. It may also be possible to use only one or two kilowatt-hour sensors to measure the total energy used by the plant. To reduce instrumentation costs, it is often acceptable to use a predetermined kilowatt draw for constant-speed fans and pumps whenever they are operating.

DDC Math and Trend Capabilities

In addition to the instrumentation requirements, efficiency monitoring requires that the DDC system chosen have good mathematical function capabilities, so that the instrumentation readings can be easily scaled, converted, calculated, displayed, and stored in trend logs for future reference.

7.6 START-UP AND COMMISSIONING ACTIVITIES

Most chilled water plants are custom designed for a particular facility. The process of design and construction involves many skilled professionals, who must perform their tasks well if the project is to be successful. Because we are all human, errors can occur. Commissioning is intended to achieve the following objectives:

- Ensure that equipment and systems are properly installed and receive adequate operational checkout by the installation contractors.
- Verify and document the proper operation and performance of equipment and systems.
- Ensure that the design intent and owner's requirements for the project are met.
- Ensure that the project is thoroughly documented.
- Ensure that the facility operating staff is adequately trained.

Depending on the size, complexity, and budget for the project, the tasks involved in commissioning can vary widely. Consequently, there can be a number of phases and levels in the commissioning process. (For details on commissioning, see Chapter 15.)

7.7 COOLING PLANTS FOR CLINICS

Most clinics are served by custom-built or packaged units with integral refrigeration components. See section 5.6 for more details.

CHAPTER 8
SPACE AND PROCESS HEATING SYSTEMS

8.1 GENERAL

Heating systems for medical facilities include those required for space heating, domestic hot water generation, utensil sterilization, food preparation, laundry, HVAC system humidification, therapeutic functions, and (in some cases) absorption refrigeration. The configuration and sizing of the heating systems and plant are significantly affected by the interrelated requirements of the heat-consuming systems. It is not unusual, for example, for more than 50% of peak boiler load in a general hospital, nursing facility, or rehabilitation facility to be associated with domestic, kitchen, laundry, and process requirements for steam and hot water. Recently, however, general hospital design has visualized the laundry facility as a separate business component, with the laundry remote from the hospital building and not connected to the central plant.

Based on the fundamental need for steam, these facility types are often served by central steam generation plants. Figure 8-1 is a diagram of a typical steam heating plant for a general hospital. Central low-temperature (<200°F [93°C]) heating water systems are also common, with separate (direct-fired or electric) steam generation. Electric heat generation is rare for large health care facilities, though sometimes encountered in smaller clinics—even in regions with relatively few heating degree-days and low electricity costs. Less frequently encountered than steam systems are central high-temperature heating water systems, which in addition to providing space heating can be used to generate steam in separate heat exchangers. High-temperature water heating is generally applied to large campus facilities only.

Steam is also generally required for sterilization and humidification. Depending upon the magnitude of the requirements, however, sterilizers and humidi-fiers are often equipped with unitary point-of-use steam generators, as central systems are often not life-cycle cost-effective. A dedicated steam generator may be justified for special areas due to unique requirements such as a laundry, kitchen, etc. The heat energy required for building heating and potable water heating is often provided by indirect gas-fired equipment and immersion electric resistance equipment.

8.2 HEATING PLANT CONSIDERATIONS

Primary equipment must be sized and configured to reliably and economically meet the maximum heating system demands imposed by building loads. The essential nature of the services provided by general hospital facilities requires that redundant, or backup, equipment be provided to ensure continued service during maintenance or repair of primary equipment. The optimum capacities and arrangement of primary heating generators should be determined on the basis of redundancy, as well as simplicity of operation and life-cycle cost-effectiveness. Although not as critical as for general hospitals, the activities in nursing and rehabilitation facilities also suggest some level of redundant equipment capacity to allow for maintenance and to ensure system continuity during periods of equipment failure.

When planning equipment room layouts, designers must consider maintenance requirements; space and a means of access must be planned to permit rapid repair or replacement of equipment. The more limited the access space, the less likely equipment will be properly maintained. Maintenance for boilers can be relatively time-intensive, requiring a single unit to be out of service for a lengthy period of

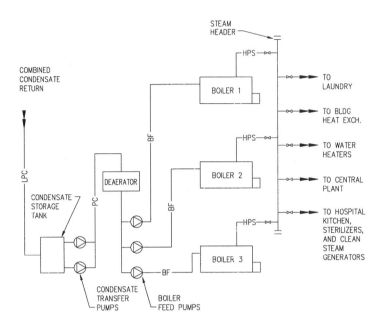

Figure 8-1   Typical steam plant schematic diagram.

time as compared to the maintenance requirements of boiler support equipment such as pumps.

8.2.1 Load Considerations and Primary Plant Capacity

Primary equipment capacity must be sufficient to meet the maximum simultaneous facility demand for all systems served by the heating system, but equipment must also respond to periods of low load. The load demand from the various systems can vary widely according to the hour of the day. Figure 8-2 illustrates a projected hourly heating plant profile, during a January day, for a general hospital located in the southeastern U.S. The total connected plant load for this facility is approximately 31,000 lb/h (8804 kW/h).

Space heating capacity must be sufficient to meet the required indoor design temperatures established by criteria for all designated areas and spaces, with minimum design outside temperature in accordance with the *ASHRAE Handbook—Fundamentals* (ASHRAE 2001a). If absorption refrigeration is utilized, the summer heat generation demand may approach winter load demand. Pickup requirements are associated with any equipment or area involved in a partial or complete shutdown (such as a cold boiler, absorption chiller, laundry equipment, or part of a building) that must be rapidly heated up to operating temperature and/or pressure. *Pickup* is the required heating capacity for the transient load

(warm-up) that is always added to steady-state peak or operating loads to determine boiler and heating system capacity. All components of the heating system must be sized for peak load *plus* pickup to maintain minimum pressure and temperature conditions for such items as sterilizers. Some operating and heat storage procedures can reduce pickup loads while minimizing *standby* losses. See Chapter 16 for information on design for energy efficiency.

8.2.2 Plant Redundancy

Key system components must be applied in multiple, parallel configurations to ensure backup capability. To provide the necessary equipment redundancy, there must be at least two separate (but connected) boilers, boiler feedwater pumps, condensate return pumps, fuel oil pumps, hydronic heat exchangers, hydronic water pumps, domestic hot water heaters, and other equipment vital for system operation—each sized to meet the required demand. Redundant equipment serves not only as a replacement in the event of primary equipment failure but permits periodic shutdown of primary equipment for routine service and maintenance. In the hospital environment, as a minimum, the capacity of *backup* system equipment should be sufficient to accommodate the systems serving critical care spaces and patient room spaces—including domestic hot water for those areas, sterilizer loads, humidification, and kitchen loads. Backup capacity should also be suffi-

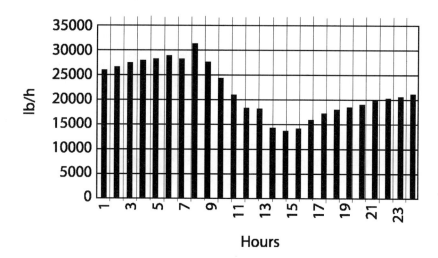

Figure 8-2 Projected daily heating plant load profile.

cient to simultaneously prevent damage from possible building freezeups in other areas of the facility. Backup system capacity for space heating may not be required in some localities where the design dry-bulb temperature exceeds 25°F (–4°C) for 99% or more of the total hours in any one heating month, as established by the *ASHRAE Handbook—Fundamentals* ("Heating and Wind Design Conditions—United States"); however, it is a strongly encouraged design practice for full-service hospitals.

The ideal minimum equipment solution employs two or three separate, interconnected steam generators sized equally to provide the indicated redundancy as illustrated in Figure 8-1. A boiler feed system with dedicated pumps for each boiler should supply the steam generators. A three-boiler array allows for one unit to be out of rotation for maintenance, while two units remain available for the minimum operational capacity. Plant operators usually favor equally sized steam generators, as they provide the most flexibility in the event of an equipment failure, and the commonality between equipment simplifies maintenance. In some cases a smaller third boiler may be more efficient. This smaller boiler can be operated in summer when the load is minimal, thereby reducing standby losses. Major overhaul or maintenance efforts should be scheduled to avoid cold system start-up and severely cold seasonal temperatures. The boilers should be equipped with isolation valves to allow maintenance and removal of a single unit without disruption to the facility.

Plant redundancy is not as critical in the outpatient facility environment. These facilities are generally considered business occupancies, and if imposed by an equipment failure, the business may be taken out of service until repairs can be implemented. However, if the essential heat equipment is designed in the minimum multiple parallel configuration for advantageous maintenance, depending on the season, an outage can be withstood.

8.2.3 Plant Configuration

In determining the optimal plant equipment arrangement, a designer may consider the maintenance advantages of utilizing primary and backup equipment of the same manufacture and capacity: simplified operation and maintenance (and operator training) and spare parts interchangeability. At the same time, however, designers should consider the potential life-cycle cost-effectiveness of mixing equipment capacities to better match seasonal or operational load profiles (including *part-load* operation and *cold starts*). Part loads and cold starting must be considered for major equipment, key components, and main control valves for four main reasons:

- Proper functioning/longevity of the equipment and components of the system
- Improved control of the equipment and components of the system
- Time-weighted average efficiency at operating points (energy conservation)
- Efficiency of low summer-load operation.

Such considerations may, for example, suggest three components in parallel sized at 20% + 40% + 40%, or 25% + 25% + 50%, of maximum required capacity instead of two components sized at 50% or one sized at 100% of capacity.

Boiler burners can be equipped with controls providing turndown rates to 25% of full-load capacity without a significant sacrifice in burner protection. Equally sized boilers (50% + 50% + 50%) are well suited to many applications, particularly where a significant level of redundancy is required, as would a configuration of 25% + 75% + 75%. Hospitals of substantial size, however, may benefit from a base-load boiler. A base-load boiler should never be applied in a manner that leaves the plant vulnerable in terms of redundancy.

8.2.4 System Steam Pressure Requirements

Steam pressure requirements for hospital appliances and equipment vary. The plant operating pressure should consider the appliance with the highest pressure requirement and a life-cycle cost justification of the steam main size. Plants serving hospitals with laundry facilities generally have the highest pressure setpoint, corresponding to the connected appliance of highest pressure. Hospitals without laundry facilities can operate at a substantially lower pressure. Significant energy saving occurs when a plant is able to operate at a lower pressure. Life-cycle cost justification of increased plant pressure based on a smaller main line size may, in some cases, be validated; it is risky, however, due to the natural growth trend in most hospital facilities.

Typical steam pressure requirements are indicated below. Designers must confirm these requirements with equipment manufacturers, building users, and local codes.

- Steam sterilizers—40 to 80 psig (276 to 552 kPa).
- Kitchen dishwasher booster heaters—15 to 30 psig (103 to 207 kPa).
- Serving line (kitchen)—5 to 15 psig (35 to 103 kPa).
- Kitchen cooking kettles and chests—15 to 30 psig (103 to 207 kPa).
- Laundry flatwork ironers—90 to 120 psig (621 to 828 kPa).
- Humidifier clean steam generators—15 to 60 psig (103 to 414 kPa).
- Hydronic heat exchangers—15 psig (103 kPa).
- Potable water heaters—15 to 60 psig (103 to 414 kPa).

Process equipment items such as sterilizers, kitchen appliances, and laundry equipment are usually limited to a confined operating pressure range. HVAC and plumbing heat transfer equipment (such as heat exchangers, water heaters, and clean steam generators) may be operated at a wider range of pressures. Potable water heaters may be selected at

increased pressures to allow for increased recovery. Clean steam generators may be selected at higher inlet pressures to minimize the unit size. In some applications, steam boilers for process loads and heating hot water boilers may be separated.

8.3 FEATURES OF HEATING EQUIPMENT

8.3.1 Boilers

Boilers used in health care facilities are characterized as steam or hot water, low and medium/high pressure, according to Chapter 27 of the *ASHRAE Handbook—HVAC Systems and Equipment* (ASHRAE 2000a). Pressure characterizations are defined as follows.

Low Pressure
- Steam boilers: less than or equal to 15 psig (103 kPa) steam.
- Hot water boilers: less than or equal to 160 psig (1103 kPa) hot water or less than or equal to 250°F (121°C) hot water.

Medium and High Pressure
- Steam boilers: greater than 15 psig (103 kPa) steam.
- Hot water boilers: greater than 160 psig (1103 kPa) hot water or greater than 250°F (121°C) hot water.

Many jurisdictions and codes define boiler operator requirements according to boiler type and capacity. For example, depending upon their capacity, medium- and high-pressure boilers may be required to be continuously supervised by a licensed boiler operator. The associated personnel costs can be significant. However, low-pressure boilers and smaller medium- and high-pressure boilers do not require a boiler operator in most jurisdictions. For these reasons, smaller facilities should consider low-pressure and multiple medium/high-pressure boilers to avoid the ongoing cost of a boiler operator.

Rules-of-thumb for boiler efficiency are:

- Typical efficiency of a boiler is 80% to 85%
- Hot water condensing boilers can be as high as 95% efficient.
- High-pressure gas boilers with an efficiency of 85% or higher are available.
- Fire tube boilers are more efficient than water tube boilers but take more space.
- Economics and space comparisons between fire tube and water tube boilers show a usual break point of 700 boiler horsepower (6867 kW).
- Further information on energy-efficient boiler plant is included in section 16.7.

8.3.2 Boiler Codes

Boiler construction and installation are influenced by a multitude of agencies. Boiler manufacturers are required to carry a high value of liability insurance to warrant their product design and essential performance. Applicable sections of boiler codes are enforced on the basis of capacity and design pressure.

Boiler codes are generally enforced at the local and state level. The most commonly accepted construction standard is the American Society of Mechanical Engineers' "Boiler and Pressure Vessel Code." Most states in the continental U.S. have adopted its requirements. Compliance with the Control and Safety Device Code (CSD-1) is also required in most states. It outlines the essential safety and operational devices required for boilers. In addition, in most jurisdictions, boilers and their components are required to be independently listed by a testing agency such as Underwriters Laboratories (UL) and/or the American Gas Association (AGA).

It may be advantageous for facility owners to comply with requirements set forth by their own insurance underwriter. National companies such as Factory Mutual (FM) and Industrial Risk Insurers (IRI) offer premium incentives for complying with basic boiler safety features. It is prudent for the designer to discuss these considerations with a client, prior to the execution of a project design.

8.3.3 Boiler Controls

Boiler design operating pressure and capacity influence the application of boiler controls. Two basic lines of definition exist; low-pressure boilers versus medium- and high-pressure boilers and below 400,000 Btu/h (117 kW) capacity versus above 400,000 Btu/h (117 kW) capacity.

Medium- and high-pressure boilers are required to be equipped with a low-water cutoff (LWCO) with automatic reset and an auxiliary low-water cutoff with manual reset. The secondary LWCO may be a probe type. Two operating controllers are also required. The first pressure or temperature setting is equipped with an automatic reset and the second (set at a higher pressure or temperature) with a manual reset. Relief valves are required on each boiler to permit the release of the total output of the boiler. A high water limit switch is required in many applications, particularly with a pressurized deaerator system, to prevent boiler operation if the water level has risen above the steam production line.

Low-pressure boilers are required to be equipped with dual low-water cutoff devices similar to medium- and high-pressure boilers. The arrangement of operating controllers and relief valves varies depending upon municipality. A high-water cutout switch is rarely required.

8.3.4 Dual-Fuel Boilers

Fuel system redundancy should be investigated for hospital plant facilities. Boilers operating on a combination of fuel sources are readily available from all major manufacturers. In view of plant component redundancy requirements, the provision of dual fuel sources is also recommended. Items to consider are reliability, guaranteed continuity of service, and facility disaster planning.

If the plant is proposed to be served by a central utility natural gas service, it should be determined whether the utility service in the area is interruptible or non-interruptible. If the service is interruptible, an alternative fuel source is warranted. Before selecting a natural gas interruptible service, the designer should perform an economic evaluation to ensure that the costs associated with an alternate fuel system can be justified. Interruptible rates are usually available only for large users (steam flow of 30,000 lb/h [8520 kW] or greater).

Some jurisdictions have adopted "Disaster Preparedness Planning" programs. Fuel redundancy, usually at the discretion of the facility owner, is strongly encouraged by these programs.

Most commonly applied in dual-fuel boilers are burners equipped to fire natural gas and number-2 grade fuel oil. The fuels are fired at different intervals rather than simultaneously. Burners can also be equipped to fire other grades of fuel oil, such as number-4 and number-6 grade. These heavier grade fuels are generally less expensive but are more difficult to pump, have a greater propensity to fouling, and have significantly higher levels of emissions. Liquefied petroleum gas (LPG) and/or mixtures of LPG are also available as a natural gas substitute.

8.3.5 Heat Recovery

Hospital facilities use tremendous amounts of heating energy due to their ventilation and process heat requirements. A number of heat recovery devices can be practically applied to the hospital plant, many of which carry a limited capital investment.

Boiler flue gas heat recovery is commonly considered. The flame temperature of most conventional forced draft burners is in the range of 1600°F to 1800°F (870°C to 980°C). Boiler efficiency is driven by an attempt to bring the boiler stack outlet temperature close to the boiler water temperature, without condensing. Stack temperatures are generally in the range of 500°F (260°C). As the flue gas exits the boiler, a great amount of energy can be recovered through a flue gas economizer. Economizer units are fire tube style shell-and-tube devices or water tube style, installed in the boiler stub stack. Boiler feedwater or condensate return water is generally circulated through the water-side component of the economizer to recover some of the flue gas heat. This application is generally quite life-cycle cost-effective as long as corrosion resistant materials are used.

Boiler blowdown economizer units are also applied. Boilers are equipped with surface blowdown systems to decrease foaming and scaling and, therefore, corrosion at the water level. The blowdown economizer is usually a shell-and-tube device. Boiler feedwater or condensate return water is circulated through the tube component of the heat exchanger to acquire heat from the blowdown water. Boiler blowdown water is, however, extremely corrosion aggressive. Units manufactured from stainless steel and cupronickel alloys are required for longevity. Although a large amount of heat may be recovered, these units are often by nature not reliable due to maintenance and replacement costs.

8.3.6 Hydronic Heat Exchangers

Heating system equipment must be rated by approved nationally recognized standards. Heat exchangers for building heating may be shell-and-tube configuration or plate-and-frame type. Shell-and-tube heat exchangers are commonly used for steam-to-hot water generation. They are also common in medium/high-temperature water to low-temperature water generation. Shell-and-tube units are often used considering the approach temperature of most steam or medium/high-temperature water applications. The essential shell-and-tube unit construction permits easy access to the interior equipment components and resists fouling.

Plate-and-frame units are found in some medium/high-temperature applications and also in low temperature source water applications. The approach temperature of plate-and-frame units can be as close as 2°F (1.1°C) to the medium to be generated. Plate-and-frame units are not usually applied in steam to hot water applications.

Heat exchangers are arranged in the building heating system as indicated in the *ASHRAE Handbook—HVAC Systems and Equipment* ("Hydronic Heating and Cooling System Design" and "Medium- and High-Temperature Water Heating Systems").

Similar to boilers, building heat exchangers should be applied in a multiple parallel configuration. In a two-heat-exchanger configuration, each should be sized to provide the heat required by critical care spaces, patient rooms, with preferably a "safety factor" to prevent freezing in other areas. Also, as with boilers, redundant heat exchange equipment capacity is often required or desired by the building owner. One option may be to provide two heat exchangers of 75% and 100% capacities. The units should be equipped with isolation valves to allow maintenance and removal of a single unit without disruption to the facility. Steam/hot water heat exchangers are recommended to be equipped with dual steam condensate traps, each trap sized at 100% of the connected load to allow for trap fouling and failure.

8.4 TERMINAL HEATING EQUIPMENT

Heating energy is used to offset winter heat loss and to provide reheat for comfort conditioning during summer. Heat is normally introduced to the air systems through finned tube heating coils in ductwork. The finned coils may be located in low velocity supply air ductwork and/or at air terminal box outlets. Finned heating coils are also found in air-handling units for comfort control and for freeze protection.

Perimeter heat is also often required to offset envelope heat loss. Heat can be provided through the use of finned-tube radiators, convectors, fan coil units, and radiant ceiling panels. Many jurisdictions and agencies prohibit finned-tube radiators in patient rooms and critical care spaces due to their fouling potential. Ceiling radiant heating panels are often used in these circumstances. Perimeter heat loss can also be offset directly through the building supply air system with an appropriate supply air diffuser selection. Linear slot type diffuser performance tests have demonstrated effective heat loss mitigation, depending upon the amount of heat loss.

8.5 PIPING SYSTEMS

8.5.1 Hot Water

Hot water is typically piped to terminal heating equipment, including baseboard heating units, radiant panels, or reheat coils. Two-pipe systems are most common, whereas four-pipe arrangements are occasionally utilized for fan-coil units. In a four-pipe configuration, two of the four pipes are used to convey the heating water and two are used to convey chilled water. In two-pipe heating/cooling system arrangements, a single piping circuit conveys heating energy and, intermittently, cooling energy, depending upon the season. The two-pipe heating/cooling piping system is not well suited to the hospital environment. A discussion of two- versus four-pipe systems is provided in the *ASHRAE Handbook—HVAC Systems and Equipment* ("Hydronic Heating and Cooling System Design"). See section 5.4.2 of this manual for additional information.

In predominantly heating climates, it may be advantageous to provide two independent space heating piping circuits, one for the building perimeter heating system (e.g., baseboard radiators) and the other for the building air-side terminal boxes and/or heating coils. The two-circuit arrangement can be served by independent perimeter and interior heat exchangers, or it can be served through a single heat exchanger with an automatic bypass, three-way mixing valve in the perimeter circuit. The objective is to allow two independent water temperatures to be circulated simultaneously. The interior system generally requires a constant hot water temperature, as coils configured for reheat experience constant supply air temperatures throughout the year. The energy expended by the perimeter system, however, can be proportional to the outdoor air temperature, allowing the water temperature to be reset as the corresponding outdoor air temperature changes.

8.5.2 Steam

Heating energy is also often conveyed to terminal equipment through a two-pipe steam/condensate system. Steam and condensate return are independently connected to all of the building's heating appliances. Steam energy is rarely used directly in the heating process, as the approach temperature of the steam to the required room temperature is excessive. In addition, the maintenance of this type system is greater than for a hydronic heating system.

Steam condensate piping should be constructed of a material thickness that compensates for naturally occurring corrosion. Generally, Schedule 80 carbon steel piping is used. For a steam condensate system that conveys steam condensate from a clean steam (not chemically treated) system, stainless steel piping materials should be considered. Steam condensate return may be by gravity or by condensate pump.

8.5.3 Steam Traps

Steam (condensate) traps are required for steam-fired appliances and devices. A multitude of trap products are available. Trap application is influenced primarily by the appliance or service intended and also by the pressure available in the system. Trap types commonly encountered in hospital environments are inverted bucket, float and thermostatic, thermodynamic, and thermostatic. Each has a particular range of service and operating characteristics. A thorough discussion of steam traps is provided in the *2000 ASHRAE Handbook—HVAC Systems and Equipment* ("Steam Systems").

The operational objective of a trap is to permit condensate, which has been condensed through a heat transfer process, to be drained away from an appliance or piping system. The trap also restricts the passage of steam from the steam piping system into the condensate system to improve energy conservation.

Trap installation should allow, to the greatest extent possible, gravity drainage at the outlet to the condensate piping system. The pressure at the trap outlet is often relied upon by designers to elevate the condensed steam to a condensate piping system above the elevation of the collection point. When this piping practice is employed, a water hammer effect occurs upon trap element opening, as the entering steam impacts the dormant liquid in the condensate piping. Although not detrimental to system dynamics, this generates unwanted noise and allows the highly corrosive condensed steam to dwell at the system's low points.

When relying on steam pressure to elevate condensate, consideration should be given to whether the application pressure is dependent upon a steam control valve at the appliance inlet or whether the application is on a steam main with no control valve. Intermittently operating or modulating steam control valves on heat exchangers, for instance, may be in the open or closed position depending upon the load requirements of the appliance. When in the closed position, no pressure is available to elevate the condensate liquid; when the control valve opens, water hammer will occur. Steam main drip traps generally have continuous pressure available, resulting in a greater level of operational predictability.

Steam trap maintenance is essential in hospital facilities to ensure system reliability and energy conservation. Facilities should establish a trap testing, cleaning, and replacement program. Electronic testing products are available to detect trap failure. An annual cleaning effort ensures proper trap life cycle.

8.6 DOMESTIC WATER SYSTEMS

8.6.1 General Considerations

The potable hot water load for a hospital can account for up to 30% of the heating energy load. Domestic, kitchen, and laundry hot water consumption rates often vary suddenly and fluctuate frequently throughout the day—by a factor of 100% or more. Because demand and consumption rates vary so suddenly and significantly, it is appropriate to store domestic, kitchen, and laundry hot water in tanks, providing a large "capacitance" for sudden changes in flow rate and quantity.

The control of *Legionella* is a concern in potable hot water systems. Storing hot water at a temperature of 140°F (60°C) will control *Legionella* within the storage tank itself. Consideration of municipality requirements and design criteria is required in order to determine the hot water storage temperature for a particular facility. If potable hot water is stored at a higher temperature than required, it must be mixed with cold water to achieve the desired system temperature at the tap.

Another factor in the control of *Legionella* is the elimination of dead-end pipe runs in a potable hot water system. This can be accomplished by effective piping design and by the utilization of a hot water recirculation system. The pipe run-out to fixtures/equipment should not exceed 25 lineal feet (7.6 meters). This measurement includes the drop from the ceiling to the fixtures/equipment. Hot water recirculation system sizing procedures are presented in the *ASHRAE Handbook—HVAC Applications* ("Service Water Heating") (ASHRAE 1999a). A hot water return flow must be established using the methods listed in the above-mentioned Handbook chapter. A minimum hot water return flow of 10 gpm (0.6 L/s) is recommended to facilitate a stable return water pump selection. Refer to Chapter 14 for more information regarding systems operations and maintenance.

Devices such as scullery equipment, dishwashers, and laboratory and sterilization equipment often require water at a temperature higher than provided by the central potable water-heating system. Washer-sterilizers and dishwashers are normally equipped with either a steam-fired or electric booster heater to elevate the water temperature. A booster heater downstream of the central potable water heater dedicated to the kitchen, for example, is often used.

Heat exchangers or tank heaters may be required by local jurisdictions or codes to be double walled to prevent contamination of potable water by the heating medium.

Consideration should also be given to connecting water heaters and recirculation pumps to building management systems for system monitoring. The building management system can also be used to cycle water heaters and pumps on and off in ambulatory care facilities, based upon the operating schedule of the facility.

8.6.2 Water Heater Features

Potable water heaters are essential equipment in health care facilities. The heat losses in potable hot water systems must be minimized through the proper application of thermal insulation. Redundant potable water heaters are recommended in all health care facilities. If two water heaters are proposed, each should be sized for 65% of the potable hot water demand. If more than two water heaters are proposed, each water heater should be sized for an equal percentage of the hot water demand.

The medium used to heat potable water varies; electricity, steam, high-temperature hot water, and gas are the most common. Different potable water heater configurations are commercially available: storage tank type, semi-instantaneous type, and instantaneous type.

Storage tank water heaters are the most commonly utilized. They must be sized to provide a facility's immediate hot water demand through the stored hot water. The heating of the water volume is spread over a period of time, which can range from a fraction of an hour to several hours. Commonly used heating mediums are steam, high-temperature hot water, gas, and electricity. One drawback to this type of water heater is the standby loss associated with the storage of hot water during periods of low demand. The input ratings of the water heaters are often low, however, due to storage tank size. *Legionella* control is a concern (see 8.6.1 above).

Semi-instantaneous water heaters store a small amount of hot water, typically ten to twenty seconds of the building's hot water demand. This allows the water heater's temperature control system to react to sudden fluctuations in water flow. The most commonly used heating medium for this type of water heater is steam. Although the standby loss associated with this type of heater is minimal, the input rating is high due to the immediate requirement for hot water. To heat the water to the water heater setpoint, a high-demand heat input energy is required.

Instantaneous water heaters must have sufficient capacity to provide the maximum hot water flow rate at the required temperature. Instantaneous water heaters find their best use where the water-heating demands are constant or where space installation restrictions are a prime consideration. Steam and high-temperature hot water are the most common heating mediums for this type of water heater.

Standby losses for instantaneous water heaters are negligible. Due to the instant demand for hot water, the input rating is high.

The domestic hot water heater can also be a direct natural-gas-fired unit. Condensing-type heaters offer the advantage of simplified venting, in that the outside vent need not necessarily route all the way to the building roof.

For smaller clinics, where domestic hot water demand is limited, water heating with electric resistance heaters or heat pumps is sometimes found to be economical.

8.6.3 Hot Water Demand

Hot water demand for fixtures should be calculated in accordance with the *ASHRAE Handbook—HVAC Applications*, chapter on "Service Water Heating." Hot water demand for equipment not indicated in the ASHRAE Handbook (i.e., laboratory and sterilization equipment) should be obtained from equipment manufacturers.

8.6.4 Water Delivery Temperature

Typically required temperatures at the point of consumption are as follows (designers must confirm local codes and design criteria):

- Domestic hot: 105°F to 125°F (41°C to 52°C), temperature issues include scalding, comfort and therapy, washing and bathing, disinfection, and janitorial.

- Kitchen dietary: 140°F (60°C), used by kitchen staff only, so scalding temperature limit is higher.

- Kitchen dishwashing final rinse: 180°F (82°C), for disinfection (this may not be required if chemical disinfection is utilized).

- Laundry: 160°F (71°C).

Prevention of scalding is a major issue in the design/maintenance of a potable hot water system. If the average adult is exposed to 140°F (60°C) water, first-degree burns will occur in approximately three seconds. Exposure to 120°F (49°C) water creates first-degree burns in approximately eight minutes. Infants and the elderly may have more sensitive skin; thus, first-degree burns can occur more rapidly.

Terminal mixing valves are commonly applied in shower and bathing facilities. The valves are typically a pressure balanced type, integral to the operational water flow valve. Other locations for terminal mixing valves include hydrotherapy rooms and laboratories.

8.7 STERILIZATION AND HUMIDIFICATION

8.7.1 General

As a rough rule of thumb, humidification and sterilization normally account for 20% and 5%, respectively, of a hospital's total heating requirements. Both systems require a high quality (that is, relatively dry) steam supply. With steam sterilizers, excess moisture can wet packs and transport pipe scale, rust, or treatment chemicals, causing instrument stains and other problems. Sterilizers require steam pressure in the range of 60-80 psi (414-552 kPa) to achieve corresponding saturation temperatures sufficient for sterilization; saturated steam is a superior sterilant to superheated steam (AHA 1985). Wet humidifier steam can lead to wetting the interiors of ductwork, filters, and other components leading to microbe growth. Humidifiers are normally served by system pressures less than 20 psig (138 kPa).

Steam for these systems may be generated in central plants or supplied by individual boilers (typically electric, gas-fired, or steam-to-steam) provided with the equipment. The decision whether to provide central generation or individual boilers should be influenced by life-cycle cost considerations including initial equipment purchase, operation and maintenance, and replacement costs. These cost factors will be significantly affected by the approach taken to deal with corrosion and by the required purity level of steam.

8.7.2 Steam Classifications

Steam used for other than space-heating applications is commonly classified as "unfiltered," "filtered," "clean," or "pure," according to the makeup water characteristics and permissible level and nature of steam impurities. These classifications are not defined by any national standard and their characteristics may, therefore, vary among different authorities, but in general:

- Unfiltered steam normally contains some system treatment chemicals, normally generated from makeup water that has been softened and often treated by other processes (deaeration or dealkalyzation, for example) to reduce corrosivity. The steam is not filtered prior to delivery.

- Filtered steam is normally generated from makeup water treated similarly to unfiltered steam, but it is filtered to remove all particles larger than some established standard, normally 1-3 microns. Filtration normally includes coalescent filter removal of liquid water droplets.

- "Clean" steam is normally generated in a dedicated steam boiler, with limited or no treatment additives permitted, and with makeup water normally only softened, although it can be treated by reverse osmosis, deionization, or even distillation.
- "Pure" steam is generated from deionized or distilled makeup water and contains no treatment additives.

The majority of medical facilities utilize unfiltered steam for sterilization. As discussed in greater detail below, most authorities will accept the presence of limited types and concentrations of system treatment additives in sterilizer steam. Unfiltered steam is also widely used for direct humidification, although the presence of treatment chemicals is much more of a concern due to the direct injection of the steam into environmental air, and its use is, therefore, banned by some authorities. Federal regulations and industry guidelines restrict the concentrations of, or prohibit altogether, certain additives to which people may be directly exposed by humidification steam.

8.7.3 Corrosion Mechanisms in Steam Generation Systems

It is important for designers to be knowledgeable of the fundamentals of steam and condensate system corrosion, so as to be aware of the implications of the different makeup and treatment alternatives and steam purity standards. Every component of the steam system, from generator to steam piping to the condensate handling components, and all fittings exposed to the makeup water, steam, or condensate, are subject to corrosion. Corrosion generates system contaminants, increases maintenance effort, reduces system reliability and performance, and dictates the frequency of equipment replacement. The primary considerations in steam system corrosion are the following.

Scale

Scale is formed in equipment and piping by the precipitation of certain chemical compounds, known as mineral salts, present in all natural water supplies. The concentration of scale-forming compounds in water is known as hardness, measured in parts per million (ppm) or grains per gallon (grams per cubic meter). Water supplies having significant levels of hardness are found in approximately 85% of the United States and Canada (Garay and Cohn 1992). Several of the more prevalent mineral salts, including magnesium and calcium carbonate, have low solubility and therefore precipitate from solution to form scale at the elevated temperatures found in boilers and other heat exchangers. Scale formation reduces equipment heat transfer and results in overheating of heating coils and elements, resulting in reduced performance and equipment failure. Water with a hardness exceeding 3.5 grains per gallon (60 grams per cubic meter) normally requires "softening," typically by ion-transfer technology, to reduce scale formation in heating equipment.

Carbon Dioxide (Carbonic Acid)

The presence of carbon dioxide in the water supply (from dissolved atmospheric CO_2 or the breakdown of carbonate and bicarbonate compounds) results in the formation of carbolic acid, which is very corrosive to materials (such as mild steel and copper alloys) commonly used in steam systems. Condensate piping, in particular, is subject to carbonic acid corrosion, which results in general wall thinning and a characteristic "troughing" or marked erosion of metal from the bottom of the pipe. The iron dissolved from carbolic acid attack often becomes a problem by clogging boiler tubes (possibly resulting in tube failure) and stopping up strainers and traps, and it can result in "red water" carryover and staining in sterilizers. In the presence of dissolved oxygen, the corrosive effect of carbolic acid is markedly increased.

Oxidation

Free oxygen dissolved in water is very corrosive to mild steel surfaces and its presence is characterized by pitting of the piping wall. As with carbolic acid corrosion, condensate piping is most vulnerable to attack. Significant iron removal is often remarked in steam piping systems as well, due to the unavoidable presence of liquid water from boiler carryover and line condensation. The iron dissolved by this corrosion process, similar to that resulting from carbolic acid attack, frequently clogs heat exchanger tubes, clogs strainers and traps, and causes stains in sterilizer packs and instrumentation.

High-Purity Water Aggressiveness

In some applications (rarely encountered in health care facilities), users desire the generation of "clean" or "pure" steam from water that has been treated to remove most of its impurities. These "reagent grade" waters, processed using distillation, demineralization, or reverse osmosis, typically range in resistivity (a measure of relative absence of dissolved ions and therefore purity) from 2 to 15 megohm/cm. A value of 18.25 megohm/cm at 25°C (77°F) is recognized as the theoretical maximum (ASPE 1994). Water of such purity is highly corrosive to many of the commonly used piping and equipment materials, including mild steel. Depending upon the purity of the water, even low-grade stainless steels can be subject to significant corrosion. High-purity water attacks not only steam generators but also the steam and condensate piping systems. As with CO_2 and oxygen corrosion, problems associated with high-purity water corrosion include reduced equipment life, system clogging, and discoloration of materials in contact with steam.

Galvanic Corrosion

When dissimilar metals are used in steam and condensate systems, galvanic corrosion can occur—in which the least noble metal (anode) corrodes to form deposits on the more noble (cathodic) metal. Examples of dissimilar metals are steel-copper or steel-stainless steel, in which the anodic steel corrodes to the relatively cathodic copper or stainless steel. Galvanic corrosion can accelerate deterioration of piping systems, thereby reducing system life and creating impurities in delivered steam.

8.7.4 Methods of Corrosion Control

Softening (Sodium Zeolite)

The most common and economical method of reducing the concentration of scale-forming compounds in water is known as sodium-zeolite water softening. In this process, the solubility of scale-forming compounds is chemically increased by replacing their magnesium or calcium cations with those of sodium, minimizing precipitation and scale formation. The sodium zeolite process can remove up to 98% of scale-producing compounds at relatively low costs—ranging in the thousands of gallons (liters) per dollar.

Deaeration – Removal of CO_2 and O_2

When water is heated, the solubility of dissolved gases is decreased. Therefore, in central steam generation plants a common process for removing oxygen and carbon dioxide from makeup water supplies is the heating of the water, often under pressure (up to 20 psi [138 kPa]), in a deaerating feedwater heater. Commercial deaerators are capable of removing dissolved oxygen to a level of 0.005 cubic centimeters per liter (cc/L).

• Dealkalyzation or Demineralization

The most common source of carbon dioxide, and therefore of carbolic acid, in steam heating systems is carbonate or bicarbonate, the anionic (negatively charged) components of the mineral salts commonly found in system makeup water. These are the same compounds associated with water hardness. While the sodium zeolite softening process reduces the scaling potential of these compounds, it does not remove the carbonates from solution. One process commonly used for carbonate removal is known as dealkalization in which chloride anions are exchanged with the carbonate/bicarbonate anions, the latter being retained by a cationic resin and removed from solution. The reverse osmosis (RO) process, which uses pressure to "filter" dissolved compounds and particles through an osmotic membrane, can be up to 95% effective in removing carbonates as well as other impurities from makeup water. The process of deionization (DI) is also very effective in removing nearly all of the carbonates and other minerals. However, with treatment costs in the neighborhood of $0.01 per gallon ($0.0026 per liter) and $0.1 per gallon ($0.026 per liter) for the RO and DI processes, respectively, these latter two are not commonly encountered in steam generation system makeup water treatment.

Corrosion-Resistant Materials

For steam generation and handling systems utilizing reagent-grade makeup water, and for systems that cannot be operated with corrosion-protecting treatment chemicals, construction using corrosion-resistant steel is highly recommended. This would apply to all portions of the steam generation and piping systems in direct contact with steam and condensate, including heat exchange surfaces, steam and condensate piping, traps, and other fittings. High-grade stainless steels are recommended for the construction of all components of steam generation systems directly exposed to the steam or condensate

Avoidance of Dissimilar Metals

Connections between dissimilar piping materials should be avoided to prevent corrosion. Dielectric couplings can be used to prevent such occurrences.

Adequate Condensate Drainage

As discussed above, the presence of oxygen and carbon dioxide in water can lead to rapid corrosion of commonly used piping materials, such as mild steel. Also, when condensate cools, it can absorb higher concentrations of oxygen and carbon dioxide (supplied by atmospheric piping leakage or carried over with steam-gas solubility increasing with lower temperature) rendering it more corrosive. Steam lines, often erroneously considered to be "dry," are exposed to more of the corrosive condensate when the liquid is inadequately trapped and removed and at times of low steam demand. It is, therefore, important that system designers provide for efficient trapping and removal of condensate from all portions of the system, minimizing opportunities for cooldown and continuous contact with piping. Design provisions include properly sloping steam lines (normally in the direction of flow), avoidance of concentric pipe fittings and other low points where condensate may pool, and the provision of adequately sized and located drip legs and traps. The latter are needed at suitable piping intervals, at the base of all risers, and immediately upstream of valves, pressure reducers, and other equipment connections where condensate can collect.

Blow-Down and Bleed-Off

When water boils in a steam generator, most of the impurities contained in the water are left behind in the heat exchange reservoir. Makeup water replacing the boiled-off steam brings in a new charge of impurities, adding to those already present and gradually increasing their overall concentration.

Unless the heat exchange surfaces are frequently cleaned of the accumulated scale and sludge, unit performance will be reduced and the equipment may eventually fail. To minimize the concentration of impurities and extend the frequency of required maintenance, many steam generators (from large plant generators to individual electric humidifier steam generators) are equipped with an automatic blow-down or bleed-off. Typically operated on a timed cycle, the bleed-off drains a certain volume of high-impurity water from the reservoir, replacing it with treated makeup water to dilute the overall impurity level.

Chemical Treatment Additives

The mechanical water treatment processes discussed above do not adequately protect the most common piping and equipment materials (i.e., mild steel) against oxygen and CO_2 corrosion. These gases may enter the piping system from ambient air via pipe and fitting connections when portions of the system experience vacuum due to condensing steam. In addition, the treatment processes cannot be depended upon to remove all traces of dissolved gas

or the compounds that form CO_2, and these may be transported throughout the system with the steam. For this reason, it is commonly necessary to add treatment chemicals that eliminate oxygen, neutralize acid, or form a barrier between system materials and the corrosion agents.

Oxygen Scavengers

Oxygen scavengers are chemicals, such as hydrazine and sodium sulfite, used to virtually eliminate or passivate any oxygen remaining in the system after deaeration of the makeup water supply. Without deaeration, the amount of scavenging chemical required to reduce dissolved oxygen would be economically and practically prohibitive. Even with efficient oxygen removal from the feedwater supply, atmospheric oxygen can reenter steam and condensate systems through vacuum breakers and atmospheric vents, condensate pumps, or flash vents, although opportunities for this are limited in sterilization and humidification steam systems in which condensate is not returned to the boilers.

Amines

Amines are alkaline treatment chemicals developed to raise pH or to shield piping system materials from direct corrosion agents. Two types of amines are utilized in the steam treatment industry: neutralizing and filming amines. The former act only to neutralize carbolic acid and have no protective effect against oxygen. The filming amines, on the other hand, act to form a molecular coating on the inside walls of piping systems, preventing direct corrosion by either carbolic acid or oxygen.

8.7.5 Treatment Chemicals and Health

A number of the treatment chemicals used in steam systems are known, or suspected, to have adverse health effects upon humans exposed to suitably high concentrations in ambient air, food, or water. The opportunities for human exposure to potentially harmful treatment chemicals in sterilizer steam is very limited, as only very small amounts of the steam are ever released into the building environment. Humidification steam, being directly injected into the building air supply, is more of a concern. Authorities have established exposure limitations for selected amines and oxygen scavengers, and it appears that in common practice, with good maintenance attention, the chemical concentrations in air humidified by treated steam fall well within these

Table 8-1. Permissible Limits for the "FDA" Amines

Chemical Name	ACGIH TWA (ppm)	OSHA PEL (ppm)	Odor Level (ppm)
Morpholine	20	20	0.14
DEAE	10	10	0.04
Cyclohexylamine	10	10	0.90

limitations. Concerns remain, however, regarding the dependability of the necessary maintenance, the potential for various environmental factors to alter the chemicals into more dangerous compounds, the potential irritant (as opposed to health endangerment) effects, and the legal implications of exposure of building occupants to any level of potentially hazardous chemical.

Regulatory Provisions

The United States Department of Health and Human Services, Food and Drug Administration (FDA), in FR 173.310 (April 1999), has limited the permissible concentration of treatment chemicals present in steam that may be in contact with food as follows:

Cyclohexylamine	10 parts per million (ppm)
Diethylaminoethanol (DEAE)	15 ppm
Hydrazine	0 ppm
Morpholine	10 ppm
Octadecylamine	3 ppm

With the exception of hydrazine, which is an oxygen scavenger, the remaining compounds are amines and have come to be regarded as "the FDA amines." The American Conference of Governmental Industrial Hygienists (ACGIH) has established a permissible Time Weighted Average exposure level (TWA) and the Occupational Safety and Health Administration (OSHA) a Permissible Exposure Level (PEL) for several amines in environmental air, as indicated in Table 8-1(ICSC 1999; ACGIH 1995). Also indicated in Table 8-1 (in the fourth column) is the odor perception level for each chemical.

To give an idea of the relative toxicity of these chemicals, the LD50 (mg of chemical per kg of body weight of animal resulting in a 50% mortality rate) for these chemicals is shown in Table 8-2. An LD50 of 50 mg/kg or less is classified as highly toxic. An LD50 between 50 and 500 mg/kg is considered toxic.

Table 8-2. Toxicity Data for the "FDA" Amines

Chemical Name	Oral Exposure - LD50	Dermal Exposure -LD50
Morpholine	3053	3083
DEAE	1300	1260
Cyclohexalamine	319	1286

The OSHA Hazard Communication Standard (29 CFR 1910.1200) requires that workers in buildings who are exposed to hazardous chemicals, as defined by the regulation (and which would include the "FDA amines"), be warned of the exposure. There is debate over whether amines introduced as part of an overall "mixture"—i.e., steam—constitute a hazard as defined by the standard in the concentrations in which they should normally be utilized in a well-managed maintenance program (Elovitz 1993).

Nonregulatory Publications

A U.S. Navy paper published in July 1990 reported the results of a Navy-funded research project by the National Research Council that investigated the use of amines in steam used for sterilization and humidification (NFEC 1990). The NRC concluded from that study that:

- Morpholine and 2-DEAE are strong irritants and can convert to nitrosamines, which are known animal carcinogens.

- "Some amines" are known to trigger asthma attacks.

- Morpholine and 2-DEAE should not be used in steam where human exposure can occur.

In a Health Hazard Evaluation Report of the effects of airborne DEAE exposure resulting from humidification steam in a museum, the National Institutes of Occupational Safety and Health (NIOSH) concluded that health problems resulted even though ambient concentrations of the chemical were well within the PEL (NIOSH 1983). In that instance, NIOSH concluded that eye and dermal irritation occurred in a number of occupants as a result of contact with condensed DEAE on building surfaces and furnishings. NIOSH recommended that

DEAE be eliminated from the humidification system.

A letter written by the U.S. Food and Drug Administration (FDA) in April 1980 offered the agency's opinion that amine concentrations within the limitations permitted for steam in direct contact with food could be safely used for steam sterilization.

Field Findings/Tests

Industry and government have published several reports of field investigations into the ambient air concentration of treatment chemicals in buildings humidified with treated air. Studies have been conducted by major chemical companies and by the Alkyl Amines Council to determine the range of amine levels that could be expected in buildings humidified by treated steam (Edgerton et al. 1989; Grattan et al. 1989; SOCMA 1988, 1991). These studies reported ambient air amine concentrations in the range of 0.0001 to 0.066 ppm, or orders of magnitude less than the regulatory exposure limitations. In another report, researchers analyzed, in a laboratory setting, the air concentrations of the three amines (morpholine, DEAE, and cyclohexylamine) introduced by a treated steam humidification system. Although the concentrations of the amines in the steam were increased to levels exceeding the regulatory limitations for dietary steam, the resulting airborne concentrations of the amines were found to be much below the regulatory exposure limitations. Other sources report similar findings (NIOSH 1996). However, most researchers and authorities advise that these low ambient air concentration levels can only be guaranteed with careful maintenance and monitoring, including metered introduction of the treatment chemicals into the steam system.

8.7.6 Practical Considerations of Treatment Chemical Application

When treatment chemicals are used in steam systems for humidification or sterilization, a good maintenance program is required in order to control the concentration of treatment chemicals in the steam, as well as to ensure that the system is adequately protected against corrosion. Excessive chemical levels in the steam may lead to adverse health effects in exposed persons (as discussed above), while inadequate levels can cause wet steam, discoloration, poor performance, and equipment failure. Slug feeding of treatment chemicals should not be permitted; rather, continuous feeding of treatment chemicals via metered feed pumps, with daily checking and adjustment of the feed rates, is necessary.

Coupons or sample ports should be provided to enable frequent checking for corrosion products. As the several amines and other treatment chemicals have differing characteristics affecting their performance in various parts of the steam system, careful attention must be paid to the appropriate selection of chemicals and to the location where they are introduced.

Neutralizing Amines

The purpose of neutralizing amines is to neutralize carbolic acid. These amines are characterized by their vapor-to-liquid (V/L) ratio, which is an indicator of their availability in the steam or condensate phase, respectively. Depending upon the size or extent of the steam and condensate distribution system, one or more different neutralizing amines, having different V/L ratios, may be required in order to protect all portions of the system. In steam distribution lines, the amines tend to disappear with the condensate collected and disposed in traps; whereas carbon dioxide, transported along with the steam, continues to travel in the system. This creates a potential for the carbolic acid level to rise, and the pH level to drop, with increasing distance from the steam generator. For extended systems, therefore, the feeding of an amine with a high vapor-to-liquid ratio will tend to better protect the more remote reaches of piping. Amines with lower V/L ratios would be more effective in protecting piping closer to the generator. To avoid the unnecessary loss of chemical in boiler blowdown, the neutralizing amines are normally fed directly into the steam supply header.

Filming Amines

Filming amines form a thin barrier on the surface of piping and equipment to guard against direct oxygen and carbonic acid exposure. Excessive dosage of filming amine can lead to "gunk ball" formation, which clogs pumps, traps, and other equipment. In addition, when first added to an existing system, filming amines may cause the release of large amounts of iron oxide and scale from piping systems, also causing plugs and fouling. Filming amines have limited volatility and should therefore be added only at the steam header to ensure their distribution throughout the system.

8.7.7 Steam for Sterilization

Effective sterilization using steam requires direct contact between the item to be sterilized and saturated steam at a temperature of 250°F (121°C) or higher—for a suitable length of time to ensure destruction of the most temperature-resistant microorganisms. To achieve this temperature, steam must be delivered at 50-80 psig (345-552 kPa). The latent energy of vaporization of saturated steam renders it a far superior sterilant to non-condensing gases, such as high-temperature air, which is why it is important to minimize any superheating of the steam supplied to the sterilizer.

Excessive superheat may result if the sterilizer jacket is maintained at a higher temperature than the chamber (an operational issue) or by excessive pressure reduction before the sterilizer connection. Sterilizer steam must be very dry – 97% quality or better – to avoid liquid droplet carryover, which can cause wetting and staining of fabrics and instruments. Condensate from the sterilizing process is considered contaminated and is not reused.

Steam Generators

Steam for sterilization may be generated by a central plant, or by integral (normally electric) generators provided with each sterilizer, as determined by life-cycle cost considerations and the operational requirements of individual facilities. Central plant steam is often the most economical alternative for large health care facilities, particularly if steam of suitable pressure is already available for heating or absorption cooling—but central systems require a high level of maintenance capability. Sterilizer manufacturers offer integral boilers of carbon steel construction for the usual filtered steam applications, recommending makeup water with a hardness not exceeding 3 to 8 grains per gallon (51-137 grams per cubic meter); stainless steel construction is normally available for applications requiring deionized or demineralized makeup water.

8.7.8 Steam for Humidification

Steam is considered by most authorities and codes to be superior to evaporative water systems for HVAC system humidification, due to its inherently sterile nature and lesser tendency to wet air-handling surfaces and contribute to microbe growth. Steam is normally injected into the air supply by one or more perforated dispersion tubes mounted in an air-handling unit casing or ductwork and directing the spray against the direction of airflow. Controls should be provided to limit the downstream relative humidity and to prevent humidifier operation when no airflow is present. Steam for humidification must be of high quality and condensate-free to prevent droplet spray and moisture accumulation in the equipment. Most manufacturers offer the steam jacketed dispersion tube arrangement preferred by many designers, wherein the actual dispersion tube is preheated by incoming steam to help dry the injected steam. For jacketed humidifiers, an automatic shut-off valve should be located upstream of the humidifier assembly. This valve should be closed during periods when humidification is not needed, reducing unnecessary heat losses from the jacket into the airstream. Even with these types of humidifiers, however, designers must carefully design to guard against water accumulation in ductwork (see additional information on this subject in Chapter 9). Depending upon the quality of available steam and the permissible level of treatment chemicals, humidifiers may use direct boiler steam or steam from a dedicated steam generation plant. When central steam is not available or economically feasible, humidifier manufacturers offer a variety of small electric, gas-fired, or steam-to-steam boilers for their equipment.

CHAPTER 9
AIR-HANDLING AND DISTRIBUTION SYSTEMS

9.1 INTRODUCTION

Air-handling and distribution systems provide health care facilities with a comfortable environment, ventilation to dilute and remove contaminants, and a supply of clean air for breathing, and they assist in controlling the transmission of airborne infection. In order to meet these requirements, HVAC systems must be properly designed to meet the applied loads and demands and facility operational requirements. In addition, the systems must be properly installed, commissioned, and maintained. The system designer has an opportunity to heavily influence the successful achievement of these features of building construction and operation. This chapter will discuss aspects of the design that help to ensure that the air-handling and distribution systems perform as required throughout the life cycle of the equipment.

9.2 CONCEPT DESIGN

Design of the air-handling and distribution systems should begin during the schematic design phase of a medical facility to permit the HVAC engineer to influence the location, arrangement, and size of spaces intended for the installation of equipment (including distribution elements). The project architect and building owner should recognize that early consideration of equipment requirements will enhance the overall functionality and economy of the facility, contributing to more efficient service distribution, reduction of maintenance traffic in occupied areas, and enhanced flexibility for future modifications or expansion. Postponing consideration of equipment space requirements until final design development often leads to poorly located, cramped, and inefficient systems and equipment that cannot be installed without compromising performance or maintainability.

9.2.1 Initial Considerations

Equipment room locations should permit easy access to equipment by maintenance personnel, with outside vehicular access available where needed. Locate equipment rooms to permit the installation of distribution elements and terminal equipment over corridors or other public spaces and to permit maintenance personnel to access the equipment without passing through or working inside of patient care spaces. Ensure that equipment room space allocations are adequate for all equipment, including electrical panels and code clearance requirements. Consider also the approximate locations and floor area requirements for piping and duct shafts. Lack of early consideration for equipment space can cause severe redesign effort in later stages of design, often impacting the architectural design and too often resulting in inadequate space for equipment installation or maintenance.

9.3 BASIC AIR-HANDLING UNIT DESIGN CONSIDERATIONS

In providing environmental comfort and ventilation for a facility, an air-handling unit simultaneously performs several functions including the intake of outside air to meet ventilation air requirements, thermal mixing of this air with recirculated air from the occupied zones, thermal conditioning, moisture control, filtration to protect equipment and to remove contaminants, and attenuation of fan-generated noise to control ambient noise levels in occupied spaces.

9.3.1 Air-Handling Unit Casing

The design of an air-handling unit casing to minimize water and dirt accumulation, resist corrosion, and permit adequate access for inspection and maintenance is of fundamental importance. It is important that no open-faced insulation be used where water accumulation is likely, such as downstream from cooling coils or humidifiers. Specifically, no lining is allowed after final filters in accordance with the AIA *Guidelines for Design and Construction of Hospital and Health Care Facilities* (AIA 2001).

Fibrous air-handling unit insulation should be isolated from the airstream using an impermeable liner, e.g., Mylar, or "sandwiched" double-wall sheet metal construction. The primary concern is that exposed fibrous insulation can collect dust and moisture to form a perfect growth environment for dangerous microorganisms, although the insulation media may be of inert material that will not of itself support microbial growth. Once contaminated, there is virtually no way of effectively cleaning or disinfecting insulation. Some manufacturers offer liner coatings, which effectively prevent fiber erosion, while still other products are available with plastic or foil coverings to exclude dirt and moisture and improve cleanability. These materials may not, however, have the long-term durability or cleanability of sheet metal. All interior air-handling unit surfaces must be accessible for inspection and cleaning; liners or interior panels should be of a light color and interior lighting should be available to enhance the effectiveness of maintenance tasks. The panels in double-wall casings should have a "thermal break" construction to prevent condensation on the outside surface in humid summer weather.

9.3.2 Outside Air Intakes

Designers must carefully consider the location of the outside air intake for an air-handling unit. Intakes must not be located near potential contaminant sources, such as boiler and generator stacks, laboratory exhaust vents, plumbing vents, cooling towers, ambulance waiting and vehicle parking areas, loading docks, and helipads. Many sources provide generally accepted criteria for minimum separation distances from the outside air intake to potential contaminant sources to ensure adequate separation and dilution. These spacings vary from 10 to 75 feet (3 to 23 m)—with 25 feet (7.6 m) recommended by the AIA *Guidelines* and 30 feet (9.1 m) suggested by the *ASHRAE Handbook—HVAC Applications* (ASHRAE 1999a). Designers must use judgement in the application of such rules, however; 30 feet (9.1 m) may be insufficient separation from a given contaminant source given the source's concen-

tration and nature, the direction of prevailing winds, and building geometry. Certain airborne pathogens, such as Legionnaire's disease bacteria, are known to have been transmitted much longer distances from aerosolized sources such as cooling towers. Designers must apply professional judgement and, when in doubt, utilize analysis techniques such as those described in the *ASHRAE Handbook—Fundamentals*, Chapter 14 (ASHRAE 2001a). Individual circumstances may justify the use of modeling techniques or field simulation to select the best outside air source locations.

Outside air intakes should be located a minimum of 8 feet (2.4 m) above grade (10 feet [3 m] according to some codes and criteria) to avoid taking in grass clippings, leaves, bird feathers, or other debris (often wet) that can clog intake louvers, screens, and filters and provide a reservoir for microbial growth. When located atop buildings, intakes should be located well above roof level (a minimum of 3 feet [0.9 m] according to most codes) to avoid intake of debris from the roof. In cold regions, designers must consider locations for air intakes that will avoid the possibility of snow drifts. All intakes should be equipped with a factory-fabricated louver designed to exclude wind-driven precipitation and with a bird screen to exclude birds or small mammals. Avoid placing an intake near horizontal surfaces (such as a shelf or ledge) that can cause rain splash to penetrate horizontally through the louver or can become a dangerous microbe growth source from collected bird droppings or other organic debris.

9.3.3 Freeze Protection

Burst coils or automatic unit shutdown due to exposure to subfreezing temperatures are frequent occurrences in buildings and result from a number of factors: inadequate air mixing, unintended exposure of coils to 100% outside air, condensate backup in steam coils, and improperly located or installed freezestats. The time required to replace a damaged coil and clean up the flooded (and possibly treatment-chemical-contaminated) air-handler casing can put an air-handling unit out of service for a long period during the most critical environmental conditions. Water leakage in a casing from a damaged cooling coil can provide an environment suitable for microbial growth and may go undetected for an extended time. The potential impact to a health care facility under such conditions can be very serious and costly. This chapter will discuss some general freeze-prevention considerations and practices. It is recommended that the design engineer pay particular attention to wintertime unit operation to ensure that he/she has accurately predicted the conditions to which the unit will be exposed—not only during normal operation but also during unoccupied, emergency, or control failure modes.

9.3.4 Air Mixing

Once outside air entry to an air-handling unit has been successfully addressed, the designer's attention should focus on the air mixing arrangement to ensure that the outside and recirculated (where permitted) airflows are adequately mixed to avoid the impingement of stratified, subfreezing temperature air on downstream equipment. Achievement of a uniform mixed-air temperature is a function of physical blending (diffusion) and heat transfer. Physical manipulation of the two airstreams is required to overcome the natural tendency for air layers of differing temperature to stratify. Manufactured air-mixing boxes are available from all major air-handling unit manufacturers, and the manufacturer will normally provide guidance as to their performance limitations. In severe climates, or where the percentage of outside air is relatively high, designers should consider supplemental air-mixing equipment or arrangements. Factory-fabricated air blenders are available from a number of manufacturers who offer cataloged airflow mixing performance data. While there is presently no national standard governing the testing of these devices, they are extensively used by HVAC designers, and if installed with proper inlet and outlet conditions, and with adequate airflow velocity, as recommended by their manufacturers, they can significantly improve airstream mixing.

9.3.5 Prefiltration

A "roughing" prefilter of approximately 30% dust spot efficiency (ASHRAE 1992) (or MERV 7 [ASHRAE 1999b]) is required within or immediately downstream of the mixing box and upstream from the heating and cooling coils. This filter removes lint, dust, and other large particles from the airstream before they can collect on or clog coils or other components. Throw-away, replaceable, cartridge filters require less maintenance than cleanable or roll-up filters and are usually specified for this reason. All filters should be provided with differential pressure gauges mounted on the air-handling unit, reading differential static pressure across the filter to indicate when the filter should be changed. When the facility is provided with a central DDC, EMCS, or BMS system, filter pressure indication

should also be available for monitoring and alarm generation on the system.

9.3.6 General Considerations for Heating and Cooling Coils

The upstream and downstream faces of all coils must be accessible for cleaning or "combing" (straightening bent fins). Access panels are normally required for this purpose. The panel and panel door should be large enough to enable a maintenance person to access and work on the entire face of the coil. Coils must be constructed of noncorrosive metals, typically copper tubing with aluminum fins. Consider the air vent discharge location and direction of automatic and manual air vents so that entrained water does not leak into the air-handling unit during air bleeding. To enable necessary testing and balancing of the coil, ensure that pressure gauges and thermometers (or ports for these instruments), flow measurement devices, and manual balancing valves are provided on the piping connections. Up and downstream air temperature sensors or sensor ports are also beneficial for unit performance monitoring and troubleshooting. Provide isolation valves and unions to facilitate coil replacement. Use caution in locating coils relative to the suction or discharge of the fan; if located too close, uneven velocity distribution across the coil face can result in loss of capacity, moisture carryover, or freeze-up problems. Generally the flow distribution across the coil face should not vary more than 10%.

9.3.7 Preheating Coil

In many applications, a preheat coil is located downstream from the prefilter and before the cooling coil. Preheat coils may utilize hot water or steam and are normally provided when the mixed air temperature is lower than the air handler's design discharge air temperature or when it is necessary to protect downstream equipment from near- or below-freezing mixed air temperatures. In addition to considering performance under design conditions, designers should think about how the coil should perform under the most severe conditions that it may encounter. For example, a fan that is designed to operate with 100% outside air during an emergency smoke evacuation mode should have a preheat coil properly sized to raise the discharge air temperature above freezing. Specific coil freeze considerations include the following.

Freeze Considerations for Steam Coils

Frequent steam coil freeze failures have resulted from exposure of the condensate-filled portions of the coil to freezing air temperatures. Designers should, therefore, pay particular attention to condensate drainage from the unit. Be aware that modulating steam control valves may cause negative atmospheric pressure in the coil, increasing the volume of condensate backup; providing a vacuum breaker will permit the condensate to drain by gravity. Many designers prefer a face-and-bypass approach for steam coil discharge temperature control, keeping the steam coil control valve fully open at all times and regulating airflow around the coil to maintain discharge setpoint. This arrangement, while undoubtedly successful in many applications, does not necessarily eliminate the danger of condensate buildup in the coil.

Freeze Considerations for Heating Water Coils

When hot water coils are used, designers must determine whether to utilize an antifreeze solution in the system. A solution containing a large percentage of glycol can provide freeze protection to well below 0°F (–18°C). In addition to reducing heat transfer and increasing the pumping energy requirement, however, there are significant maintenance considerations associated with the use of an antifreeze solution. Maintenance personnel must maintain the glycol/water percentage selected by the designer; often this is not handled properly and the maintenance personnel merely guess the glycol percentage based on the color of the solution. Care must also be given to using the correct antifreeze formulation; there are several reported instances of maintenance personnel mistakenly introducing automotive antifreeze into heating systems, leading to undesirable deposits ("gumming up") in the heating coils. When properly used and designed, however, glycol systems can be a very attractive freeze protection option. One of the most universally utilized freeze protection approaches for heating coils, whether using antifreeze solutions or untreated water, is the use of dedicated circulating pumps. The circulating pump maintains a continuous circulation of water in the coil throughout the heating season. The combination of continuous flow and pump heat can provide a significant degree of freeze protection.

9.3.8 Air-Handling Unit Freezestat

A freezestat is normally located on the upstream face of the cooling coil (the location may differ, depending upon air-handling unit design and configuration). The freezestat's function is to detect sub-freezing temperatures, sound an alarm, and shut down the air-handling unit before the coil can be damaged. Too frequently, however, improper installation of the freezestat has led to damaged coils. The freezestat consists of a long length of sensor tubing that must be installed in a serpentine fashion across the entire face of the coil so as to detect any localized freezing temperatures due to air stratification. When inadequate space is provided for sensor installation, the tubing is frequently placed as a coiled bundle, which vastly compromises its effectiveness. For this reason, as well as to enable cleaning the upstream face of the cooling coil, an upstream access panel must be provided, with suitable dimensions to enable a maintenance technician to access the entire face of the coil.

9.3.9 Cooling Coils

In addition to providing sensible cooling, a cooling coil acts as a dehumidifier and (for the latter purpose) must normally have a high heat transfer surface area consisting of at least six tubing rows with relatively tightly spaced fins. As the heat transfer surfaces remain (virtually) continuously wet, cooling coils easily collect dust and can become a microbe growth site. For this reason, an ability to clean the coil is extremely important. A large number of coil rows and close fin spacing make cleaning difficult; it is, therefore, normally recommended that coils do not exceed 6 rows or more than 12-14 fins per inch (25 mm). When additional rows are required, the cooling coil should be split into two separate coils (in the direction of airflow). Both upstream and downstream faces of the cooling coil(s) must be accessible to a maintenance worker using a power washer. Other cooling coil considerations include the following:

Moisture Carryover

In order to avoid carryover of droplets from the cooling coil into the air-handling unit casing, the air velocity through the cooling coil must be limited. Designers typically permit a maximum velocity of not more than 450-550 feet per minute (2.3-2.8 m/s), although with special fin coatings this velocity may be increased to 600-625 feet per minute (3.1-3.2 m/s). If capacity for future load growth (airflow increase) is desirable, it may be reasonable to size a coil for a velocity lower than 450 feet per minute (2.3 m/s).

Cooling coils must be provided with positively draining pans constructed of noncorrosive materials (i.e., stainless steel) for the collection and disposal of condensate and to avoid standing water. An oversized condensate drain pan can have an adverse effect and provide locations for microbial growth. Pans should reach entirely beneath the coil and extend approximately 12 inches (300 mm) from the discharge face. The pan should be at least 2 inches (50 mm) deep, with a drain pipe located so that the bottom of the pipe is flush with the bottom of the pan. When coils are stacked vertically, a separately trapped drain pan should be provided for each coil. All drain pans must be properly trapped to ensure that the condensate continues to drain during fan operation. Trap leg dimensional and configuration requirements will differ based upon whether the coil is under negative (draw-through configuration) or positive (blow-through configuration) pressure. In both cases, maintenance of the trap seal is important to avoid drawing sewage gases into the air-handling unit.

Figure 9-1 illustrates a condensate drain trap for a coil subjected to negative pressure. Unless the trap is properly constructed to provide a positive gravity head on the pan-inlet side—exceeding the negative pressure imposed by the unit fan—condensate will not drain from the unit. Dimension "A" equals "B+C," where "B" is the maximum air-handling unit static pressure plus 1 inch (w.g.) (250 Pa), and "C" is ½ B.

Figure 9-2 shows the proper configuration for a drain trap for a coil under positive pressure. In this case, the outlet leg of the trap must be high enough to offset the positive static pressure on the inlet side, which would otherwise blow out the trap seal. Dimension "A" equals the maximum air-handling unit static pressure plus ½ inch (w.g.) (125 Pa), and "B" is ½ inch (13 mm) minimum.

9.3.10 Supply Fan Considerations

Designers should apply "real world" operation and maintenance considerations to the selection of an air-handling unit supply fan to help ensure satisfactory long-term operation. The as-constructed air system pressure-flow characteristics, and, therefore, the fan operating point, often differ from the calculated values. It is a good idea to ensure that the specified fan motor horsepower is sufficient to provide for fan operation along a broad range of the fan operating curve. Select fans so that their normal operating point will not be within the surge range. Consider the need to attenuate fan-generated noise that may transmit through the distribution system to occupied spaces. Airfoil-bladed centrifugal fans and plenum-style fan arrangements tend to be less noisy than other alternatives. When final filters or coils are located downstream of the fan discharge, a discharge air diffuser may be required (depending upon conditions) to equalize the outlet velocity profile and

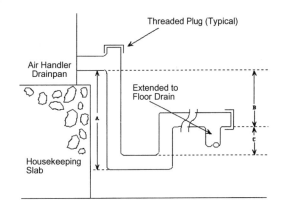

Figure 9-1   Drain trap for coil subjected to negative pressure.

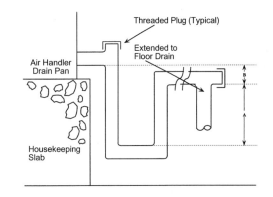

Figure 9-2   Drain trap for coil subjected to positive pressure.

avoid excessive pressure losses or velocities in the downstream components.

- *System Effect.* Cataloged fan performance is normally based upon "laboratory conditions" at the fan inlet and outlet, which often cannot be duplicated in the field and which maximize the performance of the fan. When conditions are less ideal, fan performance will be less than cataloged. The term "system effect" is used to describe the loss of performance resulting from non-idealized inlet or outlet conditions. Typically, system effect is expressed in inches of water pressure loss (pascals) or in multiples of the "velocity head" at the fan discharge. On the suction side, system effects can result from such factors as restricted inlets, flow obstructions (such as bearings or inlet vanes), and air pre-spin caused by improperly designed elbow connections. On the discharge side, system effects result from obstructions by fittings or equipment (coils, elbows, takeoffs) located too close to the fan connection or by discharge into an open plenum. Most air-handling unit manufacturers, and several industry references and standards, provide guidelines for estimating the system effect resulting from various inlet and outlet arrangements, one source being AMCA 201 (AMCA 1990). It is very important for the design engineer to read air-handling manufacturers' literature when selecting a fan to understand under what conditions the fan was tested so that the appropriate system effects can be estimated. Several manufacturers base their air-handling unit fan performance on ARI Standard 430 (ARI 1999), which tests the fans within the factory housing (suction plenum) but with several diameters of straight ductwork connected at the discharge. This is not true, however, in all cases.

- *Belt Losses.* The laboratory conditions used to test fans normally involve the fan being driven by a direct-drive dynamometer. Thus, the fan power information published in manufacturers' catalogs will often not include the effects of belt losses, which can consume up to 3-5% of total motor output, depending upon belt drive characteristics, belt tension, etc. (Carrier 1997).

Fan selection for a given application requires designer consideration of the performance characteristics, and space requirements, of the various fan types or variants available. Centrifugal fans are normally, but not exclusively, selected for supply fan applications for major air-handling units. Centrifugal fans are available with forward curved, backward curved, and airfoil-bladed scroll vanes, each variant having distinctive relative speed, noise generation, efficiency, and power (overloading versus non-overloading) characteristics. In addition, centrifugal fans are available with open (plenum) or directed discharge arrangements, involving differing noise generation, system effect, and equipment space considerations.

Vane-axial type fans are also sometimes selected for supply fan applications. Formerly, these were very commonly used for variable volume applications. With the advent of reasonably priced variable speed drives, however, this application has become less popular. Variable pitch vane-axial fans have many moving parts and they are prone to significant maintenance requirements.

9.3.11 Return Fan Considerations

Return fans are normally required for air-handling units employing an economizer ("free cooling") system. As with the supply fan, consideration must be given to fan noise generation and the need for attenuation to reduce the sound transmitted through the return ductwork to occupied spaces. Ensure that adequate space is available for personnel access to all parts of the return fan requiring inspection or periodic maintenance. As with supply fans, the design engineer will need to evaluate the "system effect" (reduced fan performance) resulting from inlet and outlet conditions. Fan type selection must consider required performance and equipment space availability for each application.

9.3.12 Humidifiers

Humidifiers are often required in health care facility air-handling systems to maintain a minimum level of relative humidity in the occupied spaces. Most criteria establish a 30% RH minimum, with possibly higher levels in critical spaces. The complexities of humidifier design and maintenance are often underestimated by designers, with the result that the devices are frequently disconnected by maintenance personnel or cited as a cause of contamination and corrosion within the air-handler or ductwork. Designers must carefully consider the selection and location of humidifiers within air-handling units or ductwork to avoid moisture accumulation in downstream components, including filters and insulation. Humidifier design considerations include the following.

Humidifier Types

Most designers, and many codes, recommend steam injection type humidifiers for health care facility applications. Steam is sterile and, therefore, eliminates the risk of introducing viable microorganisms, such as *Legionella*, into the building airstream. Steam may be generated centrally (boiler or heat exchanger) or locally at the humidifier by a separate electrical or steam-to-steam generator. Small gas-fired units are also available. Regardless of the steam source, care must be taken to ensure that only dry steam is supplied to the steam injector. Consult manufacturer's recommendation for appropriate condensate trapping and drainage provisions and ensure that appropriate details and instructions are communicated via construction drawings. Evaporative and spray mist evaporators are also available for humidification applications—where permitted by applicable codes.

Avoiding Wetting of Air-Handler or Duct Components

When saturated, dry steam is injected into the airstream, a portion of the steam is immediately condensed and forms a mist or "vapor trail" of water particles. Unless a suitable expanse of downstream duct or air-handler casing is provided to permit reevaporation, the mist will impinge on downstream equipment and cause water buildup. Filters, exposed insulating materials, and even sheet metal can easily become microbe growth sites in these circumstances, and fans and other steel air-handling and ductwork components will quickly rust. The distance required for reevaporation is a function of air temperature, relative humidity, velocity, casing or duct dimensions, and the design of the humidifier components—and can vary from a few inches (several mm) to more than 12 feet (3.6 m).

Some designers prefer to locate humidifiers within the air-handling unit. Sometimes this is the only location available due to space or other contrants. As air velocities are low in an air-handling unit casing, use of multiple humidifier manifolds (see Figure 9-3) allows the steam to be readily absorbed into the air. In some situations, a downstream moisture eliminator may be desired to provide additional protection against wetting of downsteam air-handling components. Humidifier installation in the air-handling unit will also normally allow for a final, high-efficiency filter to be installed downstream from the humidifier as an added protection against the potential presence of microbial elements.

It is also common practice for a humidifier to be installed outside of the air-handling unit casing in the discharge ductwork. In such cases, a suitable length of straight, unobstructed ductwork should be pro-

vided downstream to ensure complete evaporation of moisture droplets. Proper maintenance access is vital for this type of humidifier installation.

Sizing and Control Considerations

With VAV systems, most designers size air-handling unit humidifiers on the basis of lower winter season air flow and corresponding outside design temperature. When operating in economizer mode, a humidifier sized according to such criteria may be unable to achieve desired supply air RH setpoint.

9.3.13   Air-Handling Unit Noise Attenuation

In many cases the designer will find that attenuation of fan noise (supply, return, or both) will be required in order to achieve room background noise levels required by design criteria. This is often a concern with the double-walled air-handling units required for health care facilities because the interior sheet metal wall resists noise breakout and helps to transmit the noise through the ductwork. When attenuation is required, the designer's only options are to provide acoustically lined ductwork, active electronic silencers, or factory-fabricated sound attenuators. Packless type attenuators and active silencers have limited application and efficacy, often leaving packed-type liners and attenuators as the only practical choice. This chapter has already discussed concerns with permitting a water-permeable, unsealed insulation surface to be exposed to the airstream. Several manufacturers, however, offer double-walled attenuating ductwork or fabricated attenuators with perforated inner sheet metal housings and impermeable foil or plastic liners, which probably offer the best compromise between durability/sanitation concerns and the need for noise attenuation. The foil or plastic liners do not drastically reduce attenuation performance. Their flame spread/ smoke generation characteristics, however, should be checked against the limiting requirements of NFPA 90A or applicable codes. Due to installation space limitations, and to improve the "inspectability" and cleanability of the interior surfaces, fabricated attenuators are often chosen over attenuating ductwork.

Attenuator inlet and outlet conditions must also be considered. The noise-attenuating properties and pressure-flow characteristics cataloged by attenuator manufacturers are based upon smooth inlet and outlet duct transitions, which are normally available in their literature lines. Many designers do not realize that without proper transitions the pressure loss across a sound attenuator can be several times the cataloged value and the attenuator can actually gen-

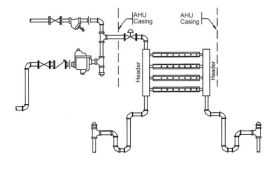

Figure 9-3   Steam humidifier with multiple manifold.

erate more noise than it attenuates. The designer needs to include suitable transition space and provide appropriate details and instructions for the contractor.

9.3.14 Second Filter Bank

Many of the spaces in a health care facility require a higher level of filtration than is provided by a prefilter (typically 30% dust spot efficiency) alone. The AIA *Guidelines,* for example, recommend a filtration level of 95% (MERV 14-15) for all patient care areas, whether in clinics or in full-service hospitals. Some codes require HEPA filtration for inpatient applications, especially where patients are particularly vulnerable to infection, such as protective isolation rooms for immunocompromised patients and orthopedic operating rooms. Designers must ensure (and require in contract documents) that space is allocated for replacing filters. All filters should be provided with a differential pressure indicating manometer mounted on the air-handling unit to indicate when replacement is required.

The second filter (normally the final filter installed in the air-handling unit) is (along with the cooling coil) a determining factor in establishing the overall dimensions of the air-handler.   Design air velocity for health care facility air-handling unit filters should not exceed 500 fpm (2.5 m/s) for filters of 95% efficiency (MERV 15) and below. HEPA and higher efficiency filters (MERV 17 and above) should be designed with a 300 fpm (1.5 m/s) velocity limit. To ensure adequate airflow throughout the range of filter resistance from clean to dirty, designers should use the filter manufacturer's recommended final resistance when calculating fan pressure requirements. If no final resistance recommendation is available, a value of 1.4 in. w.g. (350 Pa) is recommended for 80%-95% efficiency filters (MERV 13-15).   Be aware that when filters are "clean," resulting in system resistance lower than the fan selection point, the fan motor must be adequately sized to accommodate the higher brake horsepower requirements at that operating condition.

9.3.15 Airflow Monitors

Airflow monitoring arrays are often provided in the return and supply airstreams for VAV systems to enable differential supply-return fan flow control. In addition, they are frequently employed, in both VAV and constant volume systems, to monitor outside air flow. In order to accurately measure velocity (and therefore flow volume), monitoring arrays require a reasonably uniform entering velocity profile. Estab-

lishing that profile normally requires a certain extent of straight upstream duct, usually specified by the device manufacturer in terms of unit diameters, and a smoothly transitioning discharge arrangement. Designers should consult manufacturer's recommendations, ensure that the space requirements are taken into account in laying out the fan room, and reflect the requirements in the construction documents. Designers also need to consider the range of flow that they intend the device to measure to ascertain that it is not only sufficiently accurate over that range but can physically sense flow at lower velocities (a particular concern with pitot-type velocity sensing).

9.3.16 Dehumidification Equipment

Dehumidification by the primary cooling coil is often sufficient to limit relative humidity to the maximum values permitted by codes. Very stringent upper limit relative humidity requirements may dictate supplemental dehumidification using mechanical refrigeration or desiccant equipment. Some designers address this issue by providing automatic controls to reset the cooling coil discharge temperature below that required for cooling to provide dehumidification; such a strategy requires reheat of the air supply for comfort conditioning.

9.4 AIR-HANDLING SYSTEM ALTERNATIVES

Chapter 5 of this manual deals with the various HVAC systems and where they are (or are not) typically recommended for use. This chapter addresses only some of the major considerations involved in selecting among the most common system alternatives. Depending upon the facility department or area under consideration, single- and dual-duct systems, both constant and variable air volume (VAV), are frequently encountered in health care facilities. Multizone systems are less frequently encountered due to the larger number of ducts associated with these systems. Many, but not all, code authorities will permit VAV systems to serve spaces that do not have specific relative pressure requirements, including examination rooms and "normal" patient bedrooms, in addition to administrative and office spaces. Constant volume systems are commonly used for spaces such as disease isolation and ICU bedrooms, operating rooms, and laboratories, where discrete pressurization relative to contiguous spaces must be maintained. VAV systems should be able to perform in these applications given appropriate attention to pressure control and minimum ventilation requirements. When a designer has more than one system alternative to consider, the choice should be influenced by life-cycle cost analysis.

9.4.1 Variable Air Volume (VAV) Systems

VAV systems provide fan energy savings through variation of the volumetric flow rate of conditioned air when loads are less than peak. These systems may sometimes permit use of reduced fan sizes, as compared to constant volume systems, when peak loads in the areas served do not occur simultaneously. Fan capacity is normally modulated using variable inlet vanes, or variable speed motor drives, in response to static pressure sensors located downstream (usually two-thirds the distance) in the air distribution system. Another control strategy using the position of terminal volume controllers (automatic dampers) can also be considered. Single-duct VAV systems require some means of terminal or space reheat to ensure adequate zone temperature control. Dual-duct VAV systems, with separate heated and cooled air ducts, mix hot and cold air at the terminal unit to maintain the zone temperature setpoint.

With VAV systems, it is important that the terminal unit flow rate at minimum box position be sufficient to meet minimum ventilation rate criteria. Flow rate in the heating mode must be adequate to provide acceptable air distribution in the space. VAV systems are prohibited by some codes from serving spaces with relative pressurization requirements.

9.4.2 Constant Volume (CAV) Systems

Compared to VAV systems, CAV systems typically involve higher operational energy costs due to their inability to reduce fan energy during periods of low cooling demand. Their control complexity is, however, correspondingly lower, and their comparatively lower first cost and annual maintenance and first costs can make CAV systems life-cycle cost competitive with VAV. CAV systems are typically designed to distribute a cooled air supply to terminal reheat coils (single duct) or mixing boxes (dual duct) serving individual zones. Since these systems do not reduce room airflow rate during heating mode, they can provide consistent room air distribution, particularly in perimeter spaces (see Section 9.8 for further information).

9.4.3 Multizone Systems

Multizone systems are a type of constant volume system, involving a dedicated supply duct from the air-handling unit to each zone served. A multi-zone system mixes hot and cold airstreams at zone dampers located within the air-handling unit in response to the zone temperature sensor. These systems are manufactured in configurations serving as many as 12 zones per air-handler. Multizone systems offer the advantage of having the primary temperature controls and equipment located in a central location—at the air-handling unit—in lieu of being distributed throughout the facility. With so many supply ducts branching off a single air-handling unit, however, distribution space is a primary concern. The multitude of duct, cable tray, and piping systems associated with a health care facility, coupled with architectural or structural features limiting the available vertical space, often make these systems impractical.

9.4.4 Draw-Through and Blow-Through Selection Considerations

In determining the type of air-handling system to be utilized for a health care facility, the designer often has the choice of either a draw-through or a blow-through fan-cooling coil arrangement. With a draw-through arrangement the fan is located downstream of the cooling (and heating) coil. With a blow-through arrangement, the locations are reversed. With dual-duct and multizone systems, the arrangement is always blow-through. For other system types however, such as the very common single-duct constant and variable volume systems, the choice of draw-through versus blow-through requires careful consideration of several factors that can adversely affect system performance and acceptability.

• *System Effect.* The draw-through and blow-through arrangements can create different system effects. As discussed in section 9.3.10, poor fan inlet or discharge arrangements can result in lowered fan performance. Many air-handling unit manufacturers rate their fan performances with the fan operating within its inlet plenum, which takes into account any adverse effects caused by the plenum. In such cases, the design engineer does not need to evaluate the "system effect" of upstream modules or components, other than to account for their flow losses. With built-up units or special construction, however, the design engineer must use care to evaluate the system effects of upstream components or conditions. With a draw-through unit, care must be taken not to locate the upstream coil too close to the fan inlet. A minimum upstream separation between the coil and the fan casing of ½ fan wheel diameter for single-inlet centrifugal fans and 1 wheel diameter for double-inlet fans has been recommended (Trane 1982). With a blow-through arrangement, the downstream coil can cause an adverse system effect if located too close to the fan discharge. In addition to lowering performance, a coil located too close to the discharge can result in uneven velocity distribution across the coil face, diminishing coil capacity and possibly creating droplet carryover. When the coil cannot be located a suitable distance downstream from the fan discharge, a baffle plate (typically recommended to be 50% perforated) located downstream from the fan, approximately two-thirds of the distance to the coil, will provide a more even air distribution across the coil face

- *Draw-Through Fan Reheat.* The air leaving the cooling coil in an air-handling unit is often very close to the saturation point. This may also be the case if a humidifier is provided, although controls are normally set to limit the airstream relative humidity to not more than 85%. Various system factors can cause a saturated airstream to condense on downstream equipment, fittings, filters, or ductwork, contributing to microbe growth Many designers choose a draw-through design to take advantage of the "reheat" imparted by the enthalpy input at the supply fan, thus heating the airstream a few degrees above the saturation point. Blow-through fan arrangements cannot take advantage of fan heat for this purpose, and wetting of downstream components can be a significant concern.

- *Final Filter Location.* Locating the final filter too close to the fan discharge, under either arrangement, can lead to uneven air distribution across the filter and possible damage from excessively high velocities. A greater concern, however, is potential wetting of the filter if located in the saturated airstream downstream from the cooling coil or humidifier. Wet filters easily become microbe growth sites, due to the availability of moisture and nutrients (dirt) at the same location. In addition, the capture of moisture droplets by filters can vastly increase filter pressure drop, leading to reduced system ventilation performance. One major air-handling unit manufacturer recommends against locating the final filter downstream from the cooling coil in a blow-through configuration (Trane 1996). This may create a dilemma when code or criteria provisions (such as the AIA *Guidelines*) require that final filters be located downstream of the

coils. To help reduce the chance of wetting the filter, the cooling coil face velocity should be limited to 450 fpm (2.3 m/s).

- *Cooling Coil Trap Design.* The cooling coil condensate drain will be under either negative or positive pressure—depending upon which arrangement is selected—when the fan is operating. Refer to Figures 9-1 and 9-2 for design recommendations.

- *Issues Summary.* Key issues affecting the selection of a draw-through or blow-through air-handling configuration include:

    — *Draw-through advantages*: A compact unit length; more efficient fan operation when discharge is properly designed; a reduced incidence of moisture carryover from the cooling coil as a result of more uniform coil face velocities.
    — *Draw-through disadvantages*: Poor mixing of return and outside air that may cause temperature stratification and tripping of the freezestat; supply air temperature downstream of the cooling coil increases due to fan heat (a concern if not properly addressed during design).
    — *Blow-through advantages*: Heat load from high-pressure fans is absorbed by the cooling coil, permitting a higher discharge air temperature for any given space load; the fan more thoroughly mixes airstreams, reducing stratification and nuisance freezestat trips; less of the unit casing is subjected to the high-humidity environment downstream of the cooling coil.
    — *Blow-through disadvantages*: To prevent moisture carryover from the cooling coil, face velocities must be on the order of 400-450 fpm (2.0-2.3 m/s); the unit is larger; more careful design is required.

9.5 DUCTWORK

9.5.1 General Design Considerations

Duct systems for health care facilities may be designed using any of the major duct sizing approaches described in the *ASHRAE Handbook—Fundamentals* and SMACNA and other industry publications, including the equal friction, static regain, T-method, and other approaches. *Fundamentals* provides guidance as to velocity and pressure loss limitations, as well as economic considerations of the several methods. Designers should be aware that careful attention to duct system velocity limitations is especially warranted in health care facility design, due to the common imposition of background noise level criteria. Due to the variety of systems required for health care service, the ductwork design must be carefully coordinated with the electrical, fire protection, plumbing and HVAC piping, and other building services, as well as with architectural and structural elements, to ensure sufficiency of space. Most designers recommend fully ducted installations, using all-metal duct construction, particularly for inpatient facilities, and the avoidance of duct liner except when absolutely necessary to attenuate ductborne noise. Other health care facility ductwork considerations are as follows.

- Various organizations, including ASHRAE and SMACNA, publish guidelines for selecting fittings and determining pressure losses. The manufacturers of distribution equipment such as diffusers, sound attenuators, fire dampers, and inlet louvers normally publish pressure loss characteristics. Designers must be cautious, however, because the published pressure losses (as well as noise output levels) often correspond to specific "idealized" inlet or connection arrangements that may not be possible in actual building situations.

- Designers should be careful to show or specify the duct pressure classes for supply, return, and exhaust ductwork to ensure adequate construction and sealing according to SMACNA standards.

- Designers must ensure that specifications or drawings include provisions for the necessary fittings to enable testing and balancing. Splitters (when allowed and permitted) and balancing dampers must be shown or detailed wherever required. Designers should provide suitable ductwork configurations to enable accurate pitot traverses in main and branch ductwork.

- Access openings should be provided where required for system maintenance and inspection. These include not only suitably framed and gasketed (as required) openings in the duct but also coordination with the architectural design to ensure that corresponding ceiling access is provided. Duct access doors should be provided at fire and smoke dampers, on both sides of duct-mounted coils, at humidifiers, and as required by the client or codes to facilitate duct cleaning.

- Whenever permitted by space conditions, utilize long radius elbows to minimize pressure losses and improve performance and cleanliness. "Square" elbows with turning vanes should be avoided, especially in exhaust and return systems, because they collect dust and debris, leading to reduced airflow performance.

- Flexible duct use should be limited due to its higher pressure losses, particularly when crimped or coiled, and its greater susceptibility to abuse or damage. Many designers limit flexible duct connections to a maximum length of 5-6 feet (1.5–1.8 m).

9.5.2 Fully Ducted versus Plenum Returns

Most designers prefer fully ducted return systems in health care facilities, including outpatient clinics, largely due to their inherently superior sanitary characteristics. Some codes mandate fully ducted systems for all inpatient facilities. Ducted returns protect the airstream from direct exposure to such potential plenum conditions as accumulated dust, microbes or odors generated by wet materials (from piping leaks, roof leaks, or floor leaks in multi-story facilities), rodent droppings, fibers from deteriorated flame proofing or equipment, and smoke from smoldering wiring insulation or other sources during a fire. To minimize the latter possibility, NFPA codes require that electrical cables installed in plenums utilized for air movement must be of the plenum-rated type. Above-ceiling plenums, in particular, are prone to disturbance by maintenance activities that could release opportunistic fungi or allergens into a return airstream. Ducted returns in addition minimize "cross-talk" wherein audible conversations are transmitted between rooms via open return connections, particularly when room partitions do not extend above the ceilings.

9.5.3 Duct Cleaning

Ductwork collects deposits of dust and can become contaminated with microbial colonization. The extent of this problem varies with the level of filtration, HVAC system maintenance, geographic location, climate, and other factors. Accumulated dust in ductwork has been implicated by some scientific studies with increased occupant health complaints, such as itchy eyes, cough, and allergic reactions (Brosseau 2000a). Numerous studies also attribute hospital nosocomial infection outbreaks to microbes growing in ductwork or air-handling equipment. In addition, excessive dust buildup in ducts can result in significantly reduced air system performance, including underventilation. In recent years large numbers of companies have emerged that specialize in ductwork cleaning, and the National Air Duct Cleaners Association has published guidelines and specifications for this work (NADCA 2002). Cleaning processes require access into the interior of the ductwork and involve placing the duct under vacuum in combination with mechanical or power brushing, air washing, contact vacuuming, and sometimes steam cleaning. In addition, microbial biocides and encapsulants may be utilized. The effectiveness of duct cleaning in reducing the incidence of hospital nosocomial infection is in question. The process of cleaning may, particularly without careful coordination with the hospital staff and the exercise of stringent containment measures, actually increase the level of contaminants within a health care facility.

Studies have shown that dust accumulated in ductwork contains large amounts of organic materials such as human and animal hair, skin flakes, fungal spores, insect parts, and plant materials (Brosseau 2000a). These materials can provide nutrition for microbe growth and can themselves cause allergic reactions in sensitive persons. Dust buildup occurs to a much greater degree in unfiltered duct systems, such as return or exhaust ducts, and in particular upon fittings against which the airstream impacts or that cause high turbulence eddies (such as fan plenums, elbows, turning vanes, and dampers).

It is known that duct-cleaning operations can release large quantities of airborne particles, and high levels of chemical compounds, into the general hospital environment (Brosseau 2000b). Although standard procedures place the duct being cleaned under negative pressure (vacuum) during the procedure, the surrounding area can become contaminated, if the negative pressure is carelessly maintained, by not providing adequate time for disinfecting or encapsulant chemicals to dry or by work done outside of the duct to gain access for the procedure. An increase in the level of airborne particles, including opportunistic microbes such as *Aspergillus* that are a frequent component of building dust, is known to increase the risk of nosocomial infection in hospitals, particularly among the immune-compromised. Chemical applications, particularly when improperly applied or mixed, can result in occupant complaints of irritation or adverse health effects. At least one hospital investigation correlated a higher incidence of occupant health complaints during a duct-cleaning/disinfection procedure with symptoms corresponding to MSDS data for the chemicals being used (Carlson and Streifel 1996). For these reasons a number of authorities and industry associations strongly advocate that duct-cleaning projects be carefully coordinated beforehand with the facility staff, that the procedure be carried out only by prop-

erly trained and qualified personnel, and that all necessary containment and protective measures be carefully adhered to.

In order to facilitate duct cleaning, designers should provide duct access door openings in accessible locations at periodic intervals in major ductwork and at the fittings where dust is likely to most heavily accumulate (as indicated above). A survey of duct-cleaning companies also recommended that to minimize dust accumulation, designers avoid the use of interior duct linings or glass fiber ductwork.

The Centers for Disease Control (CDC) and U.S. Environmental Protection Agency (EPA) advise that there is no indication that duct cleaning results in a lower incidence of infection or other health problems (CDC 2001). It is recognized, however, that cleaning can result in improved air system performance. The general industry position for hospitals appears to be that routine duct cleaning may be justified on exhaust systems, and perhaps return systems, due to their greater potential for dust accumulation and the lesser risk of redeposition of dust into the facility, but that careful consideration be given before cleaning supply ductwork. For facilities with inpatient spaces, and particularly for those housing immune-compromised patients, duct cleaning should only be considered in cases of severe contamination, using the most carefully planned procedures, with all necessary isolation and protective measures understood and enforced by both contractor and hospital staff.

9.6 TERMINAL UNITS

Terminal units are control devices installed between the ductwork system and the room air distribution system. Depending upon the application, they could be constant volume, variable volume, or fan powered, with or without reheat. Terminal units are divided into two broad categories: constant volume and variable volume. A terminal unit is considered to be variable volume if the airflow to the space varies. If variable volume is selected, the designer must ensure that minimum air flow output is adequate to meet outside air and total air ventilation requirement. Airflow is constant for constant volume terminal units.

9.6.1 Constant Volume Terminal Unit

Constant volume terminals are connected to a constant volume fan system that serves multiple zones. Supply air is cooled to satisfy the zone with the largest cooling load. Air delivered to other zones is then reheated with heating coils (hot water, steam, or electric) installed in individual zone terminals. The reheat control is reset as required to maintain the space temperature.

9.6.2 Variable Volume Terminal Unit

This type of terminal, also known as a "throttling" terminal, has a damper in the inlet that controls the flow of supply air. A reheat coil can be installed in the discharge for spaces requiring heating. As the temperature in the space drops below the setpoint, the damper begins to close and reduce the flow of air to the space. When the airflow reaches the minimum limit, the valve on the reheat coil begins to open.

Single-duct VAV systems, which supply warm air to all zones when heating is required and cool air to all zones when cooling is required, have limited application and are used where heating is required only for morning warm-up. They should not be used if some zones require heating at the same time that others on the same air-handling unit require cooling.

9.6.3 Bypass Terminal Unit

A bypass terminal unit has a damper that diverts part of the supply air into the return plenum. The diverting damper is controlled by space temperature. When the temperature in the space drops below the setpoint, the bypass damper begins to open, routing some of the supply air to the plenum, which reduces the amount of supply air entering the space. When the bypass is fully open, the control valve for the reheat coil opens as required to maintain the space temperature. A manual balancing damper in the bypass is adjusted to match the resistance in the discharge duct. In this way, the supply of air from the primary system remains at a constant volume. The maximum airflow through the bypass should be restricted in order to maintain a minimum airflow into the space.

9.6.4 Fan-Powered Terminal Unit

This type of unit has an integral fan that supplies a constant volume of air to the space. In addition to enhancing air distribution in the space, a reheat coil can be added to maintain the space temperature when the primary system is off. When the space is occupied, the fan runs constantly to provide a constant volume of air. The fan can draw air from the return plenum to compensate for a reduced supply air flow. As the temperature in the space decreases below the setpoint, the supply air damper begins to close and the fan draws more air from the return plenum. Units serving perimeter areas of a building can

include a reheat coil. Then, when the supply air reaches its minimum level, the valve to the reheat coil begins to open. Designers should note that some authorities may not allow these units in health care applications due to possible contamination concerns.

9.6.5 Plenum Fan Terminal Unit

These units have a fan that pulls air from the return plenum and mixes it with the supply air. A reheat coil may be placed in the discharge to the space or the return plenum opening. The fan provides a minimum level of airflow to the space. Total airflow to the space is the sum of the fan output and the supply air quantity. When the space temperature drops below the setpoint, the supply air damper begins to reduce the quantity of supply air entering the terminal. Once the supply damper has reached its minimum position, the reheat coil valve starts to open.

9.6.6 Dual-Duct Constant Volume Terminal Unit

The hot-duct damper and cold-duct damper in this terminal are linked to operate in reverse directions. A space thermostat positions the mixing dampers to mix warm and cool supply air. The discharge air volume depends on the static pressure in each supply duct at that location.

9.6.7 Dual-Duct Variable Volume Terminal Unit

This unit has inlet dampers on the heating and cooling supply ducts. These dampers are interlinked to operate in opposite directions; usually each requires a control actuator. A sensor in the discharge monitors total airflow. The space thermostat controls the inlet mixing dampers directly, and the airflow controller controls the volume damper. The space thermostat resets the airflow controller from maximum to minimum flow as the sensible load on the conditioned area changes.

9.7 ROOM AIR DISTRIBUTION

At the risk of oversimplification, it may be stated that there are two different room air distribution design approaches encountered in health care facilities: (1) an approach that prioritizes the control of air movement within the space and (2) an approach that prioritizes comfort. The former, sometimes characterized as "plug" or "laminar" flow, is normally utilized in spaces where there is a high risk of patient infection, such as surgical operating rooms and (sometimes) protective isolation rooms. The intent is to limit air turbulence and achieve some degree of directional uniformity from "clean" to "dirty" areas. The application and relative efficacy of plug flow systems are discussed in more detail in Chapter 12, "Room Design," of this manual. This chapter will address the "conventional" approach, which seeks to maximize comfort and air change effectiveness.

9.7.1 The Importance of Adequate Air Distribution

Thermal comfort is of special importance in health care facilities. In examination, treatment, and diagnostic areas and bedrooms, patients are often garbed in scanty hospital gowns or partially disrobed for extensive periods of time. For seriously ill or injured patients, the additional stress of an uncomfortable environment may retard the healing process. Criteria for minimum and maximum space temperatures have been established, but thermal comfort—being a function not only of temperature but also of relative humidity, air movement, radiant exposure, clothing, and metabolism—can easily be compromised by poorly designed HVAC systems. In addition, adequate room ventilation—the effective distribution of fresh air throughout the space and the dilution and removal of contaminants—is dependent upon a carefully designed room air distribution system.

9.7.2 System Performance

As discussed above, the personal perception of thermal comfort is influenced by several factors in addition to temperature. Discomfort can result from a lack of uniform conditions or excessive fluctuation of conditions within a space. Excessive or localized drafts acting on different parts of the body, or small variations in the air temperature on different portions of the body, can lead to feelings of discomfort. A well-designed room air distribution system requires careful consideration of the type and location of the room supply air diffuser(s) in relation to the room geometry and (as applicable) outside exposure, the volumetric flow rate of air being introduced into the space, and the temperature difference between supply air and room air.

Room air movement is a function of the supply (primary) air delivered by the diffuser and movement of room air induced by this flow. When diffuser type and throw characteristics are well chosen, the combination of primary and induced flow results in good distribution of air throughout the space, avoiding uncomfortable drafts or areas of stagnation. One per-

formance indicator now frequently used by designers to relate cooling-mode occupant thermal comfort to space temperature and air movement is the Air Diffusion Performance Index (ADPI). The higher the ADPI number, the greater the comfort level, with an ADPI greater than 80% generally being considered acceptable. From a ventilation standpoint, a successful system is one that effectively distributes fresh air throughout the space; one index for rating such ventilation effectiveness is the Air Change Effectiveness (ACE). Findings indicate that systems designed to maximize ADPI also have high ACE performance characteristics.

9.7.3 Supply Outlet Performance

Diffuser performance is normally indicated by "throw"—the horizontal distance at which a diffuser will project an isothermal (supply air of same temperature as room air) air flow at a given end velocity, 50 fpm (0.25 m/s) being a typically used parameter. Throw performance is cataloged by manufacturers for their various diffuser models. The effectiveness of a diffuser in achieving good room air movement is dependent upon its throw performance, the dimensions and features of the room, and the temperature difference between the supply and room air. Throw is reduced when supply air is above room temperature (heating mode) and increased when supply air is cooler. Throw is also reduced in VAV systems when airflow controls lower the flow volume in response to lower room load.

The *ASHRAE Handbook—Fundamentals* classifies air supply outlets as shown below. The Handbook discusses the characteristics of these diffuser types in detail, and the reader is referred to this resource for further information. Group A and E diffusers predominate in medical facilities due to their throw characteristics and ceiling or high-sidewall discharge locations.

- Group A. Outlets mounted in or near the ceiling that discharge air horizontally
- Group B. Outlets mounted in or near the floor that discharge air vertically in a nonspreading jet
- Group C. Outlets mounted in or near the floor that discharge air vertically in a spreading jet
- Group D. Outlets mounted in or near the floor that discharge air horizontally
- Group E. Outlets mounted in or near the ceiling that project primary air vertically.

ADPI ranges for various diffuser configurations for the several types of commercially available supply diffusers are available from several resources to assist designers in making good cooling mode diffuser selections (see the "HVAC Computational Fluid Dynamics" chapter of *ASHRAE Handbook—Fundamentals*). At present, there is no heating mode counterpart to ADPI that diffuser manufacturers can use to establish comparative performance. Designers, therefore, often select units based upon rules of thumb or experience. For example, one major diffuser manufacturer recommends that diffusers be selected to obtain airflow velocities not exceeding 50 fpm (0.25 m/s) and a temperature gradient not exceeding 3°F (1.7°C) in the zone reaching from 6 ft to 6 ft 1 in. (1.83 to 1.85 m).

With properly selected supply diffusers, good ADPI performance is commonly achieved in the cooling mode. According to one authority, good ADPI may be expected from a properly chosen supply diffuser with a flow rate range of as much as 0.2 cfm/ft^2 to 1.0+ cfm/ft^2 (1.0 to 5.1 L/s/m^2)—rates that are a norm for many interior spaces (Dupont 1999). Data indicate that, in most cases, the cooler the supply air, the better the ADPI. Since the majority of spaces in a large health care facility are in the building interior, good ADPI is fairly easy to achieve even with variable air volume (VAV) systems.

Heating mode performance is more problematic due to the buoyancy of the relatively hotter supply air, which tends to retard the flow induced by the diffuser, preventing it from influencing the lower levels of the room. Cold perimeter exposures are a particular example where this is a problem, exacerbated when VAV systems reduce the room airflow in this mode. The following are recommended practices to address this problem.

- The temperature difference between the heating supply air and room temperature should not exceed 15°F (8.3°C) to limit the counteracting effect of buoyancy.

- Use high-induction ceiling slot diffuser(s) installed parallel to and within 5 feet (1.5 m) of the outside exposed wall, with approximately 50% of delivery projected toward the wall and diffuser throw selected to reach the floor level. Effective ADPI may require severely restricted VAV heating-mode turndown to 0.75-1.0 cfm/ft^2 (3.8-5.1 L/s/m^2) minimum and limit envelope loads to less than 200 Btu/h per lineal foot (192 W per lineal meter). This system may result in excessive floor-level drafts in the cooling mode.

- Provision of a supplemental, vertically projecting slot diffuser mounted in the ceiling in proximity to the outside wall, selected with a throw

to reach the floor below. This device may lead to objectionable drafts in the cooling mode.

- Utilization of a temperature reset control strategy that sets the supply temperature lower in the heating mode.

- Temperature reset combined with flow adjustment to ramp the supply temperature down but increase the flow volume with decreasing room temperature.

Individual project circumstances, such as room features (soffits that block diffuser throw), climatic conditions, and other factors, can result in unsatisfactory heating mode air mixing and require designer consideration of supplemental (perimeter) heating systems. Recent research by the National Institutes of Health strongly suggests that good heating-mode air mixing is difficult to achieve in the typical patient bedroom (with outside exposure mandated by fire code) with less than 4 room air changes per hour, unless perimeter heating is provided (Memarzadeh and Manning 2000).

9.8 ACOUSTICAL CONSIDERATIONS

Health care facilities require careful attention to acoustical design in order to control background noise levels and preserve privacy. High noise levels can be detrimental to the healing process, as in neonatal ICU rooms where infants are especially sensitive to background noise. High noise levels also interfere with conversation and can cause distraction and increase environmental dissatisfaction. Poorly designed return or exhaust systems or the absence of background "white noise" can lead to the intelligible transmission of confidential doctor-patient or other private conversations between adjoining spaces.

9.8.1 Room Noise Limitations

Maximum permissible background noise levels for most spaces in health care facilities are established using room criteria (RC) or noise criteria (NC) curves. Poorly designed air-handling systems can transmit excessively high noise levels generated by equipment (such as fans and terminal units) into occupied spaces via ductwork. High room noise levels may also result from noise generated by high air velocities in ductwork, duct fittings, or connections and within the space at diffusers or across restrictions (such as door undercuts).

9.8.2 Air-Handling System Fans

Air-handling system fans (supply, return, and exhaust) are a frequent source of noise and require careful designer consideration. Fan noise breakout from the fan casing to the mechanical equipment room may be transmitted into adjoining spaces through the room envelope elements. This may require locating fan rooms away from acoustically sensitive occupied spaces or careful attention to the attenuation properties of the room walls, floor, and ceiling. Fan noise will travel through ductwork, from where it may enter occupied spaces by breakout from the duct into the ceiling plenum and transmission through the ceiling. Fan noise will also travel directly through the ductwork, possibly requiring attenuation by special duct construction (additional elbows, for example), acoustical duct lining, or factory-fabricated attenuators. Designers should establish the sound power output of fans in order to estimate the need for downstream attenuation, specify the maximum permissible sound power output in design documents, and provide appropriate acoustical features in the design to limit transmission to the occupied spaces.

9.8.3 Noise Generation in Ductwork

Excessive noise generation in ductwork can usually be avoided by limiting the flow velocities. The *ASHRAE Handbook—HVAC Applications* provides guidelines for velocity limits in round and rectangular ductwork located above ceilings, in shafts, or within occupied spaces.

9.8.4 Noise Breakout and Low-Frequency "Rumble"

Noise breakout and low-frequency "rumble" are a frequent problem when large ductwork is routed over an occupied space, particularly with large-aspect-ratio rectangular ductwork. The problem can be mitigated by stiffening the ductwork with frequent bracing or reinforcement or by using more structurally rigid round or spiral seam ductwork. Rooftop air-handling installations are a frequent cause of this problem because of the proximity of noise source (fan) to the rooms served.

9.8.5 VAV Terminal Units

VAV terminal units can generate excessive noise when improperly selected or when exposed to an upstream static pressure higher than the designer anticipated. VAV unit sizes should be selected for the actual flow rate they are intended to handle, with attention to their noise characteristics when exposed to upstream static pressure calculated by design. To help ensure proper performance, the maximum sound pressure levels in each of the eight octave bands should be specified for each VAV unit for the appropriate inlet static pressure. When the designer's acoustical calculations indicate that integral (downstream) sound attenuators will be required in order to achieve the required room NC levels, this requirement should be clearly communicated to the construction contractor.

9.8.6 Proper Installation of Equipment

Manufacturer's sound performance information for various types of fittings and equipment is based upon specified upstream ductwork conditions or connection arrangements. Diffusers, for example, may generate much more noise than indicated by catalog information when the connecting ductwork is insufficiently straight or unobstructed. Designers should provide appropriate installation details and instructions and verify that physical conditions will permit the proper installation of such equipment.

9.8.7 Location of Dampers

Manual balancing dampers located on individual duct runouts should be as remotely located from the associated diffuser/register as practicable to enable the downstream duct and fitting to attenuate noise generated by airflow across the damper.

9.8.8 Noise Generated by Air Transfer

Unacceptably high noise levels may be generated within occupied spaces by in-room HVAC equipment, such as fan coil units, diffusers (see above), and high-velocity air transfer across grilles and door frames. Generally, the noise generated by fan coil units cannot economically be attenuated to meet typical NC or RC levels for occupied spaces. Noise produced by air transfer can be mitigated by limiting jet velocity to 400 ft/min.

The maintenance of patient privacy is extremely important. Doctor-patient conversations or consultations among health care providers should not be transmissible to listeners in adjoining spaces. Improperly designed return air connections can serve as a transmission pathway between rooms. This "cross-talk" situation often arises with plenum return air systems above clinical spaces, particularly when room partitions are halted at or only slightly above ceiling level and the individual room return air registers are open to the common plenum. This situation normally requires the return air fixture to be specially configured and extended into the air plenum with duct attachments incorporating one or more elbows or attenuating insulation. The problem can occur, however, even with fully ducted systems. Designers should consider the attenuating features of the duct path connecting occupied rooms to adjoining spaces, including corridors.

9.9 GENERAL CONSIDERATIONS FOR HANDLING SATURATED AIR

Generally speaking, microbial growth in the air-handling and distribution system requires the presence of liquid water (plus a nutrition source). High relative humidity alone does not support the proliferation of microbial organisms. Potential moisture problems resulting from precipitation entering outside air intakes, condensate formation at cooling coils, and droplet formation at humidifiers have been discussed. In addition, moisture accumulation in filters, fittings, and other air supply components frequently results from thermodynamic changes to saturated air, which occur in the supply system.

It is important for designers to realize that saturated or near-saturated air is a normal condition at some point within almost any air-handling and distribution system—at any time of the year. For a variety of reasons, many poorly understood by design engineers, saturated air may suddenly be exposed to a temperature below the saturation temperature, with condensation formation as a result. As one example scenario, consider a duct elbow, cooled to a temperature of 55°F (12.8°C) by the air-handling unit, suddenly exposed to a fluctuating saturated air temperature of 58°F (14.4°C) caused by control imprecision—condensation will likely form on the fitting. Due to such concerns, many designers advocate raising the cooling coil leaving air temperature above the saturation point by some form of reheat. One frequently utilized approach is a draw-through fan arrangement, wherein the fan heat provides the reheat.

9.10 DESICCANT SYSTEMS

In health care applications where a large amount of humid outside air must be used, a desiccant system can offer an alternative to the traditional method of dehumidifying supply air by cooling it to saturation temperature. When air passes through a desiccant material, the desiccant removes water from the air in the vapor state, rather than as condensed liquid. Humid air has a high water vapor pressure. Dry desiccant has a low vapor pressure. Propelled by this pressure difference, water molecules pass out of humid air into the desiccant.

In such systems, the desiccant is impregnated (or formed in place) in a honeycomb matrix in the shape of a wheel. Two airstreams are separated from each other by air seals as shown in Figure 9.4. The desiccant wheel rotates slowly (6 to 20 rph) between these two airstreams. The incoming humid airstream is called the process air. The second airstream is the reactivation air. As the wheel rotates, the desiccant collects moisture from the incoming humid air until the material becomes almost saturated. To restore its capacity, the desiccant continues its rotation and enters the second (reactivation) airstream. The reactivation air has been preheated. Hot air heats the saturated desiccant, drying it out. Moisture released by the desiccant is absorbed into the reactivation air.

Desiccant units with heated reactivation air are called "active" desiccant dehumidifiers. This distinguishes them from the "passive" desiccant wheels, which use the building's dry exhaust air instead of heated air for reactivation. Passive desiccant wheels remove much less moisture but also use much less energy than active desiccant dehumidifiers.

Sometimes, an active desiccant dehumidifier dries only a small portion of the supply air. Active desiccants dry air very deeply A small amount of very dry air removes moisture quite effectively while minimizing the size and cost of the dehumidifier.

9.10.1 Desiccant Dehumidifier Performance

The amount of moisture removed by a desiccant dehumidifier depends on the following factors:

- depth of the wheel,
- rotational speed, and
- specific sorption characteristics of the desiccant.

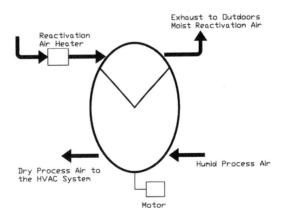

Figure 9-4 Typical desiccant system.

These variables are usually fixed by the manufacturer and the designer has little control. To predict performance, however, the HVAC designer only needs to define the temperature, humidity ratio, and volume of the entering process air, the size of the unit, and the temperature of the reactivation air. The following observations regarding performance are made.

- The drier the entering air, the drier the leaving air.
- The cooler the entering air, the drier the leaving air.
- The hotter the reactivation air, the drier the leaving air.
- The slower the process-air velocity, the drier the leaving air.

As water vapor is pulled out of the process air, the temperature of the air rises because the heat that was originally used to evaporate the water is released. The amount of heat depends upon the amount of water removed from the air. More dehumidification releases more heat.

9.10.2 Energy Wheel

Desiccant wheels are also used for energy transfer between two airstreams, for example, between outside air intake and exhaust air discharge. In this application, the device is termed an "energy wheel." In health care facilities, care must be taken to ensure that contamination between the two airstreams does not occur (see Chapter 16 for more details).

9.11 PACKAGED UNITS

Packaged rooftop cooling-only or cooling/heating units are commonly used for clinics (see Chapter 13). For further details, refer to the *ASHRAE Handbook—HVAC Systems and Equipment* (ASHRAE 2000a).

CHAPTER 10
CONTROLS AND INSTRUMENTATION

10.1 INTRODUCTION

This chapter describes characteristics and components of automatic control systems for heating, ventilating, and air-conditioning (HVAC) systems often found in hospitals and other health care facilities. General control theory and applications are discussed in detail in the *ASHRAE Handbook—Fundamentals* and in the *ASHRAE Handbook—HVAC Applications* (ASHRAE 2001a; ASHRAE 1999a).

Controls are an essential part of any HVAC system. They provide a comfortable and therapeutic environment for patients; contribute to infection control for patients, staff, and visitors; optimize energy cost and consumption; improve employee productivity; control smoke in the event of a fire; and provide cooling for hospital equipment. Controls are essential for proper and efficient operation of HVAC distribution systems and also for proper and efficient operation of central plant equipment.

Automatic controls are used to maintain a setpoint for a variable when disturbances cause a change in that variable. In HVAC systems, the most commonly controlled variables are pressure, temperature, humidity, and fluid flow rate.

One of the most significant changes in the 2001 edition of the *Guidelines for the Design and Construction of Hospitals and Health Care Facilities* (AIA 2001) is the requirement for a minimum differential static pressure of 0.01 in. w.g. (2.5 Pa) in protective isolation rooms, airborne infection isolation rooms, surgical cystoscopic rooms, bronchoscopy rooms, and autopsy rooms.

10.2 CHARACTERISTICS AND ATTRIBUTES OF CONTROL METHODS

10.2.1 Pneumatic Control Systems

Pneumatic control systems use compressed air to operate actuators, sensors, relays, and other control equipment. Pneumatic controls:

- Are naturally proportional
- Require clean dry air
- Are explosion-proof
- Provide for simple, powerful, low-cost and reliable actuators for valves and dampers
- Are commonly used for simple zone (VAV box, etc.) control
- Are the simplest modulating control means.

10.2.2 Electric Control Systems

Electric controls consist of valve/damper actuators, temperature/pressure/humidity controllers, relays, motor starters, and contactors. They are powered by low or line voltage, depending upon the circuit requirements. Controllers and actuators can be wired to perform either two-position (such as on/off or limit) or proportional, derivative, or analog control using either spring return, or nonspring return. Electric controls:

- Are most commonly used for simple on-off control
- Use integral sensor/controller
- Offer a simple sequence of control
- Can function within broad environmental limits
- Can involve complex modulating actuators, especially when spring return

10.2.3 Electronic Control Systems

In an electronic control system, an analog sensor signal is amplified, then compared to a setpoint or override signal (through a voltage or current comparison via control circuits) to actuate operations. Electronic controls:

- Provide precise control
- Offer solid-state repeatability and reliability
- Permit sensor locations 2 to 300 feet (1 to 91 meters) from a controller
- Allow simple remote setpoint adjustment
- Have a high per-loop cost
- Offer packaged complete actuators and controllers

10.2.4 Microprocessor or Direct Digital Control (DDC)

In a microprocessor-based system, sensor input is converted to digital form, where discrete instructions (algorithms) perform the comparison and control process. Microprocessor-based controllers can be used as stand-alone controllers or they can be used as controllers incorporated into a building management system (BMS) utilizing a personal computer as a host to provide additional monitoring and control functions. Microprocessor-based controls:

- Provide precise control
- Permit inherent energy management functions
- Deliver inherent high order (proportional plus integral) control
- Are compatible with building management systems (BMS)
- Can easily perform a complex sequence of control
- Support global (interloop) control via a communications bus (e.g., can optimize chillers based on demand of connected systems)
- Allow simple remote setpoint adjustment and display
- Can use pneumatic actuators

10.2.5 Computerized Building Management System

The objective of a building management system (BMS) is to centralize and simplify the monitoring, operation, and management of a building or buildings. BMS functions in health care facilities typically include monitoring environmental conditions, systems, and plants; centralized alarm reporting; reducing energy usage and cost through centralized control of energy-consuming systems; data trending;

providing historical records; supporting maintenance management programs; fire alarm; security and access control; lighting control; and start-up of the emergency generator system and transfer of power from standby to emergency.

A BMS provides an opportunity to track the operation of various control points, such as discharge air temperature, mixed air temperature, and valve or damper position. Such tracking can be done in real time. The information obtained can be very valuable in troubleshooting, problem solving, system documentation, and for efficient operation. Critical parameters can be easily monitored and can be alarmed if out of a specified range.

Using a centralized system with network communications and user-defined boundaries for comfort, it is possible to define setpoints globally and thereby optimize comfort and energy strategies. Equipment can then be operated at a minimum cost, and temperatures are controlled for maximum efficiency. Loads can be leveled and demand controlled by starting and loading the central plant based upon the demands of the air-handling systems.

Sometimes networks use the Internet or an intranet for communication. One major disadvantage of an Internet network is that the interconnection between systems may not be dedicated to the controls, may not be supervised, and could fail without notifying the central monitor or alarm system. Internet hardware and software are evolving toward robust control applications, however, that are more reliable and lower in cost than some conventional, dedicated control networks. The Internet also provides a means of establishing a common communications protocol between different control systems. It is imperative that security be the first priority of any Internet-based control system.

10.3 PRESSURIZATION, OUTSIDE AIR VENTILATION, AND OUTSIDE AIR ECONOMIZER CONTROLS

10.3.1 Pressurization Criteria

Two pressurization criteria are commonly used in health care facility design: volumetric flow rate (VFR) or room differential pressure (RDP)

- **VFR criteria:** Pressurization required for a specific hospital room is usually accomplished (under most codes) by providing differentials in the volumetric flow rates of supply, return, and exhaust air. Under these VFR design criteria, only the volumetric flow rate of supply, return, and exhaust air is considered. A room is considered positively pressurized if it has an excess of supply air volumetric flow rate into the room compared to the sum of return and exhaust air volumetric flow rate out of the room. Negatively pressurized rooms have less supply air than the sum of return and exhaust air. Most hospital rooms can be designed using only VFR criteria for pressurization. See Sections 10.3.2 and 10.3.3 for VFR criteria.

- **RDP criteria:** One of the notable changes in the 2001 edition of the *Guidelines for the Design and Construction of Hospitals and Health Care Facilities* (AIA 2001) is the requirement for minimum room differential pressure of 0.01 in. w.g. (2.5 Pa) for protective isolation rooms, airborne infection isolation rooms, surgical cystoscopic rooms, bronchoscopy rooms, and autopsy rooms. Furthermore, where there is a requirement for positive or negative room differential pressure, the pressure is to remain positive or negative at all times. When room differential pressure (RDP) criteria are the design basis, it may be necessary to consider the effects of secondary factors, such as stack effect, wind pressure, differential room pressure, the differential partial pressure of water, and (especially) leakage through walls, ceilings, and floors. See Section 10.4 for RDP criteria.

10.3.2 VFR Pressurization Criteria for a Zone

- If a room or system has constant air flow, then the volumetric flow rates required for room pressurization are established and fixed when the system is initially tested and balanced. A minimum measurable amount of air flow difference is recommended. This is the most reliable method of room pressure control.

- If variable air volume is used in areas where codes require pressure relationships between rooms, then the (supply cfm – return/exhaust cfm) relationship must be maintained at all VAV settings. This is normally done by having the return/exhaust cfm track the supply cfm minus the pressure differential cfm for both the room and the system (Lewis 1998). (Note: Unless otherwise indicated, the term "cfm" is used in this chapter as a shorthand for volumetric flow rate and does not imply a specific measurement.)

- For a room or zone (z) that has variable supply and return air and constant exhaust flow and maintains a constant pressure relationship (cfm differential) to an adjacent room or corridor, then $SA_Z - REA_Z = (EA2_Z + PRESS_Z)$,

where

SA_Z = supply air to the room,

REA_Z = return/exhaust cfm through the return air duct to the return fan before it enters an outside air economizer,

$EA2_Z$ = constant volume exhaust air cfm through a constant volume exhaust fan, and

$PRESS_Z$ = room pressurization (cfm) where $PRESS_Z$ is positive when the air flows out of the room or zone toward the reference space.

The solution of this equation for constant pressurization requires that $(SA_Z - REA_Z)$ be constant at all SA_Z and RA_Z flow rates. This means that REA_Z must track SA_Z by a constant offset—$(EA2_Z + PRESS_Z)$.

10.3.3 VFR Pressurization Criteria for a System

For a system, $SA_S - (RA_S + EA1_S) = EA2_S + PRESS_S$. The quantity $(RA_S + EA1_S)$ is often simply called "return air" (or REA) because it all passes though the return fan, even though the quantity $EA1_S$ is the cfm exhausted in the economizer and the quantity RA_S is the portion that actually mixes with outside intake air before it passes through the coils and supply fan. Note that if the return air cfm is measured upstream of the economizer section, then the system is greatly simplified. The solution of this equation for constant pressurization for an entire system requires that $(SA_S - (RA_S + EA1_S))$ be constant at all variable SA_S and REA_S flow rates. This can be accomplished on a system basis if the return fan tracks the supply fan minus a constant offset quantity, $(EA2_S + PRESS_S)$.

10.3.4 Outside Air Economizer Controls

An air-side economizer has three main functions under normal operating conditions: free cooling, minimum outdoor air ventilation, and building pressurization. Outside and exhaust air economizer dampers are closed when the system is off. The economizer may also have an emergency smoke purge mode. Three types of economizer arrangements include: supply and return fan (the most common system), supply and relief fan, and supply fan with gravity relief.

Proper selection of fan/economizer components and controls provides optimum performance with respect to free cooling, outside air ventilation, and building pressurization—often all simultaneously. The selection of fan/economizer components is critical to maintaining the desired linear and stable performance of fan/economizer systems. This includes proper selection of

- dampers by size and type (parallel or opposed-blade—opposed blade dampers provide better volume control and mixing);
- fans by size and type;
- controls:
  — pressure, including building pressure, mixing plenum pressure, and outside of building pressure;
  — dampers for pressure and VFR tracking;
  — fan speed controls.

Although some interaction is inevitable in the control loops for each of the three basic economizer control functions, this interaction should result in minimum distortion of the three basic control functions. The undesirable effects of control interaction can be minimized, and overall economizer control performance can be improved, by optimum design, selection, installation, and tuning. The best way to ensure proper operation is to provide separate supply and return fans. Air volume measurement stations may be needed for better control.

- economizer geometry (location of dampers and size of mixing box or duct, etc.).

An example of optimum economizer performance in the free cooling mode is when exhaust and outside air dampers modulate in an inversely proportional and linear manner in the free cooling mode, so that when more outside air is used, the same amount of return/exhaust air is exhausted. An example of optimum economizer performance in building pressurization mode is when the supply fan, tracking fan speeds, relief dampers, relief fan, or tracking dampers modulate to maintain stable building pressurization with minimum fan energy consumption. An example of optimum economizer performance with respect to outside air ventilation is when the same amount of outside air ventilation is provided no matter what building pressurization is required and no matter how much or little free cooling is being provided.

Economizer malfunction can be interrelated with fan or terminal unit malfunction (or controls for any of these systems) and can also result from dirty sensors or loss of calibration or adjustment. In such cases, one or more of the primary control functions (building pressurization, outside air ventilation, and/or free cooling) and associated systems and controls may have been disturbed by normal variations in environmental or process conditions, following which the control system cannot return them to the setpoints in a reasonable period of time. This can be a design problem, or a maintenance problem, or both. Symptoms of economizer, fan, or terminal unit malfunction include whistling doors that indicate improper room or system pressurization; hunting of fans, dampers, or mixed air temperatures; or excessive fan energy working against dampers. Normal disturbances include changes in outdoor air temperature, cooling or heating load, wind pressure, stack effect, opening doors, and interzonal air flows.

For design of economizer systems, see *ASHRAE Guideline 16, Selecting Outdoor, Return, and Relief Dampers for Air-Side Economizer Systems* (ASHRAE 2003). This guideline, however, does not address tracking controls, which may be required by code and should be included in some health care applications.

10.3.5 Constant or Variable Volume Box

Constant and/or variable volume boxes are often used in air distribution systems for hospitals to reduce duct distribution sizes through the use of a medium-pressure duct system and to accurately control room air flow. These boxes can be controlled pneumatically, electrically, or by DDC and are normally pressure independent (i.e., provide the same air volume regardless of duct pressure). A more detailed description of duct distribution systems is provided in Chapter 9.

10.3.6 Minimum Outside Air Ventilation with Constant or Variable Air Volume Terminals and an Economizer

If variable volume boxes are used, the controls must be adjusted to maintain minimum outside air ventilation. This is determined from the ratio of outside air to supply air in the outside air economizer and the minimum supply air quantity (ASHRAE 2003). At minimum room or zone supply-air quantity and simultaneous minimum system supply-air quantity, the room or zone outside air ventilation in air changes per hour is:

$$OAAC_{Z,min} = SAAC_{Z,min} \times \%OA_{S,min} \times 60/volume,$$

where

z = zone or room,

min = minimum,

s = system,

$OAAC$ = outside-air (OA) changes per hour in the zone,

$SAAC$ = supply-air changes per hour in the zone,

$\%OA$ = percentage of outside air through the supply fan that is introduced in the outdoor air economizer, and

$volume$ = volume of the zone or room.

Constant (worst case) values for minimum $SAAC$ and $\%OA$ at the economizer can be fixed to ensure minimum outdoor air ventilation to each room under all conditions. Alternatively, a computerized building management system can monitor and adjust minimum $SAAC$ in each zone and $\%OA$ at the system economizer to ensure minimum outdoor air ventilation to each room under all conditions. Obviously this control approach is better executed with DDC controls.

10.3.7 Dual-Duct Terminals or Variable Air Volume Induction Units

A similar approach can be used for dual-duct terminals or variable air volume induction units, considering the code requirements for each of these different types of terminals. For example, for reheat induction units, some codes require that only supply air from the central system can pass through the induction unit reheat coil.

10.4 ISOLATION ROOMS AND SIMILAR ROOMS WITH RDP CRITERIA

10.4.1 Isolation Room Static Pressure (RDP) Criteria

A room-pressure sensor measures the differential pressure between the room and the adjacent reference area or room (usually a corridor or anteroom). The key to establishing and maintaining pressurization is eliminating leaks in the walls, ceiling, and floor and keeping doors closed except during access. The sensor and transmitter (or indicator) provide a digital readout or visual indication (such as a flutter strip or ball-in-tube) of room pressure. A remote alarm panel, typically located at the nurses' station, can be installed and may be connected to the building management system for immediate response by maintenance and system operating personnel. All such systems should incorporate appropriate time delays for transient inputs. Some codes do not allow substituting a BMS for local hardwired alarms. These are the advantages of a monitored system:

- Continuous space monitoring for safety of the health care worker and protection for patient and adjacent spaces.

- Early warning to facility staff if space pressurization cannot be maintained.
- Audible and visual alarms available locally and/or remotely when the room is out of user-defined limits.
- Alarms supplied with user-defined adjustable time delays to eliminate false alarms caused by momentary changes in conditions (such as a brief door opening).
- Electronic data collection to meet Centers for Disease Control guidelines—where applicable.
- Elimination of the requirement for daily smoke testing if the room is occupied by a TB patient.

10.4.2 Specialized Sensors and Controllers

Specialized sensors and controllers are sometimes used for isolation room pressurization control in hospitals. The majority of codes require constant volume air flow with fixed volumetric differential for most situations in hospitals. Some codes now also require a minimum space pressure differential of 0.01 in. w.g. (2.5 Pa) in special rooms such as Protective Environment Isolation Rooms (PE) and Airborne Infectious Isolation Rooms (AII). Two control strategy options are generally acceptable under hospital codes (with some exceptions): (1) constant volume with fixed volumetric differential between supply and return/exhaust or (2) volumetric control (tracking) with direct pressure reset.

- *Constant Volume with Fixed Volumetric Differential In Isolation Rooms*: This involves a constant volume of supply and return/exhaust air established when the system is initially tested and balanced. Protective Isolation Rooms can return air to the central system. Infectious Isolation Rooms usually require 100% exhaust air with negative room pressurization. A fixed differential (supply cfm − return/exhaust cfm) is maintained in the isolation room. The room may have a constant volume supply air box with a reheat coil. Room differential pressure may vary somewhat, depending on the outside air conditions or the pressurization in adjacent spaces, but a minimum room pressurization can be maintained throughout all conditions if the initial pressurization is high enough. Variations of 0.03 in. w.g. (7.5 Pa) in room pressurization in a hospital in Minnesota have been reported— which coincides with seasonal variations (Steifel 2000). This may be caused primarily by stack effect; wind pressure and water partial pressure differential could also be factors. A room differential pressure monitoring device or visual indicator is provided to indicate the pressure differential between the room and the adjacent reference area or room.

- *Volumetric Control with Direct Pressure (Cascade) Reset in Isolation Rooms*: Direct pressure controls recognize and compensate for disturbances such as stack effects, infiltration, and exfiltration, but they do not, in themselves, provide volumetric flow rate stability because the system is dynamically adjusting to momentary variations in room pressure conditions caused by the opening of doors and the like. These conditions can draw air from or force air into adjacent rooms and cause pressure upsets in adjacent rooms or areas. Constant volume with a fixed volumetric differential (as described in the previous paragraph) does not compensate for disturbances such as stack effect, infiltration, or exfiltration. Volumetric control with room differential pressure reset can provide two control functions. It can reset the room point and provide volume flow differential (supply-return/exhaust cfm) within a range to maintain room pressurization.

10.4.3 Anteroom Monitoring

Isolation rooms with anterooms are provided with one monitor to measure and alarm the pressure differential between the isolation room and the anteroom and another monitor to measure and alarm the differential pressure between the anteroom and the corridor. In Protective Environment Isolation Rooms with anterooms, a fixed constant volume offset is usually maintained in the anteroom. This offset makes the anteroom negative with respect to the Protective Environment Isolation Room and slightly positive with respect to the corridor. An Infectious Isolation Room anteroom is positively pressurized with respect to the isolation room and slightly negative with respect to the corridor.

10.5 OPERATING ROOM CONTROLS

10.5.1 Temperature Controls

Operating rooms generally require wide ranges for temperature and humidity and lower than normal room temperatures. Most codes require room temperature adjustment throughout the entire range under all conditions. (e.g., 68–73°F [20.0–22.8°C] in general operating rooms) (AIA 2001). However, it is common in some operating rooms (such as cardiac surgery or organ transplant rooms) for the medical staff to prefer a room temperature of 60°F (15.6°C). To conserve energy, the chilled water temperature

requirements for the entire facility should not be dictated solely by operating room cooling requirements. One way to achieve this lower space temperature is to install two series cooling coils. One coil is connected to the normal building chilled water system and provides discharge air temperatures in the traditional range. The other coil is connected to a lower-temperature cooling medium; this could be a DX system or another cooling coil served from a special low-temperature chiller. Another method is to pre-cool or preheat outside makeup air using a heat recovery system on the exhaust air (see Chapter 16). Still another method is a dessicant cooling system for the makeup outside air.

10.5.2 Variable Air Volume and Room Static Pressure Controls in Operating Rooms and Critical Areas

Some codes require that operating rooms have constant volume systems. Other codes allow two-position or variable air volume control in operating rooms and some other critical areas for energy conservation. The latter can reduce air flow below maximum rates as long as room air change rates are met. Some codes allow further reduction of airflow when the operating room or critical area is unoccupied, as long as a means is provided to automatically increase air flow as soon as the room becomes occupied by interlocking controls with the light switch, etc. However, all codes require that directional control (pressurization) be maintained constantly (whether occupied or not) where it is required to prevent the spread of infection from one area to another. As described previously, if a variable air volume system is used, continuous room pressure monitoring and "volumetric control with direct pressure reset" is recommended because of the performance degradation of RA sensors from lint and other possible variations in room pressurization performance. This should be considered for any critical room and for the entire department or ward when a VAV system is being used.

The *Guidelines for the Design and Construction of Hospitals and Health Care Facilities* (AIA 2001) requires a minimum room static pressure of 0.01 in. w.g. (2.5 Pa) in Cystoscopic Operating Rooms.

10.5.3 Humidity Control in Operating Rooms

Dehumidification requirements for operating rooms are often extreme and require low chilled water temperatures or a desiccant cooling system for makeup outside air.

A room humidifier for each operating room may be required by code. The humidifier must have an adjustable room relative humidity setpoint, which can be changed by the operating room team. Water treatment should be evaluated to determine if the humidifier steam is safe and sufficiently odorless (see Chapter 8).

10.6 LABORATORY CONTROLS

Many hospitals and clinics have numerous types of laboratories. The most common are clinical, pathological, research, and pharmaceutical laboratories. Codes in some jurisdictions require constant volume controls in hospital laboratories. If a variable air volume system is used, it must maintain pressure relationships between the laboratory and other hospital departments. VAV control requirements are affected by large swings in airflow needs for hoods in the laboratory. Temperature control is affected by major changes in airflow to the room. Humidity control is difficult because the humidifiers must be sized to handle swings in airflow. Flow tracking is one method of maintaining a proper pressure in a laboratory if supply and exhaust air volumes vary. An offset between supply and exhaust air volume is another approach.

10.6.1 Laboratory Hoods

Laboratory hoods have a variety of different configurations. Most hoods require a minimum face velocity to capture and confine vapors and the air within. If the hood door opening size is variable, the flow through the hood must be varied to maintain the minimum velocity through the hood. Variable air volume hoods must have a local alarm at the hood to warn if the face velocity drops below the minimum.

10.6.2 Biosafety (Microbiological and Bio-medical) Laboratories

The CDC and NIH biosafety rules categorize laboratories according to the level of risk (BSL levels 1, 2, 3, and 4). Each BSL requires a specific combination of laboratory practices and techniques, safety equipment, and laboratory facilities. For further information see the *ASHRAE Handbook—HVAC Applications* (ASHRAE 1999a) and *CDC/NIH Biosafety in Microbiological and Biomedical Laboratories* (CDC 1999).

10.7 GENERAL CONTROL SEQUENCES USED IN HOSPITALS AND CLINICS

The following control sequences can be used as a design guide for typically encountered health care operational situations. For illustrative purposes, several additional examples of control sequences, along with control diagrams used in hospitals and health care facilities, are described in Appendix H. It is not intended to suggest that these are the only acceptable control sequence options but rather to illustrate typical applications.

10.7.1 Supply Fan Control by Duct Static Pressure: Supply Fan Inlet Vane or Motor Speed (Variable Frequency Drive, VFD) Control

The supply fan inlet vanes can be modulated or the VFD can control the motor speed to provide supply air system static pressure control. During the start-up mode, the supply fan should slowly ramp up to speed to maintain the setpoint of the static pressure controller (usually installed on the supply air duct, often two-thirds to ninety percent of the distance from the fan to the end of the longest duct). For dual-duct VAV systems, the supply fan pressure may be controlled to the duct static pressure of the lower of either the cold or hot duct in single-fan systems, or individually in dual-fan systems.

The return air fan can be controlled by other strategies, such as cfm matching or offset control. A control strategy using the position of terminal volume controllers (automatic dampers) can also be considered, but it is complex.

10.7.2 Fan Tracking

Return and exhaust fan inlet vane or VFD tracking control can be described as follows. Airflow stations in the supply, return, and exhaust ducts can provide control signals. The signal can input the volumetric flow rate (cfm) to the control system. The return and exhaust fans should modulate in tandem to maintain the predetermined return air and exhaust air cfm volumes or cfm differentials compared to the supply air flow rate. Volumetric air flow rate tracking assists in maintaining the entire department or facility at the correct pressure relationship with respect to other connected areas (or to the outside).

10.7.3 Humidification

The humidifier should be modulated to maintain room or exhaust air humidity. As the exhaust or room air humidity increases, the humidifier should modulate closed. The reverse should occur as the exhaust or room air humidity decreases. A high-limit humidistat should limit the signal to the humidifier if the supply air humidity exceeds 85% (hardware adjustable). Upon loss of airflow, a static pressure switch should disable the system.

10.7.4 Supply Air Temperature Control— Preheat, Economizer, and Cooling Sequence

A supply temperature control system should modulate the economizer dampers, preheating valves, and chilled water valves in sequence. Assuming that the economizer is at the minimum outside air position and that the mixed air temperature is colder than the desired supply air temperature, the preheat coil must provide some heating. As the mixed air temperature rises, the preheat valve modulates closed. As the mixed air temperature continues to rise, the economizer dampers modulate toward fully open to the outside air—if the outside air enthalpy is less than the return air enthalpy. Then, the economizer modulates as required to maintain the discharge air temperature. If the mixed air temperature is higher than the required supply air temperature, the chilled water valves modulate open. If the outside air enthalpy is greater than the return air enthalpy, then the economizer should return to the minimum outside air position. The supply air cold or hot deck temperature can sometimes be linearly reset based upon the outside air temperature if the outside air temperature is creating the primary load on the zones in the system; however, this is not typically done in a variable volume system.

10.7.5 Fan and Damper Smoke Alarm Shutdown

Upon detecting smoke at the supply or return duct smoke detector, the supply and return air smoke dampers should close through hardwired interlocks. The outside-air and return-air dampers should close and the supply, return, and exhaust fans should stop through hardwired interlocks. All control functions of the air-handling unit should return to normal condition after the smoke detector is manually reset. In some cases, an engineered smoke control system is used as described below.

10.7.6 Smoke Exhaust System Controls

As an alternative to smoke detector shutdown, the system controls can go into smoke exhaust mode to exhaust smoke and provide positive pressurization with 100% outside air to areas of egress. See Chapter 11 of this manual for further information.

10.7.7 Dual Radiator or Panel Heating and Reheat

When a room thermostat controls both a reheat coil and a wall-mounted radiator, the sequencing of the operation of the devices is very important. The most desirable condition would be that the wall-mounted radiator or heating panel control is fully operational before the duct-mounted reheat is activated. Use of this control sequence may ensure that an outside wall/window assembly will not create unpleasant drafts.

10.7.8 Thermostat and Sensor Location

A thermostat or temperature sensor must be installed at a location that samples an average condition of the zone. A thermostat should not be located where the supply air, a cold or hot outside wall, solar radiation, or heat-producing equipment would affect it.

Fouling of return-air flow sensors and airflow measuring stations with lint and dirt is a significant problem, particularly in areas where beds are made (such as in patient rooms). One solution to this problem is a special purging sensor that blows compressed air out of the sensor from time to time. These devices are complex and require maintenance. A preventive maintenance program can keep return sensors in good working order with semiannual checks of the sensors.

10.8 CONTROL "SAFETIES"

"Safeties" that protect HVAC systems are particularly important in hospitals and clinics because of the need for continuous operation with minimum downtime and maximum reliability. Most safety controls for air-handling units and smoke detectors are hardwired and independent of the BMS system. These devices should shut down equipment through hardwired interlocks and provide alarm status to the operator through the BMS front end. Safeties can also be installed through software, but a hardwired interlock is more reliable because it eliminates any error from the BMS, the software, or the operator. Confirm that in hand/auto/off switch wiring, safeties are not overridden in any switch position.

10.8.1 Cooling Coil Freeze Protection

If the outside air temperature can be lower than about 35°F (2°C), a preheat coil should be located upstream of the cooling coil to protect the cooling coil from freezing. A freezestat with a sensor just upstream of the cooling coil may have a low-limit safety and sense air temperature entering or leaving the cooling coil (set at 35°F [2°C]—adjustable), which should stop the supply, return and exhaust fans, close outside air dampers, and open chilled water valve at temperatures below the setpoint. Note that chilled water must be pumped through the coil at a significant rate of flow under such circumstances to reduce the possibility of freezing. In extremely cold conditions, this may not prevent freezing, and automatic valves should drain the coil. Before starting fans, activate the preheat control valve or provide a time delay on the freezestat so that the fan is not tripped off during start-up. The freezestat should be manually resettable, except in critical cases where airflow may not be interrupted.

10.8.2 Duct Static Pressure Safeties

When motorized smoke, isolation, or control dampers are used in a supply air system, the return-air or exhaust-air ductwork design must ensure that a closure in the supply system does not blow apart the supply ducts or collapse the return-air ducts. Duct-work can be damaged if a variable frequency drive, inlet vanes, or their controls are set improperly. The following steps can prevent this situation. Any delay in smoke damper closing, however, should be approved by the Authority Having Jurisdiction.

- A time delay after fan(s) shutdown: On a command to shut down a fan, hard-wired time delay relays should prevent dampers from closing for 30 seconds (adjustable) after the fan(s) shut off. This should prevent a buildup of pressure until the fans spin down and prevent the fan high/low static limit from tripping; or

- Upon shutdown, ensure that a differential pressure (DP) sensor across the fan indicates that a differential pressure of less than a preset value (typically 1 in. w.g. [249 Pa]) has been achieved before closing any damper; or

- A relief damper may be placed in the side of the ductwork to relieve excessive pressure.

- Upon a signal to start the air-handling unit, the supply and exhaust isolation dampers (as well as the outside air damper and smoke dampers) should open before the fans start. Isolation damper end-switches can prove that dampers are open and allow the fan(s) to start through hard-wired interlocks.

- A manual reset discharge-air high-static safety located before the supply air isolation/smoke damper should disable both supply fans and input to the DDC system upon sensing an (adjustable) static pressure above the normal operating setpoint.

- A manual reset return and exhaust air low duct-static pressure safety located before each return and exhaust fan should stop the other fans in the system and input to the DDC system upon sensing a static pressure below the normal operating setpoint.

- Fire alarm shutdown: On activation of the building fire alarm system relay, the system should shut down or operate in the smoke exhaust mode. The fire alarm should be annunciated at the BMS console.

10.9 DX SYSTEM CONTROLS

DX systems pose a challenge to the designer. Careful attention must be given to ensure that capacity control is provided under changing ambient conditions.

CHAPTER 11
SMOKE CONTROL AND LIFE SAFETY

11.1 INTRODUCTION

11.1.1 The Life Safety Approach

Hospitals present an unusual environment for life safety and fire protection. Most occupancies rely on evacuating occupants as part of their fire protection and life safety approach, but a hospital must rely on the building and building systems to protect its occupants while they remain in place. This is called a "defend-in-place" strategy. Hospitals, therefore, are well compartmented and fully sprinklered in new construction and provide many additional life safety features that may not be found in other buildings.

The defend-in-place strategy actually has three stages. Ideally, a fire can be extinguished and smoke controlled in the room where the fire originated. Only those occupants in the immediate fire area would have to be evacuated from their rooms. When a fire occurs in a smoke compartment, the nursing staff will close the doors to all patient rooms, and patients can remain in relatively clean environments, even though there is a fire in the same general area. Corridor walls are built smoke-tight, if not of rated construction, to protect patients in their rooms during this first stage.

If evacuation of patient rooms becomes necessary, the second stage is to relocate occupants of the smoke compartment where the fire originated into another compartment on the same floor. Smoke compartments are a key facet of fire protection in the building codes and in the NFPA 101 *Life Safety Code*. They allow relocating patients horizontally and provide a safe holding area on the floor where a fire originates so that patients can be wheeled or otherwise relocated without using stairs or elevators. Some hospitals use an engineered smoke evacuation system that automatically exhausts smoke from the fire zone and controls its spread by pressurizing adjacent zones.

The third stage of this strategy, which is rarely required, involves using elevators or stairs to evacuate patients from the building. If the fire protection systems work as designed, this evacuation stage should never be necessary.

Under this compartmentation concept, the HVAC system plays a major role in the life safety of patients. Transport of smoke via the HVAC system within the compartment or between compartments can overcome the defend-in-place approach. Whether smoke control is active or passive, the basic premise is that preventing smoke spread is vital. The HVAC system must, therefore, be designed in coordination with the architectural life safety layout of the building and with the fire alarm and sprinkler zoning. The life safety features of the building require a coordinated effort among the entire design team. It is important to realize that building safety components can be rendered ineffective by improper HVAC system operation during a fire. An example is excessive pressurization, which can prevent smoke doors from fully closing or make it difficult to open doors into stair towers. Maintaining proper clearances on meeting edges of doors and undercuts can minimize air and smoke leakage from a compartment and have a significant impact on the effectiveness of smoke containment.

A smoke control system may be active or passive. In hospitals, passive smoke barriers are required on almost all floors. Active smoke control may be required in atria and in high-rise (or other large) facilities, depending upon the authority having jurisdiction. The owner may also conclude that active smoke control is desirable in the facility.

When active smoke control is implemented, the conditions under which the system will operate in an emergency must be carefully considered. Clearly labeled controls with positive feedback, as well as fail-safe designs should be included. The design should allow dampers to fail in a smoke-safe position if control air or power to a damper is lost. This strategy needs to be reviewed with the infection control department so that the control of airborne infections is not compromised. The defend-in-place strategy in a hospital must provide ample time for a prolonged evacuation; thus, it is likely that pneumatic tubing or electrical wiring serving some devices will be compromised during a fire emergency.

11.1.2   Means of Smoke Spread

In designing a smoke control system for a building, the design team must consider how smoke may spread through the building. Avenues of smoke spread are well defined in other references, so this chapter merely introduces the concept and relies upon those other documents to provide details.

The stack effect is a primary means of smoke spread. The stack effect is caused by the pressure gradients that result from differences between outside and inside air temperatures. A normal stack effect occurs when the interior of the building is warmer than the outside air. A reverse stack effect occurs when the interior of the building is colder than the outside air. A normal stack effect would result in a pressure that is higher at higher elevations within the building than at lower elevations. The stack effect is also sometimes referred to as the chimney effect.

Another means of smoke spread is buoyancy. Smoke from a fire is hotter and more buoyant than the ambient air around it. This physical fact must be dealt with in attempting to limit smoke migration.

A third potential means of smoke spread is weather conditions. Wind can have an impact on the spread of smoke within a building. Wind effects can occur as a result of operable windows, but wind has a significant impact even in closed buildings. Leakage through exterior walls and operation of exterior doors can significantly alter the expected movement of smoke within an enclosed building.

As air is heated, it expands. Therefore, expansion also has an impact on smoke spread within a building. Pressure differences from a fire in a sprinklered building are generally in the range of 0.02 to 0.03 inches of water (5 to 7.5 Pa) higher than normal ambient pressures due to the expansion caused by heat. This tends to push the smoke away from the fire and into other areas of the building.

Last, the HVAC systems and other building systems can convey smoke to further portions of the building. Elevators moving up and down past a fire floor can pull smoke into the shaft and push it out onto other floors. The HVAC system, if not shut down, can convey smoke into other areas of a building. If the HVAC system is shut down without closing dampers, the ductwork creates an open passageway. This creates an opportunity for smoke spread that must be considered.

11.1.3   Key Design Concepts

Developing agreement on the expected smoke control design and performance testing procedures is of primary importance when addressing smoke control and HVAC design. This agreement should include the entire design team—the owner, infection control professionals, the authority having jurisdiction, and the insurer—so that there is confidence that the design path chosen will be acceptable to all of the stakeholders.

If an active smoke control system is chosen, it is important that the design documents clearly identify the performance of the system. These documents must clearly express the expected performance of each device in the system. In this case, the "system" is not only the mechanical system but all items that interface with the mechanical system. The drawings should include the locations of all devices that will initiate smoke control; the locations of all devices involved in the smoke control process (including control dampers, fire and smoke dampers, variable air volume controls, and fans); the identification of devices provided with emergency power; the locations of active and passive smoke barriers; the smoke control method being used; the capacities of fans involved in smoke control; the sequence of operations; and the positioning of each damper for every fire scenario. Many of these items are described further in this chapter, but it is important to recognize that they all must work together to form a viable smoke control system. It is equally important to recognize that the smoke control system is only one part of the life safety system and that without coordination with these other subsystems, the life safety system will not operate as anticipated.

HVAC system controls and fire alarm systems that are used in any way as a part of an active smoke control system should be listed for the purpose. Such listing is a common requirement of many state and regional building and fire prevention codes. Underwriters Laboratory (UL) tests equipment and provides a listing under UL864 Category UUKL for smoke control system equipment. It is important to install this equipment in strict compliance with any special provisions required in the UL listing that are outlined in the manufacturer's installation instructions. Improper installation can void such a listing.

The quantity of outside air required for active smoke control modes and the challenges of conditioning that volume of air under climatic extremes must be considered. A unit may normally take less than 25% outside air, but in the smoke control pressurization mode, it is likely to take 100%. Although the loss of space conditions is of little concern during a fire, emergency systems are regularly tested, and the impact on the coils and space conditions during testing must be considered. The operation of basic safety devices, such as coil freeze protection or static limits, must be addressed during design to avoid a critical failure during testing or emergency operations.

11.1.4 Codes and Standards

Codes and standards that will apply to a new hospital building are likely to include NFPA 101, the *Life Safety Code*, as well as other NFPA standards referenced in that code. Of primary importance to the mechanical engineer will be NFPA 90A and NFPA 92A and 92B, which address air-handling systems and smoke control systems. NFPA 90A, 92A, and 92B cannot be used, however, without understanding the approaches required by NFPA 101. Interconnection of the HVAC system to the building fire alarm system will be addressed by the requirements of NFPA 72, *National Fire Alarm Code*, which requires supervision of connections or fail-safe configuration of controlled devices.

The several model building codes also address fire protection in hospital buildings. They are not entirely consistent with the *Life Safety Code*, although in recent years the requirements of the model building codes and the *Life Safety Code* have converged. Again, the mechanical engineer must understand the requirements of the applicable codes and authority having jurisdiction *before* proceeding with design.

11.2 SMOKE COMPARTMENTS AND BARRIERS

11.2.1 The Smoke Compartment

NFPA 101 and the model building codes require separating a hospital building into smoke compartments. In general, the smoke compartments must not be larger than 22,500 square feet (2,090 square

meters), and codes limit the travel distance to a required smoke barrier from any point within a room to 200 feet (61 meters). Some codes limit the dimensions of smoke compartments rather than limiting the travel distance to reach a compartment.

A smoke compartment is intended to limit the number of people who need to be relocated and allows the transfer of beds or gurneys from (and into) adjacent compartments. It is constructed of one-hour walls and has self-closing doors across barrier openings. Smoke compartment design needs to be coordinated with HVAC smoke control provisions, automatic sprinkler design, and fire alarm system design. Generally, the HVAC system for each smoke compartment is treated as a separate zone. Where ducts penetrate smoke compartment walls or barriers, dampers may be needed as described in the following sections. Approved fire-stopping materials must also protect piping and other penetrations of these walls. Smoke barriers form a primary protective strategy in a hospital building, and penetrations must be well protected.

11.2.2 Fire Dampers

Fire dampers are devices installed in an air-distribution system that are designed to close automatically upon detecting heat. The intent of a fire damper is to interrupt migratory airflow to restrict the passage of flame. Underwriters Laboratories lists these devices under UL 555, *Standard for Safety: Fire Dampers*. Listed fire dampers have a label that gives the manufacturer's name, trademark or identifying symbol, damper type or model number, fire resistance design number or type with maximum hourly fire resistance rating, and reference to the manufacturer's installation instructions.

Fire dampers must close automatically and remain closed upon the operation of a listed fusible link or other approved heat-activated device. The fire damper must be able to close against maximum calculated airflow in the portion of the ductwork where it is installed—unless there is provision for shutting down fans that serve that duct system. Fire dampers are activated by heat and cannot be relied upon to limit smoke movement during the early stages of a fire, when large amounts of smoke may be transferred well away from a heat source at the seat of the fire.

The fusible link or heat-activated device must be able to sense an abnormal rise in temperature in a duct and should have a temperature rating approximately 50°F (28°C) above the maximum temperature normally encountered when the system is in operation or shut down. The maximum rated temperature of the link or heat activated device cannot exceed 160°F (71°C).

Unless otherwise specifically required, fire resistance ratings for fire dampers are as follows:

- ¾-hour rated in 1-hour fire resistive assemblies
- 1½-hour rated in 2-hour assemblies
- 3-hour rated in assemblies rated as 3 hours or more

Location of Dampers in Fire-Rated Walls, Floors, and Ceilings

Fire dampers are required where ducts penetrate or terminate at openings in occupancy separations, area separations, and walls protecting horizontal exit egress. Local building codes typically require fire dampers in penetrations in one-hour exit corridor walls unless the penetration is by a duct of not less than 26 gauge (0.5 mm) galvanized sheet steel and the duct has no openings into the corridor. Fire dampers are also required in any other fire-resistive rated wall when other openings must be protected. NFPA 101 does not require smoke dampers in smoke barrier walls when the HVAC system is fully ducted. If not fully ducted, smoke dampers would be required in smoke barriers.

When air ducts extend through only one floor and serve only two adjacent stories, the ducts either must be enclosed in fire resistive construction or fire dampers must be installed at each floor penetration.

Where a duct or duct opening penetrates a rated floor/ceiling or roof/ceiling assembly, such penetration or opening must be provided with a fire damper in accordance with the design of the fire resistive assembly.

Special Requirements for Dampers Located in Shafts

Fire dampers to protect openings into air shafts are required except as follows:

- Where an air duct system is used only for exhaust to the outside, serves only one story, and is contained in its own dedicated shaft.
- Where branch ducts connect to enclosed exhaust risers via steel sub-ducts that are a minimum of 22 inches (558 mm) long, the air flow in the shaft moves upward, and the riser is sized to accommodate the flow restriction created by the sub-duct.

The fire resistance rating of the enclosure (shaft) for protecting air ducts that pass through floors of buildings is required to be one hour in buildings of less than four stories and two hours in buildings of four or more stories.

Damper Location and Need for Maintenance Access

A service opening must be provided in air ducts adjacent to each fire damper. The access must be large enough to permit required maintenance and resetting of the device. Such service openings must be identified using minimum ½-inch-tall (12.7 mm) letters that note the location of the fire damper.

Maintenance of Dampers

Maintenance of fire dampers includes replacing the heat-responsive element, operating it to demonstrate that the damper closes fully, lubricating moving parts, and checking that the latch (if provided) functions properly. Activating all dampers and the associated hardware is a required maintenance practice that must be done at least once every four years.

11.2.3 Smoke Dampers

Smoke dampers are devices within the air-distribution system that are intended to control the movement of smoke. These devices are activated either via the detection of smoke (by smoke detector(s) co-located with the damper) or by a signal from the fire alarm system as part of the implementation of a building's smoke control system (see Sections 11.3 and 11.4). When smoke detectors are co-located with dampers, they must be installed in accordance with NFPA 72 and the manufacturer's installation instructions, which specify limits on air velocity, required differential pressures, and/or clearances from transitions or turns in the ductwork. A smoke damper may serve as a fire damper where a given location lends itself to multiple functions and the damper is listed as a combination fire/smoke damper. Underwriters Laboratories lists smoke dampers under UL 555S, *Standard for Safety: Leakage Rated Dampers for Use in Smoke Control Systems*. A listed smoke damper has a label that gives the manufacturer's or private labeler's name, model number or identifying symbol, date of manufacture (may be in code), arrow showing direction of airflow, installation mode (vertical and/or horizontal), leakage classification, and ambient or degradation test temperature.

Smoke dampers listed without a fire damper operator are closed automatically by springs and are manually opened. Such smoke dampers are typically used at penetrations of smoke barrier wall locations where a dynamic operating capability is not necessary for smoke control system operation.

Smoke dampers listed with a fire damper operator can be closed and opened through a fire alarm or building automation system. They are listed under

UL864 Category UUKL as "smoke control system equipment." The design must include an emergency power supply for the detectors and fail-safe design in case of interruption of control air or power to the damper. These types of smoke dampers are used in active smoke management systems. Such dampers are allowed to be positioned manually from a command station. When such dampers are installed to isolate air-handling systems whose capacity is more than 15,000 cfm (7,080 L/s), the dampers must automatically close when the system is not in operation.

Location of Dampers in Smoke Barriers

Smoke dampers are required in each air transfer opening or duct penetration in required smoke barriers. Exceptions to this requirement include:

- Ducts or transfer openings that are part of an engineered (active) smoke control system.
- When the air-handling system is designed to prevent recirculation of exhaust or return air in fire emergencies.
- Where the air transfer openings or duct penetrations are limited to an individual smoke compartment.

Smoke dampers located in smoke barrier walls are permitted to remain open when the fire warning system is activated, provided that their associated control actuators and smoke detectors remain operational.

Special Requirements for Combination Fire/Smoke Dampers

In certain locations, both a fire damper and a smoke damper may be required. In such situations, a device that is listed as a combination fire/smoke damper may be employed. These dampers must meet the listing requirements of both UL 555 and UL 555S. Such a damper will be designed to operate automatically due to heat or smoke sensed in the airstream.

When a combination fire/smoke damper is located in an air-handling system duct as part of an engineered smoke control system, the temperature rating of the fusible link or heat responsive element may be 50°F (28°C) above the maximum operating temperature of the smoke control system. However, the temperature rating cannot exceed the UL degradation test temperature rating of the combination fire/smoke damper or a maximum of 350°F (176°C).

Building Automation System Smoke Damper Controls

Smoke dampers may be controlled by a building automation system provided that the system is listed for smoke control (UL864 UUKL) and has been installed in accordance with any special provisions required by the UL-listed manufacturer's instructions, such as transient protection, secondary power, and hardware enclosures. The interface of the building automation system with smoke damper positioning must ensure that the fire safety protocols will override the normal building conditioning system in a fire emergency.

Maintenance of Smoke Dampers

A service opening must be provided in the ductwork at all smoke dampers to permit required maintenance. Refer to Chapter 14 (section 14.6.1) for additional discussion of maintenance requirements.

Smoke dampers must be tested at least every four years to verify that they close fully, in accordance with NFPA 90A, *Standard for the Installation of Air-Conditioning and Ventilating Systems*. Moving parts must be lubricated as necessary. Smoke dampers that are part of a smoke management system are required to be tested in accordance with the local building code (typically, at least once a year).

All automatic controls for smoke dampers must be tested at least annually following the guidelines of NFPA 92A (Chapter 4) or NFPA 92B (Chapter 5). Smoke detectors used in conjunction with smoke dampers must be maintained in accordance with NFPA 72, *National Fire Alarm Code*.

11.2.4 Dampers—Other Considerations

The number of devices that must operate to effectively control smoke will impact the reliability of a system. Multiple smoke and fire dampers also drive up the cost of an HVAC system. The mechanical engineer, therefore, should closely coordinate the routing of ducts with the locations of rated walls and ceilings, so that the number of dampers can be minimized.

Where dampers must be positioned in a certain way to accommodate smoke control, the local code may also require monitoring the position of those dampers. This will require end switches on the dampers and monitoring by the energy management system, building automation system, or the fire alarm system. Listing and supervision requirements of the local codes need to be followed. In most cases, if a device does not fail in a smoke/fire-safe condition upon wire break, the control wiring must be supervised to within 3 feet (0.9 meter) of the controlled device.

Some codes also contain maximum time limits for repositioning of dampers. As an example, NFPA 92A establishes a 75-second requirement. Not all dampers on the market can meet such time limits. Design specifications should address the time permitted for repositioning the damper in either the open or closed position if that is a requirement of the design.

11.2.5 Codes and Standards

Applicable codes and standards regarding fire and smoke dampers for health care facilities include NFPA 101, *Life Safety Code*; NFPA 90A, *Standard for the Installation of Air-Conditioning and Ventilating Systems*; and local building, fire, and mechanical codes.

11.3 PASSIVE SMOKE CONTROL

Since 1967, health care facilities have been required to provide passive smoke control capabilities as an integral part of their design. Passive smoke control consists primarily of smoke compartments with characteristics previously discussed. Depending upon the local authority having jurisdiction, ductwork that penetrates smoke barrier walls may or may not require combination fire and smoke dampers. All penetrations through a smoke barrier wall must have approved through-penetration assemblies that can resist the passage of smoke.

Protection of penetrations in floors and shafts that bound or serve a smoke zone is another important element of passive smoke control. These penetrations also require a listed through-penetration assembly that can maintain the fire rating and resist the passage of smoke.

As with any life safety system element, passive smoke control barriers require inspection and ongoing maintenance. The barriers must be maintained at a level that can resist the passage of smoke and contain smoke in the area of fire origin. Without using active smoke control, passive smoke barriers in combination with active fire suppression systems can provide a high degree of smoke compartmentation and containment. Smoke barriers in unsprinklered buildings greatly delay the spread of smoke but do not provide long-term smoke containment.

11.4 ACTIVE SMOKE CONTROL

Defend-in-place is a primary concept for fire protection and life safety in health care facilities. NFPA 101 and the model building codes recognize the defend-in-place approach to life safety and, in general, do not require active smoke control systems.

Some local amendments, however, require active smoke control designs. Some codes require that high-rise hospitals or clinics (over 75 feet [23 meters]) have smoke control, and all U.S. model codes require active smoke control for atrium spaces. Performance-based equivalencies may also require an active smoke control or smoke removal system. In addition, there are requirements in NFPA 99, *Standard for Health Care Facilities*, that operating rooms have the capability to prevent recirculation of smoke from a fire within the OR suite. When an active smoke control or smoke removal system is required, the basic concepts for the design are similar from code to code. This section details these basics.

11.4.1 Dedicated versus Nondedicated Systems

Active smoke control design is based upon one of the following design methods:

* Exhaust
* Pressure differential
* Opposed flow

Dedicated fans, dampers, and ductwork can be provided to meet smoke control criteria. This equipment will be used only in the smoke control mode and will be provided with adequate redundancies and emergency power backup to ensure its operation in an emergency.

Nondedicated equipment used in smoke control systems will have other day-to-day functions assigned to it. A normal supply air fan may provide makeup air to a smoke exhaust system. An economizer cycle that routes return air to the exterior may be used as the exhaust portion of a smoke control system. Emergency power must be provided for these nondedicated system components. Activation of a smoke control system using a nondedicated smoke control arrangement requires overriding all other building control functions related to the nondedicated equipment. Nondedicated systems have lower equipment costs, but they may require complicated control equipment and programming.

11.4.2 Smoke Control Mode of Operation

Automatic initial activation of the smoke control sequence is essential. In a multiple-zone smoke control system, the initial operation of the system is based on correctly locating the fire. In general, a fire can be located most reliably by using the automatic sprinkler system zone information from the building fire alarm system. This requires designing the automatic sprinkler system using sprinkler zones that correspond to the smoke control zones. Smoke detector activation of a smoke control system is discouraged in large multiple-zone buildings because smoke that migrates to an adjacent zone before it reaches activation concentrations in the zone where the fire originated may cause the smoke control system to first operate in the wrong configuration. Manual pull stations should not be used to determine the initial smoke zone because persons frequently activate them after they have left the area of the actual fire.

Some typical terms to be familiar with when developing the smoke control mode of operation are:

- original zone of operation
- adjacent zones
- nonrelated zones

The design team should develop a smoke control activation matrix during the design development and construction documents phases of a project. This matrix should be part of the HVAC systems specifications, building automation systems specifications, fire detection alarm system specifications, and the automatic sprinkler system specifications. These four systems must be coordinated to properly activate a smoke control system. The activation matrix will identify the coordination required.

The design team should also prepare a list of all fans, control dampers, ductwork, door releases, fan shutdown releases, detection device locations, smoke barrier locations, fire wall barrier locations, and other information needed to properly test the smoke control system.

Before completing the design of the smoke control system, the design team should prepare a testing method and manual for the system. This manual should incorporate the guidelines of NFPA 92A (Chapter 4); NFPA 92B (Chapter 5); and NFPA 72 (Chapter 7), as appropriate for the equipment and design. This testing manual should be shared with the contractor and the building and fire departments and coordinated between the design disciplines on the team. This testing manual will identify performance criteria for the smoke control system, the testing equipment needed, the testing protocol, the pass/fail criteria, and the documentation required for accepting the smoke control system.

Atria

Atria are common in health care facilities. An atrium, by definition, is a vertical opening that connects three or more floors. In some jurisdictions, a two-story vertical opening may also be classified as an atrium. Smoke control for an atrium usually consists of a smoke exhaust system. Smoke is exhausted at the upper levels of an atrium, and makeup air is introduced at the lower levels of the atrium—below the clear air-to-smoke interface. The "mechanical" makeup air flow rate should be between 80% and 90% of the mechanical exhaust rate. The remaining air flow would be provided through leakage at the atrium's perimeter, although the amount of air that leaks into an atrium will depend upon the construction tightness of the atrium enclosures.

Smoke Control Zones

In health care occupancies, smoke control systems must be zoned. In very rare instances will a single floor of a health care occupancy be considered one smoke zone. Smoke control systems usually cannot totally protect the floor of a fire's origin. Smoke control systems can limit and minimize the migration of smoke from the area of fire origin. In a defend-in-place occupancy, such as a health care facility, passive smoke control is provided in the form of smoke barriers. If active smoke control is required, the active system should use the smoke barriers as the zoning configuration for its smoke control strategy.

Controls

In addition to automatic control sequences, the smoke control system must have manual override controls. These controls will be provided in a place accessible to the fire department or responding agency so they can override all automatic smoke control settings. The smoke control manual override panel should be designed for ease of operation.

A smoke control system in a building is a custom-configured system. Each local jurisdiction has its own requirements related to system performance and design. It is imperative that local building and fire officials review and accept the smoke control system design, manual override, and testing procedures before the construction documents are completed. NFPA 92A includes guidelines for graphics, switches, and feedback that can be used when developing a concept for local review. Even though it is customized for site requirements, the firefighter interface panel should be UL-listed as part of a fire or smoke control system – experience indicates failure to do so is a recurring problem.

Activation and Deactivation of the Smoke Control System

As previously noted, automatic activation of the smoke control system by a reliable means, such as sprinkler water flow, is desirable. The smoke control system can also be activated manually through the manual control panel discussed previously. The system should be deactivated only by manual means. Deactivation of the smoke control system will also require resetting the fire detection alarm system to clear the resulting alarm. Reversal of supply and/or return fans is problematic and should be avoided.

11.5 STAIRWELL PRESSURIZATION

11.5.1 Introduction

Stairwell pressurization systems are designed to maintain a pressure differential from the stairwell to adjacent spaces. The NFPA 101 Life Safety Code requires a minimum pressure differential of 0.05 in. w.g. (12.4 Pa) in sprinklered buildings and a minimum of 0.10 in. w.g. (25 Pa) in unsprinkled buildings. Additionally, the pressure difference across doors should not be more than that which permits the door to begin to be opened by a force of 30 ft-lb (41 J). Depending upon the size of the door and pressure exerted by the closing device, this generally occurs when the pressure differential exceeds 0.25 in. w.g. (62 Pa).

Of course, many factors affect a pressurization system, and several variables are undefined even after construction and final testing, including the number of open doors, which can vary constantly. Other factors that affect pressurization include the stack effect, the reverse stack effect, door leakage, wall leakage, and wind effects. Design considerations for pressurization also include emergency power to the systems as required by NFPA 99 and local codes and ensuring that the system controls used are listed as "smoke control equipment."

11.5.2 Excessive Pressure Control

One method of compensating for changing conditions is the use of barometric relief dampers. These dampers relieve excess pressure (into the building or outside) if the stairwell pressurization exceeds a specified value (usually 0.25 in. [62 Pa]). Concerns associated with barometric relief dampers include additional maintenance to ensure proper operation and the effect of adverse weather conditions in some climates.

Modulating supply airflow systems is another method of controlling excessive pressure differences. A variable supply air flow rate can be achieved by using a commercially available variable flow rate fan or a fan bypass arrangement of ducts and dampers. Variable flow fans are controlled by one or more static pressure sensors that sense the pressure difference between a stairwell and the building. In a bypass system, the air flow rate into the stairwell is varied by modulating bypass dampers, which are controlled by one or more static pressure sensors as just described.

11.5.3 Air Supply Source Locations

Choosing the location of the air supply for a stairwell pressurization system involves numerous variables. The most advantageous choice is at the bottom of the stair shaft, close to the ground. The most notable advantage of a low point of supply is less likelihood of drawing contaminated air into the system (assuming that smoke from a fire in the building will probably move upward). Additionally, the wind effect in tall buildings is greater as you progress up the building, and this could have an adverse effect on fan performance.

Other considerations when locating supply inlets include the location of other exhausts and outlets for the building. Care should be taken to avoid locating supply inlets near outlets from smoke shafts and vents of the smoke control system as well as natural shaft vents such as elevator vents or other openings that may exhaust smoke from a building.

11.5.4 Types of Air Supply Fans

Several types of fans are commonly used for stairwell pressurization systems. The fans are basically either centrifugal or axial types and may be either direct drive or indirect drive.

All fans can be equipped with variable speed drives, variable inlet vanes, or dampers for changing the airflow to a stairwell. Propeller and other axial fans may use blades that are fixed, adjustable at standstill, or variable in operation and are, therefore, best suited for a stairwell pressurization system. Controllable-pitch axial fans do not need speed or vane controls.

Supply air fans may be stand-alone or part of a building HVAC system. Additional dampers and control modules are needed, however, when using building HVAC fans as part of a stairwell pressurization system. This often leads to increased complication and maintenance and should be avoided if at all possible.

11.5.5 Single and Multiple Injector Systems

Many analyses, as well as actual tests, have been conducted to study the effects of single and multiple injection point air supply systems. These studies have shown that stairwells of more than eight stories are subject to pressurization failure with single-point injection. This is due to significant stack effect, as well as to losses attributed to door openings near the source of the single-point injection.

Because the top and bottom of stair shafts are most susceptible to pressurization loss due to the stack effect, it is best to avoid these locations for single-point injection systems. Additionally, the large amount of air needed to reach sufficient pressure differentials in tall stairwells may create pressure forces on doors near the supply point that exceed allowable door opening forces.

Multiple-point injection systems use one or more fans and a ductwork system with outlets throughout the stairwell. Studies have shown that systems that have outlets on every level perform best, but systems that have outlets on alternate or every third level have also been effective.

11.6 ELEVATORS

Elevators and elevator shafts can impact the transfer of smoke between floors. Codes are inconsistent regarding protection of elevators and elevator shafts. NFPA 101 relies on quick-response automatic sprinkler protection to limit air buoyancy and the amount of smoke produced and, therefore, does not require elevator shaft or lobby protection.

Some of the model codes, however, require elevator lobbies in high-rise buildings and separating elevator openings from corridors in all buildings. All codes require enclosing elevator shafts in two-hour fire-resistive construction (with few exceptions).

If elevator lobby protection is required, generally it is accomplished by using a one-hour-rated elevator lobby. If an active smoke control system is provided, this lobby will also often be treated as a passive zone, requiring that all ductwork penetrating the lobby wall employ smoke and fire dampers. For small elevator lobbies, it may be more convenient to anticipate that elevator lobby doors will be held open and that conditioning the space immediately outside the elevator lobby can achieve the necessary air exchange. In that way, no duct penetrations are needed, and no dampers need to be provided.

Some jurisdictions allow pressurization of elevator shafts as a means of avoiding elevator lobbies. Pressurization design for elevator shafts depends upon the amount of leakage through elevator doors and the sensitivity of the elevator equipment to pressure differences within the shaft. Before using this approach, it is important to work with the elevator manufacturer and the general contractor to determine allowable pressure differences and expected leakage of the elevator shaft.

If elevator recall (ANSI A17.1, Firefighter Phase 1 Mode) is not provided or elevators must be used for firefighter access and patient evacuation, the piston effect of moving elevators can enhance smoke spread. While the mechanical engineer will not have control over whether elevator recall is provided, it is a question that should be considered because it may impact the design of the smoke control system.

11.7 CONTROLS AND SEQUENCING

11.7.1 Passive Systems

Controls and sequences for passive systems are relatively simple. However, the mechanical engineer still must consider whether closure of dampers will affect the integrity of fans and ductwork. If a fire damper in the immediate vicinity of an exhaust or supply fan closes (and there is only one branch of the system at that point), overpressurization or underpressurization of the duct could occur. In that case, it may be necessary to include a relief or a delay in the damper closure.

11.7.2 Active Systems

Controls and sequencing for active smoke control systems can be very complicated. Many smoke control system components must work together to accomplish an overall purpose. A combination of fans and dampers must start, open, or close, and that sequence must occur in a way that will not damage the HVAC system. Delays may need to be built into the system to allow fans to slow or stop before dampers are closed. The ability to properly position all VAV box dampers and control the output of variable speed drives to pressurize or exhaust a space most efficiently may also be necessary.

Manual controls are also necessary for an active system. For simple systems, control by damper and fan may be appropriate. For the typical hospital system, however, control by zone is more likely the appropriate method. In this case, a single switch would cause activation of the smoke control mode for each zone, and a single LED will likely indicate proper damper positioning for dampers within that zone. Fan controls might be individually annunciated because they are larger portions of the system. Often, a firefighter control panel controls the system.

Because the fire department is expected to operate this panel, working out the design of the panel with the fire department before fabricating it and specifying the panel as UL-listed for "smoke control applications" is strongly advised.

11.8 ENERGY MANAGEMENT AND SMOKE CONTROL

Energy management systems can add additional complexity to a smoke control system. On the other hand, by using the energy management system to control remote devices, significant wiring can be eliminated. There are advantages and disadvantages of tying together the building energy management system and the smoke control system.

- *Advantages*
- By using the energy management system to perform smoke control functions, replication of wiring and controls to many devices can be eliminated. Instead, signals between panels, generally done by dry contact, are all that would be necessary.
- By eliminating redundant wiring and control features, field priority issues can be avoided. Instead, priority can be dealt with at the panels.
- The energy management system is in normal use. Rather than functioning only in an emergency, the system has to operate on a day-to-day basis. This improves the reliability of the system.
- It has the ability to command VAV and VSD devices directly to provide efficient pressurization or exhaust modes to a zone.
- It has the ability to monitor and control coils on units directly during smoke mode operations in order to minimize loss of space conditioning and equipment damage due to large outside air volumes in extreme climatic conditions.

- *Disadvantages*
  - If the energy management system is expected to provide smoke control functions, many jurisdictions will require it to be listed as a smoke control system. Some energy management systems do not carry such a listing.
  - Energy management systems and life safety systems are often the last systems installed in a building. The building cannot open without a life safety system. If the construction schedule is tight, it may be possible to open some of the building without a properly functioning energy management system. By separating the systems, priority can be provided to the life safety system.

11.9 TESTING AND COMMISSIONING

Regardless of the quality of design and construction, an acceptance test is necessary to ensure that the smoke control system operates as intended. The acceptance testing should involve two levels. The first is a functional test, which is a test of each individual component to be certain it is operating properly. The second level of testing is a performance test to determine whether the system as a whole works in accordance with the design.

Testing will generally include measurement of air flow and pressure differences in accordance with the testing guidelines developed by the designer. The first step in the testing should be to agree on the performance goals and to review the test criteria included with the design.

ASHRAE Guideline 5 covers the commissioning of smoke management systems and is a good reference for use in this regard. This chapter summarizes some of the information from the ASHRAE guideline.

11.9.1 Functional Tests

The following items should be inspected and individually tested to confirm proper installation and operation.

- Ducts should be tested for leakage and inspected for completeness and stability. In particular, ducts that traverse smoke compartments other than the compartment they serve should be closely reviewed to be sure that smoke flowing through the duct will not leak into adjacent compartments.
- Fan capacities, power (including emergency power), speed, operation (within their curve), and direction of flow should all be reviewed and verified.
- The locations of initiation devices specified in the design should be verified, and the devices should be tested to confirm that they operate properly and report to the control panel. Outputs from the control panel will be tested later (in the performance level stage).
- Fire and smoke dampers should be tested for proper installation, operation, end switch positions, speed of opening and closing, adequate power supply (including emergency power), and location in accordance with the plans.
- Doors should be tested for proper rating, automatic closure where appropriate, and location in accordance with the plans.
- Smoke barriers should be tested for integrity and leakage.

The overall system should be reviewed for layout, including zoning and controls, and to check that assumptions regarding temperatures and conditions were realistic.

11.9.2 Performance Tests

The first and most important step in the operating test is to develop a scenario of expected inputs and outputs for each device. During design, a matrix should have been developed that indicates, in general, reactions of the devices. The testing scenario takes that matrix one step further and indicates, by specific device, the actions and reactions that should occur. For instance, a fire in Zone A should cause Dampers 1, 2, 3, 4, 5, and 6 to open; Dampers 7, 8, 9, 10, 11, and 12 to close; Fans C, D, E, and F to start; Fans G, H, I, and J to stop; Doors AA, BB, CC, and DD to close; and a pressure difference between Zone A and adjoining zones of 0.05 inch to be established. The fire incident might also cause stairwell pressurization fans to start, annunciation on the proper panels, and operating lights to indicate proper configuration. A detailed matrix (or scenario) by zone must be prepared to conduct these tests effectively and efficiently.

Depending upon the type of smoke control system, pressure differentials or exhaust rates might be measured. Operability of all other system components in alarm conditions—under normal and emergency power—would be verified.

11.9.3 Equipment

A variety of tools are needed to measure smoke control system performance. Air flow from fans and pressure differences across boundaries need to be measured, door-opening forces need to be accounted for, and air velocities may need to be measured. Some jurisdictions will also ask for a review of the direction of smoke movement. This may be done by using paper or smoke.

Artificial smoke should be used only to determine the direction of smoke flow. It does not replicate the hot smoke generated by a fire. Therefore, filling a space with cold smoke to measure time to visibility or other similar performance indicators will not serve the purpose intended. Using cold smoke to determine the general direction of air movement is appropriate.

Many smoke detection devices do not respond to cold smoke. Smoke detection testing should be done in accordance with NFPA 72 (Chapter 7) and the manufacturer's testing instructions.

11.10 HEALTH AND LIFE SAFETY

11.10.1 Maintenance

Besides the acceptance testing discussed in the previous section, ongoing testing of the life safety system and smoke control system should be conducted. This includes individual device testing, as well as overall performance testing. The ongoing reliability of smoke control systems depends upon testing and maintaining systems regularly.

To carry out such ongoing maintenance and testing, the original design and testing program must be clearly documented. The building engineer should maintain this document, and the mechanical engineer of record should also maintain a copy.

11.10.2 Infection Control/Sterile Areas

In a hospital, the unusual movement of air by a smoke control system cannot be allowed to overcome the infection control concerns necessary for day-to-day operation. When air is expected to move from one zone (or room) to another during smoke control system operation, it must be confirmed that the air is appropriate for such movement under normal circumstances. Such movement will occur during a fire, during periodic inspection and testing, and during unwanted alarms. The potential movement of infectious products through the operation of a smoke control system must be accounted for and avoided.

11.10.3 Air Movement Considerations

In addition to the concern about spreading infectious diseases, there are other considerations to take into account regarding smoke control system design. Most hospitals have cafeterias or kitchens, where fans for exhaust hoods are often quite large compared with other air-handling devices in the vicinity. Kitchen exhaust hoods can remain on during smoke control if they will not impact the performance of the system. However, if either exhaust or makeup air goes off and the other remains on, an imbalance of pressures and flows can easily occur. This must be considered under normal and emergency power conditions.

Many areas at higher or lower than standard pressures are found in hospitals. Operating rooms are a sterile environment and need to remain so. Hyperbaric chambers cannot be impacted by smoke control measures. These and other spaces must be considered when developing smoke control concepts.

11.10.4 Fire Alarm System

Throughout this chapter, coordination with the fire alarm system has been stressed as a part of smoke control system design. Zoning must be coordinated with both the fire alarm system and the automatic sprinkler system. The handoff from the fire alarm system to the energy management system or to the smoke control system must be clear. There can be no holes or redundancies passed on to the contractors for resolution. Coordinated testing of the systems must be done so that inputs and outputs can be properly identified. Smoke damper locations need to be coordinated with smoke detector locations, smoke detectors in fan systems need to be coordinated with the fire alarm system, and proper annunciation of the smoke control equipment needs to show on either a smoke control panel or fire alarm panel.

Final placement and sequence of operation programming of duct smoke detectors provided as part of the building fire alarm system must be considered during design. Local codes may require overrides for the supply duct detector air-handling unit shutdown from the firefighter's control panel. Further, placement of a return duct smoke detector may cause it to be activated when a unit is placed in smoke purge or exhaust mode; this must not interfere with the intended smoke mode operation.

In addition to coordination with the fire alarm system, a smoke control system needs proper emergency power provisions and must be coordinated with rated walls, doors, and ceilings. Proper design requires coordination among the entire design team.

11.11 ATRIUM SMOKE CONTROL

Many new or renovated hospitals incorporate an atrium, or multiple atria in some cases, as central feature spaces.

An atrium in a building provides a possible route by which smoke and fire can spread from one floor to another. Of course, smoke and fire could also spread between stories in a building that does not have an atrium, but normal horizontal compartmentation would provide a barrier to such spread, at least for a period of time (typically one hour).

Building floor slabs help achieve fire separation, and the whole building structure is designed to remain stable for at least one hour during a fire. However, smoke from a fire could get into an atrium void, bypass the floor slabs, and enter higher floors.

When an atrium enclosure does not confine the smoke from a fire to the space in which it originated, even though the building is of fire-resistant construction, the buoyancy and expansion of the fire gases can cause smoke to pass through any openings or gaps into adjacent spaces.

The flow of hot smoke into an atrium can be summarized as follows:

- Hot smoke rises from a fire to the ceiling above.

- Hot smoke spreads outward under the ceiling.

- Smoke reaches an atrium and flows around the edge of the fire floor's ceiling into the atrium void.

Although a glazed screen may or may not be fire rated, it can fulfill an extremely useful role in maintaining smoke separation between an atrium and the floors of the building and in assisting the displacement ventilation system to allow incoming fresh air to force smoke out of the atrium at a high level.

On floors open to the atrium, a clear occupancy zone is maintained below the smoke (approximately 6.5 feet [2.0 meters]) and smoke mixing is minimized as smoke and heat flow into and up the atrium where the smoke will rise to the atrium roof and collect to form a smoke cloud. By opening vents in the atrium roof or walls and/or by using smoke extraction fans and ductwork, this smoke can be exhausted to the outside, thereby reducing the smoke volume remaining and drawing smoke and heat away from the fire zone.

11.11.1 Other Considerations

- Occupants in a hospital are often asleep, too ill to be mobile without assistance, and unfamiliar with the building. The building, however, is supervised by a trained management team. It is public policy that health care buildings be properly supervised and supported by trained staff. The staff is trained to respond to a fire, which is typically announced by the fire alarm system, and to follow a procedure to ensure that occupants are moved safely away from the fire source. The problem is basically one of evacuating people safely to prevent injury from smoke by intoxication, incapacity, unconsciousness, or from panic.

The general principle of movement of patients from areas of risk to safe areas applies, but there are further considerations in buildings with atria.

- *Vertical Fire Spread.* Fire, or smoke and heat from a fire, may start to affect floors above the fire. To avoid this an atrium must be depressurized and the "neutral plane" must be above the highest occupancy level. This will ensure that air and smoke movement is toward the atrium rather than into the occupied areas.

- *Stratification of the Smoke Layer.* If the smoke from a fire cools too quickly, a cloud of cool smoke may collect within the atrium and fail to rise under buoyancy. Again, depressurization is required to draw smoke upward.

- *Human Concerns for Safety.* An atrium allows occupants on all floors to see what is happening throughout the building. In a fire, smoke will enter the atrium and will be seen by patients on floors above the fire floor. These patients will not be subject to any immediate risk, and because the atrium is depressurized, they will not come into contact with any smoke products. Nevertheless, the sight of smoke will provoke some concern and the hospital staff may have to move patients away from the atrium and to assure them of safety.

11.12 ENGINEERED FIRE SAFETY DESIGN

A fire safety engineering approach that takes into account the total fire safety package can often provide a more fundamental and economical solution than more prescriptive approaches to fire safety. It may be the only viable means of achieving a satisfactory standard of fire safety in some large and complex health care buildings.

Fire safety engineering can have many benefits. In particular, it will:

1. Provide a disciplined approach to fire safety design to the designer.

2. Allow comparison of the safety levels provided by alternative designs.

3. Provide a basis for selecting appropriate fire protection systems.

4. Provide opportunities for innovative design.

5. Provide information regarding fire safety management for a building.

When used by persons suitably qualified and experienced, a fire safety engineering approach will provide a means of establishing acceptable levels of fire safety economically and without imposing unnecessary constraints on aspects of building design.

11.13 CLIMATIC EFFECTS ON BUILDING SYSTEMS

The designer is responsible for ensuring that varying climatic conditions are considered and properly accounted for in the design and implementation of building systems. Wind and temperature are among the leading climatic factors that will have to be accommodated to ensure that the building systems operate according to their specifications. Certain types of buildings and building systems are more vulnerable to the adverse effects of the environment. Having an understanding of the potential pitfalls associated with the local climate will enable the designer to create more reliable and functional systems. Conversely, if an utter lack of understanding exists, it is conceivable that inadequate or unsafe conditions could arise as a result of interactions between the building systems and the exterior environment. This is especially true with life safety systems.

Temperature will affect air movements and pressures to a significant degree, as is evidenced by such phenomena as the stack effect, stratification, and buoyancy. For example, a designer who is trying to specify a pressurization system that relies on air flows with predictable densities, must have adequate knowledge of the extreme winter and summer temperatures that will be experienced. Climatic data sources can provide this information. The required air flow capacities to maintain pressure gradients vary from summer to winter (when the greatest air capacities are required and when the greatest interior to exterior temperature differences exist).

The interior climate in health care facilities is often precisely controlled. This may lead to extreme differences between the temperatures inside and outside of a building. As some building systems rely heavily on unconditioned exterior air, having a qualitative understanding of the design effects of temperature conditions is mandatory.

Wind affects building systems principally via its introduction into the interior environment of the building as a result of leakage (observed in all building constructions) as well as through more direct means, such as air intake or exhaust openings. Air intakes should be placed only after considering the local wind characteristics and the location of exhaust openings, lest a system be designed that introduces contaminated air into the building supply system. The key wind characteristics of which the designer must be aware are wind speed and direction. It is generally true that the more prone the interior environment is to exterior wind effects, the more challenging it will be to design effective building systems.

Computer models, such as CONTAM, may be used to quantify the varying effects of wind on the interior environment of a building. By defining leakage areas and flow modes between the inside of the facility and the outside, the designer can learn how varying wind conditions affect air and smoke movement and, hence, required air capacities and pressure differentials. Furthermore, the impact of wind direction may be analyzed with complex flow tools such as CONTAM, thereby allowing the designer to better orient the building with respect to its surroundings. The source and nature of wind data must be carefully considered to ensure that the most representative conditions are accommodated in designing the building systems.

CHAPTER 12
ROOM DESIGN

12.1 GENERAL INFORMATION

This chapter describes ventilation designs for various spaces in a health care facility. These designs have been used in practice to restrict air movement between spaces, dilute and remove airborne microorganisms and odors, and maintain required temperature and humidity levels. The designs are intended to perform their functions dependably with no more than normal maintenance. See Chapter 14 for additional details.

The information in Chapter 4 provides a background for the design of ventilation for the various spaces discussed in this chapter. Information provided herein includes diffuser types, layout suggestions, typical loads, and system applications for environmental control, infection control, and process cooling. Information regarding the physical size and shape of the rooms, the processes they may hold, potential equipment, people, and lighting loads, and specific infection control needs can be found in Chapter 3, "Facility Descriptions."

12.2 ROLE OF VENTILATION IN INFECTION CONTROL AND COMFORT

12.2.1 How Does Airborne Infection Occur?

In order to determine the role of ventilation in health care infection control, the process of acquiring an infection in either an open wound or via respiration must be understood. Particles that are found in every environment are not necessarily viable particles and are not necessarily infectious particles. Infectious particles may not necessarily cause infections. Infectious particles may, if in high enough concentrations, become an infectious dose that in turn may overwhelm a host's immune defenses. This process is described by the biological force of infection relationship (Heirholzer 1993):

$$\text{Infection} \cong \text{Dose} \times \text{Site} \times \text{Virulence} \times \text{Time} / \text{Level of Host Defense}$$

This equation states that airborne infectious particles must be present in a concentration equal to or greater than the infectious dose for a long enough time in a susceptible host for a colonization to occur to the point where an infection begins. Infection then may or may not lead to disease.

12.2.2 What Role Can Ventilation Design Play?

Among the biological forces of infection parameters in the above relationship, ventilation can affect the infectious dose by control of the airborne infectious particle concentration and the time of exposure by lowering the mean age of air in a space. By concentrating on the control of contaminant concentration and time of exposure, real engineering can be accomplished with measurable results. In this way, rational ventilation rates, filter efficiencies, and pressure relationships can be determined (Hermans 2000).

No single generalized ventilation design solution can solve all airborne infectious particle concentration problems and be continuously cost-effective. Ventilation designers, who must always consider the cost of installation and operation of their systems, need effective control strategies for air systems to make a design work in practice. Unfortunately, ventilation control systems do not measure the concentration of infectious particles in a space. A ventilation system cannot, therefore, increase airflow rates, vary the air cleanliness, or improve air distribution in response to a burst of airborne infectious particles. Until a real-time and cost-effective monitor for infectious particles (or a valid surrogate) is created, ventilation systems will be designed for fixed conditions of source generation of contaminants. Ventilation system design will be controlled by the traditional parameters of temperature, humidity, flow rate, and pressure. These are the tools the designer has available to address infection and comfort control.

12.2.3 Which Infectious Particles Should Be Controlled?

The choice of which particles to focus upon for ventilation design (or for a ventilation standard), depends entirely upon the expected clinical use of the space. Airborne candidates for control in most common patient-occupied spaces are *M. tuberculosis*, measles virus, Varicella zoster, and some fungal spores. These particles all have been shown to be transported between spaces by ventilation systems (Riley 1980; Murray et al. 1988; Streifel et al. 1989; Riley et al. 1978).

Patients with *M. tuberculosis*, measles, or chicken pox should be in Airborne Infectious Isolation rooms. Patients who are susceptible to infection will be in a Protective Environment. These spaces will require ventilation designs that are concerned with concentration control or with protection. Of these infectious agents, M. tuberculosis is a good organism for control focus simply because there has been enough research to suggest a ventilation effectiveness. A minimum ventilation rate is suggested in the next section.

Finding a design organism for the general patient room is difficult. Although any patient room could contain an undiagnosed infectious patient, providing ventilation to every room for such a possibility would be prohibitively expensive. General patient rooms need to be cooled and heated to maintain conditions described in Table 4-1 for the comfort of the patient. Patient rooms need ventilation to make up the exhaust from the toilet room if one is attached.

12.2.4 Can Ventilation Design Contribute to Airborne Infection?

Ventilation systems can be a source of infectious particles and must be designed in such a way as to avoid becoming amplifying sites for organisms to grow and become aerosolized. Air systems are rarely the original source of pathogens but can quickly become a reservoir for amplification. All places where moisture and a food source can accumulate in the ducts or air-handler must be eliminated. Air systems can distribute pathogens from an internal source to a susceptible person nearly anywhere in the distribution system if there is inadequate filtration. Any place where dust and dirt can accumulate in a patient room and subsequently become wet is a result of bad design practice. Air cooling coils located within the patient room to cool air below its dew point are particularly bad, due to the moisture they create mixing with the dust they collect. Any finned element, whether cooling or heating, may become a amplifier for pathogens.

12.2.5 Ultraviolet Germicidal Irradiation in a Room

Properly maintained upper-room ultraviolet germicidal irradiation (UVGI) lamps can kill a significant percentage of the viable particles floating in the air of a room. The best ventilation rates for effective UVGI are in the range of 10-12 ACH for winter (with an all-air heating system) and 6 ACH for summer (or in winter with a convective heat source below the window) (Memarzadeh 2000). Well-mixed air is a critical requirement for effective killing.

12.2.6 Why Is Filtered Air Important in Health Care Settings?

Basically, without air filtration, particle concentrations in indoor environments tend to build up. Even inert or dead particles can cause toxic effects in some people, even normally healthy people. For patients with respiratory problems, high particle counts are detrimental.

The most compelling argument for filtration is to reduce the transmission of pathogenic substances that will travel from person to person (or from the environment to a susceptible person) and be deposited either in an open wound, as in the case of an invasive procedure, or into the respiratory system. Particles have a tendency to become deposited either in the upper respiratory tract or the lower respiratory tract, depending upon their size (Morrow 1980).

The physics of particle deposition probability in the lung has been theorized to be based upon the size of the particle, as shown in Figure 12-1. Upper respiratory tract (URT) deposition for the larger particles helps protect the more sensitive lower membranes of the lung. Notice the range of 0.2 micron to 5.0 micron where the deposition fraction in the upper tract drops off and the fraction in the lower tract (LRT) increases. This range of particles will tend to enter the lung and become deposited in the deepest areas, there to colonize and potentially infect and cause disease. Some particles that fall in this range

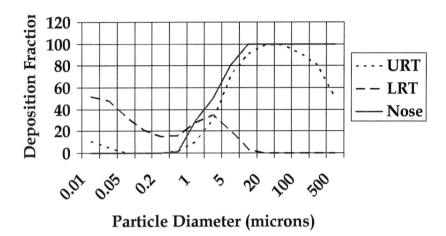

Particle Diameter (microns)

Figure 12-1   Particle deposition in the lung.

are *Streptococcus*, anthrax, *aspergillus*, diphtheria, and tuberculosis.

These types of organisms are dangerous to healthy humans and much more so to those with suppressed immune systems. The likelihood of coming across these kinds of pathogens is greater in hospitals than in a private home or on the city street. It is, therefore, necessary for the health care ventilation designer to be aware of the risk of transmission of these organisms through ventilation systems and of the opportunity to capture them on appropriate filter media.

12.2.7   Application of Standard 52.2 to Health Care Ventilation Systems

The requirement for air filtration in hospitals has a long history. In the October 22, 1947, *Federal Register*, the Public Health Service published rules for construction of hospitals funded with federal funds. Commonly referred to as the "Hill Burton" rules, the requirements set minimum conditions for the environments of certain critical areas inside hospitals. The rules said in part: "The operating and delivery rooms shall be provided with a supply ventilating system with heaters and humidifiers which will change the air at least eight times per hour by supplying fresh filtered air humidified to prevent static." The humidifier requirement was necessary due to the use of explosive anesthetics. The filter requirement is not as obvious. Since these systems were required to be 100% outside air, the intent wasn't to prevent recirculating internally generated airborne pathogens. The heating coils during this time may have needed filters for protection if they used closely

spaced fins on tubes, but this type of coil was not common in 1947. It is more likely that the heating coil was a cast iron type not unlike the room radiators of the period (and not likely to require filters). What remains, as a logical reason for the filter requirement, is to protect the patient from airborne contaminants present in the supply air. This is the primary reason high-efficiency filters are used today in health care ventilation systems.

Health care ventilation filtration systems are required to be tested using ASHRAE Standard 52 (ASHRAE 1992, 1999b). The minimum efficiencies of required filters are listed in several guidelines and design handbooks (ASHRAE 1999a; AIA 2001).

The *Guidelines for Design and Construction of Hospitals and Health Care Facilities* provide the filtration requirements adopted in most states for health care design (AIA 2001). These requirements, converted to equivalent MERV ratings, are shown in Table 12-1.

All health care facilities, whether or not they are governed by the guidelines, should follow the above minimum requirements for filter efficiencies. Following are further thoughts on filtration.

• The deposition versus particle size graph (Figure 12-1) suggests filters should stop particles that will pass by the upper respiratory tract (URT) and deposit on the lower respiratory tract (LRT). Viruses are generally below 0.3 μm in diameter and, if they are free floating, they will very likely deposit deep into the lung. Not much can be done about this by using filtration. Kowalski et al. (1999) suggest that filter efficiencies for virus-sized particles are difficult to deter-

**Table 12-1. Filter Efficiencies for Central Ventilation and
Air-Conditioning Systems in General Hospitals**

Area Designation	No. Filter Beds	Filter Bed No. 1 (MERV)	Filter Bed No. 2 (MERV)
All areas for inpatient care, treatment, and diagnosis, and those areas providing direct service or clean supplies such as sterile and clean processing, etc.	2	8	15
Protective environment room	2	8	17[a]
Laboratories	1	12	–
Administrative, bulk storage, soiled holding areas, food preparation areas, and laundries	1	8	–

Notes: Additional roughing or pre-filters should be considered to reduce maintenance for filters with efficiencies higher than 75 percent. The minimum efficiency Reporting Value (MERV) is based on ASHRAE 52.2-1999.

a. HEPA

mine because of problems in modeling filter performance using the diffusion model (Kowalski et al. 1999).

- Since the effect of filtration on free viruses is not understood sufficiently to make a recommendation for filter efficiencies, it has been suggested that the best method to control virus concentrations in room air is dilution with outside air (Hermans and Streifel 1993).

- If viruses are not the particles to establish filter efficiency, then some other particle is needed.

- Bacteria fall into the size range of 0.2 μm to 2.0 μm. This particle size range is within the ability of present day filter media. This range is also the size particle most likely to be deposited deep in the lung. Notable pathogens that fit this range and are communicable are *Chlamydia Pneumonia* at 0.28 μm and *Mycobacterium tuberculosis* at 0.64 μm logmean diameter.

- The choice of filters for patient care areas is 90% by the dust spot method. However, under Standard 52.2 this filter may only have an efficiency of 84% at the 0.3 to 1.0 μm particle size range. Since the infectious dose for TB is as low as 1 bacillus (Ryan 1994), this filter would not be the best choice.

- There is a choice of filters above 90% dust spot efficiency. The MERV chart shows several filters in this range. MERV 15 is probably necessary for use in any area involving a patient where respiratory infections exist. Fungal spores are another threat to patients. Stopping such spores is relatively easy with filters of MERV 13 and higher. These could be used with any patients having normal immune systems and no open wounds.

- Laboratories can be served by filters of MERV 12 and higher.

- Pre-filters should be at least MERV 8.

12.2.8 Surgical Site Infections

A distinction between infection and contamination must be made. An *infection* is defined as a pathologic condition of tissue characterized by signs of inflammation (redness, swelling, pain, heat, purulent secretion) with or without general bodily reaction (fever, prostration, etc.). *Contamination* is defined as the seeding of microorganisms that may or may not develop into an actual infection, depending on such factors as susceptibility of the host, the quantitative load and virulence of the invading microorganisms, and other factors. A surgical wound infection is initiated by contamination of the wound, may develop within a few days after surgery, or may be delayed and not become evident until months, or even years, after contamination. Surgical wound infections may be superficial, involving skin and subcuticular tissue, or deep, involving deeper subcutaneous tissues, fascia, muscle, bone, joints, internal organs, or body cavities (peritonitis, pleuritis).

Sources of contamination and infection may be endogenous (originating from the patient) or exogenous (from anywhere outside the patient). Contact contamination is contamination carried into the surgical wound by touching or penetrating the raw tissue of the surgical wound with contaminated surgical instruments or foreign body implants or by contact with contaminated gloves or apparel of the surgical team. Airborne contamination is carried into the surgical wound by means of microorganisms present in the air. Contamination may reach an open surgical wound by direct or indirect pathways. Indirect contamination occurs when instruments are seeded by airborne microorganisms and then placed into the surgical wound, thereby combining airborne with contact contamination. Bioparticles are microscopic particles that carry microorganisms (bacteria, viruses, fungi, etc.). Airborne bacteria or viruses may be carried on bioparticles—such as dust particles, lint particles, shed skin scales (scurf)—or in moisture globules or may be airborne as actual bacteria or spores, singly or in clusters.

No more than an estimated 2% of all surgical wound infections are attributable to airborne contamination (2% of the 1-3% wound infection rate in clean-clean operations, or 0.02% to 0.06% of all surgical wound infections). Clean-clean operations are defined as surgical operations in which no preexisting infection is encountered, no break in technique has occurred, or in which the gastrointestinal, billiary, gentiolurinary, or respiratory tracts have not been entered. Airborne organisms assume a more important role as a cause of wound infection when (1) an air-handling system becomes grossly contaminated due to faulty design, faulty installation, poor maintenance, misuse, or abuse; (2) a large foreign body is surgically implanted, as in complete joint replacement; (3) the patient's immune mechanism is suppressed; and (4) the quantity and/or virulence of the invading microorganisms is overwhelming.

12.3 HEALTH CARE ROOM DESIGN CRITERIA

12.3.1 Inpatient Care Units

The general medical/surgical patient room ventilation design is intended for patients with near normal immune systems that protect the patient from the normal airborne organisms found in the ambient environment. General patient rooms should have the following design parameters.

Ordinary or general patient rooms should have neutral or slightly positive pressure differential with respect to the corridor. Pressure differentials should be maintained between patient rooms and any adjacent sterile area, soiled utility, toilet, locker room, or isolation room. This requirement is intended to limit the migration of smoke, but in the health care setting it has the added benefit of limiting the transfer of airborne organisms into the room. Positive pressures to the corridor should be maintained where allowed. Exhaust all air from patient toilets at 2.0 cfm per square foot (10.2 L/s per square meter) or at code-required flow rates, whichever is larger. Introduce replacement air to the toilet room, if necessary, equal to or slightly less than exhausted air as part of a central ventilation system. Provide all necessary cooling with air from a central air-handling system. Use no wet coils in the room, such as with fan-coil arrangements. If radiant cooling panels are used, ensure that the chilled water temperature always remains above

the room dew-point temperature. Provide heating by air or from flat and smooth radiant panels. Use no fin tubes or convectors. Diffusers can be of Group A and Group E, but not Groups B, C, and D (refer to Chapter 9, Section 9.8.3). Pay close attention to the air diffuser performance. Minimum required ventilation flow rates are increased by poor air diffusion. The entire room volume should be well mixed with supply air. Choose diffuser throw lengths that allow no stagnant areas. Provide air volumes to offset the heat gains in the room or as required by the local authority having jurisdiction (AHJ), whichever is greater. Assume internal heat gain from a television set.

12.3.2 Nursing Station

Equipment loads should assume four ordinary personal computers, two cardiac patient monitors, and possibly a pneumatic tube station. Exhaust a nourishment room as if it were a kitchen; makeup air should come from the nursing station. Provide an accurate thermometer on an adjustable thermostat for staff use.

12.3.3 Isolation Rooms

Isolation bedrooms may generally be classified into two types: Airborne Infectious Isolation Rooms (AII) for patients having an airborne-communicable disease and Protective Environment (PE) rooms for patients suffering from weakened immune systems and who require protection against infectious airborne agents. For the AII room, the HVAC system functions as one of the multiple levels of infection control designed to contain patient-generated infectious microbials within the room in order to prevent the spread of infection to other patients and staff. In the case of the PE room, it is the patient who must be protected against infectious microbials, including opportunistic pathogens that would normally not pose an infection risk to healthy individuals. Design requirements for each type of isolation room follow.

12.3.4 Airborne Infectious Isolation Rooms (AII)

AII rooms are used to house patients with suspected or known respiratory diseases such as *Mycobacterium tuberculosis*. These rooms provide a volume within which airborne particles are contained, diluted, and directed outside. AII rooms have two major ventilation design criteria: (1) negative air pressure relative to all adjoining spaces and (2) an air distribution pattern within the room that is favorable to airborne infection control.

Negative Air Pressure

Measuring a negative differential air pressure between the AII room and the corridor may provide evidence that all air movement is into the room. There are a number of factors, however, that may well allow air to escape from an AII room in spite of a negative room-to-corridor pressure relationship. One such factor is the opening and closing of the room door.

The truly significant factor in determining the amount of air volume migration (AVM) from the room to the corridor is the airflow volume differential (Hayden et al. 1998). In all cases, some air volume migration occurs through an open door when the air pressure difference is essentially zero. In one study, for a range of room air exhaust from 50 to 220 cfm (23 to 104 L/s), the AVM between an isolation room and its anteroom was found to be 35 to 65 ft^3 (1.0 to 1.8 m^3) (Hayden et al. 1998). Through dilution, a 500 ft^3 (14 m^3) anteroom (for example) with an AVM of 50 ft^3 (1.4 m^3) would experience a 90% reduction in the transmission of contaminated air to and from the isolation room. An anteroom is recommended as a means of controlling airborne contaminant concentration via containment and dilution of the migrating air.

Provide a tight envelope to maintain effective control of infectious organisms generated within the room. Walls must extend from floor to structure and all openings must be sealed. Maintain a specific differential airflow rate. Airflow from one space to another occurs through cracks or gaps in walls, ceilings, and floors, and around doors. The sum of the areas of all these pathways is called the leakage area. The infiltration or exfiltration from an AII room is a function of the leakage area and the pressure differential across each of the five surfaces of the room. Isolation is maintained only when the airflow is inward on each of the five surfaces. Air pressure differential is a measurable quantity and should be maintained at 0.01 in. w.g. (2.5 Pa). A reasonable differential airflow rate for a patient room is 100 cfm (47.2 L/s). The designer must coordinate with the architect to seal the AII room to allow a 0.01 inch (2.5 Pa) pressure difference with a fixed air volume difference. This is accomplished by estimating the maximum allowable leakage area of all uncontrolled openings. The *ASHRAE Handbook—Fundamentals* provides a method to estimate the allowable leakage area as follows:

$$A_L = C_5 Q_r ((\rho/2\Delta p_r)^{1/2})/C_D \Delta p_r$$

A_L = air leakage area, in.^{2}

C_5 = units conversion, 0.186

Q_r = air leakage volume, cfm

ρ = air density, 0.0724 lbm/ft^3 at normal room temperature

C_D = discharge coefficient, approximately 0.186

Δp_r = reference pressure difference—for AII, 0.01 in. w.g.

The coefficient C_D is a parameter that depends upon the gaps through which the air flows. An estimate of this parameter has been made (and tested empirically) to be 0.186 (ASHRAE 2001a). The designer should estimate the leakage area using this method from the *ASHRAE Fundamentals* chapter on infiltration. If the leakage area cannot be reduced to that needed for an airflow differential of 100 cfm (47.2 L/s), recalculate with the known air leakage area and solve for Q_r. Minimum Q_r is 50 cfm (23.6 L/s) and Δp_r is 0.01 in. w.g. (2.5 Pa). In most cases, Q must be much larger and can even equal the total cooling supply air volume. In order to reduce the value of Q the ventilation designer should influence the envelope tightness as a means of decreasing the leakage area. Leakage areas of 35 in.^{2} (22,575 mm^2) require Q = 100 cfm (47.2 L/s) at 0.01 in. w.g. (2.5 Pa) (Coogan 1996). Maintaining a negative air pressure difference between the AII and the corridor may not be enough to provide isolation. Since there are up to five possible shared bounding surfaces for any room, and since there may be adverse pressure relationships across any of these surfaces, each surface must be considered. Pressures in adjoining rooms may be lower than in the AII room and air may flow out. In order to prevent such flows, the Q may need to be increased beyond that required to maintain appropriate corridor flow. The value of Q must be set to ensure that the AII will pull air from all of the surrounding spaces. See the sample ventilation worksheet (Table 12-2).

Air Distribution Patterns within Airborne Infectious Isolation (AII) Rooms

Within the isolation room itself, the goal of the HVAC system is to establish an airflow arrangement that will reduce exposure of uninfected occupants who visit or work in the space. The recommended design approach favors creating maximized air mixing and dilution effectiveness and, thereby, maximized microorganism removal.

While "laminar flow" systems are of proven efficacy in clean-room and other applications involving much higher airflow exchange rates, designers cannot expect to achieve or maintain true unidirec-

Table 12-2. Example Ventilation Worksheet: AII Room with Anteroom

	Room Name	Airborne Infectious Isolation
	Room Number:	1-100
	Room Floor Area:	120 ft² (11.2 m²)
	Room Volume:	960 ft³ (27.2 m³)
	Room Cooling Load:	4000 Btuh (1172 W)
A	Toilet Exhaust Volume:	100 cfm (47.2 L/s)
B	Room Supply Volume for Cooling:	185 cfm (87.3 L/s)
	Room Leakage Area:	35 in.² (22,575 mm²)
C	Differential Air Volume:	100 cfm (47.2 L/s) for P = 0.01 in. w.g. (2.5 Pa)
D	Anteroom Supply Volume:	75 cfm (35.4 L/s)
	Room Exhaust: B + C + D – A	260 cfm (122.7 L/s)
	Room Air Change Rate:	16.25 (12 ach = 192 cfm [90.6 L/s] exh.)

Table 12-3. Example Ventilation Worksheet: PE Room with Anteroom

	Room Name	Airborne Infectious Isolation
	Room Number:	1-100
	Room Floor Area:	120 ft² (11.2 m²)
	Room Volume:	960 ft³ (27.2 m³)
	Room Cooling Load:	4000 Btuh (1172 W)
A	Toilet Exhaust Volume:	100 cfm (47.2 L/s)
B	Room Supply Volume for Cooling:	185 cfm (87.3 L/s)
	Room Leakage Area:	35 in.² (22,575 mm²)
C	Differential Air Volume:	100 cfm (47.2 L/s) for P = 0.01 in. w.g. (2.5 Pa)
D	Anteroom Supply Volume:	75 cfm (35.4 L/s)
	Room Supply: Larger of B or A + C + D	275 cfm (129.8 L/s)
	Room Air Change Rate:	16.25 (12 ach = 192 cfm [90.6 L/s] sup.)

tional flow in infectious isolation rooms (one need only consider that at an air change rate of 12 ACH, the average air molecule travels about the space for an average of five minutes before exiting).

The preferred design approach emphasizes air mixing effectiveness and dilution ventilation without attempting to establish unidirectional airflow. Occupant protection is afforded by minimizing the airborne concentration of infectious microorganisms. As discussed in more detail in the *ASHRAE Handbook—Fundamentals*, ventilation effectiveness is maximized, particularly for perimeter rooms in cooling-dominated climates, by Type A ceiling-mounted, horizontal-throw diffusers, with maximum throw reaching the far wall and with ceiling-mounted exhaust registers. In addition to its contribution to ventilation effectiveness, the exhaust register—if located over the patient bed—has the potential of increasing the system's overall efficacy by its location in the path of the patient's cough-induced plume. The designer should be cautious with supply diffuser location and throw design, to avoid high-velocity throw reaching the doorway to the anteroom or corri-

dor and potentially counteracting the desired air transfer pattern. Provide enough conditioned air to satisfy the cooling loads within the room. The internal heat gains in the typical patient room demonstrate one possible ventilation design. These rooms generally have televisions like any other patient room. When totaled with two room occupants (a patient and a caregiver), lights, solar loads, and wall conduction, heat gains easily exceed 4000 Btu/h (1172 W). This gain will require about 185 cfm (87 L/s) of 55°F (12.8°C) air.

Provide more exhaust volume than supply in this type room. Either the supply airflow or both supply and exhaust air volumes should be controlled by a relative-pressure-sensing device. The sensor should always be located within the wall of the patient room exit, regardless of the presence of an anteroom. If the sensing device measures relative pressure, set the control for 0.01 in. w.g. (2.5 Pa). See the sample ventilation worksheet (Table 12-3).

Provide an alarm mechanism to alert clinical staff of loss of negative pressure. Supply air to the room does not have to be 100% outside air. Supply air must be filtered at least to the levels of the general patient spaces. All air must be exhausted directly to the outside. Locate exhaust grilles or registers directly above the patient bed. Consider locating the exhaust grille near the head of the bed. Use Group A or E outlets (see Chapter 9) for supply air. Place the supply diffuser in the center of the room or slightly toward the entrance. Provide high airflow rates and high air diffusion performance. Air in this room should be well mixed. A 95% ADPI (Air Diffusion Performance Index) can be achieved with a good Group A diffuser moving 15 air changes per hour and a single ceiling return (Riskowski 1996). Exhaust grilles in AII rooms require special design attention. Low sidewall grilles, if used, have the potential of becoming clogged with lint from bed-making and gowns. Failure to keep grilles clean often results in overpressurization of the AII room, creating an effect opposite to that of containing infectious disease (Hermans and Streifel 1993).

The actual air flow volumes for these rooms will depend heavily upon the cooling load and on the size of the leakage area. If the cooling needs are lower, the air change rate can be less—down to a minimum of 12 air changes per hour. If the leakage area is larger, the exhaust must be greater to achieve the 0.01 in. w.g. (2.5 Pa) pressure differential.

12.3.5   Protective Environment (PE) Rooms

Protective Environment rooms include Bone Marrow Transplant, Oncology, Hematology, and rooms for any condition that leaves a patient immunocompromised. The PE room has an objective very different from the AII room. Whereas an AII room seeks to protect uninfected occupants and the general population outside the room from the infection source (the patient), a PE room seeks to protect the patient from all potential airborne infectious organisms, some of which may be benign to normal immune systems. Among these otherwise harmless organisms are fungal spores. In many climates, fungal spores are found in the ambient air both inside and outside of environmentally controlled buildings. Spores from *Aspergillis fumigatus*, for example, are ubiquitous and exist in the outside environment in concentrations of several hundred colony-forming units per cubic meter of air (cfu/m^3). Thermo-tolerant species, i.e., those that grow in cultures at 37°C (98°F), are particularly hazardous to the immunosuppressed patient. Low concentrations (~2.0 cfu/m^3) of *A. fumigatus* in the indoor air surrounding such patients may cause aspergillosis (Rhame et al. 1984). The PE room has design consid-

erations similar to the AII room: (1) room air pressure control, in this case positive pressure with respect to all adjoining spaces, and (2) an air distribution pattern within the room that is favorable to airborne infection control, in this case for the protection of the patient.

Positive Air Pressure

Maintaining positive pressure, possibly with anterooms and continuous alarms, requires daily or continuous monitoring of pressurization. Seal PE rooms to reduce air leakage area and/or increase differential air volume to maintain a differential pressure of 0.01 in. w.g. (2.5 Pa). As an example (see Table 12-3), with a 35-square-inch (22,575 square millimeters) air leakage area, the differential air volume needs to be 100 cfm (47.2 L/s). The toilet room then needs to be exhausted at 100 cfm (47.2 L/s) and the anteroom must be exhausted. If the anteroom is exhausted at 75 cfm (35.4 m/s), the patient room would be supplied with a minimum of 275 cfm (129.8 L/s). This equals 17.2 air changes per hour.

Room Air Distribution

A unidirectional flow approach is recommended, where air is introduced at low velocity (100 fpm or less) from ceiling-mounted non-aspirating flow diffusers. Use non-aspirating unidirectional flow diffusers of Group E, including HEPA filters within the diffuser. Air is exhausted at the floor level near the entrance to the room. The intent is to establish a vertically downward wash of clean air through the breathing zone of the patient, picking up contaminants as the air passes through the lower level of the room and out through the exhaust registers. This approach may require more air than the well-mixed room in order to maintain the cleanest air at the patient. In the cooling season, some advantage can be taken by allowing the air to "dump" somewhat down to the bed. However, in the heating season in colder climates, the air must be forced down to bed level at velocities around 50-75 fpm (0.25-0.38 m/s) without entraining room air. A higher room temperature can allow cooler supply air to fall to the bed (even in the heating season), so a radiant heat source near the window, controlled independently from the supply air temperature, is an advantage.

For example, set the room supply air temperature at a fixed temperature and vary the radiant panel using a room thermostat to maintain 75°F to 78°F (23.9°C to 25.6°C) in the heating season.

12.3.6   Critical Care Units

The critical care unit environment has an impact on the recovery of traumatized patients. The air in critical care units must be nearly sterile and of low velocity at the patient. Patients in critical care have wounds that are still susceptible to airborne infection.

Convective heating elements using fins or other closely spaced surfaces trap dirt, dust, and lint that can be re-aerosolized into the room air. Fin-tube convectors should not be used in critical care. If perimeter heating is required, use radiant ceiling panels or linear air diffusers with hot air discharged down the window.

General ICU

Design is similar to that of patient care rooms with higher air change rates. Use Group A and E outlets; use no fin-tube radiation. Make this a well-mixed room. An ICU that is also an AII room must be designed to the standards of AII.

Wound Intensive Care (Burn Units)

This room type requires careful humidity control; maintain 40-60% RH. Air velocity must be below 50 fpm (0.25 m/s) at patient bed level. Deliver unidirectional airflow throughout the room, using non-aspirating ceiling diffusers of Group E with HEPA filtration within the diffuser. Use low sidewall returns near the door to the room. Keep the room under positive pressure at all times.

Neonatal Intensive Care

Air movement patterns must avoid velocities above 50 fpm (0.25 m/s) at isolet levels. Provide Group A and E outlets; use no fin-tube radiation; use low sidewall returns.

Examination Rooms

A typical examination room may require more air changes than a patient room to satisfy the cooling requirements of the space. Supply and return location is not as critical as in a Trauma Room (see Section 12.3.7), but distribution device locations must be considered to thoroughly wash the space. Supply outlets of any groups may be used.

Cast Rooms

Provide special ventilation and exhaust for the high concentration of plaster dust. This should be a negative pressure space. Most casts today are made of glass fiber and epoxy resin. These rooms may or may not require special exhaust due to volatile gases. Ask the emergency department about the type of cast material used.

Psychiatric Nursing Units

These spaces require special attention to sound control. These spaces may require security diffusers. Ask the department about the patient protection needs.

Physical Therapy

Such spaces need lower than normal temperature settings that may require a special thermostat.

Occupational Therapy

These areas often include working kitchens and/or garages that have special ventilation needs.

Cardiology (Telemetry) Step Down Units

Avoid any equipment that may interfere with the RF telemetry units. These rooms may have unusual cooling loads for monitors, ventilators, or thermal blankets.

12.3.7 Surgical Suites

Operating rooms, as a class of space within health care facilities, are very special. The operating room environment is unique among patient treatment areas of a hospital. It is a special-care area where patients are put at greater risk than elsewhere. Patients are being rendered insensitive to pain by means of general or regional anesthesia. Instruments and devices are inserted into the body to conduct invasive surgical procedures. Surgical procedures expose varying amount of exposed interior tissue to the environment. The environment may engender its own hazards and risks to both user and patient (Laufman 1994). Airborne infectious contamination comes from two primary sources: (1) aerosolized microorganisms generated within the operating room and (2) aerosolized microorganisms introduced by ventilation or infiltration.

The surgical suite contains operating rooms as well as substerile rooms, clean supply, preoperative preparation, and postoperative recovery care (postanesthesia care unit or PACU). Common usage of the term "OR" is often intended to include both the surgical room and the above-mentioned support areas. In some hospitals, other spaces such as locker rooms, doctors' lounges, control desks, anesthesia workrooms, and even surgical waiting areas may be included in the general term. The OR special environment, however, embraces only the restricted area of the surgical suite.

General Purpose OR

Surgeons want the operating room air to be clean enough to not contribute to the hazard of wound infection and tolerable enough in temperature and humidity to provide a comfortable working environment for the surgical team and an optimal environment for the patient (Laufman 1999). Surgeons may mistake high humidity in the operating room for high temperature and request a lower room temperature when, in fact, the reason for their discomfort lies in the excessive humidity.

Operating rooms should be maintained at positive pressure with respect to corridors and adjacent areas. Positive pressure should be maintained at all times, regardless of room occupancy. Positive pressure should be between 10% and 15% of air volume. Provide ceiling diffusers of low-velocity and high-volume output. Design for lower velocity and lower volumetric flow rate while maintaining stable direction and low-turbulent (low mixing) characteristics; this results in less possibility of contamination impinging upon the surgical wound and lower operating cost (Lewis 1993; Memarzadeh 2002). Provide low sidewall returns. Provide Group E outlets only, located in the ceiling and of non-aspirating type.

A key design parameter for air distribution is to maintain a low enough velocity at the surgical site to allow the wound's thermal plume to carry away any airborne particles released into the sterile field. Diffuser face air velocities should be no higher than 30 fpm (0/15 m/s) (Memarzadeh and Manning 2002). Recirculate no more than 80% of the supply air back through the air-handling system. Provide two stages of filtration: MERV 8, then MERV 15.

Provide occupant control of temperature and humidity using thermostats and humidistats with a wide range of control. Both thermostats and humidistats should be operable by operating room staff through the full range of available room temperatures and humidities. Provide individual room duct humidifiers with stainless steel duct sections and condensate drains from the duct. Provide HVAC systems that are powerful enough to offer a range of conditions depending upon the needs of the room. Some jurisdictions require a system to provide all environmental conditions within the range of temperature and humidity listed in Table 4-1, e.g., 68°F (20°C) at any humidity from 30% to 60% RH regardless of ambient conditions. Airflow should be purposefully directed from clean (beginning at the wound site) outward to less clean (low and at the room perimeter.) An anesthesia gas scavenging system is necessary whenever anesthetic gases are used.

Local gas scavenging exhausts can take the form of either an adapted connection to the medical vacuum system or a custom-ducted low-pressure system.

Recovery and Pre-Op

These spaces within the surgical suite should have filtration similar to the general OR. They should have positive pressure relative to the corridor. Spaces such as pre- and post-op (recovery) have high equipment loads. Provide good air mixing using Group A ceiling diffusers and airflow rates according to Table 4-1.

Sterilization

Substerile rooms, flash sterilizer rooms, or other rooms with sterilizers should be exhausted to maintain negative pressure relative to all adjoining spaces. Use manufacturer's information to obtain heat gains from sterilizers. Place an exhaust register directly above the sterilizer door to capture fugitive steam.

Eye Surgery

Special environments for microscopes are required. Eye surgery requires critical air velocities at the eye. Provide less than 50 fpm (0.25 m/s) at the patient head level. Microscopes require very stable anchors to eliminate vibration. These anchors may obstruct airflow.

Cardiac Surgery

Expect more than the normal equipment and personnel in cardiovascular operations. These surgical rooms are generally larger than general-purpose rooms. A pump room with direct access is usually situated adjacent to the cardiovascular room. Because of the back-and-forth traffic, the quality of the air in the pump room should be equal to that in the adjoining OR. In some cardiac operations, surgeons may request that the room temperature be rapidly lowered below the usual 68°F (20°C) to as low as 60°F (15.6°C). They may also want the room rapidly heated to 78°F (25.6°C) during the same operation. Because of the power necessary to accomplish such rapid changes, a supplemental cooling and heating system is used. Auxiliary cooling coils can be used to provide such cooling for individual rooms. Such coils may require glycol-water solutions operating at or below the freezing point of water to provide the necessary air temperatures.

Neuro-Surgery

Operating rooms in which neurological surgery is performed are usually as large as those used for orthopedic or cardiovascular surgery. In fact, in many institutions the "large" ORs are used interchangeably for all three types of surgery. Specifications for air handling for orthopedic, cardiovascular, and neurological surgery ORs are virtually the same Ceiling rails for mounting equipment such as microscopes are not recommended; they increase the risk of particulate fallout onto the sterile field during movement of the instrument. A preferable mounting for an overhead microscope is a ceiling-mounted pod located peripherally to the ceiling air diffuser with an articulated arm for positioning the microscope.

Laser Surgery

Any procedure that creates aerosolized particles (such as smoke from laser surgery) should be directly exhausted as close to the source as possible. Local exhaust systems often consist of a flexible hose and capture-bell mouth arrangement, sometimes referred to as a snorkel exhaust.

Orthopedics

Orthopedic surgery requires large rooms, with HEPA-filtered airflow rates higher than internal heat gains require. These spaces involve a wide range of temperatures and large internal heat gains from people, lights, and equipment. Some surgeons require "laminar flow" or clean-room-like systems (either vertical or horizontal) with very high airflow rates. The general operating room issues regarding impingement of particles into the surgical site also apply to orthopedic rooms. Make sure the velocity of the airstream is low at the surgical site.

Solid Organ Transplant

Transplant rooms require the highest ventilation concern. Transplant procedures involve open wounds for the longest time and are performed on patients with artificially suppressed immune systems. These rooms are often large and may even be paired: one room for a donor and an adjacent room for the recipient. Rooms of this type have the largest internal heat gains due to lights, people, and especially equipment. The number of people may reach as high as 12. In addition to anesthesia machines, this room may have heart pump machines and thermal blankets. Room temperatures may need to be quickly lowered to 65°F (18.3°C) (or lower) during the procedure. Discharge air temperatures of 45°F (7.2°C) or less are required to accomplish this. Supplemental cooling coils are typically used to lower discharge temperatures to these levels.

12.3.8 Emergency/Trauma Center

Emergency Rooms

As a point of uncontrolled entry into the hospital, the ER is a potential location for TB contact (in some geographic areas). The ER waiting area requires special consideration for directed airflow of relatively high volumes and low sidewall exhaust. Some ERs have special decontamination rooms immediately off the entrance that require dedicated exhaust.

Trauma Rooms

The term "Trauma Room" may refer to rooms of two different uses. See Chapters 2 and 3 and Table 4-1. The HVAC systems will normally supply air to satisfy the cooling load or meet code requirements. Air should be supplied overhead directly above the patient bed, with the return grilles located at the perimeter. Sometimes the return grilles are located at opposite corners of the space at the floor. This design will tend to create a sterile field around the patient and staff.

Shock or Crisis Rooms are frequently open to other spaces. Space pressurization is not possible. Use a directional flow to control contaminants. Air should be moving inward towards these rooms and then totally exhausted.

12.3.9 Diagnostic Imaging/Radiology

Imaging Suite

The heat produced by the various equipment components can require a supply airflow of substantial air changes to maintain thermal conditions. While typical overhead distribution can be utilized, special consideration should be given to patient location so as to minimize drafts. If the lead shielding extends across the ceiling, penetrations for the air devices will also need to be protected.

MRI

Temperature and humidity requirements, coupled with the extensive electronics, usually require that a computer-room-style air-conditioning unit serve an equipment room. Adding an auxiliary chilled water coil to a packaged DX unit is the best method to build in required redundancy. The MRI and associated control console space could be served by the normal building HVAC systems. Some MRI systems require chilled-water cooling for the magnet itself. All electrical and mechanical penetrations of the radio frequency (RF) shielding grid must be provided with dielectric connections for piping and waveguide connections for ductwork. Air devices in the space itself must be nonferrous, usually aluminum. It is almost impossible to generalize the design of an MRI room and its supporting spaces into a typical air change rate or cfm per square foot (L/s per square meter) value.

CT Scanning

As with an MRI suite, site-specific information for the CT scan should be the basis for each design. Peak heat gain rate must be the basis of design.

12.3.10 Other Areas

Renal Dialysis

Because of people and equipment concentrations, air supply to dialysis areas is usually greater than for a typical patient room. Location of the supply diffusers is important because the patients are seated in reclining chairs throughout the treatment. Keep air velocities well below 50 fpm (0.25 m/s) at the treatment chair.

Environmental conditions for this space should be identical to a patient room. Consider locating a radiant ceiling heater directly above the chair. Provide thermostats for individual patient control. Dialysis patients are frequently cold because they are sedentary as well as anemic due to their condition. The staff is typically too warm as they are continually moving around the treatment area caring for patients. Provide a separate zone of control for staff desk areas.

Cystoscopy

Cystoscopy rooms may be located in several different areas of a hospital. They may be in an inpatient department, in radiology, or in the surgical suite. These rooms should be ventilated first to accommodate the cooling load of the equipment (which may include fluoroscopic equipment). If located in the surgical suite, the room should be provided with a balanced positive pressure. If located anywhere else, the room may be neutral or slightly negative. Consider exhausting all air from this room to control odors, regardless of where it is located.

Endoscopy

The endoscopy suite may require specialized equipment for scope cleaning and storage. The room must be balanced negative relative to all surrounding spaces. It must be completely exhausted to the outside. Conventional overhead air distribution should

be utilized, with the air supply located directly over the procedure table and with the exhaust inlets located at the perimeter. Air can be exhausted to a general exhaust system.

Interview Spaces

Direct airflow from behind the staff person toward the patient, exhaust from behind the patient.

Visitor Waiting Areas

Evaluate the facility for the potential for undiagnosed TB cases appearing in the waiting area. This space requires a large air change rate and directional flow away from the admitting/desk area.

Respiratory Therapy

This space may involve sputum collection and pentamadine administration. Both of these may require a patient hood system. If a hood is used, it may be recirculating with a HEPA filter or require venting to an exhaust. During design, ask the clinical staff about HIV drug therapy.

Central Sterile Supply

This is a clean space. Ventilate and filter to provide air quality equal to the surgical suite. This space must be balanced positive to all surrounding spaces. Provide exhausts at and around steam sterilizers, especially above the doors. There may be a gas sterilizer, which requires special venting either directly from the sterilizer or from an ETO disposer that will burn up the gas and pass it along as hot combustion products. Either way, a special exhaust system is usually required.

Materials Management

This area usually will involve a space for hazardous material storage, which may require special ventilation.

Loading Dock

The loading dock may contain a "Red Bag" storage area. Consider this space a biohazard area and exhaust all air.

Morgue and Autopsy

Body holding spaces require negative pressure and TB control protocol. There will be high internal heat gains due to refrigeration units. This space must be completely exhausted. Provide air velocity from 50 to 75 fpm (0.25-0.38 m/s) at the table. Use low sidewall exhaust grills. Ventilation is well mixed to reduce general concentration levels in the room. Provide HEPA-filtered snorkel exhaust for bone dust.

Pharmacy

A pharmacy may contain drug production spaces. These will require a clean-room environment ranging from class 10,000 in the general space to class 100 inside laminar flow hoods. A pharmacy may also contain radiochemistry products.

Film Processing Areas

Modern radiology departments are moving away from chemical process film developers. New film processors are more like large photocopiers and require no special ventilation other than removal of the heat they generate.

Film Library

Provide special humidifiers for film libraries. The humidifier may be portable or duct-mounted such as in a surgical suite.

Histology

Provide exhaust for slide trays, grossing station, and chemical hoods. This space will contain a microscope. The grossing table will usually require a special exhaust connection. Countertops may also need exhaust in the wall over the backsplash.

Cytology

This area may contain a chemical hood.

Hematology

This area will contain blood refrigerators.

Soiled Utility

Exhaust this area the same as a toilet. Transfer air from a nearby clean utility room if possible.

CHAPTER 13
CLINICS AND OTHER
HEALTH CARE FACILITIES

13.1 OCCUPANCY CLASSIFICATIONS

The economic forces of managed care are shifting the focus of the health care industry from centralized to decentralized facilities. Health care providers are making a strategic change from the large central campus to a network of electronically interconnected, special-purpose, freestanding facilities located closer to patient populations—more for disease prevention than for medical intervention. Hospitals and physicians' group practices have experimented with the decentralized approach. Facilities for sub-acute care, intermediate care, skilled nursing, post-surgical recovery, and birthing have had mixed results. Health care facilities that move out from the campus may not look like hospitals. Medical malls are providing outpatient clinics, diagnostic/screening, and health-related retail services. Workplace fitness centers and wellness centers are blending into the corporate and suburban landscape.

In some cases, the largest distinction between hospital and clinic buildings is the life safety design. Refer to Chapter 11 for a detailed analysis of life safety systems in these facilities. Most jurisdictions want to separate life safety systems in clinics and hospitals. This usually means that ventilation systems must not cross occupancy separations. Clinic and hospital spaces usually have different occupancy schedules and so would benefit from separate HVAC systems.

13.1.1 Primary Care Outpatient Centers

The primary care facility is often the first point of contact with patients. These buildings require the least equipment and can be located within neighborhoods far from a hospital campus or as separate buildings on the campus. They can be solitary, freestanding buildings or part of a medical office building. They are traditionally open only during normal business hours, similar to retail stores. The services are often based upon family practice or specialty group practice. One characteristic of primary care is linkage to a secondary or tertiary care facility.

13.1.2 Outpatient Surgical Facility or Ambulatory Surgery Center

Some of the procedures common in busy hospital-based outpatient and emergency departments may be performed in a same-day or ambulatory surgery center. These include oral surgical procedures, dental, plastic and radiological procedures, and almost all endoscopies (Bregande 1974). Most of these procedures are performed under either local or inhalation anesthesia and in either a sterile or nonsterile environment. The surgical environment in the freestanding surgical facility must be both sterile and able to accommodate inhalation anesthetics, just as in the general hospital. These surgical facilities include spaces with functions similar to the office-type areas found in hospital surgical suites: a space for controlling access to sterile areas, a control desk, an admitting space, a consult room, and interview rooms. Surgical preoperative screening, lab prep, and radiology spaces are like hospital exam rooms. Patient dressing areas should be treated like locker rooms. Post-anesthesia recovery is exactly like the hospital space of the same name. This is an anesthetizing location. Use ceiling-mounted Type A diffusers and provide well-mixed air. Returns are ducted, low sidewall type.

Operating Rooms

These rooms may not be as large, nor contain as much equipment, as the hospital-based equivalent.

They are identical with respect to the ventilation requirements.

Only those procedures in which there is the expectation of discharge from the facility within a reasonably short period of time should be done. The types of procedures that can be expected in this facility fall into three classes (American College of Surgeons 1996):

- Class A: Provides for minor surgical procedures performed under topical local or regional anesthesia without preoperative sedation. Excluded are intravenous, spinal, and epidural routes; these methods are appropriate for Class B and C facilities.
- Class B: Provides for minor or major surgical procedures performed in conjunction with oral, parenteral, or intravenous sedation or under analgesic or dissociative drugs.
- Class C: Provides for major surgical procedures that require general or regional block anesthesia and support of vital bodily functions.

Class A facilities usually provide care for normal healthy patients and patients who have mild systemic disease that does not limit physical activity. Class B and C facilities provide care for patients who have severe systemic disease that limits normal activity and is a constant threat to life. Moribund patients, not expected to survive with or without the operation, are not appropriate for this type facility.

Operating rooms in these facilities will involve the following support spaces:

- Substerile area: Exhaust this space as if it were a soiled utility from a grille directly above the sterilizer door
- Scrub area: The scrub area is part of the sterile zone
- Clean workroom: This area needs positive pressure relative to the corridor and especially the soiled workroom
- Soiled workroom: This area needs negative pressure relative to all other spaces.

These facilities require medical gas alarms, scavenging systems, positive pressure, sterilizer exhaust, specific minimum air flow rates, minimum filtration and humidity control in exactly the same way as the equivalent hospital space.

Patient holding is a space type unique to the ambulatory center. The patient hold room is a non-threatening environment used before surgery to stage patients without preoperative sedation. Most preoperative functions such as vital signs, IV start, preop-erative skin-site prep, and attachment of monitor leads occur in holding. This space is part general medical-surgical patient room and part hospital pre-operative room.

13.1.3 Freestanding Emergency Facility (Urgent Care)

The freestanding emergency center (FEC) offers a variety of health care services to patients independently of a hospital. Any facility with the term "Emergency" in its name or advertising should be expected to have the capability of handling life- or limb-threatening conditions (Wilk 1985). Such facilities should be held to the same standard of construction as the hospital emergency department. They should include on-premises laboratories, radiology, oxygen and vacuum systems, trauma rooms, exam rooms, and treatment rooms identical to hospitals. All spaces for patient care should maintain equivalent infection control and comfort control of temperature and humidity. These spaces are sometimes called Urgent Care. The capabilities of Urgent Care may differ from Emergency Centers. The designer should be guided by the services provided, not the name of the building. If the facility provides services equivalent to a hospital, hospital standards apply.

13.1.4 Freestanding Birthing Center

Freestanding birthing centers (FBC) are facilities that provide labor, delivery, recovery, and possibly postpartum services. The FBC is an inpatient facility. It is usually classified as an "I" occupancy by most code officials and is treated as an inpatient hospital by local health departments. It usually contains at least one delivery room for emergency cesarean sections. This room is identical to a hospital delivery room and provides complete inhalation anesthetics.

Support services, including food service, housekeeping, sterile processing, pharmacy, and laundry collection and storage, are also present in these centers.

13.1.5 Freestanding Outpatient Diagnostic and/or Treatment Clinics

13.1.5.1 Cancer Centers

Cancer centers are dominated by diagnostic and therapeutic radiology. Equipment heat gains and stringent environmental requirements dictate highly sophisticated ventilation and process cooling systems.

These buildings are designed to hospital ventilation standards and contain most of the oncology services provided in inpatient facilities, such as chemotherapy, radiation treatments, CT and MRI, nuclear medicine, mammography, ultrasound, as well as exam rooms, pharmacy, and laboratories. There are neither overnight stays nor bedrooms for patients.

13.1.5.2 Dialysis Center

Kidney dialysis centers are most notable for the unique water treatment plant used for the dialysis process. These buildings have special exhaust systems as well. All of the dialysis stations should be predominantly exhausted. Air from the nursing station and other clean support space can be recirculated, but most of the treatment space should be exhausted. These centers may also have infectious isolation dialysis rooms that require separate exhaust systems.

Opportunities exist in these buildings for heat recovery from the high quantities of exhaust air. Most of the spaces require ducted returns for controlling odors and for effective heat recovery.

13.2 CLINIC SPACES

13.2.1 Exam Rooms

These spaces are often used in outpatient settings because they frequently take the place of an inpatient bedroom. Preparation and postprocedure recovery usually take place in rooms like these, which may have names such as Patient Hold, Patient Cubicle, Stretcher, or Prep Registration or may be called Exam Rooms by some medical planners. They all involve types of medical services that could include local anesthesia. Exam rooms should have ducted returns and ventilation based on hospital standards.

13.2.2 Laboratory

Laboratories in clinics follow the same rules as for ventilation as in hospitals.

13.2.3 Pharmacy

The pharmacy in an outpatient setting is likely to be similar to a retail pharmacy and can be ventilated as retail. If any specialty preparations are made, such as for chemotherapy or nuclear medicine, hospital pharmacy design rules should apply. Fume hoods require attention both to exhaust and room diffusion, regardless of their location.

13.2.4 X-Ray

Any level of facility could have X-ray equipment. Radiological equipment is getting smaller and more portable. The designer is cautioned to get as much information as possible about the equipment to determine heat gains and environmental requirements.

Some authorities having jurisdiction require separating "process" cooling loads from the comfort air-conditioning system. Radiology often uses the most process cooling in a clinic.

13.2.5 MRI

MRI suites in outpatient settings are no different than those in hospitals. The equipment manufacturer determines the environmental requirements. These temperature and humidity requirements, coupled with extensive electronics, usually require this space to be served with a computer-room-style air-conditioning unit. Adding an auxiliary chilled water coil to a packaged DX unit is the best way to build in required redundancy. Some MRI systems require a chilled-water cooling source for the magnet itself. All electrical and mechanical penetrations of the shielding grid must have a dielectric connection for piping and flexible fabric connections for ductwork. Air devices in the space itself must be nonmagnetic, usually stainless steel or aluminum. It is almost impossible to generalize the design of an MRI room and its supporting spaces into "typical" values for air change rate or supply airflow per unit floor area.

13.2.6 Ophthalmology and Optometry

These departments have no unusual mechanical requirements beyond good filtration and low-velocity air distribution in the exam room.

13.2.7 Endoscopy

An endoscopy suite may require specialized equipment for scope cleaning and storage. It must have negative air pressure relative to all surrounding spaces and is completely exhausted to the outside. The air supply to an Endoscopy Room would be in the range of 6–10 air changes per hour. Conventional overhead air distribution should be used. The air supply should be located directly over the procedure table, and the exhaust inlets should be at the perimeter. Exhausting the air to a general exhaust system is suggested.

13.2.8 Bronchoscopy

Treat a Bronchoscopy Exam Room as if it were an infectious isolation room. This may require pressure controls and alarms. Make the room pressure negative, and exhaust the room completely.

13.2.9 Cardiac Catheterization and Angiography

Heart catheterization rooms are very equipment-intensive. The equipment supplier determines the environmental requirements. Treatment rooms should have low sidewall returns and low-velocity, non-aspirating ceiling supply diffusers over the tables. The equipment room is best served by a process air cooler or modular cooler. The control and treatment rooms require close control of temperature and humidity and limits on the rate of change in these parameters over time.

13.2.10 Ambulatory Surgery

Surgery is an invasive procedure, regardless of the general health of the patient. The surgery suite should be treated just as if it were in a hospital using the same mechanical design parameters. The design should comply with state and local fire and life safety codes.

These facilities are generally Class A type, but some facilities may perform Class B procedures if an anesthesiologist is on staff. Clinics that have only general treatment rooms are not considered ambulatory surgery.

13.2.11 Surgicenter

The surgicenter is a department somewhat unique to the outpatient setting. It provides the functions of preoperative prep, postoperative recovery, and patient holding (in place of a regular patient room). Patients who need an Intensive Care Unit are generally not ambulatory patients. Preoperative, recovery, and holding should be designed with the same parameters as their inpatient facility counterparts.

CHAPTER 14
OPERATION AND MAINTENANCE

14.1 INTRODUCTION

Harteen et al. (2000) state that constructing a building represents only 11% of total building costs over 40 years. Operations, on the other hand, make up 50%. Inappropriate facility operation and maintenance can mean ignoring the largest single component of building costs. It means wasting limited budgets on equipment replacement and higher energy costs. Worse yet, it can mean random disruptions (even patient care disruptions) due to mechanical system and equipment failure, which is not acceptable in hospitals or clinics.

The operating and maintenance functions in hospitals and clinics can be provided in different ways (Ferguson 2000). Many facilities have in-house maintenance personnel who provide minimum to extensive maintenance, often on very sophisticated and technically complex systems. Some facilities perform the minimum (usually the life-safety related functions) in-house and outsource all other functions. Another model is a completely outsourced maintenance department. Some departments are unionized and have specialized work practices, and some are not unionized and are more functionally diverse. This chapter is not intended to discuss the merits of various maintenance delivery systems. The intent is to show the importance of the maintenance function in health care facilities.

For tasks that in-house staff cannot handle, consider contractors or consultants. Ensure that the contractor uses the best maintenance practices and has specific training. To save time and avoid communication problems, make sure the contractor can provide both diagnostic and corrective services. Finally, to ensure that the roots of problems are addressed, find a contractor who takes a holistic view of the facility.

A good maintenance and operating program must be implemented to ensure that a health care facility's buildings and systems operate reliably to provide the core mission, which is patient care.

14.2 MAINTENANCE

Everything that has moving parts breaks or fails eventually. A hospital or clinic, like any other facility, requires maintenance. At one time, maintenance was considered a largely uncontrollable component of hospital operating cost. In the present climate of pressure on operating costs, maintenance practices must be carefully reviewed. Blind acceptance of O&M schedules, such as chiller teardowns or preventive maintenance based simply on time intervals, can be very expensive. Similarly, maintenance performed only when equipment fails (reactive maintenance) can cause unacceptable loss of function.

The four common approaches to maintenance—reactive, preventive, predictive, and proactive—have evolved over the years as progress in diagnostic systems has occurred. An *Industry Week* article (1994) listed the following maintenance costs per horsepower:

- $18 for a reactive approach
- $13 for a preventive approach
- $8 for a predictive approach.

More detailed information on maintenance approaches is provided below (adapted from Harteen et al. 2000).

14.2.1 Reactive Maintenance

Reactive maintenance is run-to-fail maintenance, replacing equipment only when it breaks. Reactive maintenance is perfectly acceptable for non-critical equipment if the cost to replace or repair the equipment is less than the cost of monitoring it and preventing problems. This may be the case, for example, with a small motor that costs only $400 to replace. It may also be the right choice for inexpensive items such as lightbulbs. The disadvantages are as follows:

Costly Downtime

Machinery often fails with little or no warning, so equipment is out of service until replacement parts arrive. If the equipment is critical to the area, patient care delivery is disrupted. If parts are hard to find, a long out-of-service period can result. Even inexpensive equipment can cause downtime and a significant negative business impact.

Higher Overall Maintenance Costs

Unexpected failures may result in costly overtime for emergency repairs. Parts costs increase because delivery may need to be expedited and there may be insufficient time for competitive bidding. In addition, failures are more likely to be severe when failure is unexpected, possibly damaging or destroying other parts. Just as a failed timing belt on a car can cause valve damage, a failed bearing can damage shafts, couplings, impellers, fan cages and blades, gearing, and housings.

Safety Hazards

The failure of equipment, especially vane-axial fans, can injure nearby persons. For example, parts of fan blades can cut through ductwork.

14.2.2 Preventive Maintenance

Preventive maintenance involves scheduling maintenance or tasks at specific intervals. For example, it means changing the oil in a car every 3000 miles or changing the timing belt every 60,000 miles. In an HVAC system, it includes such tasks as changing the oil and filter and cleaning equipment.

By offering a first line of defense, preventive maintenance avoids many of the problems of a reactive approach. Unfortunately, preventive maintenance has these disadvantages:

Is Often Wasteful

Preventive maintenance replaces equipment that may still have a long useful life ahead. A car's timing belt may last 100,000 miles, so replacing it at 60,000 to avoid failure may be wasteful. Similarly, a chiller teardown that is unnecessarily scheduled may waste approximately $15,000 or more and may end up replacing perfectly good bearings.

Does Not Prevent All Failures

Preventive maintenance fails to catch some problems. If leaking oil is weakening a belt, for example, a new belt will immediately begin to break down. Similarly, if imbalance or misalignment is causing bearing wear, bearings could fail before the next scheduled maintenance.

Can Introduce Problems

Preventive maintenance can actually cause new problems. Every disassembly creates the potential for mistakes during reassembly or the early failure of a new component. Both events can lead to failure sooner than if the machine were allowed to run with its original components.

Requires Large Inventories

Preventive maintenance requires a large parts inventory to address all of the problems that could arise in a piece of equipment or could be required during a scheduled teardown.

14.2.3 Predictive Maintenance

Predictive maintenance checks the condition of equipment as it operates. Equipment condition, rather than time intervals, determines the need for service. If an analysis shows problems, facility managers can schedule repairs before total failure occurs. Identifying problems early helps avoid unscheduled downtime and the costs of secondary damage.

Predictive maintenance squeezes the greatest possible life out of parts—without letting them fail. By doing so, it reduces maintenance costs and downtime. For a car, knowing that a timing belt would not fail until 110,000 miles would allow the owner to forego the scheduled replacement at 60,000 miles. In a facility, predictive maintenance allows managers to eliminate scheduled overhauls when predictive techniques show that equipment is in good condition.

The appeal of predictive maintenance is threefold. First, it uncovers problems before they cause failures. Second, it extends service intervals for equipment in good condition. Finally, it determines the condition of equipment as it operates—without taking the machine apart. Predictive maintenance techniques reduce expenses by revealing the optimal time for maintenance. The following predictive techniques are used and will be described in more detail in Section 14.3.

- Vibrational analysis
- Infrared thermographic inspection
- Motor current analysis
- Oil analysis
- Refrigerant analysis

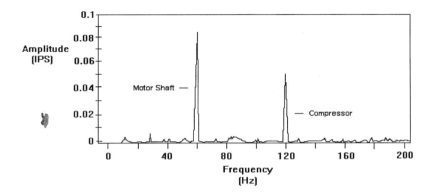

Figure 14-1   Example vibrational analysis of a chiller.

14.2.4   Proactive Maintenance

Proactive maintenance relies on predictive methods (such as vibrational analysis) to point out parts that are deteriorating. Rather than being satisfied with knowing when parts will fail, however, proactive maintenance eliminates the sources of failure altogether. For example, rather than simply replacing worn bearings, proactive maintenance seeks to eliminate the causes of wear. By getting at the root causes of fan and pump failure (imbalance and misalignment, for example), the proactive approach reduces downtime costs, eliminates recurring problems, extends machine life, reduces energy costs, and identifies ineffective operational approaches.

14.2.5   Computerized Maintenance Systems

Computers can be useful in implementing any of the above maintenance approaches. Most modern hospitals have some kind of computerized work order system that is useful in implementing required maintenance on an HVAC system, controlling an inventory of spare parts, efficiently allocating available manpower to required tasks, etc. There are several excellent computerized maintenance management software systems (CMMS) and computer-aided facility management systems (CAFM) available.

14.3   MODERN MAINTENANCE TOOLS

The information provided here is adapted from Harteen et al. (2000).

14.3.1   Vibrational Analysis

Vibrational analysis is one of the most effective techniques for analyzing the condition of rotating equipment. It is the cornerstone of a predictive main-

tenance program because it detects a wide range of equipment problems before they can cause failure.

* Misalignment and imbalance (which account for 60–80% of fan and pump problems)
* Resonance and bearing defects
* Gear and belt problems
* Sheave and impeller problems
* Looseness and bent shafts
* Flow-related problems (cavitation and recirculation)
* Electrical problems (rotor bar problems)

In environments that are critical to the facility mission, the greatest benefit of vibrational analysis is that it forecasts the most appropriate time to correct machine problems, which eliminates unscheduled downtime.

Performing Vibrational Analysis

Vibrational analysis involves attaching small sensors at predetermined locations on selected equipment. A technician connects these sensors to an accelerometer. The accelerometer collects data and converts mechanical motion (vibration) into electrical signals. Plotting these signals produces a graph called a vibrational signature that tells technicians which components are vibrating and how much.

Figure 14-1 shows a typical vibrational signature for a chiller. Amplitude and frequency are the two characteristics of vibration used to diagnose equipment problems. Amplitude is the amount of vibration. It indicates the severity of a problem. The greater the amplitude, the greater the problem. Amplitude is measured in inches per second (ips), mils of displacement, or g's of acceleration.

Frequency identifies the source of a vibration. For example, a motor shaft may vibrate at 50 Hz,

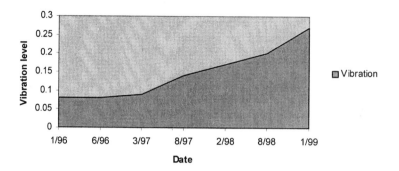

Figure 14-2   Vibrational trending of a chiller.

while a compressor may vibrate at 120 Hz. In addition, different mechanical problems cause vibrations at different frequencies.

Frequency is measured in revolutions per minute (rpm), cycles per minute (cpm), and cycles per second (cps or hertz [Hz]). Machinery rpm is a measure of frequency. Under imbalance, one cycle occurs during each revolution. Therefore, the frequency for imbalance is 1 × rpm. Different machines run at different rpms. A motor that operates at 1800 rpm has a frequency of imbalance of 1 × rpm or 1800 cpm.

Trending Vibrational Levels

The big picture offered by trending—measuring vibrational levels over time—helps determine more precisely when a machine will fail. A single vibrational measurement gives a snapshot of a machine's condition, but trending gives a full view of the equipment's performance.

As shown in Figure 14-2, a machine's vibration in August 1997 was 0.13 ips, which is within specifications. Given that measurement alone, the machine has no problem. The trend chart, however, shows that vibrational levels have been rising at an increasing rate, a sign of upcoming problems.

Vibrational Trending

Trending forecasts the future condition of equipment and provides time to prepare for necessary maintenance. Rather than make emergency fixes, managers can schedule repairs for planned outages on off-peak hours. Every trend measurement gathered reduces the risk of unscheduled downtime. The importance of the space being served by equipment dictates the frequency of trend measurements.

Overall Vibration

Overall vibration (measured in ips) is the total vibration within a piece of equipment, the vibration caused by all of the equipment's problems. Measuring the overall vibration of a machine quickly reveals whether it is in good condition; it does not tell you, however, what the problem is. High overall vibration points to a need to analyze the vibrational signature further.

14.3.2   Infrared Thermographic Inspection

Thermography involves analyzing heat transfer by electromagnetic radiation. All animate and inanimate objects (for example, electrical control panels, motors, and boiler doors) emit electromagnetic radiation in the infrared spectrum. Only an infrared camera can see such radiation. Thermographic inspection is an accurate, quick, and effective technique for avoiding equipment breakdowns by gathering and presenting thermal performance information about a system. It does not, however, ensure proper equipment operation, however; other tests and proper maintenance are necessary to ensure reliable performance.

An infrared scanner looks like a video camera. It records site-collected information on diskettes or on standard VHS videotapes for later review and investigation. A display screen helps to identify potential problem areas immediately.

Conducting a Thermographic Inspection

In a thermographic inspection, plant equipment is systematically scanned for temperature profiles in order to find and correct developing problems before equipment failure occurs. Analysis can isolate a source of overheating or other problem areas. Temperature anomalies in equipment—both hot spots and cold spots—can be investigated. The relative severity of a hot spot can be determined, and its root cause can be isolated and identified.

Other Uses of Thermographic Inspection

Electrical inspections are one of many applications of thermographic technology. Think of an electrical system as a chain. Stress causes the chain to break at its weakest link. In an electrical system, hot spots caused by a small temperature rise weaken the chain. When a component deteriorates, its temperature rises, and eventually it burns up or short circuits.

14.3.3   Motor Current Analysis

Motor current analysis is used to diagnose rotor problems, including:

- Broken or cracked rotor bars or shorting rings
- Bad high-resistance joints between rotor bars and shorting rings
- Shorted rotor lamination
- Loose or open rotor bars not making good contact with end rings.

Current analysis eliminates the need for Variac or Growler tests that diagnose the same problems but require turning off and disassembling the equipment. Motor current analysis can generally be performed while the equipment is running. One exception is high-voltage machines; these should be shut down to avoid the risk of electrocution.

**How Is a Motor Current
Analysis Performed?**

A motor current analysis is performed with a multimeter and a motor current clamp that measures the current drawn by the motor. Motor current can be measured on either the main phase circuit or on the secondary control circuit. The secondary circuit is safer; always use this for equipment at more than 600 volts.

When performing a motor current analysis, an analyst measures the three-phase power line leads one at a time. Then, the analyst compares the currents in each phase. The current in each phase should be within approximately 3% of the others. Variations higher than 3% point to stator problems such as those listed earlier.

14.3.4   Oil Analysis

Oil analysis is one of the oldest, most common, and useful predictive technologies. It helps to prevent failure and unscheduled downtime by displaying the wear metal count and types of contaminants in oil. The wear metal count indicates whether equipment is experiencing unusual wear. The types of contaminants in the oil, as well as the oil's physical characteristics, determine whether the time interval between oil changes can be extended.

Common methods for determining oil quality include spectrochemical analysis, physical tests, and ferrography. Spectrochemical analysis identifies wear particles (metals such as zinc, aluminum, copper, nickel, and chromium) in the oil. Friction between bearings and gears causes these metals to wear from the surfaces and circulate in the lubricant. A high level of metals indicates that components are wearing.

Physical tests show how well a lubricant is doing its job. Contaminated lubricants can be changed before they accelerate component wear. The most common physical tests include the following.

Viscosity

Viscosity is a lubricant's internal resistance to flow. It is the single most important physical property of oil. Changes in viscosity indicate lubricant breakdown, contamination, or improper servicing. Each of these occurrences leads to premature component failure.

Water in Oil

Water promotes oxidation and rust in components. It also prevents a lubricant from doing its job.

Total Acid Number

Total acid number (TAN) is the level of acidic material in a lubricant. It indicates acidic contamination of the oil or increased oil oxidation. Both increase the potential for corrosive wear.

Ferrography is a useful technique for analyzing centrifugal equipment with transmissions and for screw compressors. It determines the condition of a component by directly examining wear metal particles. Wear metals and contaminant particles are magnetically separated from the oil and arranged according to size and composition. Direct reading (DR) ferrography monitors and measures trends in the concentration of ferrous wear particles. DR ferrography trends indicate abnormal or critical wear that can be used to trigger analytical ferrography. Direct reading ferrography is usually unnecessary if vibrational analysis is being used because vibrational analysis assesses the condition of gears more accurately.

Regular sampling is important to successful oil analysis. Sampling determines the suitability of the oil for continued service. It can also provide crucial information about the presence of wear metals, acids, moisture, and other contaminants.

14.3.5   Refrigerant Analysis

Refrigerant analysis checks physical properties, vapor-phase contaminants, and liquid-phase contaminants to determine the condition of a refrigerant. Moisture and acidity are the two most important levels to monitor. High moisture levels lead to increases in acid levels. This in turn causes motor insulation to deteriorate and tube metal to erode. Once acid is in the system, it migrates into the oil. In the oil, the acid accelerates the wear of rotating components such as bearings and gears. This leads to premature component failures.

A refrigerant analysis can also verify that the refrigerant purchased meets acceptable standards. ARI Standard 700-99 (ARI 1999b) is typically used to assess refrigerant condition. An analysis should be conducted after repairing leaks, adding refrigerant, or performing major repairs that have a high potential for moisture contamination.

The accuracy of a refrigerant test depends upon the sampling technique. It is important to not contaminate a sample with outside moisture because moisture level is an important indicator of condition.

14.3.6   Shaft Alignment

Improper alignment may be the most common cause of high vibration and premature failure in equipment. High vibrational levels lead to excessive wear on bearings, bushings, couplings, shaft seals, and gears. Proper alignment can slow the deterioration of equipment. Alignment means adjusting a piece of equipment so that its shaft is in line with the machine to which it is coupled. When the driver and driven machines are connected through a common coupling and rotate together at operating equilibrium, the unit rotates along a common axis of rotation as one continuous unit without excessive vibration.

The three most common types of alignment are:

- *Parallel*, in which the coupling hub faces are parallel, but the two shaft centerlines are offset; essentially there is a distance between the two shaft centerlines.
- *Angular*, in which the coupling hub faces are not parallel and the shaft centerlines are not concentric.
- *Perfect*, in which the coupling hub faces are parallel and shaft centerlines are concentric.

Correcting Shaft Misalignment

When alignment and shimming procedures are performed, the adjustments are made only to one machine. This machine is the driver unit. The machine not adjusted (because of size or other physical constraints) is usually the stationary machine or driven unit.

Newer alignment methods and tools make alignment relatively fast and easy. Alignment methods include:

- Reverse indicator
- Laser
- Optical
- Straightedge.

Any alignment, even a straightedge alignment, is better than no alignment at all.

14.3.7   Dynamic Balancing

Imbalance occurs when the center of mass of a rotating system does not coincide with the center of rotation. Excessive mass on one side of the rotor results in an imbalance. The centrifugal force that acts on the heavy side exceeds the centrifugal force exerted by the unequal forces. The magnitude of the rotating-speed vibration due to imbalance is directly proportional to the amount of imbalance. Imbalance can be caused by a number of things, including incorrect assembly, material buildup, or rotor sag.

An unbalanced rotor causes elevated vibrational levels and increased stress in the rotating element. Elevated vibrational levels in the rotor of an assembly affect the entire machine and cause excessive wear on the supporting structure, bearings, bushings, shafts, and gears.

An unbalanced condition can be in a single plane (static imbalance) or multiple planes (coupled imbalance). The combination is called dynamic imbalance and results in a vector that rotates with the shaft and produces a once per revolution vibrational signature. Dynamically balancing a unit:

- Extends the life of the bearings, bushings, shafts, and gears
- Reduces vibration to an acceptable level that will not accelerate equipment deterioration
- Reduces stress that causes equipment fatigue
- Minimizes audible noise, operator fatigue, and dissatisfaction
- Reduces energy losses.

Identifying Imbalance

Imbalance needs to be distinguished from other sources of vibration before beginning any balancing procedure. A vibrational peak at or near the rotating speed of the rotor can have several causes, such as misalignment, a bent or cracked shaft, eccentricity, open rotor bars, or imbalance. Verify the presence of imbalance before proceeding with a balancing procedure. Analytical techniques—such as spectrum waveform or phase analysis—can isolate imbalance as the cause of vibration. Imbalance is characterized by:

- Dominant vibrational magnitude at the rotating speed of the rotor
- Highest vibration in the radial and vertical planes and lower vibrational levels in the axial plane
- An amplitude and phase angle of vibration that is repeatable and steady
- Radial versus vertical-phase-angle vibrational measurements

14.4 OPERATION

Ferguson (2000) describes the following unique operational characteristics for systems and equipment in hospitals and clinics.

14.4.1 Continuity of Services

Hospitals never close. They operate 24 hours per day, 7 days per week. Facilities must be designed to allow for maintenance shutdowns and adding new features to systems. Two words can easily sum up an appropriate design philosophy: isolation and redundancy.

The procedures that are performed in outpatient facilities and clinics are becoming increasingly more complex. Although classified as a business occupancy rather than a hospital, a facility manager should look carefully at the requirements for each function within this type of building. Many house hospital-grade systems simply operate less than 24 hours a day.

14.4.2 Need for Collaboration

Close collaboration and teamwork are required between the maintenance department and other entities of the hospital. These entities include the infection control department, respiratory therapy, biomedical engineering, police and security, and/or environmental services.

For example, the maintenance department collaborates with others to ensure that building systems operate properly to reduce infection. Improper use of a negative pressure isolation room may allow infectious agents from the room to enter a corridor and infect hospital workers, other patients, or visitors. Improper hot water temperature may allow microbial growth. Improper filter application or maintenance may create infection control problems.

14.5 COMPLYING WITH JOINT COMMISSION REQUIREMENTS

The maintenance department works closely with other departments and a facility's Safety Committee to obtain Joint Commission on Accreditation of Healthcare Organizations (JCAHO) compliance. The following are key areas of concern relative to such compliance.

14.5.1 Statement of Conditions (SOC)

The JCAHO requires that all health care facilities keep up-to-date information on the condition of the facility. This document is called the Statement of Conditions (SOC). It lists all corrective measures in a Plan for Correction (PFC). The SOC is a living document. It should be continuously updated as a facility is changed, renovated, and improved. The maintenance department plays a central role in preparing the SOC document and carrying out the PFC.

14.5.2 Hospital Disaster Preparedness

State licensure usually requires a health care facility to have a disaster plan in addition to a JCAHO mandate. The maintenance department plays an important role in formulating and implementing such a plan. This is another example of the close collaboration required between the maintenance department and other departments. A health care facility's Disaster Planning Committee usually includes representatives from the following:

- Medical staff (ER physician or trauma surgeon)
- Administration (includes risk manager)
- OR nursing staff manager
- Emergency department
- Security/Communications
- Public relations
- Medical records and Admissions
- Laboratory
- Radiology
- Respiratory therapy.

14.5.3 Interim Life Safety

Creating a safe building environment is the goal of life safety codes and standards that cover egress, stairs, fire detection devices, and general occupancy. As long as the building design remains unchanged, the design integrity of life safety systems remains. However, health care facilities are always changing. As buildings undergo renovation and construction (both planned and unplanned), the integrity of life safety systems may diminish. This potential for a decrease in life safety results in the creation of interim life safety measures.

Interim life safety is generally overlooked during the design of renovations and is often not dealt with until construction actually begins. It is never too late to make necessary adjustments to the design and construction process. Otherwise, patients and visitors may be exposed to grave dangers. The maintenance department may be called upon to support additional fire and evacuation drills and exercise control over cutting, soldering, and the use of flame in the construction process. Some maintenance departments issue an internal flame permit to outside contractors and secure fire alarm zones as required to allow construction in existing buildings. After construction is complete, the fire alarm system is returned to its normal operating condition.

14.5.4 Utilities Management

Utilities management has become a complex function in today's health care facility. Quality improvements, along with trending occurrences in utility systems and equipment, will help the facility manager reduce maintenance service calls due to recurring problems. The facilities manager of record needs to be aware of confined-space issues as they pertain to maintainability, safety, and code requirements (i.e., OSHA).

14.5.5 Self-Assessment and Resolution of Indoor Air Quality Problems

Indoor air quality (IAQ) problems originate from many different sources within facilities. These sources may involve building systems, processes and procedures, management practices, employees, and outside influences. Maintenance departments usually get the first call regarding these problems, and they need to follow a systematic investigative process.

14.5.6 Prevention of Legionnaire's Disease

Health care facilities can be prone to *Legionella* outbreaks. Maintenance departments are the first line of defense against this problem. Butkus et al. (1999), ASHE (1993, 1994), and ASHRAE (2000b) provide an excellent discussion of this problem and potential solutions. *Legionellae* are bacteria. The name of the disease is derived from a well-known 1976 outbreak at an American Legion convention in Philadelphia attributed to a cooling tower. *Legionellae* occur in natural water sources and municipal water systems in low or undetectable concentrations. Under certain conditions, however, the concentration may increase

dramatically, a process called "amplification." Conditions favorable for amplification include:

- Water temperature of 77-108°F (25-42°C)
- Stagnation
- Scale and sediment
- Biofilms
- Presence of amoebae
- Certain materials—natural rubber, wood, some plastics.

Transmission to humans occurs when water that contains the organism is aerosolized in respirable droplets (1-5 microns) and inhaled by a susceptible host. Infections initially occur in the upper or lower respiratory tract. The risk is greater for older people, those who smoke, those who have chronic lung disease, and those who are immunosuppressed. Promising technologies for *Legionella* abatement or control include treatment with chlorine dioxide, chloramines, or silver-copper ion injection in the domestic water supply.

It has long been known that cooling towers are a potential cause of Legionellosis. The key recommendations for minimizing the risk from cooling towers involve clean surfaces and a biocide program. Professional help with chemical treatment is recommended. Mechanical filtration should be considered to minimize fouling. Drift eliminators should be regularly inspected, cleaned, and repaired as needed. It is sound practice to alternate biocides used for cooling water treatment to avoid developing resistant strains of microbes. Weekly changes in dose and frequency are recommended.

Shutting down and starting a cooling tower system requires specific attention. When a system is shut down for more than three days, draining the entire system to waste is recommended. When not practical to do so, stagnant water must be pretreated with a biocide regimen before tower start-up. Circulation of water for up to six hours is suggested for both drained and undrained system shutdowns after adding biocide and before tower fans are operated.

14.5.7 Pressure Monitoring Systems for Isolation Rooms

NIOSH recommends a smoke-tube verification of directional airflow as a qualitative "calibration" check of differential pressure. If a pressure monitoring system is installed, it is recommended that quantitative calibration be performed at some interval to ensure that the system is accurately monitoring pressure.

14.5.8 First Response

Coordination in preparing for unexpected shutdowns and system failures is essential. Careful planning for those who will be available and addressing how they will communicate with health care givers is essential. The management decision chain must be clearly defined, and contingencies must be built in for personnel absences.

14.6 CONSTRUCTION

Ferguson (2000) provides an excellent review of construction issues. Many maintenance departments provide in-house construction services for renovation or new construction projects. If well managed, they can usually provide construction at a lower cost than outside contractors. They also have an advantage in conducting shutdowns and if needed can move from location to location in a short time. Construction and maintenance functions must be clearly defined and separated. There is always a danger that too much construction can divert departmental resources from maintenance functions.

Infection risk assessment by a health care facility's infection control group should be an integral part of the construction process. Always include the infection control group in plan review meetings and construction prebid meetings. See Appendix A for additional information.

Assigning an owner's representative to all construction projects is highly recommended. In most instances, this is the key individual to determine whether the owner's money is well spent and how well the design/construction team is performing. This individual must know construction by the various trades, must understand the contract being administered, and be flexible enough to work out inevitable coordination issues between the contractor and owner. Shutdowns, night work, and windows of opportunity for noisy activities (such as cutting and hammering) are coordinated through this individual, who may also be responsible for welding and other hot-work permits.

A small team from the maintenance department working with the owner's representative can identify performance and maintenance concerns before ceilings and walls are closed in. An on-site inspection by the maintenance group is highly recommended. This inspection should be controlled and scheduled by the owner's representative or the maintenance office.

14.6.1 Construction Plan Review

Maintenance departments are usually asked to (and should) become involved in reviewing new construction and renovation projects. The following checklist can be helpful during this process.

General Mechanical and Electrical Equipment Rooms

Ideally, mechanical rooms for major equipment such as air-handling equipment and chillers should be directly accessible from the outside of the building for ease of replacement. This feature may not, however, be practical. At a minimum, mechanical room locations should minimize the intrusion of maintenance personnel into the medical floors. If possible, direct vehicle transport for maintenance items and equipment would be desirable. Direct elevator access to mechanical spaces in upper floors is most helpful.

Roof-Mounted Equipment

Roof-mounted equipment in general should be avoided for critical applications because access is usually difficult and working conditions are not safe for maintenance personnel. However, roof-mounted HVAC equipment is a very cost- effective option for clinics. Also, exhaust fans, cooling towers, and other heat rejection equipment must often be on the roof. Whenever roof-mounted equipment is used, providing pavers or other personnel access pathways that will not damage the roof is highly recommended. A fixed ladder and/or catwalk should be considered for any equipment that requires maintenance access (including valves) and is not readily accessible from a 6-ft-high portable ladder. Hose bibbs and electrical service receptacles should be included near the equipment.

Mechanical Room Layout

Mechanical room layout should include sufficient space for access to equipment for operation, maintenance, and replacement, including permanent catwalks or ladders for access to equipment that cannot be reached from the floor. Verify that practical means are provided for removing/replacing the largest and/or heaviest equipment item(s) located in the facility and that pull space is provided for all coils, heat exchangers, chillers, boiler tubes, and filters.

Chillers and Boilers

Provisions should be made for moving these units in and out of the building. For large chillers, consider installing a beam attached to the structure to move or replace large compressors or motors.

General Personnel Access

Safe and practical means of personnel access should be provided. A minimum of 2 ft (0.6 m) of clearance is generally required at all service points to mechanical equipment to allow personnel access and working space. Greater space may be required for particular equipment and maintenance applications. During plan review, serviceability requirements for equipment for mechanical equipment rooms, corridors, occupied spaces, behind walls, above ceiling, and/or buried in the ground should be verified.

Separate Energy Plants

When chilled water, heating water, or steam generators are located in a separate energy plant exterior to the primary facility, installing the connecting utility lines in a tunnel or other accessible enclosure to provide maintenance and inspection access and protection from the elements is highly desirable. Accessibility to the entire utility main runs is desirable to facilitate inspection and repairs of insulation, fittings, thermal expansion compensation, air vents, etc., as well as to facilitate future replacement or expansion. Safe and convenient accessibility is essential for those elements that require periodic inspection or service, including isolation valves, condensate drainage traps (both manual and automatic), sump pumps, and ventilation fans.

Cooling Towers

Cooling tower location and placement should be reviewed. The spray or plume could be a source of *Legionella*. Determine the distance to the nearest air handler intakes. Do not accept the "prevailing wind" excuse if it is too close; have it relocated. Stainless steel pans are recommended for their long service life and help in restricting microbial growth. Review with the designers the service options for motor removal. Look at different options for basin heating, including controls for the heaters. Be careful that they are not running year-round. Refer to Chapter 7 for additional information.

Chemical Treatment

Chemical treatment is an integral part of ensuring that the piping systems in the physical plant are in good internal condition. Dirty pipes cost energy and can lead to lower system efficiencies and discomfort for occupants. Improper water treatment on the condenser-water side can lead to excessive bleed-off and wasted water. Too much boiler blowdown

also wastes water, so a treatment program for boilers is needed as well.

Test coupons placed at strategic locations should be retrieved and checked on a routine basis. Chemical shot feeders should be located in an area that is easily accessed and can be washed down. Air-handling unit drain pans should be treated regularly with biocide tablets. The product drums typically weight 60 lb (28 kilograms), so a means for moving and lifting them is needed.

Cooling Coils

Coil thickness should not exceed six rows to facilitate cleaning. Coils finer than 14 fins per inch are increasingly more difficult to clean with industrial coil cleaning compounds. These cleaners are typically applied on the upstream side of the coil and allowed to penetrate into the rows of the coil. Once the cleaner has done its job by softening scale and removing biological growth, a high-pressure washer is used for final cleanup. When more than six rows are required to effect dehumidification, the coil could be separated into two 4- or 6-row units with access provided to both upstream and downstream coil faces. Typically, a 24-in. (610 mm) space between coils is adequate.

Stainless Steel Drain Pans

Stainless steel drain pans should be provided to optimize cleaning and reduce microbial growth. To ensure pan drainage, facilities managers should review the dimensions of the traps to verify that they compensate for the effects of fan static pressure.

Freeze Protection Features

Freeze protection is a very important feature. Freezestats are designed to protect air-handling equipment and coils from freezing. If this system is not designed and installed correctly, the air-handling equipment would frequently trip off and shut down. This nuisance tripping causes a loss of airflow pressure control and can also be a safety hazard. Many maintenance personnel attempt to compensate for this situation by increasing the supply air temperature. The resulting high temperature causes difficulty in providing cooling.

Balancing Features

To facilitate future troubleshooting or system balancing, check for measurement devices and balancing dampers in all HVAC equipment. This may include temperature and pressure measurement ports or devices on inlet and outlet connections to all coils, as well as balancing valves, flow measurement apparatus, and temperature-measuring ports or devices at various locations in the air-handling unit. Pressure ports or gauges upstream and downstream of the fan and ports for pitot traverse and airflow should also be provided. To facilitate periodic rebalancing or future modification, manual balancing dampers should be provided on all branch duct runouts, located as far upstream from the terminal fixture (diffuser, register) as practicable to reduce air-generated noise.

Central Station Air-Handling Units

To reduce the possibility of microbial growth in unit insulation, air-handling units used in medical facilities should be the internally insulated, double-wall type with a corrosion-resistant inner wall. Perforated inner wall surfaces are not generally recommended. When final filtration is provided in an air-handling unit that is downstream from cooling coils, provision must be made to avoid wetting the filters. Carefully evaluate a draw-through versus a blow-through design.

Ductwork Design Considerations

Access panels for inspection or servicing of duct-mounted equipment (including fire dampers, smoke dampers, and controls) and to facilitate periodic cleaning or disinfecting must be properly sized and installed in accessible locations. Turning vanes should not be installed in return and exhaust ductwork. Refer to Chapter 9 for additional information.

Smoke Dampers and Smoke Control Systems

Even though this issue may be part of commissioning, it is important to restate that an initial acceptance testing must be performed to ensure that a smoke control system operates as intended. The first part of the testing includes the functional aspects of the system, which involve two areas. First, the passive fire protection systems (completeness and integrity of fire-rated assemblies, firestopping, fire doors, etc.) must be evaluated. Then, the following subsystems must be tested to the extent that they affect the operation of the smoke control system:

- Fire protective signaling system
- Building management system
- HVAC equipment
- Electrical equipment
- Temperature control system
- Power sources
- Standby power
- Automatic suppression systems
- Automatically operating doors and closures
- Emergency elevator operation

The second part of the acceptance testing is performance oriented. This portion of the testing determines whether the entire system performs under all required modes of operation.

Note that the model codes (including building, mechanical, and fire prevention codes) contain requirements for testing, inspecting, and maintaining smoke control systems. In addition, ANSI/NFPA 92A and 92B contain guidelines for testing.

After the installation is approved, the contractor should supply a certificate indicating that the smoke control system was installed in compliance with the code and that all of the acceptance tests were performed. ANSI/NFPA 92A requires that a copy of all operational testing documentation be provided to the owner.

Periodic testing and maintenance is essential to ensure that a smoke control system works as intended in a fire scenario. Components, including initiating devices, fans, dampers, controls, and doors, must be tested on a scheduled basis. ANSI/NFPA 92A recommends testing dedicated systems semiannually and nondedicated systems annually. The following standards prescribe the requirements for these systems.

- ANSI/NFPA 92A. 2000. *Recommended Practice for Smoke-Control Systems.* National Fire Protection Association, Quincy, MA.
- ANSI/NFPA 92B. 2000. *Guide for Smoke Management Systems in Malls, Atria, and Large Areas.* National Fire Protection Association, Quincy, MA.

Fire Dampers/Smoke Dampers

The NFPA requires damper maintenance and inspection every five years. JCAHO inspectors look at proper fire damper installation, performance, and maintenance records. They require testing a portion of the dampers for proper operation. This operation requires replacing the fusible link. Once the link has been removed, the spring-loaded damper should drop immediately. Moving the damper back into position is difficult and typically requires two people. Therefore, access panels should be installed on each side of a fire damper. Usually, one person gets on each side of the damper, and together they push the damper back into place using a wood stud or similar lever; then the fusible link is reinstalled. This is a complicated, labor-intensive task.

Attempt to minimize the number of fire and smoke dampers through the design process. Indicate and provide access on both sides of the dampers whenever possible. "Breakaway" connections at duct risers are generally overlooked for access. Adequate access doors must be provided for utility shafts.

Duct Cleaning When Existing Ducts Are Used

Before embarking on a duct-cleaning project, carefully investigate the cost and benefit versus risk. Consult a hygienist and send samples of the offending material to the lab for analysis. Cleaning ductwork may give mixed results. Lined ductwork typically should be replaced rather than cleaned, when possible. The cleaning process strips away the insulating inner liner. Externally insulating an existing duct is labor-intensive and in some cases impossible without removing all surrounding utilities.

Pumps

There are several configurations for pumps: end suction, vertical split case, vertical inline, etc. Space constraints, cost, mechanical room layout, and efficiency all dictate pump configuration. Provide pressure taps and trumpet valves so that maintenance personnel can check pump performance. Specify training for maintenance personnel for each pump type. If very large motors (more than 15 hp [11 kW]) and pumps are installed, provide a beam or rail system for removing these heavy items over or out of a crowded mechanical room.

Fire Protection Systems

The trend of oversizing these systems has resulted in large and expensive overpressure relief piping. Examine the submittals carefully, and be certain that street pressure has been properly accounted for in the calculations. A bypass line with a flow meter is a good option and saves tremendous amounts of water because hospital systems must be checked weekly.

Emergency Generators

The facility manager must determine if cogeneration, load-sharing programs, or leak shaving will be part of the emergency power system.

Generator placement is extremely important but is generally dictated by architectural issues rather than performance or ventilation concerns. Diesel engine discharge at ground level is nearly always an odor problem. Take generator exhaust to the roof whenever possible. Cooling louvers should be located in an area that provides the free area recommended by the manufacturer. Be very cautious about

generator specifications. It is common for specifications to name NFPA 70, *National Electrical Code*, as part of the generator specification, but NFPA 110, *Standard for Emergency and Standby Power Systems*, is referred to by NFPA 70 and has some very specific requirements for emergency generator construction and operation (NFPA 2002a, 2003). Review these documents carefully, and adjust the specifications if needed.

Emergency Recovery Plan

Determine whether the health care facility can run its entire operation on emergency power. It is also not uncommon to find that there is simply not enough fuel storage to run the building(s) for an extended period. The facility manager should carefully review the facility's requirements and codes for required run times.

Outside Air Intakes

Improper location of outside air louvers near a contamination source can cause IAQ problems. Do not allow the architect to place fresh air louvers near a loading dock. Similarly, do not allow the architect to put the diesel generator near fresh air louvers. Diesel exhaust is detectable by humans in concentrations as low as 6 parts per billion! Medical vacuum pumps discharge many unknowns. Finding a safe location for vacuum pump discharge is typically overlooked.

Domestic Water Pumps

The use of variable speed drives for domestic water pumps must be carefully evaluated; otherwise the system may not respond properly to rapid changes in building water demand.

Water Heaters

Quality units are stainless steel or glass-lined and thermally efficient. Inspection ports must be accessible. Temperature and pressure gauges should be provided on the outlet and inlet of each unit. Water flows must be properly balanced. Venting is a major concern for gas-fired units. Gas-fired units may not share space with refrigeration equipment.

Redundancy

In a hospital, 100% redundancy is often advised. Multiple electrical services and HVAC systems are recommended. At the same time, space for future growth is recommended because growth is inevitable. An example whereby redundancy in mechanical systems can be achieved is in the use of looping piping systems. Two paths of distribution within the plant allow more options in case of emergency. Looping can be used effectively for gases and liquids. Examine your requirements carefully, and look at costs as well.

Valves

There are never enough valves. Let us qualify that statement by saying that valves are seldom in the right locations to isolate equipment properly for maintenance. Valves are inexpensive by comparison to the alternative. An emergency stop valve (or emergency line plug) is typically 100 times more expensive than a valve in the same location. It is typical to provide a valve between each piece of equipment on a loop or header but almost never on the header.

Filter Replacement

Filtration requirements for medical facilities are not a new concept. The original requirements were published in 1947 under the Hill–Burton Act. In the 50 or more years since then, the requirements have been modified to current technologies for filtration and microbial contamination control.

Guidelines for the Design and Construction of Hospitals and Health Care Facilities (AIA 2001) publishes requirements for minimum levels of air filtration efficiency (AIA 2001). The requirements also define filtration by area and note additional items such as required air changes per hour, recommended temperatures, recommended relative humidity, and room pressure relative to the rest of the facility.

Medical facility HVAC systems are unusual in that two filter beds are recommended, one upstream of the coil and a final filter bank downstream of the coil. Standard HVAC systems place both stages upstream of the coil.

In orthopedic, bone marrow transplant, and organ transplant suites and recovery rooms, an additional stage of HEPA filtration is recommended at the air outlets. HEPA filters are also recommended for TB isolation rooms where recirculation is employed to maintain the high air change requirements or where 100% exhaust to the outside is not possible. See Chapter 9 for additional information on the subject.

Rigid filters are preferred in hospitals. Bag filters collapse during normal maintenance of the air handler. When bag filters collapse, particles of dust on the outer surface of the filter media are released into the airstream. Rigid filters by their nature do not have this problem.

Typically, charcoal filters are used for odor control of external sources such as diesel exhaust. Acti-vated charcoal may also be used for odor control in air supply systems where required within medical care facilities.

Efficiencies are listed by dust spot efficiency as rated under ASHRAE Standard 52.1-1992. As ASHRAE Standard 52.2 (which deals with testing filters based on particle size versus efficiency) becomes the common methodology, the filters for typical applications will have minimum efficiency rating values (MERVs) of MERV 7 before the coil and MERV 14 as the final or secondary filter.

Additionally, AIA Guidelines recommend air intake locations and air outlet requirements. Outdoor intakes should be located as far as possible above the ground—at a minimum level of 6 ft (1.8 m). Roof level intakes should be located at least 3 ft (0.9 m) above the roof. Outdoor intakes must also be at least 25 ft (7.6 m) from any exhausts or combustion equipment (venting). Room air supplies should be located at or near ceiling height.

Maintenance Considerations

Air handlers: The frequency of changing air handler filters is a function of the filter replacement costs, air handler fan curve, local electrical costs, labor costs, and the terminal static pressure of the filter in use. As static pressure increases, the costs of running the units fans also increase. The costs must be measured against the labor and material costs of replacing filters. The optimum loading for a particular filter type is available from filter manufacturers.

HEPA: Bag-in/bag-out filter housings and filters should be changed by mechanics who are trained and certified in infection control and bag-in/bag-out techniques for the housing and seals in use.

The maintenance manager should be made aware of odd size filters during the construction process. This item can be covered in the contract filter specifications in the general mechanical conditions but is often missed for smaller pieces of equipment. Filter selection may also be influenced by direct conversation with the mechanical contractors who bid on the project.

14.6.2 Construction Project Acceptance

Fast-track construction seems to be the norm, rather than the exception, in today's construction market. Maintenance departments are more often being asked to accept a project that has not been completed before users begin to move in.

So-called beneficial occupancy is becoming prevalent. Beneficial occupancy tends to muddy the contract waters by introducing confusion over the dates on which an owner actually takes possession of the building, when owner-conducted maintenance begins, and when the warranty periods provided by contractors end. When a decision for early occupancy is made, the owner must review the consequences of the contractual arrangements with the contractor, with input from the design team.

Multi-phase projects are particularly difficult to close out. A contract must spell out clearly what is to be provided at the end of each phase. Phased projects can go on for years, so it is necessary that as-built drawings, operating and maintenance manuals, and spare materials for each phase be delivered to the owner as each phase is completed.

Finally, retaining a firm to commission a building will improve owner representation, field inspection for each trade, suggested design guidance, maintainability, proof of proper operation, and field inspection of materials and equipment bought for the project. See Chapter 15, "Commissioning," for more detailed information.

14.7 SPECIAL MAINTENANCE CONSIDERATIONS FOR HVAC SYSTEMS /EQUIPMENT

Ferguson (2000) provides the following descriptions of special maintenance considerations for health care equipment and systems.

Fan-Coil Units

Each fan-coil unit with a cooling coil has a drain pan that could become a reservoir for microbial growth. Periodic inspection of the condensate pan is necessary to avoid stoppages that may cause overflows and wet surrounding materials, thereby creating additional sites for microbial amplification. Because these units are typically located within the spaces served, maintenance personnel will need access to occupied areas.

Fin-Tube Radiation and Convection Units

These units also require frequent cleaning to minimize the collection of dirt and debris. This equipment also requires frequent access for maintenance personnel to occupied spaces.

Fan-Powered Terminal Units

Fan-powered terminal units require inspection and maintenance. Frequent access to filters is required. These units have a fan motor and fan that may need to be replaced. Separate ventilation air and primary air supplies may be provided and should be periodically checked.

Secondary Air Systems

An example of this type of system is a laminar flow system in an Orthopedic Operating Room or a HEPA-filtered recirculating unit for a Bone Marrow Transplant Unit. These may be provided with filters that need to be replaced, as well as a motor that may require periodic service or replacement.

14.8 BUILDING COMMISSIONING

Commissioning is a quality-focused process for achieving, validating, and documenting that a facility and its systems are planned, designed, installed, tested, and capable of being operated and maintained to perform in conformity with the design intent. The commissioning process extends through all phases of a new or renovation project, from conceptualization to occupancy and operation, and has checks at each stage of the process to ensure validation of performance to meet the owner's design requirements.

These are the fundamental objectives of the commissioning process:

- To verify and provide documentation that the performance of the facility and its systems meets the owner's requirements
- To enhance communication by documenting information and decisions throughout all phases of the project
- To validate and report that building system performance meets the design intent

The active and ongoing participation of maintenance and operations personnel in the commissioning process is critical to its success. For an expanded discussion of commissioning, see Chapter 15.

14.9 CAPITAL INVESTMENT PLANNING

Ferguson (2000) notes that maintenance departments generally are responsible for budgeting for a facility's infrastructural upgrade. Careful attention must be paid to assessing a facility's need for future growth as presented in a capital budget. Maintenance departments should also request funding for repairing and/or replacing mechanical and electrical items that must be replaced regularly.

Understand the medical community's needs when upgrading systems or equipment. For example, replacing a Bone Marrow Unit would require bringing the current unit down, relocating patients to another area, and returning them. These types of secondary costs are often overlooked, but they must be included during budgeting.

CHAPTER 15
COMMISSIONING

15.1 INTRODUCTION

Commissioning is a quality assurance, quality control process that provides the essential documentation, testing, and training to ensure that a system meets both its design intent and operational needs. Commissioning practices may be implemented to various degrees for a particular project depending upon its specific needs and requirements.

Commissioning practices have proven beneficial because of the increasing overall complexity of mechanical and electrical systems and the "fast track" mode of much construction. Commissioning adds tangible value by implementing a quality review process throughout a project, along with detailed documentation, testing, and systematic training.

Commissioning has been defined as a systematic process that begins in the predesign phase and continues until at least a year after construction is completed. Properly executed, the process includes preparing the facility's staff to operate systems and ensuring (through documented verification) that all building systems perform individually and interactively according to documented design intent and the owner's operational needs. Commissioning is most valuable when system performance is evaluated under a full range of load and climatic conditions. Assessing system performance under part-load or extreme conditions is often the best way to discover problems in buildings and correct them before occupancy.

Commissioning is a team effort. The participants include the owner, design professionals, the contractor, and a commissioning team leader or specialist. The objective of the commissioning team is to guide the process of quality control and quality assurance. This is accomplished by implementing elements of the major components of commissioning described below.

This chapter presents a framework for the commissioning process and outlines general requirements that can be adapted to health care facilities. *ASHRAE Guideline 1* (ASHRAE 1996) is the most widely cited document on commissioning. Many commissioning projects involve building systems beyond heating, ventilating, and air-conditioning. In this manner, a well-conceived commissioning program can serve as an overall quality assurance measure to integrate complex building systems. Such additional building systems could include the building envelope, electrical systems, power and communications systems, transport systems, fire and life safety systems, water systems, areas requiring specialized control, and building management systems.

15.2 COMMISSIONING AUTHORITY

The commissioning authority (CA) is the person (or entity) who leads the commissioning process. The CA assembles the commissioning team, coordinates all commissioning activities, writes the commissioning plan, and develops the commissioning specifications. The commissioning authority must develop the commissioning schedule, make it a part of the overall construction schedule, and develop agendas for and conduct monthly or weekly commissioning meetings.

The CA must be an excellent communicator—both orally and in writing. The individual must understand the systems and facilities that are to be commissioned but will typically not be in a position to know everything about a facility. This is the reason that commissioning of complex facilities requires a team—so that someone on the team knows and understands all the building systems.

Because commissioning does not clearly come under the purview of any single design discipline, a commissioning authority with broad experience with building systems is recommended as the responsible party to guide the commissioning process. An independent commissioning authority who reports directly to the building owner is essential to effective commissioning.

15.2.1 The Owner as Commissioning Authority

Owners are often the most obvious choice to act as commissioning authority because they have a vested interest in ensuring that work is held to the highest quality standards. By using in-house staff as commissioning authority, the owner can take control of the commissioning process to ensure that the contractor delivers the building properly. Disadvantages of this approach are that permanent staff must be assigned to deal with ongoing projects (which may result in delays in other areas of the project) and/or in-house staff may lack the appropriate expertise to serve effectively as a CA.

15.2.2 An Outside Expert

The owner can still act as commissioning authority by hiring an outside expert to serve in the role of the CA. The expert would report directly to the owner on the contractor's performance and provide effective monitoring of the commissioning progress. This requires giving the outside consultant appropriate authority to coordinate outside subcontractors to undertake many of the required commissioning activities. For an effective program, the line of authority from the owner to the commissioning authority must be clearly defined.

15.2.3 The General Contractor

It is logical to hold the contractor accountable for quality control, which takes into account many of the activities required for effective commissioning of a building. Furthermore, it is the general contractor who is responsible for construction sequencing and who can effectively police the quality of workmanship on the job. The general contractor has a stake in the successful completion and timely delivery of the entire project. There is also direct financial benefit if the general contractor can reduce warranty and service calls. Of course, the major drawback is the possibility of a conflict of interest because the contractor would be responsible for replacing any items found deficient. To try to avoid such conflict of interest, the owner could retain the prerogative of approving the

general contractor's work through spot checks and quality assurance of the contractor's commissioning efforts. By doing this, however, the owner may generate animosity and ill will because exercising this authority will directly undermine the activities of the general contractor as the commissioning authority.

15.2.4 The Engineer of Record

The advantages of using the design engineer as the commissioning authority include that fact that the engineer has full knowledge of the system design and is intimately familiar with its sequence of operation. This could achieve significant economies of time. There is a potential conflict of interest, however, because design engineers may not acknowledge problems that are in fact design errors for which they are responsible. In addition, a major benefit of commissioning, that of outside peer review, is lost using this approach. Areas of design that could be deficient may not be captured because the engineer may not see them as deficient.

15.3 THE COMMISSIONING PROCESS

15.3.1 Phase 1: Predesign

The building/HVAC commissioning process begins by

- designating a commissioning authority (CA),
- establishing the parameters for design and acceptance,
- designating the responsibilities of the various parties,
- delineating the documentation requirements for the entire project.

The CA, the design team, and the owner review the building program and identify the information required for effective design and the criteria for system and building acceptance.

15.3.2 Phase II: Design

The commissioning authority is often thought of as a quality control element for the design team. As such, the CA is responsible for reviewing and documenting discrepancies between architectural/HVAC design and specifications and the owner's building system performance criteria. As the design review proceeds, the CA is also responsible for reviewing value-engineering proposals for conformance to codes, occupant needs, and general reasonableness and for providing an opinion regarding the resulting effects of such changes.

Early in the design phase, the CA is responsible for preparing and distributing a commissioning plan that identifies the responsibilities of each of the key members of the team and schedules commissioning activities and deliverables. This plan should be in sufficient detail so that the required submittals will designate parties and instrumentation that need to be present for each test. In addition, the master construction schedule should include the schedule of commissioning activities and link commissioning activities with other construction activities.

The commissioning authority must ensure that the design team takes explicit responsibility for documenting the following items:

Design Criteria and Underlying Assumptions

The design criteria should address all of the following environmental considerations:

Thermal conditions	Special loads
Humidity	Air quality design criteria
Occupancy (hours and levels of activity)	Pressurization and infiltration requirements
Lighting	Fire safety
Vibration	Energy efficiency
Total and outside air requirements	Maintainability
Code requirements and impact on design	

Functional Performance Test Specifications

These specifications are developed during the design phase and allow the design team to better anticipate the commissioning process requirements. These test specifications are required, at a minimum, to do the following.

- *Describe the equipment or systems to be tested.* The HVAC system description includes type, components, intended operation, capacity, temperature control, and sequences of operation.
- *Identify the functions to be tested.* Operation and performance data should address each seasonal mode, seasonal changeover, and part-load operational strategies, as well as the design setpoints of the control system(s) and the range of permissible adjustments. Other items to be considered include the life safety modes of operation and any applicable energy conservation procedures.
- *Define the conditions under which the test is to be performed.* It is important to consider all possible operating modes, for example, full and partial loads and the extremes of operating temperatures and pressures. The documentation

that is provided to support this is critical because it will clearly show the completeness of the engineer's design.

- *Specify acceptance criteria.* It is essential to present the acceptance criteria in clear, unambiguous terms. Where possible, the acceptance criteria should be quantitative, and the accuracy and precision required should be consistent with the limitations of the equipment and system design.

15.3.3 Phase III: Construction

During the construction phase, the commissioning authority is responsible for on-site inspection of materials, workmanship, and installation of building/HVAC systems and components (including verification of pressure tests of piping and duct systems). The CA should also observe and/or independently audit testing, adjusting, and balancing; fire stopping of walls; calibrating of system components; and pressure testing of specialty rooms.

Other activities that an effective commissioning authority performs during the construction phase include (1) reviewing warranty and retaining policies before the completion of construction, (2) reviewing copies of the contractor's approved equipment submittals, (3) ensuring that effective construction containment techniques are used, and (4) documenting and reporting discrepancies for the owner.

Finally, it is essential that personnel who will be responsible for operating the completed systems receive adequate training before system acceptance. This is best done during the construction phase. The commissioning authority should take responsibility to ensure that appropriate personnel (often equipment manufacturers, through the design engineer) provide this training for the numerous components of the HVAC system(s).

15.3.4 Training

The successful transition from construction to owner occupancy and use largely depends on complete and competent training. Often, operations and maintenance personnel are excluded from the project during the planning and construction phases. An effective commissioning program avoids this problem. The operations and maintenance (O&M) staff must be well versed in all aspects of operation and maintenance of building systems to maintain an appropriate level of serviceability and functionality.

The commissioning team interacts with O&M personnel throughout a project, culminating in a training program that offers key personnel the advantage of both classroom and "hands-on" training. The training program includes a system overview by the design professional supported by narratives, flow diagrams, one-line diagrams, and appropriate specifications sections. It is augmented by training from qualified instructors on individual systems and equipment, supported by operations and maintenance manuals, wiring diagrams, audiovisual equipment, and calibration and troubleshooting devices, in addition to actual "hands-on" demonstrations.

15.3.5   Phase IV: Acceptance

Acceptance should follow the commissioning plan established during the design phase. The functional performance test specifications form the basis for documenting the performance tests. The commissioning authority either conducts or observes the appropriate parties testing the functional performance of each system. This testing should start at the lowest reasonable level (system components), then move on to subsystems, then finally systems, until every piece of equipment has been tested. The CA must also ensure that all essential activities involve valid performance tests (e.g., hydrostatic testing, testing and air balancing [TAB] work, and calibration of automatic controls) and that the tests have been completed to a satisfactory conclusion before starting the acceptance verification procedures. It is critical to test in all modes of system operation, including full load and emergency conditions.

All required documentation should be compiled to form the basis of the system operating manual. Furthermore, as-built documents should be revised to ensure that accurate drawings are available, showing all relevant control points and values.

The commissioning authority will produce and distribute to appropriate parties a document detailing all discovered deficiencies in the form of an action list. After the required work has been completed, the CA will revisit the site and perform follow-up performance testing, where required, to verify that all action list items have been successfully resolved.

15.3.6   Phase V: Post-acceptance

The post-acceptance phase can best be thought of as an ongoing audit of the building's systems and the building's occupancies. Periodic retesting is often advisable, especially during the first year. This can be particularly important during extreme seasonal variations from the original commissioning conditions or during design extremes. The commissioning authority should document the building operator's adjusted setpoints to ensure that they are consistent with the original design. Where differences exist, the CA should evaluate the impact of such deviations and reconcile their effects in a written report.

15.3.7   Overview of the Process

Hospitals are one of the most difficult facility types encountered in commissioning work. Even though many of the tasks are the same as in the commissioning of office buildings or schools, they are more complex. In hospitals, there are pressurization issues, infection issues, immunocompromised patients, isolation room issues, specialty gases and equipment, along with energy concerns. For a commissioning project to be a true success, commissioning must start with the owner's desire to build the facility. Then, the owner must support the effort to the fullest extent.

The commissioning authority should be selected before (or not later than when) the design team is chosen and should work with the team and the owner in developing the owner's program and design intent. Both of these documents must become an integral part of the commissioning plan to be developed by the commissioning authority. The designer must also develop a basis of design, a document that details the reasons why certain systems and equipment have been selected.

Once the owner's program and intent, along with the basis of design, have been finalized, the commissioning authority develops commissioning specifications. These specifications outline the contractual responsibilities and duties of the commissioning authority, owner, and the contractors who will be responsible for systems to be commissioned (such as the mechanical, electrical, and fire protection systems). The mechanical contractor's contract should assign responsibility for the HVAC&R controls, medical gas, plumbing, sheet metal, piping, HVAC equipment, insulation, etc. The electrical contractor will be responsible for the generator, fire alarm, and all of the electrical wiring and electrical apparatus. The fire protection contractor will be responsible for the sprinkler system, hose reels, and all fire apparatus. All of these contractors should have a working contract with the general contractor or construction manager that defines commissioning responsibilities. It is imperative to spell out the working relationships between the responsible contractors, general contractor, and commissioning authority in the respective contracts between the parties.

Once contracts have been awarded, it is critical that the commissioning authority hold an initial commissioning meeting and review the responsibilities of the various contractors.

15.4 DOCUMENTATION

The overall success of a project may depend on how well and accurately decisions, criteria, and concepts are documented. From the basis of design to the functional testing protocols for mechanical and electrical systems, it is essential that all phases of a project include appropriate documentation. The commissioning team coordinates, reviews, communicates, and archives documentation to substantiate that system integrity is acceptable and meets the owner's requirements. Commissioning may include assistance with developing and quality review of any or all of the following:

- Basis of design documentation
- Design development documents
- Construction documents (plans and specifications)
- Meeting notes and project correspondence
- Shop drawings
- Product data submittals
- Installation procedures
- Construction practices
- Static testing procedures (duct, pipe, equipment)
- Cleaning procedures (systems)
- Functional performance testing procedures
- Training procedures
- Testing and balancing procedures and reports
- Operating and maintenance manuals.

15.4.1 Functional Performance Testing Protocols

Often components of a system are tested individually or are assumed to be "factory calibrated" and are not tested at all. When a system is turned over to the owner and operated under actual conditions, it frequently falls short of expectations. This is generally evidenced by negative feedback from building occupants or process users. By subjecting mechanical and electrical systems to functional performance testing, the commissioning team observes, evaluates, identifies deficiencies and recommends modifications, tunes, and documents systems and system equipment performance over a range of loads and functional levels.

A functional performance test protocol is a step-by-step procedure developed to advance building systems from a state of substantial completion to full dynamic operation. The details of functional testing of building systems vary from system to system and are subject to the type and intended use of the facility or process. The following systems are typically subjected to functional performance testing.

Mechanical	Electrical
HVAC air-handling systems	Substations
Specialty ventilation systems	
Exhaust systems	Distribution equipment
Energy recovery loop systems	Motor control centers
Chilled water systems	Grounding systems
Boiler systems	Automatic transfer switches
Pumping systems	Intercommunication systems
	Smoke/fire protection systems
Heating systems	Fire alarm systems
Domestic hot/cold water systems	Smoke management systems
Cooling tower systems	Delayed exiting systems
Waste and vent systems	Security systems
Medical gas systems	
Specialty gas systems	Closed-circuit television systems
Natural gas systems	Emergency generator systems
Fire protection systems	Uninterruptible power supply systems
Process cooling water systems	Process control systems
HVAC&R control systems	Nurse call systems
High-purity water systems	Isolated power systems
Specialty process systems	Lighting systems
Sterile processing systems	
Plumbing systems	Variable speed drives
Smoke/fire protection systems	Automatic doors

15.4.2 Commissioning Plan

A commissioning plan is a document that outlines the various commissioning activities and responsibilities in detail. The commissioning plan also includes the different forms that are to be used. There should be a prefunctional and functional performance testing form for each piece of equipment. The prefunctional form should have line items for installation, specifications, and start-up of the equipment The functional performance test form should identify how a particular piece of equipment is to operate individually and how it operates as part of a total system.

The HVAC&R control, fire alarm, and smoke control systems have to be verified, and their operation with the various other building systems has to be documented. The test form should outline in step-by-step detail how the systems are to function. The various stages and steps of testing and verification have to be identified.

The commissioning plan must identify the various parties to commissioning and the responsibilities of each. The parties should include the following, as a minimum:

- Owner
  — Facility Manager
  — Operations and Maintenance Personnel

- Authority Having Jurisdiction
  — Plan Reviewer
  — Inspector
  — Licensure Authority
- Architect
- Engineers
- General Contractor
- Mechanical Contractor
- Electrical Contractor
- Control Contractor
- Test and Balance Contractor

15.4.3 Owner

The owner is involved in commissioning documentation in one or more of the following roles:

- A single entity, a corporation, or a board
- The person who gives the A/E design and operational criteria for the facility
- A person whom the owner designates as a representative. That person can be the facility manager, chief engineer, building operator, or another party. This person should have authorization from the owner to make decisions for the owner up to a certain dollar value that must be documented. The owner's representative must attend commissioning meetings and construction progress meetings. The representative must report directly to the owner and advise the owner of the progress of the project. The representative may also be charged to review and approve monthly pay requests. The representative must also be responsible for meeting with the A/E and contractors as needed. The representative must become familiar with the contract documents so that binding decisions can be rendered.
- The owner must provide infectious control specifications on projects where applicable.

On a health care project, the facility users should attend the initial commissioning meeting and should be involved in the design review. When satisfied, they should sign off on the drawings and specifications to indicate that they accept or agree to the design of their particular area.

These are examples of user groups who should attend the initial commissioning meeting:

- Administration
  — Financial
  — Chief Operating Officer
  — Department Assistant Operating Officer
  — Chairman of Respective Department
     (or designee)
- Operating Rooms Supervisor
- Chief of Staff (for respective services)
- Chief of Medicine
- Pharmacy
- Food Service
- Housekeeping
- Laundry
- Maintenance
- Emergency Department
- Central Sterile Supply
- Laboratories
- Information Systems
- Biomedical (Clinical Engineering)
- Radiology
- Security
- Pediatrics

- Specialty area representatives
  — Orthopedic
  — Coronary Care
  — Isolation Personnel
  — Transplantation
  — Intensive Care
  — Americans with Disabilities Act (ADA)
  — Transportation (vertical and horizontal)

- Infectious Control
  — Risk Management
  — Patient Relationships
  — Public Relationships

All of these disciplines may not attend every meeting, but they should attend the design meeting to ensure that their needs are met. They may not attend all commissioning meetings, but they should be kept informed, and an invitation to attend the commissioning meetings must be extended. The users should be involved in all decisions relating to substitutions and to their departments, as deemed necessary.

Additional meetings may have to be scheduled to keep people continually involved and informed. Minutes of meetings should be taken and forwarded (with supporting documentation) to all parties who participated in the initial meetings, plus department heads and others who are considered important to the project.

15.4.4 Architect/Engineer (A/E)

The A/E is responsible (with the owner's input) for developing the design intent, the basis of design, and the contract documents. The design professionals must assign a representative from each discipline to make design decisions on their behalf. The representatives must attend construction progress meetings and commissioning meetings.

They architect and engineer(s) must also visit the site monthly and issue a report based upon their findings and observations. These reports should be filed with the owner and the commissioning authority (this must be spelled out in the contracts) within 72 hours of each visit to the site. The A/E must address a request for information (RFI) within 5 calendar days and a change order request (COR) within 10 calendar days (this must also be spelled out in the contract documents). These response requirements are critical for compliance with the construction schedule.

15.5 CONSTRUCTION PROCESS AND COMMISSIONING INTERFACE

15.5.1 Predesign Phase

This is the phase when the owner decides whether to build a facility or remodel an area of an existing facility. This is when the owner commences to think about the wants, needs, and requirements of the proposed facility. The owner also must start to think about the professional design team and issue a request for qualifications (RFQ). Once the owner has received the RFQs, a meeting is set up to determine a short list and, after this is accomplished, a short list is prepared. From the short list, interviews are established and the design team is selected. Once this is accomplished, the owner in conjunction with the design team develops the design.

Once the owner's program has been accepted, the A/E must develop design intent, a basis of design, and the design documents. The design intent must clearly state how systems are to operate. Design intent must be developed for operating rooms, the emergency department, patient rooms, food service, housekeeping, etc. Once the design intent has been developed and accepted, the design can commence.

15.5.2 Design Phase

During the design phase, the commissioning authority should review the contract documents at various stages (35%, 50%, 75%, and 100% completion). Comments on the design should be issued at the various review stages. The designer should furnish, at the next stage of review, highlighted documents for comparison and verification that previous comments have been incorporated into the current documents. During the design phase, the owner may want to engage a test and balance contractor to review the documents for system test and balancing capabilities.

During this phase, there is an opportunity to investigate the possibility of obtaining a guaranteed maximum price (GMP) from selected contractors. If this option is adopted, the commissioning authority should be involved.

During the design phase, a set of commissioning specifications must be developed and inserted into the contract documents. These specifications must convey to the contractors that commissioning will be conducted and must include the responsibilities of the owner, designer, general contractor, and subcontractors relative to commissioning activities.

15.5.3 Construction Phase

During the construction phase, the main objective is to build the building on time and within budget. During this phase, the various contractors must submit commissioning (test) plans that explain how they are going to commission their particular portions of the project. The subcontractors must have their vendors furnish delivery schedules for materials and equipment and include these schedules in the overall commissioning plan and project schedule. The submittal process should require that submittals go the commissioning authority and the A/E simultaneously so they can be reviewed for compliance with the commissioning objectives. Should the commissioning authority have substantive comments or comments of noncompliance, the submittals should be returned to the subcontractor for corrective action and resubmitted through the same process.

Once the submittals have been accepted, they can be returned to the various contractors and subcontractors so that equipment and materials can be ordered. Once the equipment and materials have been ordered, the subcontractors should prepare coordination drawings and submit them for approval. Coordination drawings must be developed and reviewed by the respective contractors, i.e., mechanical and electrical. These drawings should be overlaid to determine if there is interference among water pipes, ductwork, conduit, lights, equipment, etc. The commissioning authority and the A/E must approve these drawings. Once these drawings have been approved, they must be used to install the systems.

During the construction phase, the commissioning authority must attend project coordination meetings and be on the agenda. The CA must also conduct commissioning meetings. These are commonly held the day before the coordination meetings so that commissioning issues can be documented and recorded in the minutes of the coordination meetings, along with commissioning meeting minutes.

The commissioning authority must inspect and verify that equipment and systems are installed in accordance with the submittals, coordination drawings, and contract documents. Deficiencies must be brought to the attention of the respective contractors in written form and the contractors must answer within five calendar days with a resolution. If the deficiency cannot be corrected within the allotted time, the response should tell the commissioning authority when it will be corrected and should contain appropriate backup data.

During the construction phase, the commissioning authority must develop pre-functional and functional testing plans. In the pre-functional tests, equipment is to be started up and systems flushed and cleaned in accordance with the contract documents. The pre-functional test forms should be transmitted to the contractor for completion and sign-off. The commissioning authority initials and forwards the forms to the general contractor or construction manager for signature. When the pre-functional test forms are completed and signed, they are given back to the commissioning authority to verify that there are no outstanding issues. The commissioning authority signs off and accepts this portion of the process. Upon acceptance of the pre-functional tests, the respective contractor and general contractor (or construction manager), along with the commissioning authority, agree that the systems have been started up, ductwork has been cleaned, water pipes have been flushed, controls are functioning, and systems have been debugged. The pre-functional tests verify that equipment and systems are in satisfactory operational condition and are ready for functional testing.

The commissioning authority must maintain a presence on the construction site once equipment has been set in place and testing has started. The CA must also continually review the quality of the construction under the contract. Systems that have not been designed or contracted for cannot be commissioned.

15.5.4 Special Health Care Facility Considerations

Maintaining a clean worksite can be an issue on all projects but is especially critical on health care projects. The responsibility for maintaining the mechanical work in a relatively clean state belongs to the contractors. The designers and the commissioning authority—as well as the contractors—need to be cognizant of the effects of cleanliness on the completed systems.

Construction dust and debris and moisture in uncompleted systems are issues on all projects. In most cases, ducts and piping systems are normally left "open-ended" until the next phase of activity. As an example, a supply air system is being installed. The first activity would probably have the main ducts installed. A second "pass" would install the air terminal units, connect them to the main ducts, and then install low-velocity distribution ducts downstream of the terminal units. The final "pass" would be to install the air devices in the final locations and connect the devices to the low-velocity distribution ducts. Days, weeks, or months may have transpired between each of these phases. If the system was left "open-ended" at the completion of each day, shift, or activity phase, it can, and will, collect anything and everything from construction dirt and drywall dust to leaves, sandwich wrappers, and wind-blown rain.

This example can be applied to other components of the mechanical systems, such as the air-handling equipment, medical gas piping, etc. Storage of construction materials can also be a major concern. Air terminal units are normally shipped to a project on pallets and covered with plastic "shrink-wrap." This is an excellent method of protecting the equipment until installation. Once the plastic is removed to install the first air terminal, the remainder of the terminals on the pallet are then exposed to the same ambient conditions as open-ended duct and piping.

15.6 RETRO-COMMISSIONING

Retro-commissioning is a process that evaluates the means by which functional requirements in an existing (uncommissioned) facility are met. Functional evaluation is a subset of performance evaluation. Retro-commissioning is generally performed by a third-party commissioning authority to avoid conflicts of interest. A similar process in a previously commissioned facility is typically termed "re-commissioning" or "continuous commissioning."

Such performance evaluation (testing, metering/monitoring, and troubleshooting) of existing system operations is conducted to establish conformance with design intent, optimized energy utilization targets, and current operational requirements. It is an application of expertise, rather than an application of technology to reduce costs.

Typical retro-commissioning projects might include:

- Evaluation and adjustment of automation or control system parameters.
- Implementation of alternative operational strategies.
- Optimized equipment staging and sequencing.
- Identification of undetected equipment impairment and/or failure.
- Damper actuator optimization, economizer rehabilitation.
- Variable speed drive control adjustments.
- Reset and changeover strategies.
- Tailored equipment scheduling and sequencing.
- General automation "tweaks."

Retro-commissioning projects involve numerous benefits, such as:

- Low cost.
- Generally little or no capital expenditure required to implement savings opportunities.
- Recommendations can be carried out through control sequence modifications and/or conventional maintenance work in many instances.
- Rapid payback (payback on program cost is typically much less than one year).
- Efforts can typically be self-funded through the operational budget.
- Similar projects have demonstrated proven results.
- Annual operational cost savings of 3% to 7% are common, with early savings often higher.

Although retro-commissioning can be very attractive, there are several potential shortfalls:

- The primary difficulty with retro-commissioning efforts is maintenance of benefits ("savings persistence").
- Performance "slippage" is unavoidable in any dynamically operated facility—parts wear, activities change, schedules are modified.
- Performance slippage can often occur without affecting system functional behavior.

- Commissioning personnel are seldom available on an ongoing basis to adapt their recommendations and strategies to changing conditions.
- Operational staff is frequently not apprised of the underlying logic motivating strategies, making in-house detection and correction of performance slippage difficult.

Successful retro-commissioning projects require the following elements:

- Staff buy-in: It is imperative that operations staff understand the what, why, and how of retro-commissioning strategies. Without operations staff buy-in, any strategy predicated on new or counterintuitive operational practices will lapse.
- The commissioning authority must work closely and cooperatively with operations staff.

Data and information collection: The information required to monitor operational performance may not correspond with existing indicators of functional performance. Identify bellwether status indicators that are simple and direct for each major strategy.

- Status indicators should be "actionable" and unambiguous (not open to conflicting interpretation). Structure data to indicate operational quality and/or relative significance.
- Do not over-collect data or collect data that require follow-up operator evaluation and post-processing. This will eventually result in abandonment of monitoring efforts.

Simple indicative monitoring practices that are put to use surpass "sophisticated" practices that are not used.

- Operational tools: Integrate persistence-enhancing monitoring and diagnostic tools into the regular operational routine to ingrain monitoring processes.
- Attempt to utilize or augment existing practices where possible. Do not create "new work."
- Tools should automatically perform necessary data manipulation. Summarization of bellwether indicators should be embedded in the process and be conveniently generated for staff review.
- Tools should be simple to use and understand. Something that looks like a BAS front end (or an F-16 control panel) is too idiosyncratic for ongoing use by general operations personnel.
- Data validation routines should be used to screen for bad data and prevent false alarms.

Ongoing retention of the benefits of retro-com-missioning can be enhanced through the following actions:

- Staff must understand, be included in, and buy into the program agenda.
- Information that reflects system performance should be collected and reviewed on an ongoing basis. As needed, develop data relationships that signify performance "quality."
- Concise monitoring and evaluation tools should be available to, and understood by, staff.
- Data manipulation should be automated.
- Historic data should be available on demand.
- Data should be presented graphically for trend detection.
- Findings and results should be shared.

15.7 COSTS, OFFSETS, AND BENEFITS

There is currently no standard approach to cost-ing commissioning services. Some of the more com-mon methods are discussed below. No matter which budgeting approach is selected, contracts with the general and specialized contractors must clearly state that although the commissioning authority is initially paid by the owner, additional charges incurred by the CA will be paid by the contractors if systems fail or cause delays in the established commissioning or project schedules.

15.7.1 Budget a Percentage of the Total Mechanical/Electrical Cost of a Project

A range of 1.5% to 6.0% is generally considered reasonable. The higher percentages are generally used for those projects that are smaller in scope or those that are more complex, such as a health care facility.

15.7.2 A Separate Commissioning Budget Independent of the Project Budget

This approach is often useful when an owner has an ongoing construction program, such as that found in many health care facilities. Setting aside a com-missioning budget that represents between $0.10 and $0.28 per square foot ($1.10 and $3.00 per square meter) allows carrying out work on a number of projects during a year's time. Most owners use an operations budget, although some do capitalize this work.

15.7.3 Payment Schedule Based on Time Estimates

Use a payment schedule based on time estimates provided to the owner by the commissioning author-ity. In these types of projects, it is important that all parties agree in writing as to what constitutes a com-pleted commissioning plan, as well as an appropriate payment schedule.

15.7.4 Commissioning Offsets

McCarthy and Dykens (2000) provide a good discussion of the "commissioning offset," which can be summarized as follows.

Although commissioning is often seen as an added cost to a project, owners experienced with commissioning do not find an overall cost increase when constructing buildings. The commissioning costs discussed above compare favorably with other cost parameters normally associated with building construction. For example, 2–6% of M/E project cost compares favorably with the 9–18% range for change orders and claims generally encountered on capital projects.

In addition to the benefits cited earlier, experi-ence shows that an effective commissioning program can also

- reduce change orders and claims by 50% to 90%;
- provide energy savings in the first year of opera-tion that generally exceed the cost of commis-sioning;
- reduce overall system maintenance costs during the first year by an amount that is comparable to (and often exceeds) the cost of the commission-ing program.

15.7.5 Commissioning Benefits

Levin (1997) lists the benefits of commissioning reported by an extensive survey that included 146 case studies. The results are reproduced in Tables 15-1, 15-2, and 15-3. The data reported in these tables clearly indicate that commissioning programs pro-vide important economic and operational benefits to an owner.

Data do not exist to conclusively demonstrate improvements in worker productivity or reduced ill-ness rates due to commissioning activities, although such benefits are anecdotally reported. Many groups have extensively evaluated the impacts of commis-sioning on energy conservation or energy efficiency measures. Piette and Nordman (1996) studied the commissioning of energy conservation programs in 16 buildings in the Pacific Northwest and found that

Table 15-1. Benefits of Commissioning

Benefits of Commissioning	Percentage of Survey Respondents Reporting the Benefit
Energy savings[a]	82
Thermal comfort	46
Improved operation and maintenance	42
Indoor air quality	25
Improved occupant morale	8
Improved productivity	8
Reduced change orders	8
Timely project completion	7
Liability avoidance	6

Reprinted from PECI (1996).

a. More than 70% energy savings was documented by metering or monitoring.

Table 15-2. Thermal Comfort Benefits of Commissioning

Benefit	Percentage of Survey Respondents Reporting the Benefit
Improved thermal control	90
Reduced humidity control requirements	52
Improved air balances	30
Reduced occupant complaints	30

Reprinted from PECI (1996).

Table 15-3. Indoor Air Quality Benefits of Commissioning

Benefit	Percentage of Survey Respondents Reporting the Benefit
Improved ventilation	70
Better contaminant control	22
Improved carbon dioxide levels	19
Improved moisture control	11
Improved containment: clean rooms or laboratories	8

Reprinted from PECI (1996).

the investment in commissioning was cost-effective based on energy savings alone.

All participants—owners, design team, and contractors—can realize the benefits of commissioning the building systems on a project. Commissioning achieves a win-win-win situation for all team members.

The owner receives documentation and training resulting in increased knowledge of building systems, installations, and operations. Because of testing, upon occupancy the owner experiences fewer operational problems, less dependence on the contractor, and increased satisfaction with the project. Projects are more often completed on time and with an overall cost saving (when typically required first-year remedial actions are considered).

The design team becomes more familiar with owner requirements, system installation techniques,

and procedures. They are more involved in problem identification and resolution. Because of on-time project completion and cost savings, owner satisfaction with the design team is improved.

The contractor can identify problems early and meet the project schedule. There is less reactive repair at project completion and fewer callbacks. There is increased efficiency in system installation, start-up, operation, testing, and training, which results in cost savings.

The value of commissioning is most often cited with respect to new building construction projects. Part of HVAC commissioning involves formally documenting performance objectives. Basing acceptance upon these performance objectives, from construction through to system operation, results in a better functioning building. These procedures can be equally valuable in renovation projects and energy conservation programs. Many times, the start-up, control, and operational problems that occur due to "minor" changes in local areas can compromise the performance or efficiency of entire buildings. Furthermore, when one considers the impact that deficiently operating HVAC systems can have on indoor air quality and health, the benefit of incorporating proper building commissioning activities in all HVAC-related projects is obvious.

Specific benefits that can be realized from a successful commissioning program include:

- Higher quality building systems and the knowledge that a facility operates consistently with the owner's design intent and meets occupant needs.
- Identification of system faults and discrepancies early in the construction process so that they can be resolved in a timely manner while appropriate contractors are still on the job. This will reduce the number of contractor callbacks.
- Improved documentation, training, and education for operators and facility managers to ensure longer equipment life and improved performance.
- Increased equipment reliability by discovering system problems during construction. In this way, commissioning prevents costly downtime due to premature equipment failure and reduces wear and tear on equipment by ensuring that it operates properly.
- Reduced operating and maintenance costs.
- Improved occupant comfort and indoor air quality. Managing these factors effectively can reduce employee absenteeism and improve pro-

ductivity and morale of health care workers. Furthermore, the reduction in occupant and patient complaints of discomfort minimizes service calls to building operators during the life of the building.

- Better infection control.
- Reduced potential for liability and litigation. This is true for owners (from personal injury cases) and for engineers and contractors (due to claims from owners).

15.8 SUMMARY

Commissioning is a systematic, detailed process that requires the mutual commitment of the owner and the commissioning authority to ensure its success. The goal of commissioning is to turn over to the owner a building that meets the design intent with appropriate safeguards (such as operator training and required documentation) to ensure that it will continue to function properly. As owners, contractors, architects, and engineers see the benefits of commissioning, they are incorporating it into their building projects. Although there are many definitions of commissioning, it is important to bear in mind that this is the ultimate quality assurance program in the life of a building. As such, it must clearly and unequivocally set the standards of acceptability. The commissioning authority has a responsibility to the owner and to the community of professionals involved in the building process to ensure that the highest standards are met and to ensure that a building performs according to the owner's project requirements and its occupants' needs.

CHAPTER 16
ENERGY EFFICIENT DESIGN AND
CONSERVATION OF ENERGY RESOURCES

16.1 INTRODUCTION

According to the U.S. Department of Energy (1998) the average health care facility consumes 2.7 times the energy per unit floor area as the average commercial building. The department (USDOE) has documented the average energy consumption of health care facilities in the U.S. as 240,400 Btu per square foot per year (75 kWh per square meter per year) with an average cost of approximately $2.26 per square foot per year. The average acute care, full-service hospital is documented to have an even higher average consumption of about 330,000 Btu per square foot per year (1040 kWh per square meter per year) with an average cost of approximately $3 per square foot per year ($32 per square meter per year).

Energy efficiency is the *efficient* use of the energy resources consumed by a health care facility. Resource optimization is efficiently *utilizing* all the *available* energy *resources*, including recoverable, nonrenewable, and renewable resources. Energy efficiency opportunities (EEOs) are strategies that use improved design and operation of systems, equipment, building characteristics, and energy management systems to efficiently utilize the available energy resources. These strategies are important means to achieving the goal of reducing the cost of health care facilities operations within a reasonable return-on-investment and while conserving precious global energy resources.

This chapter will present energy efficient design concepts that can be applied in the design of new health care facility buildings, systems, and equipment or can be applied in the retrofit of existing health care buildings, systems, and equipment. These energy efficient design strategies will reduce the consumption of energy resources while maintaining all the important health, safety, and comfort constraints unique to health care facilities.

16.2 HEALTH CARE CONSTRAINTS

16.2.1 Health Care Functions

The particular functions and requirements of health care facilities provide unique opportunities for implementing energy design alternatives. The implementation of energy efficiency opportunities in health care facilities, however, must not adversely affect or compromise health care objectives or functions (including diagnosis, treatment, recovery and recuperation, infection control, and a wide variety of support functions). The energy efficiency opportunities must also be addressed in such a manner as to maintain the safety and comfort of patients, staff, and visitors and support the maintenance of environmental conditions necessary for operation of hospital equipment.

Energy efficiency considerations for health care facilities are similar to those in other types of commercial and institutional facilities. Energy efficient design alternatives are especially effective in health care facilities, however, due to unique health care functions. Health care functions and requirements that result in significant energy use include 24/7 occupancy, strict indoor air quality and high ventilation air requirements, and intensive (strict) room temperature and humidity requirements.

16.2.2 Hospital Mission

Some areas of hospitals (such as emergency, labor/delivery, surgery, and cardiac and intensive care) must maintain a status of constant readiness for urgent health care needs and emergencies. Most hospitals are also part of a disaster response system. The implementation of energy conservation opportunities must not compromise these missions.

16.3   ENERGY USAGE IN HEALTH CARE FACILITIES

In order to best understand how to reduce consumption of energy resources in new health care facilities, or to retrofit existing health care facilities to be more energy efficient, it is important to understand where energy is normally consumed in a typical heath care facility.

16.3.1   Study of an Example Facility

The example facility is a 350,000 ft^2 (32,500 m^2), full-service metropolitan health care facility with all the typical health care facility functions: surgery suites, recovery suites, labor/delivery areas including nurseries and c-section suites, cardiac catherization areas, radiology, mammography, nuclear medicine areas, laboratory areas, physical and occupational therapy areas, outpatient examination and surgery areas, dietary, laundry, nursing floors, emergency room and waiting areas, maintenance services, offices, and special services.

This example facility is heated and cooled by 27 constant volume air-handling systems with chilled water cooling coils, steam heating coils, and steam humidification. All of the air-handling systems have enthalpy-based air-side economizer controls. About 50% of the HVAC systems are constant volume dual-duct systems and 50% are constant volume reheat systems. The HVAC systems introduce a varying percentage of minimum outdoor air, from 10% to 100% of the total HVAC system airflow quantity. Total supply air volume was 420,000 cfm (198,200 L/s).

This example facility has a central Energy Center with electrical centrifugal chillers, primary and secondary chilled water pumping systems with some variable speed pumps, constant speed cooling tower fans, and constant speed condenser water pumps. The Energy Center also contains steam boilers that produce steam for heating, sterilization, and humidification.

Heating water for reheat coils and finned-tube radiation is produced using steam-to-water heat exchangers. The heating water pumping systems are constant speed systems.

The lighting in the facility had been partially retrofitted by conversion to T-8 fluorescent lamps and energy efficient electronic ballasts. A fairly conscientious lighting management program is also in place.

The energy rates for the example facility are $0.055/kWh (or $16.15/MMBtu) for electricity and $0.50/therm (or $5.00/MMBtu [$0.017/kWh]) for natural gas.

The following tables illustrating facility energy usage were developed using a DOE 2.1 computer model of an actual health care facility in the Midwest (Farnsworth 2001). The facility was modeled using climate files for different geographical locations to investigate how different climates would affect energy consumption (using TMY weather files from the U.S. Department of Energy).

Tables 16-1 through 16-5 provide a definitive breakdown of energy usage patterns for a prototypical health care facility. Table 16.1 lists typical electrical energy usage components and their relationship to total electrical energy consumption. Table 16-2 lists typical primary cooling energy usage components and their percentage of total cooling energy. Table 16-3 lists typical thermal energy usage breakdown by component and their relationship to total thermal energy consumption. Table 16-4 lists typical primary heating energy consumption components and their contribution to total heating energy. Table 16-5 shows a typical breakdown of annual costs by all energy-using components.

The tables illustrate how energy is used in typical health care facilities in various climates and the percentages of a health care facility's total energy expenditures that are spent on given energy-consuming components. The distributions of energy consumption and utility costs will vary somewhat from facility to facility, but the percentages listed in these tables may be considered generally accurate in their portrayal of how energy is used in a typical health care facility, whether small or large, in a range of different geographic locales.

Although the information in Tables 16-1 through 16-5 is based upon this prototypical facility, DOE-2 models of a 750,000 ft^2 (69,700 m^2) suburban health care facility, a 260,000 ft^2 (24,200 m^2) regional health care facility, and a 175,000 ft^2 (16,300 m^2) eye institute/general hospital show very similar results.

Table 16-5 was developed using the noted $16.15/MMBtu ($0.055/kWh) utility rates for electricity and $5.00/MMBtu ($0.017/kWh) for natural gas throughout the country. Utility rate structures are actually different in the varying locales listed in the table, but for comparison a uniform set of rates was used for each location. In fact, these rates would be considered quite low compared to most rate structures on the East and West coasts. The accuracy of the table will still apply as long as the ratio of electrical costs to natural gas costs remains the same.

16.3.2   Important Assumptions for the Existing Facility and Discussion of Results

Some important assumptions should be noted that will affect the distribution of energy usage by components in any individual facility versus those listed in Tables 16-1 through 16-5.

Table 16-1. Typical Hospital Electrical Usage Profile (% of kWh/year) By Component (1)

Component	NE (Boston)	Mid-Atl. (Phila.)	SE (Atlanta)	Florida (Miami)	Midwest (St. Louis)	Upper Ctrl. (Chicago)	North (Minneapolis)	South Ctrl. (Houston)	Southwest (Tucson)	S. Calif. (L.A.)	Northwest (Seattle)
					% of Electrical Energy Use						
Lighting (retrofitted T-8 lamps/ electronic ballasts/ lighting control)	18	17	16	13	17	17	17	14	16	16	14
kWh	1,626,240	1,626,240	1,626,240	1,626,240	1,626,240	1,626,240	1,626,240	1,626,240	1,626,240	1,626,240	1,626,240
Miscellaneous Electrical (receptacle load, computers, equipment, exterior lighting, etc.)	19	19	17	14	18	19	19	15	18	18	24
kWh	1,797,417	1,797,417	1,797,417	1,797,417	1,797,417	1,797,417	1,797,417	1,797,417	1,797,417	1,797,417	1,797,417
Primary Cooling	14	16	21	33	15	14	13	27	20	20	10
OA Cooling (% of Total Cooling)	1	1	3	8	1	1	1	5	1	6	1
kWh	84,096	133,693	343,848	1,031,842	153,100	133,670	105,000	642,234	106,073	598,958	133,643
Space Cooling (% of Total Cooling)	11	12	14	20	11	10	10	17	16	11	7
kWh	973,997	1,147,738	1,502,227	2,591,141	1,070,418	997,426	993,870	2,044,687	1,553,618	1,097,039	569,684
Fan Heat/Losses/ Thermal Mixing (% of Total Cooling)	2	3	4	5	3	3	2	5	3	3	2
kWh	243,499	286,934	375,557	647,785	267,505	249,386	233,468	511,172	388,424	274,260	142,431
Cooling Towers/ Condenser Water Pumping (Constant Vol.)	5	6	7	10	6	6	5	9	6	6	4
kWh	453,406	568,150	744,834	1,304,571	553,260	537,667	498,391	1,049,951	629,035	617,175	327,548
Chilled Water/ Heating Water Pumping (Constant Vol.)	6	6	7	6	6	6	6	6	6	6	6
kWh	584,225	580,989	662,380	778,035	617,651	595,278	600,501	719,087	670,367	681,012	527,946
Ventilation Fans (100% CAV)	29	28	26	21	28	29	29	24	28	28	35
kWh	2,700,503	2,700,503	2,700,503	2,700,503	2,700,503	2,700,503	2,700,503	2,700,503	2,700,503	2,700,503	2,700,503
Heating Auxiliaries	9	8	6	3	10	9	11	5	5	5	7
kWh	793,872	734,333	675,958	424,435	944,037	889,788	797,322	636,050	509,542	487,756	610,730
TOTAL	100	100	100	100	100	100	100	100	100	100	100
kWh	9,257,255	9,575,997	10,428,964	12,901,969	9,730,131	9,527,375	9,352,712	11,727,341	9,981,219	9,880,360	8,436,142

Table 16-2. Typical Hospital Electrical Usage Profile (% of kWh/year) By Component (1)

Component	NE (Boston) Primary Cooling %	Mid-Atl. (Phila.) Primary Cooling %	SE (Atlanta) Primary Cooling %	Florida (Miami) Primary Cooling %	Midwest (St. Louis) Primary Cooling %	Upper Ctrl. (Chicago) Primary Cooling %	North (Minapls.) Primary Cooling %	South Ctrl. (Houston) Primary Cooling %	Southwest (Tucson) Primary Cooling %	S. Calif. (L.A.) Primary Cooling %	Northwest (Seattle) Primary Cooling %
Primary Cooling											
OA Cooling (% of Total Cooling)	6	9	18	24	10	10	8	20	5	30	16
Space Cooling (% of Total Cooling)	75	73	68	61	72	72	73	64	76	56	67
Fan Heat/Losses/ Thermal Mixing (% of Total Cooling)	19	18	14	15	18	18	19	16	19	14	17
TOTAL	100	100	100	100	100	100	100	100	100	100	100

Table 16-3. Typical Hospital Thermal Energy Usage Profile (% of Total Btu/year) By Component

Component	NE (Boston)	Mid-Atl. (Phila.)	SE (Atlanta)	Florida (Miami)	Midwest (St. Louis)	Upper Ctrl. (Chicago)	North (Minpls.)	South Ctrl. (Houston)	Southwest (Tucson)	S. Calif. (L.A.)	Northwest (Seattle)
						% of Thermal Energy Use					
Primary Heating Use	% 90	% 89	% 88	% 86	% 90	% 90	% 90	% 87	% 87	% 87	% 89
OA Heating (% Total Thermal Use)	13	11	11	4	15	15	17	7	5	5	9
Therms	62,643	48,417	41,048	11,262	73,461	74,299	92,113	21,432	16,439	2,970	37,200
Reheating/Thermal Mixing (% Total Thermal Use)	56	58	59	69	55	55	53	65	58	69	61
Therms	267,792	255,384	218,987	182,175	269,426	266,803	282,298	206,156	182,644	223,116	256,350
Space Sensible Heating (% of Total Thermal Use)	21	20	18	13	20	20	20	15	24	13	19
Therms	95,113	89,044	66,504	34,869	96,350	97,630	110,619	49,484	73,324	55,678	73,324
DHW Heating	2	2	3	5	3	3	2	3	3	3	3
Therms	7,790	7,790	7,790	7,790	7,790	7,790	7,790	7,790	7,790	7,790	7,790
Dietary/Sterilizers	4	4	4	4	3	4	4	5	5	5	3
Therms	17,840	17,840	17,840	17,840	17,840	17,840	17,840	17,840	17,840	17,840	17,840
Distribution System/ Losses	4	5	5	5	4	3	4	5	5	5	5
Therms	23,470	22,085	18,535	13,365	24,467	24,440	26,877	15,930	15,686	16,179	20,668
TOTAL	100	100	100	100	100	100	100	100	100	100	100
Therms	474,648	440,560	370,704	267,301	489,334	488,802	537,537	318,632	313,723	323,573	413,172

Table 16-4. Primary Heating Energy Usage (% of Total Btu/year) By Component

Component	NE (Boston) Primary Heating %	Mid-Atl. (Phila.) Primary Heating %	SE (Atlanta) Primary Heating %	Florida (Miami) Primary Heating %	Midwest (St. Louis) Primary Heating %	Upper Ctrl. (Chicago) Primary Heating %	North (Minpls.) Primary Heating %	South Ctrl. (Houston) Primary Heating %	Southwest (Tucson) Primary Heating %	S. Calif. (L.A.) Primary Heating %	Northwest (Seattle) Primary Heating %
Primary Heating Use											
OA Heating (% Total Heating Use)	15	12	13	5	17	17	19	8	6	6	10
Reheating/Thermal Mixing (% Total Heating Use)	63	65	67	80	61	61	58	74	67	79	70
Space Sensor Heating (% of Total Cooling)	22	23	20	15	22	22	23	18	27	15	20
TOTAL	100	100	100	100	100	100	100	100	100	100	100

Table 16-5. Typical Hospital Energy Costs By Component

% of Total Annual Energy Costs

Component	NE (Boston)	Mid-Atlantic (Philadelphia)	SE (Atlanta)	Florida (Miami)	Midwest (St. Louis)	Upper Central (Chicago)	North (Minneapolis)	South Central (Houston)	SW (Tucson)	S. Calif. (L.A.)	NW (Seattle)
Lighting (T-8 Lamps)	12%	12%	12%	11%	11%	12%	11%	11%	13%	13%	13%
Miscellaneous Electrical	13%	13%	13%	12%	13%	13%	13%	12%	14%	14%	15%
OA Cooling	1%	1%	2%	7%	1%	1%	1%	5%	1%	4%	1%
Space Sensible Cooling	7%	8%	11%	17%	7%	7%	6%	14%	12%	9%	5%
Cooling—Fan Heat/Thermal Mixing	2%	2%	3%	4%	2%	2%	2%	3%	3%	2%	2%
OA Heating	4%	3%	3%	1%	5%	5%	6%	1%	1%	1%	3%
Reheating/Thermal Mixing	18%	18%	14%	11%	17%	17%	18%	14%	13%	15%	19%
Space Heating	6%	6%	4%	2%	6%	6%	7%	3%	5%	4%	5%
Cooling Towers/Condenser Water Pumping	3%	4%	5%	8%	4%	4%	3%	7%	5%	5%	3%
Chilled Water/Heating Water Pumping	4%	4%	5%	5%	4%	4%	4%	5%	5%	5%	4%
Ventilation Fans	20%	20%	20%	17%	19%	19%	19%	18%	21%	21%	22%
Heating Auxiliaries	6%	5%	5%	2%	7%	6%	7%	4%	4%	4%	5%
DHW Heating/Sterilizers/Humidification	1%	1%	1%	1%	1%	1%	1%	1%	1%	1%	1%
Dietary/Sterilizers	1%	1%	1%	1%	1%	1%	1%	1%	1%	1%	1%
Thermal Distribution	2%	2%	1%	1%	2%	2%	2%	1%	1%	1%	2%
Total	100%	100%	100%	100%	100%	100%	100%	100%	100%	100%	100%

- If some of the air-handling systems in a facility are variable air volume (VAV) systems and are designed for reduced static pressure loss, the total ventilation fan energy usage may be reduced to as low as 15-20% of the total electrical energy usage and as low as 14% of the total energy cost of the facility. In most existing health care facilities, only about 20% of the air-handling units are variable volume systems. In the example facility, the air-handling systems were all constant volume.

- In existing health care facilities, many of the air-handling systems are constant volume, dual-path, thermal mixing systems (dual-duct or multizone systems), with fixed cooling coil and heating coil discharge temperatures. In these cases, the cooling and reheating thermal mixing energy consumption would be much higher than listed in Tables 16.1-16.5. Most new facility HVAC systems are designed as either constant volume or variable volume reheat systems. Fifty percent of the systems in this representative facility were constant volume dual-duct or multizone systems and fifty percent were constant volume reheat systems.

- Lighting system energy consumption could be much higher than in this representative facility, if lighting management techniques are not being employed or if energy efficient ballasts are not used. The lighting in the representative facility had been retrofit, using energy efficient T-8 fluorescent lamps and electronic ballasts.

- The chilled water and heating water pumping systems in this representative facility had primary-secondary pumping configurations with variable speed control of secondary pumps. The energy consumption for these use categories will be significantly higher if variable speed pumping control systems are not implemented. These strategies are, in fact, typically not implemented in health care facilities. The cooling tower fans and condenser water pumps in the modeled facility were constant speed/constant volume systems.

- The primary cooling energy use percentages are representative of a facility where approximately 70% of the air-handling systems used air-side "enthalpy based free cooling" economizer systems. If these free-cooling strategies are not implemented in a facility, the primary cooling energy consumption would be higher and the energy consumption required for heating and cooling of outdoor air would be much higher than listed for the prototypical facility.

- The minimum outdoor air quantities provided for the air-handling units in this prototypical facility varied from 10% of the total airflow to 100% of the total airflow, depending upon the areas served. Makeup air units for patient wings were 100% outdoor air. If a health care facility has a larger percentage of 100% outdoor air units, the energy consumption cost for outdoor air cooling, dehumidifying, humidifying, and heating will be much greater.

- Component energy cost percentages will vary from the example facility if there is a significantly different ratio of natural gas costs to electricity costs at another facility than illustrated here. The ratio for the prototype facility has electricity costing approximately 3.3 times more per 10^6 Btu (1.06×10^6 kJ) than natural gas. If electrical rates in a given area are significantly higher than indicated in this example and natural gas rates are similar, then the electrical energy end-use components will have a greater cost effect. If the natural gas rates are significantly higher and electrical rates are similar, then the thermal energy end-use components will have a greater cost effect.

- The example facility had electrical centrifugal chilled water plants with medium efficiency chillers (0.75 kW/ton [0.21 kW/kW]). Other types of electrical cooling with more or less efficient performance (or the use of absorption chillers or gas-engine-driven centrifugal chillers) would cause the electrical and thermal energy cost percentage profiles to change.

Even if the energy cost percentages vary somewhat from health care facility to health care facility and with geographic location, several important observations can be extracted from a review of the data in these tables. First, because of the significant minimum total air change requirements and minimum outdoor air change code requirements for health care facilities, between 31% and 41% of the annual energy cost of the typical facility is used for ventilation fan energy and for overcooling and then reheating space ventilation air in excess of that required to heat or cool the space. Additionally, another 13-20% of the annual energy cost of the facility is used for auxiliary or "parasitic" energy usage components, composed of pumping energy and cooling tower energy. Between 5% and 10% of the annual energy costs are required for outdoor air heating, cooling, humidification, and dehumidification, depending upon location.

These observations provide a roadmap for determining the types of energy efficiency improvements that should be incorporated into any health care facility. Such improvements can be easily made in a manner that will make a significant impact on energy consumption without affecting space comfort, health, or life safety requirements.

16.4 DESIGN OF ENERGY EFFICIENT HVAC SYSTEMS

As illustrated by the energy usage tables in the previous section, between 36% and 46% of the annual energy costs of the typical health care facility are related to the operation of the HVAC systems. This includes ventilation fan energy, outdoor air cooling and dehumidification, outdoor air heating and humidification, as well as thermal mixing and reheating required to maintain space comfort. For this reason, it is especially important to implement energy efficient strategies in the design of new (or retrofit) HVAC systems. (See Appendix H for sample control strategies.)

16.4.1 Variable Air Volume (VAV) System Application Opportunity

In most locations, state health codes may allow a reduction in minimum total air flow rates and minimum outdoor air flow rates during unoccupied periods (see Table 4-1). This reduction can apply to any of the spaces in a health care facility that are in unoccupied status as long as the required directional pressurization control is maintained for the space. Significant energy savings can be achieved by designing the air-handling systems serving these spaces as variable air volume systems. The AIA (American Institute of Architects) and ASHRAE allow ventilation rates to be reduced to 25% of the occupied period rates as long as continuous directional control and space pressurization are maintained at all times and the full (occupied) ventilation air change rates can be reestablished any time the space is being utilized (see further discussion below under unoccupied period control strategies).

A designer should consider the following factors when evaluating how effective a variable volume HVAC system will be in a health care facility:

A. Hours of operation of the spaces being served by the HVAC system.

B. Magnitude of the difference between the minimum ventilation air changes per hour (see Table 4-1 in Chapter 4) and the air flow required to meet space sensible cooling load requirements.

C. Requirements for continuous directional control—positive, negative, neutral, or no requirement (see Table 4-1 in Chapter 4).

For example, in spaces that are occupied 24 hours daily (i.e., emergency rooms, 24-hour laboratory or pharmacy areas, intensive care units, nurseries, etc.) and/or where the space sensible cooling air flow requirements are not significantly greater than the minimum ventilation air change rate requirements, reducing air flow will probably not reduce energy consumption greatly.

However, in spaces where

1. no continuous directional control or minimum ventilation air change rates are required, or

2. there are significant unoccupied hours, or

3. where space sensible cooling air flow requirements are significantly greater than the minimum ventilation air requirements,

then significant reductions in energy consumption can be achieved through use of variable volume control of the HVAC systems. Most spaces in health care facilities fall into these categories, including:

- Most surgery and recovery suites
- C-section suites
- Radiology, X-ray, mammogram, nuclear medicine, CAT scan, ultrasound, MRI, and PET areas
- Physical/occupational therapy areas
- Office areas
- Dietary areas
- Laundries
- Outpatient areas and surgeries
- Cardiac catherization areas
- Waiting areas
- Maintenance departments and other support areas
- Examination rooms and treatment rooms

In a typical health care facility, only about 20% of the facility is occupied more than 60-70 hours per week. Operating suites and surgical prep areas are rarely used more than 60-80 hours per week, except for a few operating suites, recovery areas, and radiology areas dedicated to emergency services. Such spaces usually only constitute about 20% of the total surgery areas in a facility. Typical schedules are illustrated in Table 16-6, using data derived from multiple field surveys.

A variable volume air-handling system should be provided with variable frequency controllers for the supply air and return/relief air fans. The design should also include a separate minimum outdoor air

Table 16-6. Typical Occupancy Patterns for Various Health Care Facility Spaces

Spaces	Typical Occupied Hours/Week
Patient Rooms	80% of rooms normally occupied 24 hours, 7 days/week
ICU Rooms	75% of rooms normally occupied 24 hours, 7 days/week
Nurses' Stations	24 hours, 7 days/week
Emergency Room Areas/Exam Rooms	24 hours, 7 days/week
Labs Areas (normally 50% of total areas)	24 hours, 7 days/week
Emergency Radiology Areas (normally 10%-20% of total areas)	24 hours, 7 days/week
Emergency Surgery/Recovery Areas (normally 10%-20% of total areas)	24 hours, 7 days/week
Autopsy	24 hours, 7 days/week
Central Sterile Supply	24 hours, 7 days/week
Nursery	24 hours, 7 days/week
Corridors/Waiting Areas	24 hours, 7 days/week
Medical Records	24 hours, 7 days/week
Receiving	60 hours/week
Clean Linen Storage	50 hours/week
Purchasing	50 hours/week
Maintenance Offices	50 hours/week
Ultrasound Areas – General	50 hours/week
Mammography Areas – General	50 hours/week
Nuclear Medicine Areas – General	50 hours/week
Fluoroscopy Areas – General	60 hours/week
Endoscopy Areas – General	60 hours/week
X-Ray Areas – General	60 hours/week
Surgery Prep Areas – General	65 hours/week
Operating Rooms – General	65 hours/week
Outpatient Operating Rooms – General	50 hours/week
C-Section Operating Rooms	40 hours/week
Administration Offices/Conference Rooms	50 hours/week
Recovery – General	55 hours/week
Physical/Occupational Therapy	60 hours/week
Outpatient Exam/Office Areas	65 hours/week
Cardiac Catherization Labs	55 hours/week
Dietary	98 hours/week
Dining Areas	98 hours/week
Laundry	60 hours/week

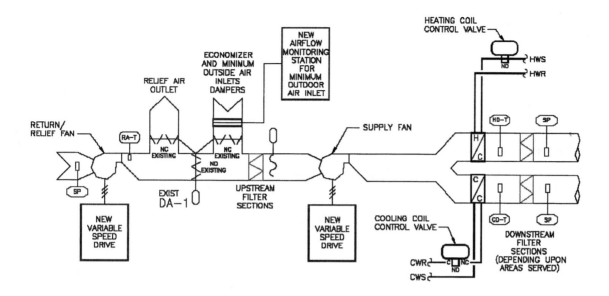

Figure 16-1   Variable air volume air-handling unit schematic. Dual-duct or multizone air-handing units.

control damper for control of minimum outside air (see Table 4-1) separate from control of outside air for "free-cooling economizer" operation. In an energy retrofit application, the dampers should be separated if there is currently only one damper. The building automation system (BAS) should include supply ductwork static pressure sensors and control sequences to vary the supply fan speed and return air ductwork static pressure sensors and control sequences to vary return/relief air fan speed. Space pressurization control in critical spaces can be maintained by using return air terminal units as discussed in Section 16.4.4.

16.4.2 VAV Systems for Existing Hospitals

In hospitals that experienced substantial building construction during the 1960s and 1970s, existing air-handling systems are most likely either constant volume single-duct, dual-duct, or sometimes even constant volume multizone. Facilities with substantial construction in the 1980s and 1990s will more likely have air-handling systems with constant volume reheat operation. Most new facilities are currently designed with either constant volume or variable volume reheat air-handling systems. All of these systems can be easily retrofit to VAV operation with significant reductions in ventilation fan energy, thermal mixing and reheating energy, and cooling energy use. Figure 16-1 indicates retrofit modifications to a typical dual-duct or multizone air-handling unit, although these modifications will also

apply to reheat systems. Figure 16-2 illustrates how an existing dual-duct terminal unit can be easily retrofit to variable volume operation. Figures 16-3 and 16-4 indicate how an existing multizone system can be easily retrofit to variable volume operation.

In cases where critical care areas require a certain minimum total ventilation air change rate (see Table 4-1), the terminal unit maximum and minimum airflow setpoints may need to be the same during occupied periods and the terminal unit be programmed to act like a constant volume terminal unit during occupied periods.

In critical spaces where pressure relationships must be maintained, the designer should note the possibility of lint accumulation on the return air terminal volume measurement element. This condition may affect pressure relationship.

Documented energy retrofit experiences with existing health care facility air-handling systems are very favorable. Generally, a three- to four-year simple payback can be achieved for an energy retrofit conversion of dual-duct and multizone air-handling systems, and a two- to four-year simple payback can be achieved for an energy retrofit conversion of constant volume reheat systems using utility rates as discussed for the prototypical facility. Higher utility rates may produce an even quicker return on investment. In new construction, the additional incremental cost to add variable frequency controllers, additional building automation controls, return air terminal units, and dampers to change from constant

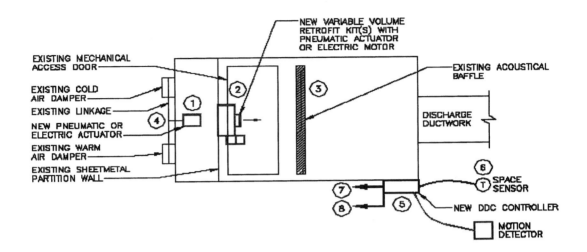

① THE EXISTING PNEUMATIC DAMPER ACTUATOR AND DAMPER LINKAGE ARE VERIFIED TO BE OPERATIONAL OR A NEW PNEUMATIC OR ELECTRONIC ACTUATOR IS PROVIDED

② THE EXISTING MECHANICAL CONSTANT VOLUME REGULATOR IS REMOVED AND A NEW VARIABLE VOLUME DAMPER ASSEMBLY WITH ASSOCIATED PNEUMATIC OR ELECTRIC ACTUATOR IS BUILT INTO THE LOCATION WHERE THE PREVIOUS REGULATOR WAS REMOVED.

③ THE ENTIRE TERMINAL UNIT IS CLEANED FOR IAQ AND ALL BAFFLES ARE CHECKED FOR EFFICIENCY

④ THE EXISTING COLD AIR DUCTWORK AND WARM AIR DUCTWORK DAMPERS AND LINKAGES ARE CHECKED AND REPAIRED AS REQUIRED DURING COMMISSIONING.

⑤ A NEW DIRECT DIGITAL CONTROL (DDC) TERMINAL UNIT CONTROLLER IS PROVIDED FOR CONTROLLING SPACE TEMPERATURE, THE NEW VAV DAMPER, AND EXISTING COLD AIR AND WARM AIR DUCTWORK DAMPERS.

⑥ A NEW DDC ELECTRONIC SPACE TEMPERATURE SENSOR IS INSTALLED AND A NEW MOTION DETECTOR IS INSTALLED AND INPUTS ARE SENT TO THE CONTROLLER.

⑦ NEW POWER WIRING IS PROVIDED FOR THE CONTROLLER.

⑧ THE DDC TERMINAL UNIT CONTROLLER IS CONNECTED BY A NETWORK TO ALL OTHER CONTROLLERS AND CENTRAL BUILDING AUTOMATION SYSTEM.

Figure 16-2   Modified dual-duct terminal units for variable volume operation.

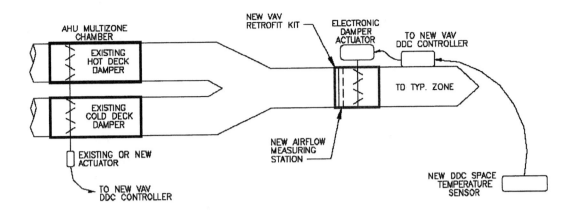

Figure 16-3 Multizone, variable air volume control ductwork schematic.

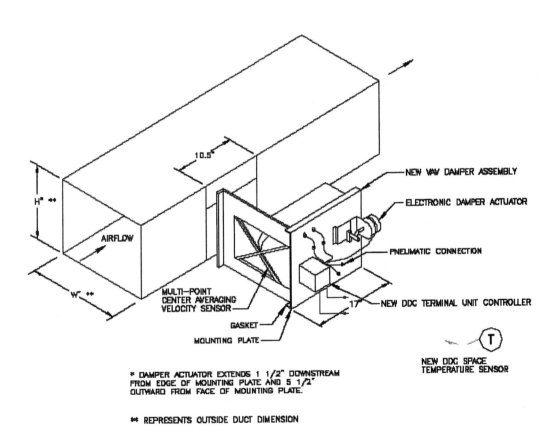

Figure 16-4 Modified constant volume, multizone systems for variable volume operation.

volume reheat systems to variable volume reheat systems generally shows a simple payback of only one to two years.

16.4.3 Variable Volume Occupied and Unoccupied Period Control for Noncritical Care Spaces

Many of the spaces in a health care facility (such as dietary and dining areas, outpatient administrative offices, outpatient treatment areas, many radiology and outpatient therapy areas, and many common areas) do not have continuous pressurization control requirements. These areas can be easily served by a traditional VAV air-handling system, which can substantially reduce energy consumption through use of several occupied and unoccupied period control strategies.

1. During occupied periods, the DDC building automation system (BAS) will modulate air flow from terminal unit maximum occupied air flow setpoints to minimum occupied period air flow setpoints to maintain space temperature setpoint. Minimum occupied period airflow setpoints should be established to provide adequate ventilation effectiveness and adequate indoor air quality for occupants and to provide makeup air for exhaust or pressurization requirements.

2. During unoccupied periods, the BAS will modulate airflow to maintain space temperature in the same manner; however, the DDC building automation system should reduce all terminal unit minimum airflow setpoints to their unoccupied period minimum airflow values. These unoccupied period minimum airflow setpoints should provide only as much air as required to make up for exhaust or pressurization requirements. The unoccupied period minimum airflow setpoint could be zero if no exhaust or pressurization requirements exist. This will produce a significant reduction in reheat energy usage, cooling energy usage, and ventilation fan energy usage.

3. During unoccupied periods, the BAS should also reset the HVAC system minimum outdoor air setpoint to a new unoccupied period value to adjust for the reduced occupancy of the spaces. This will produce a significant reduction in the energy required for cooling, heating, dehumidifying, and/ or humidifying minimum outdoor air.

16.4.4 Variable Volume Occupied and Unoccupied Period Control for Critical Care Spaces

In areas of a health care facility where continuous directional pressurization control is required (either positive or negative) and significant minimum air flow rates are required during occupied periods, substantial reductions in energy usage and costs can be achieved by reducing air flow rates during unoccupied periods. (See Table 4-1 in Chapter 4, which illustrates the changes that can be made to ventilation rates during unoccupied periods according to ASHRAE [1999a], AIA [2001], and most state departments of health.) Figure 16-5 illustrates a

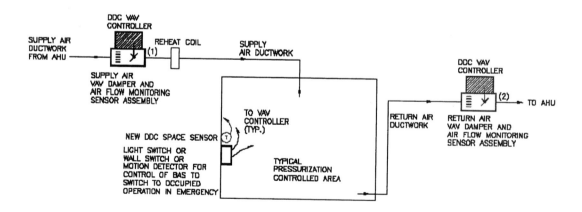

(1) SUPPLY AIR MINIMUM AIRFLOW SET POINT CHANGES FROM OCCUPIED TO UNOCCUPIED MINIMUM AIR CHANGE REQUIREMENTS BASED ON SCHEDULE OR OCCUPANCY SWITCH.

(2) RETURN AIRFLOW SETPOINT IS CONTROLLED TO MAINTAIN AN OFFSET CFM OR A SPACE DIFFERENTIAL PRESSURE SETPOINT. THE SETPOINT IS RESET FROM OCCUPIED TO UNOCCUPIED PERIODS.

Figure 16-5   Critical care area schematic. Typical for directional pressurization control.

method for achieving these savings by retrofitting a constant volume reheat system or using a new variable volume reheat tracking system. The same procedures would apply equally well to dual-duct or multizone systems.

In critical care areas, significant reductions in ventilation fan energy usage, reheat or thermal mixing energy usage, space cooling energy usage, and energy usage for treatment of outdoor air can be achieved during unoccupied periods by designing new air-handling systems or modifying existing air-handling systems to meet the following building automation control strategies.

- During occupied periods, the DDC building automation systems will control the terminal unit to maintain space temperature setpoint by modulating the airflow between maximum airflow setpoint and minimum airflow setpoint. The VAV supply air controller/damper assembly will provide the required supply air from the air-handler to meet the space sensible cooling load requirement or to provide the minimum occupied period total space ventilation requirements (Table 4-1), whichever is greater. The minimum airflow setpoint of the terminal unit controller should be set for the occupied minimum total space air changes per hour (Table 4-1). This may require the terminal unit to act as a constant volume terminal during occupied periods.

- During occupied periods, the BAS will control the VAV return air controller/damper assembly to track the supply air controller, providing the required return air from the space to maintain either a constant positive or negative air volume offset in the space or a space differential pressure (positive or negative) setpoint.

- The BAS will control the minimum outside air controller in the air-handling system serving these spaces to provide adequate minimum outside air to meet all of the occupied period minimum space outside air ventilation (Table 4.1) requirements.

- During unoccupied periods, the BAS will control the supply air control/damper assembly to provide the required supply air to meet the space sensible cooling load requirement or the minimum unoccupied period total space ventilation requirements (Table 4-1), whichever is greater. The minimum airflow setpoint of the terminal unit controller is set for the unoccupied minimum total air changes per hour (Table 4-1).

- During unoccupied periods, the return air controller tracks the supply air controller in the same manner as discussed above, except using different setpoints.

- The BAS will control the minimum outside air controller in the air-handling system to provide adequate minimum outside air to meet all of the unoccupied period minimum outside air space ventilation requirements (Table 4-1).

16.5 AIR-TO-AIR HEAT RECOVERY STRATEGIES

Due to the significant amount of outside air required to meet code requirements in health care facilities, air-to-air heat recovery strategies are a very cost-effective means of reducing energy consumption. Specific savings will depend upon the percentage of minimum outdoor air used for a facility and its geographic location/climate.

There are four air-to-air heat recovery systems that are commonly used; runaround coil systems, fixed plate heat exchanger systems, heat pipe systems, and rotary desiccant heat exchanger systems (heat wheels). These system types are illustrated in Figure 16-6.

The effectiveness of these systems depends upon the temperature differences between the airstreams, latent energy differences, air flow, device efficiency, and hours of operation. Increased maintenance may be required with the implementation of such systems, and a ventilation fan energy penalty will be incurred.

16.5.1 Runaround Coil System

This system is composed of two or more extended-surface coils installed in air ducts and interconnected by a piping system. The heat exchanger fluid, usually consisting of ethylene glycol and water, is circulated through the system by a pump, removing heat from the hot airstream and transferring it to the cold airstream. A runaround-coil system may be used in winter to recover heat from warm exhaust air in order to preheat cold outdoor air and in summer to cool hot outdoor air by transferring heat to cooler exhaust air.

Runaround coil systems normally have a heat transfer efficiency of between 60% and 80% of the sensible heat available. These systems are frequently the only practical heat recovery option in retrofit situations, as the other options need to have the outdoor air and exhaust/relief ducts close to each other. Run-

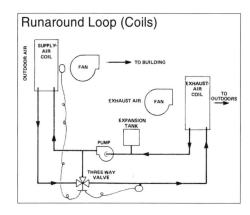

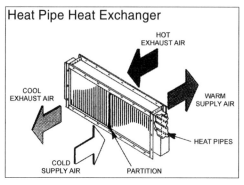

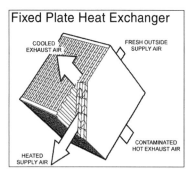

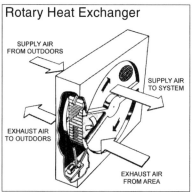

Graphics Source: ASHRAE. 2000.
*2000 ASHRAE Handbook—HVAC
Systems and Equipment.* Atlanta:
American Society of Heating,
Refrigerating and Air-Condition-
ing Engineers, Inc.

Figure 16-6   Energy recovery technologies.

around systems usually have a 3-5 year simple pay-back if implemented in an energy retrofit application and usually have a 0.5-2 year payback if implemented as part of a new design project—especially if overall heating and cooling plant sizes can be reduced as a result of the heat recovery.

16.5.2   Heat Pipe Systems

Heat pipe systems are composed of extended-surface finned tubes extending between adjacent air ducts. The tubes are continuous on the same horizontal plane from one duct to the other. Each tube contains liquid refrigerant that evaporates at the warm end (absorbing heat from the warmer airstream) and migrates as a gas to the cold end where it condenses (and releases heat into the cold airstream). The condensed liquid then runs back to the hot end of the tube to complete the cycle. These systems require that supply and exhaust ducts be installed side by side.

Heat pipe systems also usually have an efficiency of between 60% and 80% of the sensible heat available. They have simple paybacks on investment, similar to the runaround coil systems, but may be

difficult to implement in a retrofit application unless the airstreams are very close together and the duct-work can be modified to facilitate installation.

16.5.3   Plate Heat Exchanger

Plate-type air-to-air heat exchangers transfer heat from one airstream to another via indirect contact through a metal heat-transfer surface. The systems have no crossover flow. Plate heat exchangers require that supply and exhaust ducts be installed side by side.

These systems also have an efficiency of between 60% and 80% of the sensible heat available. New technologies allow latent heat transfer as well. They have simple paybacks, similar to the runaround coil systems, but may be difficult to implement in a retrofit application unless the airstreams are very close together and the ductwork can be modified to facilitate installation.

16.5.4   Heat Wheels

Rotating heat wheels are an air-to-air heat recovery system that can transfer both sensible heat and water vapor between airstreams.

If properly designed, these systems can achieve up to 80% efficiency in recovering the total (sensible and latent) heat available. These systems have the added benefit of dehumidifying and cooling incoming hot and humid air in cooling months and humidifying and warming incoming cold dry air in heating months. The payback for installing these systems, like the other air-to-air heat recovery systems, is highly dependent upon climate and hours of operation. In health care applications, however, these systems can have a three- to five-year simple payback if installed in a retrofit application (although ductwork for exhaust and outdoor airstreams must be close together or a separate heat recovery unit used). If incorporated into a new design, the simple payback can be as low as 0.5-1.5 years, especially if the central heating and cooling plant sizes can be reduced due to the installation of the heat recovery system.

It is essential that heat wheel systems be properly designed to minimize any possibility of cross-contamination between airstreams and that the air entering both sides is properly filtered. An essential component of heat wheel design requires that the outdoor air be introduced with a fan blowing into the inlet side of the wheel (positive) and the exhaust air removed from the building with an exhaust fan on the leaving side of the wheel (negative). In this manner, potential leakage will always flow from the fresh air (positive) side to the exhaust air (negative) side of the heat exchanger.

It should be noted that the AIA *Guidelines for Design and Construction of Hospital and Health Care Facilities* (section 7.31.D2) prohibits use of a heat wheel for infectious isolation rooms.

16.6 DESIGN OF ENERGY EFFICIENT CHILLED WATER AND CONDENSER WATER SYSTEMS

The energy use analysis discussed earlier in this chapter indicates that a significant portion of the annual energy costs of a typical hospital is related to primary cooling systems. Energy conservative strategies related to the design, operation, and control of these systems can dramatically reduce the annual energy usage of these systems in both new and existing health care facilities.

16.6.1 Water-side "Free-Cooling" Economizer

Many existing health care facilities have significant areas (i.e., patient rooms, ICU rooms, confer-

ence rooms, offices, etc.) served by two-pipe or four-pipe fan-coil systems or air-handling systems without air-side (free cooling) economizers, many of which need cooling a significant part of the year. This normally requires some percentage of the chiller capacity to be in use all year. In many climates with low wet-bulb temperatures in winter months (usually November-April), water-side "free-cooling" for these spaces, using cooling tower water as the heat exchange medium, can be easily accomplished. This system can be controlled, based on outside wet-bulb temperature and condenser water supply temperature, to use the heat exchanger during appropriate periods and switch to chiller operation during periods when the wet-bulb temperature and condenser water supply temperature are too high. This scenario will require the use of variable frequency controllers for the cooling tower fans and installation of a cooling tower bypass valve to bypass the condenser water return from the cooling tower hot water basins in cold weather.

This strategy can also be used in design of new health care facilities in lieu of an "air-side" free cooling economizer, obviously depending upon geographic location and climate. If this strategy is installed as part of a new project, the incremental simple payback will usually only be 0.5-2 years, depending on the climate. In energy retrofit projects, it normally has a two- to four-year simple payback. Figures 16-8 and 16-9 illustrate the implementation of this energy conservation strategy.

16.6.2 Variable Speed Control of Chilled Water and Condenser Water Pumping Systems

Many existing health care facilities, especially those designed over 10 years ago, have chilled water and condenser water piping systems configured as indicated in Figures 16-7 and 16-9. Such systems are parallel pumping systems that are sized for the peak load of the plant and include control strategies for chilled water delivery that require all of the pumping to be operated since the cooling coil control valves are three-way-type bypass valves that do not vary flow to the coil. These systems often operate with a very low chilled water temperature difference (3-4°F [1.4-1.9°C]) at the chillers, requiring several chillers to operate at part-load conditions. Additionally, when fewer than the total number of parallel pumps are operating, the operating pumps will flow more

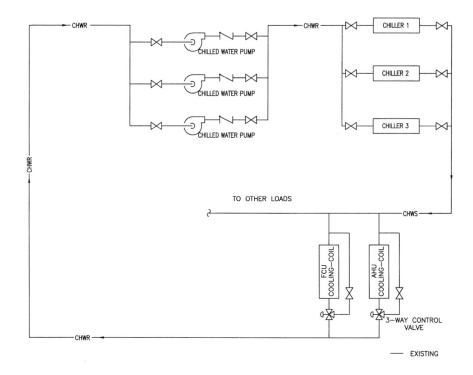

Figure 16-7   Energy Center chilled water flow diagram—pre-retrofit.

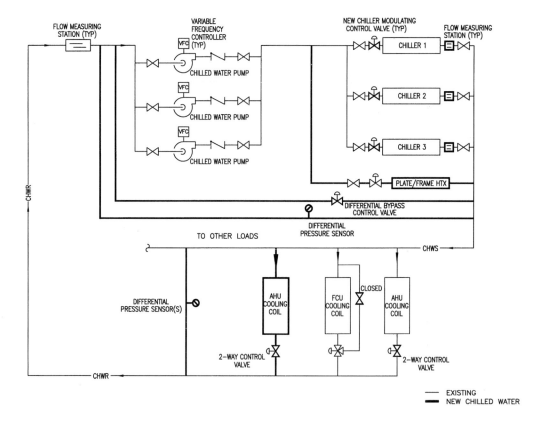

Figure 16-8   Energy Center chilled water flow diagram—post-retrofit.

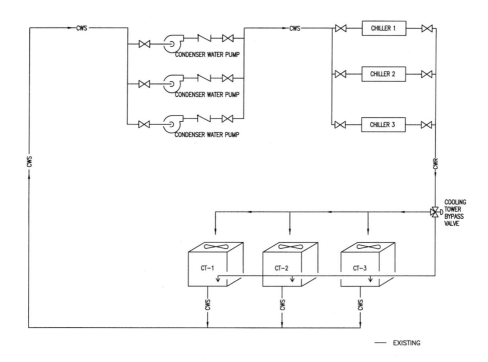

Figure 16-9 Energy Center condenser water flow diagram—pre-retrofit.

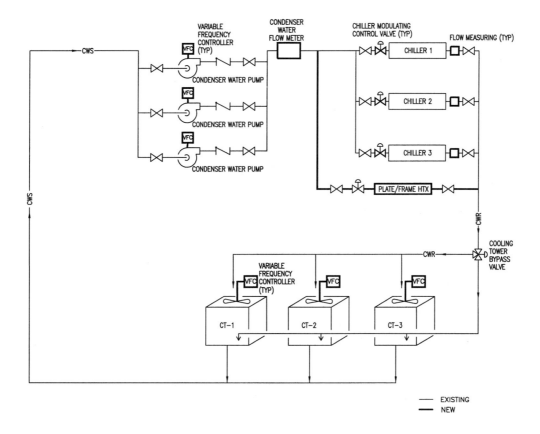

Figure 16-10 Energy Center condenser water flow diagram—post-retrofit.

water than required and use more energy than required.

An initial (or retrofit) system design that allows for variable chilled water and condenser water flow will reduce pumping energy consumption dramatically and will also improve chiller operating efficiency, since each chiller will be operating at more efficient loading points more often. These designs are illustrated in Figures 16-8 and 16-9. The following strategies should be implemented:

1. Provide new variable frequency controllers for condenser water pumps. Vary the condenser water flow to maintain the desired differential head pressure required by the chiller manufacturer, except always maintain the minimum condenser water flow required by the manufacturer. Use only the number of pumps required to meet the overall flow requirements and switch to additional pumps as additional chillers are started. The condenser water flow must be maintained at a minimum flow rate or minimum chiller differential pressure setpoint as prescribed by the chiller manufacturer.

2. Have the cooling tower fan variable frequency controllers modulate to maintain the coldest condenser water temperature allowed by the chiller manufacturer (usually as low as 68-75°F [20.0-23.9°C]).

3. Provide new two-way modulating control valves for each air-handling system and fan-coil unit cooling coil, or shut off operation of the three-way bypass on the existing control valves (if allowed by the manufacturer).

4. Provide new variable frequency controllers for each chilled water pump and vary chilled water flow to meet the differential pressure setpoint controllers located in the chilled water system. If the flow reaches the minimum allowed through the chiller or chillers by the manufacturer, the variable frequency controllers will not vary speed any lower and the chilled water bypass controller will modulate to maintain the differential pressure setpoint and minimum flow rate through the chillers.

When implemented as part of the design of a new health care facility, these strategies will have a one- to three-year simple payback. As an energy retrofit for an existing facility, the simple payback usually averages three to five years, depending upon the hours of operation of the chiller plant and whether air-side or water-side economizer systems are available.

16.6.3 Variable Speed Cooling Tower Fan Control/Condenser Water Reset

The use of variable speed cooling tower fans to control condenser water supply temperature to the chillers improves condenser water temperature control and is an excellent opportunity to reduce electrical energy consumption. This strategy will have a two- to three-year simple payback as a retrofit project and usually less than a year simple payback if implemented as part of a new design. Chillers of recent vintage can operate with as low as 65-70°F (18.3-21.1°C) entering condenser water temperatures when wet-bulb conditions are favorable, dramatically reducing energy consumption of the chiller. The cooling tower fans should operate to maintain as low an entering condenser water temperature as possible.

16.6.4 Variable Speed Chiller Control

Variable speed control of chillers can also be an excellent energy efficient design feature if the chillers need to operate at low load conditions (usually less than 60% of chiller capacity) for a significant number of hours. Variable speed control of chillers also allows operation at low condenser water entering temperatures, improving the efficiency of the chillers. Careful evaluation of this measure requires an understanding of the load profile on the chillers with regard to the chiller operating hours at various chiller load points.

16.7 ENERGY CONSERVATION DESIGN OF CENTRAL HEATING SYSTEMS

16.7.1 High Efficiency Condensing Boilers

High efficiency or condensing heating water boilers can be an excellent energy-conserving design feature in health care facility hot water space heating systems. These boilers can have combustion efficiencies as high as 88-92%. Since health care facilities have steam requirements for domestic water heating, dietary needs, sterilization, laundries, and humidification, use of high efficiency hot water boilers will require separate steam systems for these other hospital thermal requirements (see 16.6.3). High efficiency heating water boilers usually come in relatively small sizes and therefore may be impractical for use in large health care facilities.

16.7.2 Boiler Economizers

Boiler economizers are an excellent energy-conserving design feature that can be implemented in existing health care heating plants as an energy retrofit project or incorporated into new heating plant designs. A boiler economizer is an air-to-water heat exchanger that takes heat from the exhaust flue gas stream leaving the boiler and uses it to preheat boiler feed water or other water sources (domestic hot water, etc.). Boiler economizers can usually save approximately 3-8% of total heating energy if a consistent heat sink is available. Care in design is necessary to ensure that the economizer control prevents condensation in the flue gas exhaust ductwork. These projects will usually have a two-to four-year simple payback when implemented as a retrofit project and a one- to three-year simple payback when implemented as part of a new design. The payback will be dependent upon the operating hours of the boiler system and the boiler system load profile, as well as the ability to effectively use the heat for another heating load.

16.7.3 Dedicated Steam Boilers for DHW Heating, Humidification, Sterilization, and Laundry Requirements

Health care facilities have consistent thermal loads that are not weather related. These include heating for dietary, sterilization, laundry, humidification, and domestic hot water applications. These loads may frequently require higher operating steam pressures than needed for space heating loads and are usually (depending upon the climate) a small percentage of the peak heating plant capacity for space heating and reheating. When this is the case, the heating plant will operate very inefficiently during nonheating months, when very low loads are imposed on large boilers. Therefore, it is often an excellent energy conservation measure to provide a separate dedicated boiler system for these non-space-heating loads and a separate heating system (frequently designed as a hot water system instead of steam) for space heating and reheating loads. Paybacks for boiler optimization projects will vary depending upon the ratio of space heating loads to non-space-heating loads but frequently can be in the range of a three- to six-year simple payback.

16.7.4 Central Heating Plant Vs. Distributed Heating Plants

In campus-type health care facilities, an evaluation should be made of multiple distributed or process stream plants in lieu of a central large steam/high-temperature hot water/energy plant and associated distribution system. Use of a large central system can be energy inefficient, especially during low-load conditions, due to distribution losses.

16.7.5 High-Temperature Hot Water Heating Systems

In large new health care environments, high-temperature heating water systems with large temperature differentials (usually greater than 350°F [176°C]) can reduce pumping horsepower and be an effective energy efficiency measure.

16.7.6 Steam Turbine Generators Versus Pressure-Reducing Valves

In many health care operations, different steam pressures are required for different health care functions: dietary, laundry, sterilization, humidification, and space heating and reheating. Higher pressure requirements may be needed at 60 psig to 80 psig (414-552 kPa), while space heating and reheating are most usually accomplished with 15 psig (103 kPa) steam.

In many large health care facilities, only one central steam system is used, and multiple pressure reductions are required to meet the various needs. In these cases, the use of small steam turbine generators for steam pressure reductions from the highest pressure to the space-heating pressure may be an effective energy efficiency opportunity.

16.7.7 Variable Speed Pumping for Heating Systems

Most existing health care facilities have heating water piping systems configured as indicated in Figure 16-11. In a manner similar to chilled water systems, a three-way control valve setup requires constant volume heating water flow even at very low loads and operates the boilers at very low temperature differences, which are inefficient.

A system design that allows for variable heating water flow will reduce heating water pumping energy consumption and improve boiler operating efficiency, since only the required number of boilers will be operating, and they will be operating more efficiently.

The following strategies should be implemented:

- Provide new variable frequency controllers for heating water pumps. Vary the flow to maintain the desired differential pressure setpoint in the heating water piping system, except that the minimum acceptable flow through the boiler or boilers must be maintained. When minimum flow is reached, the variable frequency controllers will not vary speed any lower and the differential pressure bypass valve will modulate to

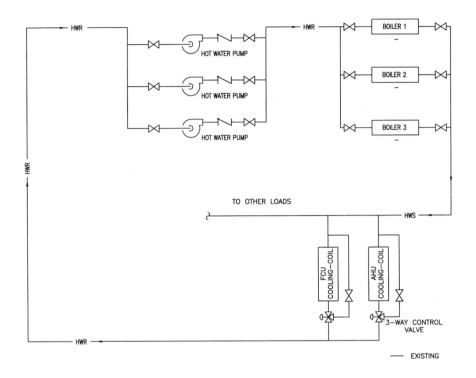

Figure 16-11 Energy Center hot water flow diagram—pre-retrofit.

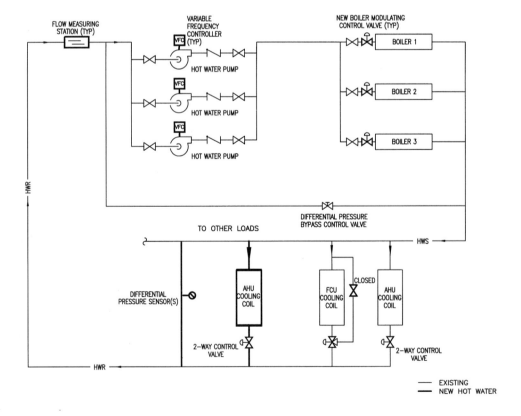

Figure 16-12 Energy Center hot water flow diagram—post-retrofit.

maintain the differential pressure setpoint and minimum flow rate through the boilers.

- Provide new two-way valve controls for fan-coil unit heating coils or shut off operation of the bypass on the existing heating control valves.

These retrofits are illustrated in Figure 16-12. When implemented as part of a new project, this strategy will have a one- to two-year simple payback. In energy retrofit case studies, the simple payback is usually three to six years.

16.8 DESIGN OF ENERGY EFFICIENT BUILDING ENVELOPES

Energy efficient building envelopes—considering items such as orientation, building shape, glazing selection, insulation, passive solar features, shading, reflection, and effective use of materials—should be considered as part of any new building design strategy. Incorporating these features in a new building often has an infinite return on investment, since they will reduce annual operating costs with minimal or no increase in initial building construction costs. Energy retrofit projects incorporating these features often have very long paybacks if viewed as only an isolated effort. Paybacks can be immensely improved, however, if envelope retrofits are incorporated into a boiler or chiller replacement project where the envelope project permits purchase of smaller central heating or cooling equipment.

16.9 OPERATIONS AND MAINTENANCE

Continuous maintenance of building HVAC systems (including control systems) is essential to energy-conservative operation of a health care facility. If systems are allowed to operate in an un-maintained state, energy-efficient features of the design will degrade and the energy consumption of the facility will increase. See Chapter 14 for operations and maintenance procedures.

16.10 COMMISSIONING/ RECOMMISSIONING

Commissioning new health care HVAC systems, or recommissioning existing HVAC systems, almost always provides a quick payback from energy savings. The commissioning process is even more essential today than in the past because of the use of sophisticated computerized strategies to control health care HVAC systems. Subtle changes in these strategies can have significant effects on building energy consumption. See Chapter 15 for commissioning and recommissioning information.

16.11 FINANCING AN ENERGY EFFICIENCY PROGRAM

Many financing options exist to assist health care facility owners in implementing energy efficiency programs in new construction and for retrofit of existing facilities.

Internal Financing

This method often proves to be the most cost-effective approach to energy savings. The building owner, manager, or occupant simply makes a decision to finance the modifications internally, taking advantage of all the savings and assuming all the risk.

Shared Savings Contracts

Under this approach, independent contractors typically install energy-related modifications at their expense. The building owner then pays a prearranged fee, which is usually related to the savings achieved. The length of these contracts runs from several years to as long as 20 years. The terms and conditions of the contract must be carefully documented in advance. In particular, methods of determining energy savings and of accounting for other influences on energy consumption must be carefully and precisely described. In using this approach, there is a need for caution regarding potential fraud and overpricing of construction costs since the contractors have complete control of the assigned prices.

Guaranteed Savings Contracts

These are similar to shared savings contracts, except that the costs of the modifications are specified up front. Energy savings are guaranteed, usually on an annual basis. The owner can pay for the retrofit at the beginning of the contract and finance it over a period of years or have the contractor finance it with repayment out of the savings. If greater savings are achieved, some contracts require that a bonus be paid to the contractor. If less than the guaranteed savings are realized, the owner is reimbursed for the difference. The owner should enter into these agreements carefully, with an understanding of the financial liability if the savings do not materialize and the contractor is unable to make good on the guarantee. With this type of contract, the performance record of the contractor should be examined.

Demand Side Management

Demand side management (DSM) programs are offered by many utilities and commonly subsidize the installation of energy modifications. These programs usually take the form of rebates to contractors or building owners for the installation of specified equipment, and are often carried out by subcontractors or unregulated subsidiaries of utilities. The purpose of these programs is to reduce demand or consumption of the particular form of energy supplied by the utility. Contact the applicable utilities at the beginning of a project to ensure that the highest potential rebates are obtained.

Government Programs

There are numerous federal, state, and local government programs that provide subsidies or tax credits for certain energy modifications.

APPENDIX A
MANAGING CONSTRUCTION AND
RENOVATION TO REDUCE RISK IN
HEALTH CARE FACILITIES

A.1 INTRODUCTION

Risk implies a probability that harm, injury, or disease will occur. Such a probability is obvious when one takes risks beyond reason, for example, accelerating an automobile to 100 mph (161 km/h) in a 30-mph (48 km/h) speed zone. Risk management in today's health care facilities is usually responsive to medical-legal considerations in patient care relating to patient harm from medication, surgical procedures, or misdiagnosis. Safety relating to construction and renovation in health care facilities has focused upon fire and life safety and rarely on infection control. The hazard of ill health to a patient is presented to the health system team that defines an illness and returns the patient to good health. During treatment, patients are exposed to a variety of hazards common to the respective diagnostic and therapeutic treatments. Health care is truly an industry of hazard management. The health care professional must understand the extent of the hazards and implement procedures for patient and employee safety.

Construction and renovation are continuous in health care facilities as organizations upgrade utilities, communications, and diagnostic/therapeutic equipment. As medical technology advances, more hospitals are providing modern treatment modalities for severely ill individuals. Immunocompromising treatments that result from this advancement make opportunistic infectious environmental microbes an emerging threat to patients. It is necessary, therefore, to recognize the risks and investigate the effects on the users of health care facilities (AIA 2001).

A.2 RISK ASSESSMENT

Health care risk assessment must be based upon potential for harm to patients and occupants (Streifel and Hendrikson 2002). These questions should be asked regarding construction projects or maintenance efforts:

- Which patient groups and employees are susceptible to risks from the proposed construction process?
- Which ventilation systems may be involved and how close are they to the construction?
- What effect on pressure relationships in the building may occur when ventilation systems are interrupted?
- Are the current ventilation controls operating according to original design intent?
- Will supplemental ventilation be required during the project?
- How will fire code and interim life safety requirements during construction affect ventilation requirements?
- Is special ventilation for infectious disease prevention (tuberculosis or aspergillosis) affected during construction?
- What impact will noise and vibration have on occupants? Will sound or vibration affect sensitive procedures or equipment?
- How will perceptions affect patients during various noisy or odorous procedures?
- Is there a history of water damage in renovated areas?

Project planning can find and implement methods and procedures to reduce the risks of construction hazards. Such risks can be circumvented by good communication. That generally means two-way, routine communication with the occupants and a means to question or complain to the construction management. This communication must not needlessly interfere with a project but must be taken seriously by the designated owner's representative so that hazards can be controlled. Once a hazard is recognized, a procedure should be in place for investigating it immediately or temporarily stopping the project (Streifel 1997).

A.3   PLANNING

As a project is conceptualized, a plan is started to program the project for the users. The decision to build new or renovate is often made at this stage. The impact of a renovation on current occupants should be considered. Factoring in such concerns at this stage is up to the members of the planning team. Often the program plan does not fully consider the impacts on occupants of a health care building. The team should be multidisciplinary and capable of understanding the impact of construction on buildings. This includes outages necessary for utility work, how work will be conducted to modify mechanical systems, ventilation management in critical areas during phasing, barrier management for airflow, and traffic control. The cost of such planning and subsequent implementation of the control measures is always a factor that administrators consider important to the feasibility of a project. Although at first imposing, the costs can be controlled by appropriate experience and preplanning. A contractor experienced in health care construction has the opportunity to develop a routine, which includes recognizing and handling hazards through routine interventions. For example, a contractor assigned to replace a CT scanner in Diagnostic Radiology understands that substantial barriers are needed along with portable HEPA filtration for certain hospital patients. The bid acceptance procedure should not be based entirely upon low bids. The bid procedure should be based on experience in health care construction and ability to work in that environment.

A.3.1   At-Risk Groups/Areas/Activities

The risk from environmental, opportunistic microorganisms is paramount for certain patients. Current medical practice can include procedures that severely compromise a patient's ability to resist infection.

Patient groups at high risk can include:

- Patients who receive solid organ transplants,
- Premature birth babies,
- Patients who receive bone marrow transplants,
- Oncology patients,
- Patents who receive steroid therapy.

Employee at-risk groups include:

- Employees with solid organ transplants,
- Atopic/allergic employees,
- HIV-infected employees.

Areas with chemical or physical hazard include:

- Medicated aerosol treatment areas,
- Vapor or fumes from disinfection or sterilization,
- Electrocautery smoke plume,
- Laboratory hoods,
- Surgical pathology/morgue.

Mechanical system interventions with high risk potential include:

- Ventilation maintenance or repair,
- Fire management testing,
- Plumbing outages.

Planning for construction demolition must address:

- Dust control,
- Internal versus external projects,
- Filter integrity.

A.4   ENVIRONMENTAL ASSESSMENT

The patient care environment should be evaluated before construction to determine if deficiencies exist in critical areas. Ventilation of protective and airborne infection isolation areas is essential to ensure infection control. Measles, chicken pox, and tuberculosis are airborne infectious diseases that are disseminated when droplets from sneezes or coughs evaporate to create droplet nuclei (which are less than 5.0 μm in diameter). These droplet nuclei are concentrations of infectious particles, which are aerodynamically buoyant and remain airborne for long periods. Buoyant airborne particles increase the probability of inhalation (University of Minnesota 2001).

Airborne environmental-opportunistic spore-forming fungi such as *Aspergillus fumigatus* are a threat to severely immunocompromised patients. These patients are being treated for malignant hematological or solid tumor disorders, solid organ transplants, or other immune-deficient treatments that render them susceptible to common airborne fungi. The case fatality rate for aspergillosis in these patient groups is high due to the difficulty in diagnosing and treating this disease. These fungi are common indoors and outdoors, and it is a challenge to exclude them from the critical patient's environment.

A.5 VENTILATION CONTROL

Rooms for airborne infection isolation (AII) should have definable ventilation parameters. These parameters include room air exchanges, filtration, and airflow direction (pressurization). The parameters for these rooms have been recommended as part of prudent practice. The criteria that define the benchmark parameters for these special ventilation rooms are important to understand. The differences for AII rooms and PE rooms pertain to exhaust for all air in the AII setting and filtration requirements for the supply air in the PE room, or, if air is recirculated from the AII room, it should be HEPA filtered.

The following is a list of recommended parameters for all special ventilation rooms:

- Air exchanges per hour: >12
- Filtration: 90% dust spot efficiency or MERV 14
- Pressurization: 0.01–0.03 in. w.g. (2.5 to 7.5 Pa) filtration verification

It is essential for the protective environment that a reduction of particles be verified after filtration. If a HEPA (99.97% efficient for a 0.3-μm particle) filter is used, PE room criteria should be provided. These criteria would establish a rank order of particle concentration. The analysis can be of viable or nonviable particles. The viable particle is important, but the incubation time to get the data requires more than seven days for analysis. What good are the data after that time should be the question. Efforts to benchmark performance before occupancy are ideal when using viable culture methods. Using comparison sampling of areas, results should indicate that areas with the highest level of filtration have the lowest particle counts—both viable and nonviable. The advantage of using an optical or laser particle counter is real-time data retrieval. Particle-count information does not indicate whether airborne particles are opportunistic microbial agents, but a particle count will demonstrate particle removal that ensures ventilation integrity.

A.5.1 Room Air Exchanges

Air exchanges for critical rooms should be as specified by design guidelines established by the American Institute of Architects and the American Society of Heating, Refrigerating and Air-Conditioning Engineers, Inc., for health care construction. Refer to Table 4-1 in this manual for air exchange rates. These rates should be site-verified before spe-

cially ventilated patient care areas are occupied (ASHRAE 1999a).

The location of diffusers and the type of air "throw" are also important in managing airborne particles and controlling gas or fumes. Open doors and windows can negate special ventilation requirements for infection control. Sufficient outside air should be provided to ensure recommended fresh air requirements.

A.5.2 Pressure or Airflow Direction

Room pressurization is often described as airflow "in" or "out" of respective special ventilation areas. These special ventilation rooms should have self-closing doors to ensure the special ventilation requirements can be maintained. Pressure criteria should be defined via a performance range. The range for special ventilation rooms should be between 0.01 and 0.03 in. w.g. (2.5 to 7.5 Pa). Maintaining such pressure requires a tight room and an offset of supply or exhaust/return ventilation. The room tightness can be defined in square feet of openings. For example, if there are 0.5 ft^2 (0.004 m^2) of openings, there should be an offset of 125 cfm (59 L/s) to provide 0.01 in. w.g. (2.5 Pa) pressure differential. Leakage, which can prevent proper pressurization, can occur around plumbing penetrations, light fixtures, and windows.

These ventilation parameters should be evaluated and altered to conform to infection control criteria before a project begins in critical health care areas. Too often, administrators who are unfamiliar with the infection risk of construction and maintenance activities make uninformed management decisions that impact safe patient care.

A.6 PROJECT IMPLEMENTATION

A project is conducted either internally or external to a facility. The impact of any project must be categorized. A project risk assessment should include the impact of demolition and excavation on the integrity of the building's exterior and building penetrations. If windows are deteriorating, for example, they should be sealed. Air filtration should be ensured before a project begins. Filters that are improperly installed in a filter housing can allow air to bypass the filter. During excavation, particles can pass significantly around improperly maintained filters and cause patient infections. Methods to determine filter leaks have been developed using particle counters to ensure that the filtration efficacy is similar to the filter rating. During internal, and at times external, projects, barrier protection is important for preventing movement of dirty-to-clean construction air. Therefore, a smoke barrier is essential for preventing smoke and construction aerosol movement into critical health care spaces. Due to the chimney effect, unfiltered air can enter high-rise buildings via underground utility tunnels during demolition and excavation.

Risk assessment in anticipation of emergencies is difficult. When a gas leak occurs, what should be done if patients are receiving invasive therapies, such as kidney dialysis or oral surgery? Such accidents happen during complex demolition projects in areas where plans showing buried utilities are not readily available. Fires, water main breaks, and crumbling buildings can all contribute risks to complex demolition and construction projects in health care settings. An infection control tool in the form of a check list (Table A-1) should be developed to provide guidance and documentation for respective projects. Communication and planning will help to prepare an enlight-

ened construction manager for the unusual occurrence (Kuehn et al. 1996).

A.7 COMMUNICATION

Communication during construction should be considered a "given," but there are essential elements that must be defined. For example, who has the authority to stop a project and under what conditions? Such issues must be addressed before a project begins. Who will handle complaints about the project? The complaint might be about excessive vibration affecting microscope-assisted brain surgery or an odor in the bone marrow transplant unit. Which one is potentially an infection control issue? What response is appropriate during such conditions? The project team should develop construction implementation logic before project work begins. The team should consist of infection control, safety, construction administration, facilities management, and contractor's representatives. The team should prepare a

Table A-1. Sample Infection Control Monitoring Checklist

Infection Control	Yes	No	Comments
All barriers are in place and integrity is maintained.			
Airflow is maintained from clean to dirty.			
There is compliance with traffic patterns.			
There is compliance with covering clothing requirements when appropriate for infection control.			
Equipment is in place to prevent airborne particles from migrating to PT areas: portable HEPA filters, HEPA filter vacuums, exhaust fans, self-closing construction entrance doors, exhaust fans, or debris chutes.			
Doors closed to project and properly signed.			
Appropriate debris transport: covered cart, dedicated elevator, designated route, etc.			
All windows, doors, and debris chutes to the outside are secured when not in use.			
Carpet or other track-dirt compliance aids are in place at the doors leading to the hospital/clinic/support space. Housekeeping is notified for "as needed" cleaning.			
Areas are cleaned at the end of the day; trash is removed.			
Water leakage is handled as it occurs in occupied clinical areas. There is immediate notification of facilities management. Immediate action is taken to ensure drying in less than 72 hours.			
Pest control: no visible signs of mice, insects, birds, squirrels, or other vermin.			
Roof protection is in place.			
Other Notes:			

safe plan or project implementation for the shared mission of occupant protection from certain exposures due to a disrupted health care environment. Bid document and specification language should be consistent with expectations. Radio and phone contact must be available to critical team members to prevent confusion and to facilitate corrective action when emergencies occur.

Perception plays a large role in how people react to risk. If someone in an operating room smells something like smoke, the first instinct is avoiding risk to the surgical patient. This perception usually results in a delay in the procedure and ultimately causes problems with scheduling in a busy operating room. If, however, the construction management notifies the OR control supervisor that odors due to welding may occur on a given shift, the issue could be understood and schedules maintained. This applies to noise and vibration, construction traffic, utility outage, and ventilation adjustment in almost any area of a health care facility.

Construction meetings during most projects are generally routine. Who participates in the meetings and the protocols for information dissemination, however, are not routine. These issues vary according to the size of the project. Reducing risk by using clearly understood communication pathways will help to avoid confusion and help focus on logical ways of reducing risk when and if an emergency develops.

A.8 COMMISSIONING

Specially ventilated areas should have their operating parameters verified before acceptance by the owner. Commissioning can accomplish such verification. Verification requirements should be part of the bid documentation. Disputes regarding critical ventilation issues should be avoided by providing direction to the architect, construction manager, and contractors as part of the commissioning process. The owner should provide commissioning information from the perspectives of infection control and safety. The AIA, and the CDC's *Guideline for Environmental Infection Control* (2001), address infection control design and construction issues (AIA 2001; JCAHO 2002).

A.9 LEGAL ISSUES

This contentious topic must be addressed. If litigation occurs due to perceived or real infection control factors, resources will be used either to defend or accuse. Recently, a lawsuit that resulted from construction and fungal infection problems was settled out of court in Massachusetts ("Verdicts and Settlements" 1999). The hospital settled because critical environmental factors were not acted upon as a result of construction-related issues associated with environmental testing, construction practice, and air balance. Plaintiffs and defendants are currently litigating to resolve disputes through the use of definable environmental parameters. Neglect or competence in the management of engineering controls in the health care environment is often subject to legal interpretation (Laurel et al. 1999).

In construction and renovation, it is often challenging to provide a finished product on time. The dynamic nature of health care and the essential element of safety in continuously occupied facilities provide even more challenge. The concepts of risk assessment, communication, and emergency preparation are essential in providing a safe environment for patient care (Davis 1998).

APPENDIX B
DISASTER MANAGEMENT

B.1 INTRODUCTION

Health care organizations are subject to both internal and external disasters that might affect an institution's mechanical systems to the point of disrupting services. Hospital reactions to internal disasters such as fire are published in NFPA 101, Life Safety Code (NFPA 2000). JCAHO Standard EC.1.4 requires that a hospital plan address emergency management (JCAHO 2000). Item 1 states, "An alternative means of meeting essential building utility needs (for example, electricity, water, ventilation, fuel sources, medical gas/vacuum systems) when the hospital is designated by its emergency plan to provide continuous service during a disaster or emergency." The AIA Guidelines, Section 1.4, addresses disasters that affect the hospital itself (AIA 1996).

An external or community disaster such as an earthquake, train wreck, chemical spill, bioterrorism, or infectious epidemic presents an added set of considerations, primarily the designation of emergency spaces to serve larger than usual numbers of victims. Hospital staffs are remarkably resourceful and innovative when confronted with emergencies; nevertheless, their provision of care can be greatly aided if spaces such as lobbies and meeting rooms have mechanical capabilities already in place that allow them to function as emergency treatment areas. Some communities may be located near chemical plants, nuclear plants, or other industrial complexes that could predispose the community to contamination or to industrial injuries. Terrorist attack, explosion, biological threat, chemical spill, or multiple shootings can strike any place, possibly in areas where few suspect such threats. Hospital governing bodies and communities can decide if their hospitals are to be prepared to respond to community disasters. The Joint Commission on Accreditation of

Healthcare Organizations advises in its Standards overview that "planning and designing is consistent with the hospital's mission and vision (JCAHO 1997)."

Emergency protocols are set into motion by a designated member of the hospital staff. Trauma disaster is immediately evident by the size of the occurrence and the number of people involved. A recognition of biological disasters, on the other hand, might be delayed. A cluster of patients who have bizarre or unexplained symptoms might trigger the suspicion of biological disaster. Once disaster is declared, necessary personnel must be contacted to come to the hospital. If ordinary communication routes are out of commission, alternate emergency communication capabilities must be available. In some cases, local law enforcement agencies or hospital maintenance vehicles may be needed to bring personnel to the hospital.

Traumatic, chemical, nuclear, and biological disasters will not preclude using normal hospital treatment areas, unless (1) available hospital beds and areas are inadequate to handle the number of victims or (2) the hospital itself is damaged by the disaster, as in seismic or terrorist disasters. Emergency stores (water, food, medication, fuel) might be required if a disaster occurs within the hospital or to a portion of the hospital itself, if ordinary external supply mechanisms are hindered, or if patients from a damaged hospital must be evacuated to a host hospital.

B.2 TERRORISM

The events of September 11, 2001, have brought the realities of terrorism to our doorstep. Disaster preparation for our institutions and our communities is no longer an afterthought. Community facilities such as schools, buses, and hospitals are likely targets of terrorism. Terrorists have a tendency to hit the most vulnerable, the most populous, and the most emotionally charged targets. Many governmental and institutional committees are presently working on recommendations for protection. In the meantime, the following aspects of the problem can be considered, as well as the recommendations in the following sections.

Basically, three types of terrorism delivery routes are available: (1) delivery from afar (nuclear, chemical, biological bombs); (2) delivery from within (sabotage or contamination of water, food, or air) where the culprits try to save themselves; and (3) delivery by suicidal fanatics.

Prevention is the most effective remedy for terrorist activity, just as prevention is the most effective remedy for disease. In the case of delivery from afar, military/intelligence interception is the most effective protection. If a terrorist organization has gone to the trouble and the expense of inserting many operatives into an area, it is unlikely that it would destroy its own organization by a generally lethal airborne attack. On the other hand, suppose that such insanity does indeed exist and that smallpox is released into the air of a community (terrorist operatives might consider themselves protected by immunization). The first problem would be detection. There are, as yet, no electronic sensors that detect smallpox in the air. Detection would result from recognition that a cluster of unusual cases is smallpox, diagnoses that will not be easy or rapid. Instituting protective measures at this point would be shutting the barn door after the horse has gone. Should this cluster of patients be evacuated? Should the hospital be evacuated? Should the community be evacuated? Evacuation raises the possibility of infecting other, previously uninfected, areas. This raises the specter of quarantine. Should the hospital outside air intake be protected by HEPA filtration, by carbon filtration, or by UV radiation? The original cluster of patients contracted the disease outside the hospital. All of the hospital workers left the hospital and circulated in the community during the several days between the release of the virus and its detection. Very little would be achieved by sterilizing the hospital's outside air intake. In the case of smallpox, the disease enters the hospital through the emergency room, not through the air intake. Universal immunization seems a better option than equipping all hospital outside air intakes with fan-power-consuming HEPA and carbon filtration.

On the other hand, a cloud of contamination could drift over the hospital. HEPA filtration would protect the hospital from microbial attack, and carbon filtration would protect from chemical attack. Does the possibility of such attacks warrant the expenditures for sophisticated filtration systems and permanently increased fan power for all hospitals? Perhaps the air intake could simply be closed off until the cloud passes. Perhaps minimally recirculating air could be augmented by bottled oxygen. Detecting noxious air and predicting hospital involvement would be necessary to institute these measures. "Purging" (noxious air removal) from the hospital is a valid defense, particularly in cases of localized contamination. Ordinary smoke control systems and defend-in-place strategies can be used for purging, but this would require planning and education of personnel.

The second case, delivery from within, presents a different set of considerations. The recent anthrax disaster taught a very valuable lesson: in-place delivery systems can be used for transmitting deadly microbes as well as explosives (the Unabomber). Irradiation of mail will probably protect us from microbe dissemination. Irradiation is a possible protection for all mail and package delivery systems, not only for the U.S. Mail. Hospitals can protect themselves by ensuring that air intakes are inaccessible to the public, ventilation in public areas is isolated, mechanical rooms are protected by heightened security, and supplies (water, food, medicines) are protected by heightened security. The ability to "purge" affected areas is advisable.

The third case, delivery by suicidal fanatic, would initiate the same hospital responses as the first two cases: detection, identification, notification of authorities, isolation if the malady is communicable (or undiagnosed), treatment, immunization in cases such as smallpox, prophylactic antibiotics in cases such as anthrax, and possible evacuation if the community is no longer viable. It may be less likely that suicide fanatics can be recruited to undergo a slow and painful entry into paradise by disease rather than by explosion.

B.3 DISASTER CLASSIFICATION

This classification is developed for this publication and is not an institutionally recognized classification system.

B.3.1 Internal Disasters

An internal disaster is one that affects the hospital itself, its patients, its systems, its personnel, and/or its spaces. A fire within the hospital, for example, is an internal disaster. A hurricane, on the other hand, is an external disaster, but it might affect internal hospital systems such as the power supply. In such a case, internal disaster contingencies would be initiated, and the emergency generators would be switched on. The following are possible internal disasters that require planned emergency and/or backup planning:

1. Fire

2. Power disruption

3. Water supply disruption or contamination

4. Ventilation system failure or contamination

5. Heating system failure

6. Fuel supply disruption

7. Medical gas system disruption

8. Steam supply disruption resulting in inoperable autoclaves and humidification failure

9. Nosocomial infection outbreaks (possible pressurization failure)

10. Loss of internal communications

11. Loss of external communications

12. Structural failure (earthquake, flood, tornado, explosion)

13. Supplies deficit (food, drugs, linens, medical gases, blood products)

14. Terrorist attack on the hospital itself (chemical, biological, explosive)

15. Elevator failure

See Paragraph 1.4.C, 1996-97 *Guidelines for Design and Construction of Hospital and -Healthcare Facilities* (AIA).

B.3.2 External Disasters

Disasters such as large or multiple vehicular accidents, accidental release of gaseous chemicals into the community, and multiple trauma due to natural disasters and large fires can happen in any community. Some communities may be near chemical plants, nuclear plants, or other industrial complexes. External disasters might produce so many victims that the normal hospital treatment areas and protocols are overwhelmed and alternate emergency spaces and procedures must be used. The following is a suggested classification of external disasters:

- *Multiple trauma disasters*
  a. Accidental (vehicular pile-up, hurricane, tornado, fire, earthquake)
  b. Terrorist (explosion)

- *Chemical disasters*
  a. Accidental (train wreck involving chemical tank car)
  b. Terrorist (water supply contamination, airborne/explosive, food contamination)

- *Biological disasters*
  a. Unidentified severe illness, possibly infectious
  b. Epidemic (waterborne, airborne, insect vector)
  c. Terrorist (water supply contamination, airborne/explosive, food contamination)

- *Nuclear disasters*
  a. Accidental (industrial)
  b. Terrorist

- *Evacuation disaster*
  a. Accommodation of patients and staff from an evacuated health care facility

B.3.2.1 Trauma Disasters

Readiness for trauma disasters is the basic and minimum degree of preparation for disaster readiness, and, it is mandated by the JCAHO *Hospital Accreditation Standards* (1997). A sudden volume of trauma victims, a volume larger than can be accommodated by the hospital's normal emergency facilities, requires a triage area, treatment areas (first aid, medical, surgical, and casting), sterilization capability, observation space, convalescent space, in-hospital communications, extra-hospital communications, in-hospital transportation, extra-hospital transportation, and supplies of water, medicines, cots, stretchers, food, fuel, clothing, medical gases, and first aid.

B.3.2.2 Chemical Disasters

Readiness for chemical disasters requires the basic (trauma) preparations listed in B.3.2.1 plus decontamination (wash) and special waste containment capabilities. Preparation of the decontamination area is clearly outlined in *Managing Hazardous Materials Incidents, Volume II, Hospital Emergency Departments* (USDHS 1992), obtainable on the U.S. Centers for Disease Control and Prevention web site: http://wonder.cdc.gov/wonder/prevguid/p0000019/p0000019.asp.

Although diseases due to chemical exposure are not contagious, ventilation isolation is advisable to prevent entry of deleterious chemicals from contaminated clothing, debris, or air.

B.3.2.3 Biological Disasters

- *Unidentified severe illness, possibly infectious* (such as Hanta or Ebola viruses): This classification is more of a potential disaster when it is recognized than a disaster that involves many victims. Lack of recognition and lack of proper handling can then predispose a hospital to a disaster that involves many victims, particularly hospital personnel and patients. Initial isolation and heightened suspicion are paramount in this situation. See *Bioterrorism Readiness Plan*.

- *Epidemic* (Hospital Infection Control Practices Advisory Committee 1996): An epidemic is a disaster that involves multiple victims of a possibly contagious disease. This situation requires basic preparations (B.3.2.1) as well as isolation protocols, waste isolation, and separate ventilation. Patients should be isolated from the general hospital population but not necessarily from each other; thus, a single large space with multiple beds (and screens) can be used (see Simon 1997).

- *Bioterrorism* (Simon 1997): The preparations for a bioterrorism disaster are similar to those for chemical disasters. Basic preparations (B.3.2.1) plus decontamination (wash) procedures, waste containment, and ventilation isolation are required.

B.3.2.4 Nuclear Disasters

Wash/decontamination facilities are the central component of nuclear disaster readiness. As in chemical disasters, specialized protective gear and clothing are necessary for workers in the wash area, in this case, radiation protective gear and clothing. As in chemical disasters, everyone in the community exposed to the radiation must be decontaminated and supplied with safe clothing. Basic preparations (B.3.2.1) and nuclear waste containment capabilities are also required. Communication with outside authorities and community rescue teams is essential (FEMA 1984; Ricks 1984).

B.3.2.5 Evacuation Disasters

a. *Hospital Evacuation*. The hospital may become dysfunctional and require evacuation due to destruction or failure of internal ser-

vices. Special areas are obviously not required, but communication and transportation (of patients) capabilities are critical. Elevator service in a multistory building is essential.

b. *Evacuation Reception*. A nearby hospital may become nonfunctional and need to evacuate its patients to a receiving facility. That facility may already be full with its own patients and therefore require the use of alternate patient care spaces. These spaces require all of the mechanical and supply services that are necessary in ordinary treatment and convalescent areas. Communication and transportation capabilities are paramount.

B.4 SPACE DEFINITIONS

B.4.1 Triage Space

Victims of a disaster are brought to a triage area where those who have the most life-threatening injuries are identified for immediate treatment. In nuclear exposure and chemical exposure, victims must first be brought through a total body cleaning and clothing disposal area before entering triage. Workers in the bathing area must have appropriate protective clothing. The triage area of a hospital is usually the emergency room. The emergency room's waiting room and/or other hospital waiting rooms can be used for additional triage space if they are accessible to the outside and are equipped with isolated ventilation, electricity, water, communications, etc. (see Sections B.5.1 to B.5.6).

B.4.2 Wash Area (Decontamination)

Nuclear disasters require total body washing and total clothing change of all exposed victims (ambulatory and non-ambulatory) whether admitted into the facility or not. Decontamination facilities are located outside the facility and can be collapsible tent-like enclosures.

Total body washing and new clothing are also necessary in massive chemical exposures and in terrorist biological exposures. Special protective gear and clothing are necessary for the wash area personnel. Note that not only will victims require decontamination but so, too, will those in the community who have responded to the emergency, such as firemen, EMS personnel, and other civil agents.

B.4.3 Waste Isolation

Trauma disasters: Waste/clothing can be disposed of in the usual manner.

Chemical disasters: Waste/clothing must be held in such a manner that all personnel are safe from contact with the waste. In chemical terrorism, the waste must be retained and made available for examination by the proper authorities.

Nuclear disasters: Waste/clothing must be held in a radiation-shielded area and disposed of later in a manner dictated by the proper authorities. Incineration is not an option because of the possibility of introducing radioactive molecules into the air.

Biological disasters: In an epidemic of an identified disease, waste/clothing can be disposed of according to standard isolation and disposal techniques. In bioterrorism, waste must be held isolated for examination by proper authorities. In the case of unidentified infective agents, waste must be held isolated for examination by proper authorities and by appropriate laboratories.

B.4.4 Isolation Space

A space other than the triage area and the general hospital can be designated for isolation of patients thought to be infectious. The designated isolation area should have total exhaust and negative pressurization. Care must be taken that air is exhausted well away from habitable areas.

B.4.5 Treatment Space

Ordinarily, emergency rooms and operating rooms serve as treatment areas and should be sufficient for serving as disaster treatment areas, unless they are damaged by the disaster. Delivery rooms can be taken over as disaster treatment and operating rooms. If the hospital medical staff is large (more available doctors than existing treatment rooms), auxiliary areas can be designated as disaster treatment areas and should be equipped with clean air and emergency power.

Sterilization capability (autoclave) is a critical component of the treatment area. Designated auxiliary treatment areas as well as existing treatment areas must have access to fail-safe sterilization capability. This may consist of an emergency autoclave fueled by the emergency electrical system or by liquid petroleum. Gas sterilization systems are unacceptable as the only method of sterilization in disaster situations because of the increased time they require for sterilization and for evacuating gas.

B.5 REQUIRED SERVICES IN EMERGENCY AND DISASTER

The following are the initial emergency priorities in managing a critically ill or injured patient:

1. Establish an airway (breathing and heartbeat, i.e., resuscitation),

2. Stop bleeding,

3. Establish vascular access (fluids, blood products, medications),

4. Establish vascular stability (treat shock),

5. Diagnostic procedures (monitoring, X ray, ECG, lab),

6. Surgery and/or treatment.

All mechanical services necessary for these procedures must be in place for optimal and successful emergency response.

B.5.1 Power

Guidelines exist for design of emergency power grids (NFPA 2000; JCAHO 2000; AIA 2001). Power must be supplied to all of the designated auxiliary emergency treatment areas. The triage area requires power for light, ventilation, communication, diagnostic equipment, suction machines, defibrillators, monitors, portable X-ray machines, IV pumps, respiratory therapy equipment, and possibly for sterilization equipment. Power outlets for these uses must be available in spaces designed for alternate treatment areas (see Paragraph 1.4.A1, 1996-97 *Guidelines for Design and Construction of Hospital and Healthcare Facilities*).

B.5.2 Water

Uncontaminated water is necessary for washing (hands, patients, instruments, equipment), food preparation, sterilization, and possibly medicinal preparation. Disruption or contamination of the ordinary hospital water supply requires access to an alternate supply. This alternate supply can be from a well or from storage tanks. The capacity should be sufficient to last for four continuous days (see Paragraph 1.4.C, 1996-97 *Guidelines for Design and Construction of Hospital and Healthcare Facilities*).

B.5.3 Ventilation

Paragraph 7.9D2, 1996-97 *Guidelines for Design and Construction of Hospital and Healthcare Facilities* requires that the triage area (of the ordinary hospital emergency facility) "be designed and ventilated to reduce exposure of staff, patients and families to airborne infectious diseases." This is best accomplished by 100% exhaust and transfer or by intake of uncontaminated air. Recirculating 99.7% HEPA-filtered air is an acceptable alternative but would require more fan power.

B.5.4 Sterilization

Sterilization can become a problem if the hospital's steam generation capability is interrupted. Autoclaves that use an alternative energy source are required. Sterilization is necessary for surgical instruments, fluids, linens, and reusable equipment.

B.5.5 Communication

Communications and transport of data within a hospital are very important to day-to-day operations but become critical during extraordinary circumstances such as a disaster.

In a disaster, extra-hospital communications become critical. Communications with rescue vehicles and teams, hospital vehicles, police, laboratories, federal agencies such as the FBI and the CDC, fire department, and off-duty hospital personnel are critical.

B.5.6 Transportation

A hospital functions very much like a factory. Its "product," the patient, must be transported from function to function, sometimes rapidly (triage to surgery). Pure mechanical transport of patients (assembly line) is unacceptable. Patients are transported by people, often by several people if life support equipment is involved. The greater the distances between stations (triage to X-ray, for instance), the greater will be delays in treatment and the greater will be the need for transport personnel. Functioning elevators are essential. All hospital elevators must be on the emergency electrical grid and must be large enough to transport patients on stretchers since some

of the elevators may be damaged or not functioning during an emergency. One cannot predict which elevators will fail.

Extra-hospital transportation capability is necessary to bring patients into the hospital setting, to transfer patients to other facilities, to bring in supplies, to transport laboratory specimens, and to bring in extra and off-duty staff.

B.6 SUMMARY

B.6.1 General Principles of Management

The mechanical services required to manage the various types of disasters are remarkably similar. Several general considerations are helpful in planning:

1. Designate alternative diagnostic and treatment areas for use when ordinary hospital areas are overrun or out of commission.

2. Install exhaust capability in areas that might be used to treat people who have communicable disease and in areas accessible to the general public.

3. Designate large areas for use that already have ventilation isolation, such as lobbies or waiting areas.

4. Install external wash/decontamination capability.

5. Provide redundant storage of ordinary supplies, food, water, medicines, cots, etc.

6. Provide redundant communication and transportation capabilities.

7. Provide redundant sterilization capability.

8. Use existing smoke-control systems and defend-in-place procedures in cases of internal chemical or biological contamination.

9. Provide security for hospital air intakes, mechanical equipment, and entrances for people and materials.

Table B-1. Mechanical Services Required in Disaster Situations

Disaster Type	Condition	Space Designation	Emergency Power	Total Exhaust (L)	Ventilation Isolation	Positive Pressure	Negative Pressure	Hepa Filtration	Heat	Water	Sterilization (D)	Hot Water (G)	Total Body Washing	Protective Gear	Eyewash	Medical Gases	Waste Isolation	Food	Clothing	Medicines (Drugs, IVs, etc.)	First Aid Supplies	Surgical Supplies	Respiratory Therapy	Communication In-Hosp	Communication Extra-Hosp	Transportation In-Hosp	Transportation Extra-Hosp
Multiple trauma — Accidental or terrorism	Basic	Triage	+	B	B		B		+	+	+	+	+		+	+			+	+	+		+	+	+	+	+
		Surgery	+			+				+	+	+				+				+	+	+		+		+	
		Observation	+						+	+						+		+	+	+			+	+			
		Convalescent	+						+	+		+				+		+	+	+			+	+			
		Storage																+	+	+	+	+	+				
		Lab, X-ray	+							+						+								+		+	+
	If hospital involved	Food Prep (E), Pharmacy (A)	+						+	+														+	+	+	+
Chemical — Accidental or terrorism	Basic	Wash/Decontam	+	+	+		+		+	+		+	++(F)	+	+	+	+		++	+			+	+	+	+	+
		Treatment	+	+	+		+		+	+		+			+	+		+		+	+		+	+	+		
		Triage	+						+	+		+				+				+	+		+	+			
	If event is too large to be absorbed by hospital	Observation	+						+	+						+		+	+	+			+	+			
		Convalescent	+						+	+		+						+	+			+	+	+			
	If hospital involved (C)	Storage								+																	
		Lab, X-ray	+						+	+														+	+	+	
		Food Prep (E), Pharmacy (A)	+						+	+														+	+	+	+

Table B-1. Mechanical Services Required in Disaster Situations (Continued)

Category	Sub-category	Service	Mechanical Services
Biological	Unknown epidemic or terrorism with hospital involved — Basic	Wash/Decontam	+ + + + + H + + + + + + + + + + + + + + + + +
		Isolation	+ + + + H + + + + + + + + + + + + + + + +
		Treatment	+ + + + H + + + + + + + + + + + + + + + +
		Lab, X-ray (I)	+ + + + H + + + + + + + + + + + + + + + + + +
	Epidemic too large to be absorbed by hospital	Triage	+ L J +
		Storage	+ L J + + + + + + + + + + + +
		Observation	+ + + + + + + + + + + + +
		Convalescent	+ L J + + + + + + + + + + + + + + +
		Food Prep (E), Pharmacy (A)	+ + + + + + + + +
	Terrorism, hospital not involved — Basic	Wash/Decontam	+ L K + + + + + + + + + + + + + + + +
		Triage	+ L K + + + + + + + + + + + + + + + + + +
		Treatment	+ L K + + + + + + + + + + + + + +
		Observation	+ L K + + + + + + + + + + + + + +
		Convalescent	+ L K + + + + + + + + + + + + + +
		Storage	+ + + + + + + + + + +
	If too large to be absorbed by hospital	Lab, X-ray (I)	+ L K + + + + + + + + + + + + + +
		Food Prep (E), Pharmacy (A)	+ + + + + +
Nuclear	Basic	Wash/Decontam	+ + + + + + + + + + + + + + + + + + +
		Triage	+ + + + + + + + + + + + + + + + + + +
		Treatment	+ + + + + + + + + + + +
		Observation	+ + + + + + + + +
		Convalescent	+ + + + + + + + +
		Storage	+ + + + + + +
	If too large to be absorbed by hospital	Lab, X-ray	+ + + + + + +
		Food Prep (E), Pharmacy (A)	+ + + + + + + + +

Table B-1. Mechanical Services Required in Disaster Situations (Continued)

Table B-1 Notes

A. *Food Prep*: Alternate area for food preparation if hospital kitchen is too small or damaged. *Pharmacy*: Alternate area for medication preparation if hospital pharmacy is damaged. Emergency food and medicine supplies are included under "storage."

B. The triage area ventilation should be isolated (total exhaust, treated or filtered return) because hospital ventilation generally should be protected against return air from uncontrolled areas and from potentially contaminated public areas.

C. Local release of noxious chemicals in a hospital can be devastating. The defence for such a release is similar to the NFPA defend-in-place strategy for fire and smoke control in health care facilities (see Chapter 11); i.e., evacuation of people from affected area, air evacuation, and pressurization of unaffected areas.

D. Sterilization capability is a paramount feature of hospitals, especially in emergency conditions. An independent form of sterilization will be necessary should central hospital services fail.

E. Backup cooking fuel source is needed.

F. Double-plus sign emphasizes importance under these circumstances.

G. Hand washing is by far the most effective means of preventing the spread of microbes and other pathogenic materials. Washing facilities should, therefore, be easily available in all hospital areas and to all personnel. Hand washing is more comfortable with warm water, but can be done with only cold water. Items marked here are those that need hot water—over and above that needed for hand washing.

H. HEPA filtration is most necessary in situations of unknown infective agents. Ventilation isolation (separation) may be sufficient in other biological emergency situations.

I. In this case, the X-ray machine or facility should be separate from the main X-ray department whether the main X-ray department is down or not.

J. A biological spill or attack within the hospital can be handled by the same defend-in-place strategy as in chemical or smoke control, i.e., evacuation (and isolation in this case) of people, evacuation of air, and pressurization of other areas.

K. The necessity for ventilation isolation may be determined by the agent involved. In cases such as anthrax, where the victim is not contagious, ventilation isolation might not be necessary once the victim is decontaminated. In cases of more infectious and secondarily transmitted or unknown agents, ventilation isolation is necessary.

L. Listing "Total Exhaust," "Ventilation Isolation," and "Negative Pressurization" seems somewhat redundant. "Total Exhaust" is listed because it is probably the least expensive method of achieving both ventilation isolation and negative pressurization. Care must be taken, however, to exhaust possibly contaminated air well away from people and from air intakes.

APPENDIX C
LOAD CALCULATIONS AND
EQUIPMENT HEAT GAINS

C.1 INTRODUCTION

This appendix is not intended to duplicate any of the chapters in the *ASHRAE Handbook—Fundamentals* on air-conditioning load calculations or the thousands of pages written in support of DOE-2 or commercially available computer load programs. The intention is to highlight specific aspects of cooling and heating load calculations for health care facilities.

C.2 OUTDOOR AND INDOOR DESIGN CONDITIONS

The outdoor design conditions (temperature, humidity, and other factors) relate to the location of the building. They are the given, based upon historical climatic data, and must be clearly defined in the project design criteria or basis of design. To calculate cooling and heating loads, the design summer and winter conditions will suffice. To select a system based on life-cycle cost analysis or to design a central plant where the cooling and heating might intertwine, however, climatic conditions during an entire year must be considered. Annual cooling and heating loads and daily load profiles are typically calculated using energy analysis computer programs.

The indoor design conditions are the conditions under which the building must operate. They are established as design criteria early in design; they are not statistically derived but are established according to the occupancy needs of each space in a building. Variations in indoor design conditions over time must also be established in accordance with the schedule of operation of the individual spaces.

Refer to Chapter 4 for general design criteria and approach and to Chapters 12 and 13 for specific indoor design criteria for various types of spaces.

C.3 DESIGN LOADS

C.3.1 Lighting Loads

Intensive lighting must be installed in many health care facility spaces to facilitate medical procedures. These loads, apart from general lighting, could be of short duration or may very well last for hours. Most of the time, the schedule for use of these lights is uncertain. Therefore, it is prudent to incorporate them into load calculations at their peak load conditions and to design the system flexibly enough to operate without wasting energy at lower loads.

C.3.2 Occupancy Loads

Sensible and latent heat gains from people in different states of activity that are specific to health care facilities must be considered. Design uncertainties may result from a high population density occurring for an unknown or difficult-to-predict period of time. This is true for waiting rooms, surgery rooms, and the emergency department. Again, it is prudent to incorporate these as peak loads in the calculations, and the system design must be flexible enough to operate without wasting energy at reduced loadings.

C.3.3 Medical Equipment Loads

A major portion of the internal cooling load in a health care facility is due to the heat produced by medical equipment installed in the various spaces. These loads, based upon manufacturers' data, must be evaluated in detail and documented during design. Data for selected equipment may be found in Table C-1.

Table C-1. Typical Medical Equipment Heat Gains

Equipment Type	Peak Watts	Average Watts
Anesthesia System	177	166
Blood Warmer	204	114
Blood Pressure Meter	33	29
Blanket Warmer	504	221
Endoscope	605	596
Electrosurgery	147	109
ECG/RESP	54	50
Harmonical Scalpel	60	59
Hysteroscopic Pump	35	34
Laser Sonics	256	229
Optical Microscope	65	63
Pulse Oximeter	21	20
Stress Treadmill	198	173
X-Ray (Portable C-Arm)	534	480
X-Ray (GX-PAN)	—	82
X-Ray (Portable)	—	18
Vacuum Suction (Portable)	337	302
Ultra-Sound System	1063	1050
Film Viewer, 4 bank	0.3-0.6 kW	
Angiographic Injector	0.6-1.5 kW	
Laser Imager	2.4-3.5 kW	
Film Viewer, Motorized	1.5-2.0 kW	
Bi-Plane Angiographic Imager	7.0-10.5 kW	
CathLab Computer	0.6-1.2 kW	

C.3.4 Ventilation Loads

A significant component of the cooling and heating load is a result of the outside air that has to be brought in to ventilate a space. Many of the health care facility spaces have specific requirements regarding minimum outside air, mandatory requirements regarding the rate of exhaust air, and mandatory requirements regarding the pressure relationships between rooms. These requirements must be established as design criteria based upon the occupancy of each space. Specific data can be found in Chapter 4 and Chapter 12.

C.4 DIVERSITY FACTORS AND SCHEDULE OF OPERATIONS

Many rooms in health care facilities house several pieces of heat-releasing equipment. The resulting internal loads are time dependent. Variations in the operating schedules of the lighting and heat-producing equipment located in the same room greatly affect the peak load of a space. This is probably the most difficult factor to determine and the least precise to calculate.

There are two methods for calculating the heating/cooling loads in these spaces. Both methods must be applied with caution and must be based on an in-depth analysis of the operation of the equipment in the space.

The Diversity Factor Method

The diversity factor is defined as the ratio of the average use of a group of heat-producing equipment items and the sum of their peak heat releases. A diversity factor is determined on the basis of experience or published data and is applied to the sum of the maximum heat releases of all equipment items.

The Schedule of Operation Method

A schedule of operation is assigned to each piece of equipment, and the hourly loads thus resulting are added, hour by hour, to determine the peak load of the space at each hour of the day.

C.5 SUPPLY AIR

The quantity of conditioned air that has to be delivered to a space to satisfy its sensible load is calculated from the formula:

$$\text{cfm} = Q_{max} / 1.1 \times DT \, [\text{L/s} = Q_{max}/1.2 \times DT]$$

where

- Q is the sensible load expressed in Btu/h (W),
- DT is the difference between the room temperature and the temperature of the supply air in °F (°C), and
- 1.1 is the product of the specific weight of dry air at sea level (0.075 lb/ft^3 [1.2 kg/m^3]), the specific heat of moist air at 55°F dry bulb (24.4 Btu/°F lb dry air [1000 J/kg°K]), and 60 min/h.

In regular building occupancies, the supply temperature is predetermined, and the load establishes the air quantity to be delivered to the space. In health care facilities, many spaces have to follow code requirements regarding the minimum quantity of air to be supplied to the room, or room air has to be exhausted to the outside at a minimum rate, or a certain pressure differential must be maintained between rooms. These conditions could make the supply air quantity larger than calculated on the basis of the space load or could require that the systems that serve such spaces be constant volume instead of variable volume systems.

C.6 AIR BALANCE

For reasons previously discussed, system air balance plays an important role in determining health care facility cooling and heating loads. Final calculations of the loads that are seen by the cooling or heating equipment can be determined only after all of the air quantities have been calculated and the entire building has been air balanced.

C.7 HVAC EQUIPMENT SIZING

Numerous factors involved in load calculations, such as weather data and heat transmission coefficients for building materials and assemblies, involve uncertainty. Characteristics of the materials used in the actual construction may be different from those assumed during design. The quality of construction differs from one building to another. Buildings are operated in different ways. Occupancy patterns and the operating schedules of heat-producing equipment are uncertain most of the time. All of these factors make calculation of air-conditioning load numerically imprecise. The best a designer can do is to provide a good estimate of the load. For this reason, a 10% safety margin added to the calculated load is good engineering practice.

Two methods can be used to account for the additional uncertainty of pick-up or transient loads (such as warm-up or cool-down):

- Load calculations that take into account the degree of setback and the necessary recovery time, or
- Estimates that increase the design loads by a certain percentage. California's energy standards, for example, allow a maximum 30% adjustment for heating and 10% for cooling.

Furthermore, equipment sizing should follow the principles enunciated in Chapter 4 for reliability, redundancy, and flexibility, according to the use of the space being served.

APPENDIX D
INFECTION CONTROL ISSUES

D.1 INTRODUCTION

Airborne transmission of disease has been a problem since mankind has lived indoors. Sunlight (UV radiation) kills most microbes that cause disease in humans. Many respiratory pathogens have adapted to our comfortable indoor environments, thereby escaping the deadly sunlight. Airborne pathogens have always been a problem. Current concerns, such as microbial resistance to antibiotics, the incidence of other nosocomial infections, and the high cost and morbidity of nosocomial infections, magnify the problem.

Robert Bazell of NBC News reported on December 27, 2000: "It's a danger of staggering proportions. Every year, one in twenty Americans—8 million people—develop an infection, with 88,000 of them dying. The biggest threat: "supergerms" resistant to antibiotics...."

Although HVAC engineers are primarily concerned with problems that are "airborne" (respiratory infections), other nosocomial infections can be ameliorated by engineering and/or architectural considerations. Kowalski and Bahnfleth produced a superb review of airborne respiratory disease, control of microbes, and mechanical systems published by *HPAC* in July 1998. The paper is reproduced at the end of this appendix.

Health care facilities are the only places where nosocomial infections can be acquired. Patients who have the worst infections wind up at a hospital. Patients who have the most drug-resistant organisms wind up at a hospital. Infected patients without regular medical care (without medical insurance) wind up in hospital emergency rooms (and waiting rooms) after they have put off seeking help as long as possible. A community's worst and most drug-resistant infections are, therefore, concentrated in a single community location—the hospital where we take our most vulnerable and susceptible loved ones. It is incumbent upon us as citizens, hospital workers, architects, and engineers to do our utmost to prevent the spread and proliferation of infection.

D.2 CONTEXT FOR INFECTION CONTROL

Our current health care system has a few quirks that might discourage all-out infection control. Hospitals are not compensated directly for the costs of instituting infection control programs. Also, hospital *revenues* are *higher* as infections and complications increase. The incentive for hospitals to control infections is lacking in the milieu of "running hospitals like businesses." The situation is similar to the "change-order" mechanism in design-construction. Hospital stays are becoming shorter, so infections (and other complications) may not become evident until after a patient is discharged. Thus, an infection might be treated outside of the hospital and therefore not be reported in hospital infection statistics. Hospital infection statistics are difficult to obtain because many hospitals consider that data proprietary information.

D.3 NOSOCOMIAL INFECTION COSTS AND MORBIDITY

"The total number of nosocomial and other institutional infections exceeds 4 million per year, a number substantially larger than the total number of admissions for all cancer, accidents and acute myocardial infarctions combined" (Martone et al. 1998). Table D-1, reflecting the costs of nosocomial infections, is taken from Chapter 30 in *Hospital Infections* (Martone et al. 1998).

The numbers in the table do not reflect the extra pain and suffering that patients and their families

Table D-1. Estimated Extra Days, Extra Charges, and Deaths Attributable to Nosocomial Infections Annually in U.S. Hospitals

	Extra Days		Extra Charges			Deaths Directly Caused by Infections		Deaths Contributed by Infection	
	Avg. per infection[a]	Est. U.S. total[b]	Avg. per infection [1975][a]	Avg. per infection [1992][c]	Est. U.S. total [1992][b]	[%][d]	Est. U.S. total[b]	[%][d]	Est. U.S. Total[b]
Surgical wound infection	7.3	3,726,000	$ 838.00	$ 3,152.00	$1,609,000,000.00	0.64	3,251	1.91	9,726
Pneumonia	5.9	1,339,000	$1,511.00	$ 5,683.00	$1,290,000,000.00	3.12	7,087	10.13	22,983
Bacteremia	7.4	762,000	$ 935.00	$ 3,517.00	$ 362,000,000.00	4.37	4,496	8.59	8,844
Urinary tract infection	1.0	903,000	$ 181.00	$ 680.00	$ 615,000,000.00	0.10	947	0.72	6,503
Other site	4.8	1,946,000	$ 430.00	$11,617.00	$ 656,000,000.00	0.80	3,246	2.48	10,036
All sites	4.0	8,676,000	$ 560.00	$ 2,100.00	$4,532,000,000.00	0.90	19,027	2.70	58,092

a. Adapted from R.W. Haley et al., *American Journal of Medicine*, 1981, 70:51.
b. Estimated by multiplying the total number of nosocomial infections estimated in the SENIC Project [*American Journal of Epidemiology* 1985, 121:159] by the average extra days, average extra charges, or percentage of infections causing or contributing to death, respectively.
c. Estimated from Haley et al., *American Journal of Medicine* 1981; 70:51, by pooling data and adjusting for inflation.
d. Unpublished analysis of data reported to the National Nosocomial Infections Surveillance System in 1980-1982, J.M. Hughes et al.

must undergo when these infections occur, nor do they reflect such things as 6-12 months of waiting, while debilitated, before an orthopedic prosthesis can be replaced.

D.4 ISOLATION

Patients who have infectious diseases are placed in isolation *after* they have been diagnosed. Undiagnosed patients are transported through hospital corridors and to imaging labs before being diagnosed as infectious. More and more invasive procedures are being performed in imaging labs, even though those labs have not been designed for sterile procedures and have not been designed for adequate cleaning and disinfecting after serving infected patients. Hospital personnel make multiple contacts with undiagnosed patients before they are recognized as infectious. Less trained hospital workers make inappropriate contact with infected patients even while in isolation.

Hospitals are hiring more and more untrained people for patient care because of cost concerns. Hospital turnover often outpaces universal infection control training. Hand washing is by far the most important procedure in infection control. Handwashing sinks or supplies, however, are often not placed conveniently near the exits of patients' rooms. Obviously, all of these problems do not exist in all hospitals.

The growing cost and morbidity of nosocomial infections to society suggests that a concerted multidisciplinary approach to solutions is necessary. Solutions that may have significantly high first costs should not be rejected out of hand.

D.5 ANTEROOMS

The incidence of nosocomial tuberculosis infections rose steadily until 1993. Improved ventilation techniques are responsible for significantly reversing that trend in the past several years. Ventilation strategies make a difference. Infectious patients are placed in rooms that are negatively pressurized to prevent infecting microbes from spreading. Immunosuppressed patients are placed in positively pressurized rooms to prevent them from coming into contact with infectious organisms. Immunosuppressed patients who are also infected are placed in rooms that have anterooms.

Why not place all infectious patients and immunosuppressed patients in rooms with anterooms? After all, many infected patients, particularly, tuberculosis patients, are somewhat immunosuppressed from debilitation and are highly susceptible to secondary infections. Likewise many immunosuppressed patients, particularly AIDS patients, already harbor communicable secondary infections. It makes no difference whether their room is negatively pressurized or positively pressurized. The important point is that their air is separated from everybody else's air—which anterooms can do. Undiagnosed patients should be placed, upon admission, in rooms with anterooms, so that there is less chance of spreading organisms before diagnosis. This would require more anterooms and higher first costs, but it would cut down the confusion of pressurization, cut down the number of room transfers, afford flexibility in the number of available isolation rooms, decrease the spread of organisms before diagnosis, and, probably prevent a few cases of nosocomial infection.

More infections are spread by the droplet route and by contact than by the airborne route. Anterooms prevent infection from spreading by the airborne route—and also by the droplet and contact routes. Anterooms control access to patient rooms. Food service personnel leave patients' trays in the anterooms rather than taking them to the patients' bedsides and then going directly to another bedside. Only trained personnel are allowed into the room proper. Although more breaks in isolation technique result from personnel error than from HVAC or architectural inadequacy, anterooms and designs cognizant of infection dangers can augment and enforce compliance with isolation techniques. Anterooms allow easy access to isolation materials: sinks, masks, gowns, gloves, and soap. Anterooms that are positively pressurized to both the patient room and to the corridor—combined with patient room air supply over the patient's bed and exhaust low between the bed and the door—achieve effective isolation in all circumstances.

D.6 INFECTION

Infections are caused by microorganisms, not by just any microorganism, but microorganisms that have evolved to use us (humans) as a place to live or as something to eat without regard to our ultimate well-being or survival. Microorganisms (viruses, rickettsia, bacteria, protozoa, fungi) predate us by hundreds of millions of years and will no doubt postdate us as well. Our ability to eradicate microorganisms is far overshadowed by their ability to eradicate us. Microorganisms evolve rapidly into new forms or into old forms with new processes to adapt to whatever environment they enter or to whatever environmental danger (antibiotics) they encounter. They accomplish this by replicating themselves (and mutating) at warp speeds compared to our ability to replicate ourselves. Microorganisms can evolve into resistant forms faster than we can develop and test antibiotics and faster than we can develop measures of protection and treatment.

Most microorganisms are not harmful to humanity. Many microorganisms are necessary for our well-being, not just those that produce our wine, our bread, our cheese, and our medicines, but those that make our soil fertile and those that enter at the bottom of the food chain. Some microorganisms are even necessary within our own bodies (coliforms such as *E. coli*) to break down unneeded materials.

We humans (and all other organisms that inhabit our planet) have developed elaborate protections against the invasion of disease-producing (pathological) microorganisms. Some of our protective measures are skin; an immune system; white blood cells that act like protozoans themselves and devour bacteria; mucus in our digestive and respiratory systems; ear wax; strong acids in our stomachs; colonization of friendly bacteria (*Lactobacillus*); tears; microscopic hairs that line our respiratory systems and carry away debris and microbes; and, brains that have learned how to make antibiotics, develop isolation protocols, and design protective ventilation systems. Breakdown of any one of these protections can result in successful invasion by destructive microorganisms. Many microorganisms (virulent microorganisms) can invade us, even if all of our protective mechanisms are intact.

In this manual, we are primarily concerned with the last mentioned item, that is, the provision of safe ventilation in health care facilities—air movement that is not laden with noxious microorganisms, chemicals, odors, or particles; air movement that does not transfer disease from one person to another. This goal can better be accomplished with knowledge and understanding of how disease spreads (epidemiology); with understanding of how hospitals house, board, transport, and manage diseased patients; and with realization that health care provision scenarios are changing, population and crowding are increasing, intercontinental travel and commerce are increasing, hospital stays are shortening, inpatients are more debilitated, the costs and morbidity resulting from hospital-acquired infections are staggering, and microorganism resistance to antibiotics is increasing. It is the hospital that we all turn to in cases of disease and disaster. It behooves us to make this last bastion of our health as safe as possible. Perhaps we should not reject measures of infection protection because they have not yet proven to be effective but, rather, reject them only when they have proven to be ineffective.

Airborne Respiratory Diseases and Mechanical Systems for
CONTROL OF MICROBES

Airborne respiratory pathogens and diseases in health care facilities are numerous and dangerous. HVAC systems are critical in controlling them.

By W. J. Kowalski, PE,
Graduate Researcher, and
William Bahnfleth, PhD, PE,
*Assistant Professor,
The Pennsylvania State
University, Architectural
Engineering Dept.,
University Park, Pa.*

1 Airborne transmission of respiratory diseases in indoor environments remains a problem of indoor air quality (IAQ) with few engineering alternatives and for which performance goals and design parameters are unclear. The engineer who attempts to deal with microbial IAQ finds that pertinent microbiological information exists in abundance but not in easily digestible forms. This article summarizes the relevant literature of medical microbiology and aerobiology in a manner that engineers may find useful and informative and that will facilitate the design of HVAC systems intended to reduce the threat. The general principles presented here can be applied to any indoor environment, including office buildings, schools, residences, hospitals, and isolation wards.

Origin of respiratory diseases

The first indoor environments, built by man over half a million years ago, included caves with leather-draped interiors, fur-carpeted tents, and huts covered with animal hides. Microbial predators existed from time immemorial, but transmission had always required direct contact because they could not tolerate the sunlight and temperature extremes outdoors. Man's cozy new habitats made it possible for these ancient parasites to survive short airborne trips between hosts.

Animal husbandry seems to have resulted in a number of pathogens jumping species and then becoming adapted to indoor transmission to the exclusion of outdoor transmission. These include rhinoviruses, diphtheria, TB, smallpox, measles, and influenza, which appear to have come variously from horses, cows, dogs, pigs, and chickens. Most contagious human pathogens have evolved to such dependence on man's habitats for transmission that they lack any ability to survive outdoors for long.[1]

In contrast, the non-contagious pathogens, including the fungi, environmental bacteria, and some animal pathogens, have maintained the ability to survive in the environment. Even so, direct sunlight is rapidly fatal to almost anything but spores.[1]

Classification of pathogens

Pathogens are any disease-causing microorganism, but the term applies to any microbial agent of respiratory irritation, including allergens or toxigenic fungi. Respiratory pathogens fall into three major taxonomic groups: viruses, bacteria, and fungi. The fungi and some bacteria, most notably the actinomycetes, form spores. Since spores are characteristically larger and more resistant to factors that will destroy viruses and bacteria, the engineer may find it more convenient to consider spores a definitive and separate category.

The single most important physical characteristic by which to classify airborne pathogens is size since it directly impacts filtration efficiency.[2] Fig. 1 presents a graphic comparison of airborne respiratory pathogens in which the spores, bacteria, and viruses can be observed to differentiate well, based on size alone. The left axis indicates the "average" or typical diameter or width. The areas of the circles do not represent the actual sizes of the microbes, but each represents the diameter in proportion to one another. The span of diameters is seen to be almost four orders of magnitude. Some microbes are oval or rod-shaped, and for these only, the smaller dimension is indicated.

[1]*Superscript numerals indicate references listed at end of article.*

This article originally was published in HPAC Engineering in July 1998. Some corrections and slight modifications were made in collaboration with the authors during the republication process.

Perhaps the most important classification is that of communicable versus non-communicable, a distinction that has both medical and engineering relevance. The term *communicable* is synonymous with the term *contagious*. Communicable diseases come mainly from humans, while non-communicable diseases hail mostly from the environment. However, many microbes that are endogenous to humans or are environmentally common may cause opportunistic infections in those whose health has been compromised. These occur primarily as nosocomial, or hospital-acquired, infections. These three categories then define all airborne pathogens:

- Communicable
- Non-communicable
- Primarily nosocomial

Table 1 lists all respiratory pathogens under these three categories, along with major diseases, common sources, and average diameters. In the column identifying microbial group, the term *actinomycetes* refers only to the spore-forming actinomycetes. Some general observations can be made from these charts such as the fact that most contagious pathogens come from humans, most non-contagious pathogens come from the environment, and most primarily nosocomial infections tend to be endogenous. These tables are not necessarily inclusive since a number of pathogens, such as *E. coli*, *Bacillus subtilis*, and some other strains of *Legionella*, can, on rare occasions, cause respiratory disease or allergic reactions.[3] The abbreviation "spp." denotes that infections may be caused by more than one species of the genera but does not imply that all species are pathogenic.

Table 1 lists only respiratory pathogens, although non-respiratory pathogens can also be airborne. Certain infections of the skin or eyes, nosocomial infections of open wounds and burns, and contamination of medical equipment may occur by the airborne route. Although these types of infections have not been well studied, any pathogen that transmits by the airborne route will be subject to the same principles and removal processes described in this article.

Communicable diseases

Table 1 lists all the main respiratory diseases that can transmit between human hosts via the airborne route. Humans are the natural reservoir for most contagious pathogens but some notable exceptions exist. Pneumonic plague and Arenavirus epidemics originate with rodents or other mammals.[1] In regards to the mysterious origin of *Influenza*, humans apparently share the function of natural reservoir with birds and pigs, as strains of this virus periodically jump between species.[3]

continued on page 37

Figure 1. Relative size of airborne respiratory pathogens.

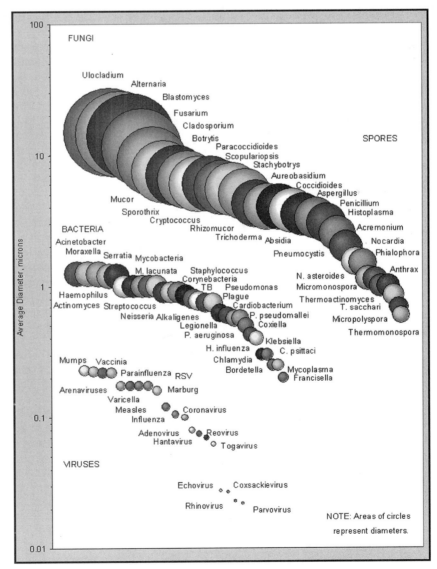

Table 1: Communicable Respiratory Pathogens

AIRBORNE PATHOGEN	MICROBIAL GROUP	DISEASE	SOURCE	Diameter microns	Notes
Adenovirus	VIRUS	colds	Humans	0.08	
Arenavirus	VIRUS	hemorrhagic fever	Rodents	0.18	F
Coronavirus	VIRUS	colds	Humans	0.11	
Coxsackievirus	VIRUS	colds	Humans	0.027	
Echovirus	VIRUS	colds	Humans	0.028	
Morbillivirus	VIRUS	measles (rubeola)	Humans	0.12	F, N
Influenza	VIRUS	flu	Humans, birds	0.1	F, N
Parainfluenza	VIRUS	flu	Humans	0.22	N
Paramyxovirus	VIRUS	mumps	Humans	0.23	F, N
Parvovirus B19	VIRUS	fifth disease, anemia	Humans	0.022	F
Reovirus	VIRUS	colds	Humans	0.075	
Respiratory Syncytial Virus	VIRUS	pneumonia	Humans	0.22	F, N
Rhinovirus	VIRUS	colds	Humans	0.023	
Togavirus	VIRUS	rubella (German measles)	Humans	0.063	N
Varicella-zoster	VIRUS	chickenpox	Humans	0.16	N
Chlamydia pneumoniae	BACTERIA	pneumonia, bronchitis	Humans	0.3	N
Mycobacterium tuberculosis	BACTERIA	TB	Humans	0.86	F, N
Yersinia pestis	BACTERIA	pneumonic plague	Rodents	0.75	F

Table 1: Primarily Nosocomial Respiratory Pathogens

AIRBORNE PATHOGEN	MICROBIAL GROUP	DISEASE	SOURCE	Diameter microns	NOTES
Acinetobacter	BACTERIA	opportunistic infections	Environmental	1.3	E, N
Actinomyces israelii	BACTERIA	actinomycosis	Humans	1.0	E, N
Alkaligenes	BACTERIA	opportunistic infections	Humans	0.75	E, N
Bordetella pertussis	BACTERIA	whooping cough	Humans	0.25	E, N
Cardiobacterium	BACTERIA	opportunistic infections	Humans	0.63	E, N
Corynebacteria diphtheria	BACTERIA	diptheria	Humans	1.0	E, N
Haemophilus influenzae	BACTERIA	meningitis, pneumonia	Humans	0.43	E, N, F
Haemophilus parainfluenzae	BACTERIA	opportunistic infections	Humans	1	E, N
Klebsiella pneumoniae	BACTERIA	opportunistic infections	Environmental	0.4	E, N
Moraxella catarrhalis	BACTERIA	opportunistic infections	Humans	1.3	E, N
Moraxella lacunata	BACTERIA	opportunistic infections	Humans	1	E, N
Mycobacterium avium	BACTERIA	cavitary pulmonary dis.	Environmental	1.2	N
Mycoplasma pneumoniae	BACTERIA	pneumonia	Humans	0.25	E, N
Neisseria meningitidis	BACTERIA	meningitis	Humans	0.8	E, N, F
Pseudomonas aeruginosa	BACTERIA	opportunistic infections	Environmental	0.57	N
Pseudomonas mallei	BACTERIA	opportunistic infections	Environmental	0.77	N
Pseudomonas pseudomallei	BACTERIA	opportunistic infections	Environmental	0.57	N
Serratia marcescens	BACTERIA	opportunistic infections	Environmental	1.3	E, N
Staphylococcus aureus	BACTERIA	opportunistic infections	Humans	1	E, N
Streptococcus pneumoniae	BACTERIA	pneumonia, otitis media	Humans	0.9	E, N, F
Streptococcus pyogenes	BACTERIA	scarlet fever, pharyngitis	Humans	0.9	N
Pneumocystis carinii	Protozoa / Fungi	pneumocystosis	Environmental	2	S, N
Cryptococcus neoformans	FUNGI	cryptococcosis	Environmental	5.5	S, N

NOTES:

E = Endogenous, common as human flora
F = Fatalities occur (excluding nosocomial)
HP = Hypersensitivity Pneumonitis
N = Nosocomial, common as (purple blocks)

EAA = Extrinsic Allergic Alveolitis
S = Spores
VOC = Volatile Organic Compounds produced
References: 1, 3, 4, 5, 8

Table 1: Non-Communicable Respiratory Pathogens

AIRBORNE PATHOGEN	MICROBIAL GROUP	DISEASE common (potential)	SOURCE	Diameter microns	NOTES
Hantavirus	VIRUS	hantavirus	Rodents	0.07	F
Poxvirus - Vaccinia	VIRUS	cowpox	Agricultural	0.23	
Bacillus anthracis	BACTERIA	anthrax	Cattle, sheep	1.1	S, F
Chlamydia psittaci	BACTERIA	psittacosis	Birds	0.3	
Coxiella burnetii	BACTERIA	Q fever	Cattle, sheep	0.5	
Francisella tularensis	BACTERIA	tularemia	wild animals	0.2	F
Legionella pneumophila	BACTERIA	LD, Pontiac fever	Environmental	0.6	F, N
Mycobacterium intracellulare	BACTERIA	cavitary pulmonary dis.	Environmental	1.2	
Mycobacterium kansasii	BACTERIA	cavitary pulmonary dis.	unknown	0.86	
Micromonospora faeni	ACTINOMYCETES	Farmer's Lung, HP	Agricultural	1	S
Micropolyspora faeni	ACTINOMYCETES	Farmer's Lung, HP	Agricultural	0.69	S
Nocardia asteroides	ACTINOMYCETES	nocardiosis	Environmental	1.1	S, N
Nocardia brasiliensis	ACTINOMYCETES	pulmonary mycetoma	Environmental	1.5	S, N
Nocardia caviae	ACTINOMYCETES	nocardiosis	Environmental	1.5	S, N
Thermoactinomyces sacchari	ACTINOMYCETES	bagassosis, HP	Agricultural	0.86	S
Thermoactinomyces vulgaris	ACTINOMYCETES	Farmer's Lung, HP	Agricultural	1	S
Thermomonospora viridis	ACTINOMYCETES	Farmer's Lung, HP	Environmental	0.6	S
Absidia corymbifera	FUNGI	zygomycosis	Environmental	3.8	S
Acremonium spp.	FUNGI	(EAA)	Environmental	2.5	S
Alternaria alternata	FUNGI	mycotoxicosis	Environmental	14.4	S
Aspergillus spp.	FUNGI	aspergillosis, VOC	Environmental	3.5	S, N
Aureobasidium pullulans	FUNGI	chromomycosis, EAA	Environmental	5	S
Blastomyces dermatitidis	FUNGI	blastomycosis	Environmental	14	S, N
Botrytis cinera	FUNGI	EAA	Environmental	7	S
Chaetomium globosum	FUNGI	chromomycosis, VOC	Environmental	5.5	S
Cladosporium spp.	FUNGI	chromoblastomycosis	Environmental	9	S
Coccidioides immitis	FUNGI	coccidioidomycosis	Environmental	4	S, N
Emericella nidulans	FUNGI	(mycotoxicosis)	Environmental	3.3	S
Epicoccum nigrum	FUNGI	(EAA)	Environmental	20	S
Eurotium spp.	FUNGI	EAA	Environmental	5.8	S
Exophiala jeanselmei	FUNGI	chromomycosis	Environmental	2.0	S
Fusarium spp.	FUNGI	mycotoxicosis, VOC	Environmental	11.5	S
Geomyces pannorum	FUNGI	EAA	Environmental	3	S
Helminthosporium	FUNGI	EAA	Environmental	12.5	S
Histoplasma capsulatum	FUNGI	histoplasmosis	Environmental	3	S, N
Mucor plumbeus	FUNGI	mucormycosis	Environmental	7.5	S, N
Paecilomyces variotii	FUNGI	mycotoxicosis	Environmental	3	S
Paracoccidioides brasiliensis	FUNGI	paracoccidioidomycosis	Environmental	23	S
Penicillium spp.	FUNGI	mycotoxicosis, VOC	Environmental	3.3	S
Phialophora spp.	FUNGI	chromomycosis	Environmental	1.5	S
Phoma spp.	FUNGI	mycotoxicosis	Environmental	3.3	S
Rhizomucor pusillus	FUNGI	zygomycosis	Environmental	4.3	S
Rhizopus stolonifer	FUNGI	zygomycosis	Environmental	8	S, N
Rhodotorula spp.	FUNGI	(EAA)	Environmental	14	S
Scopulariopsis spp.	FUNGI	onychomycosis	Environmental	6	S
Sporothrix schenckii	FUNGI	sporotrichosis	Environmental	6.5	S
Stachybotrys spp.	FUNGI	stachybotryotoxicosis	Environmental	5.7	S, F
Trichoderma spp.	FUNGI	mycotoxicosis, VOC	Environmental	4.1	S
Ulocladium spp.	FUNGI	EAA	Environmental	15	S
Wallemia sebi	FUNGI	EAA	Environmental	3	S

continued from page 35

Many contagious respiratory pathogens also transmit by direct contact through the exchange of infectious droplets or particles called fomites.[4] The eyes and nasal passages are vulnerable to fomite transmission. The predominance of these direct routes in comparison with the inhalation route has not been well established but can be very species-dependent.[5] Infectivity is also lost upon drying, and therefore hand or surface contact may require the exchange of moisture as well as an infectious dose.[1,6]

Barely 20 pathogens account for the overwhelming number of contagious respiratory infections. Table 2 lists the characteristics of these infections, while the typical course of these infections is depicted in Fig. 2. The infection rate refers to the fraction of those exposed to an infectious dose who contract the disease. This type of information can be useful to engineers attempting risk assessment or procedural control of infectious occupants or patients. Few infectious doses have been established, but for purposes of making rough or conservative estimations, as few as 1-10 TB bacilli can be infectious for humans—while a total of 200 Rhinovirus virions may be required to cause a cold.[4]

Most respiratory parasites induce their hosts to aerosolize large quantities of infectious bioaerosols by nasopharyngeal irritation, which causes coughing and sneezing.[4,5] Consider the profiles of the particle sizes shown in Fig. 3. A single sneeze can generate a hundred thousand floating bioaerosol particles, and many may contain viable microorganisms.[7] A single cough typically produces about one percent of this amount, but coughs occur about 10 times more frequently than sneezes.[7] Bioaerosols produced by talking are negligible, but extended shouting and singing can transmit infections.

Some limited data from Duguid[7] is available in generation rates stating that A TB infective can produce 1-249 bacilli per hr,[8] while a person in the infectious stage of a cold may produce 6200 droplet nuclei per hr containing viable viruses that remain airborne longer than 10 min. In one measles epidemic, 5480 virions were generated per hr.[8]

The dose received from an airborne concentration of microbes could be considered a factor under engineering control since it

TABLE 2: Communicable Respiratory Infection Characteristics							
PATHOGEN		Common Disease	Annual Cases (U.S.)	Average Incubation (days)	Infectious Peak (days)	Maximum Duration (days)	Infection Rate (fraction)
VIRUS	BACTERIA						
Adenovirus		colds	*	4	4-9	19	0.51-0.75
Coronavirus		colds	*	3	(3-4)	18	0.45-0.5
Coxsackievirus		colds	*	3	3-12	20	0.53-0.64
Echovirus		colds	*	3	(3-4)	18	0.43-0.80
Influenza		flu	200000*	2	2-7	21	0.2-0.8
Morbillivirus		measles	25000	12	8-16	29	0.85
Parainfluenza		flu	*	3	3-12	21	0.2-0.75
Paramyxovirus		mumps	10000	17	10-26	39	0.6-0.85
Parvovirus B19		fifth disease	-	8	7-14	28	0.3-0.6
Respiratory Synctial Virus		pneumonia	*	2	5-7	14	0.5-0.9
Rhinovirus		colds	*	2	2-7	7	0.38-0.89
Togavirus		rubella	3000	17	24-31	31	0.3-0.8
Varicella-zoster		varicella	*	16	12-20	25	0.75-0.96
	Bordetella pertussis	whpg cough	2000	8	15-22	42	high
	Chlamydia pneumoniae	pharyngitis	-	7	7-21	28	0.5
	Corynebacteria diptheria	diptheria	490000	3	2-10	10	varies
	Haemophilus influenzae	meningitis	8000	3	3-4	(14)	0.2-0.5
	Mycobacterium tuberculosis	TB	21000	28	varies	--	0.33
	Neisseria meningitidis	meningitis	4500	3	3-4	(21)	high
	Streptococcus pneumoniae	pneumonia	500000	2	(2-10)	21	0.1-0.3
	Yersinia pestis	pn. plague	14	2	2-3	3	varies

References   3, 4, 5, 8, 13

*(Common respiratory infections are often not reported.)

Figure 2. Generic curve for duration of symptoms of respiratory infections

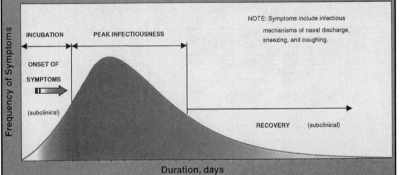

depends on the local air change rate and degree of mixing as well as the generation rate. The successful transmission of an infection, however, depends on all of the following factors:

- Susceptibility of the individual (immunity).
- Duration of exposure.
- Concentration of infectious agent.
- Virulence of infectious agent.
- Breathing rate.
- Route of infection (inhalation, eyes, nasopharynx, etc.).

None of these factors is necessarily an absolute determinant. Health and degree of immunity can be as important as the dose received from prolonged exposure.

Computations of infectious airborne doses can be fraught with uncertainty. Epidemiological studies on colds avoid these problems by computing actual risks. Fig. 4 shows how duration and proximity to an infectious person can increase the likelihood of infection, based on data from Lidwell's studies of the common cold.[9] These data suggest that there may be a threshold distance beyond which risk decreases sharply. This risk may result from local airborne concentrations but may also include the risk of contact with fomites.

Non-communicable diseases

The list of non-communicable pathogens in Table 1 includes all known that cause respiratory infections, allergic reactions, and toxic reactions. Included among the diseases are EAA and HP (see notes),

continued on page 40

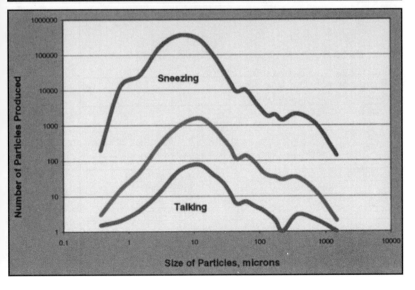

Figure 3. Profile of particle sizes produced by an infectious person.

Based on data from Duguid et al 1945.

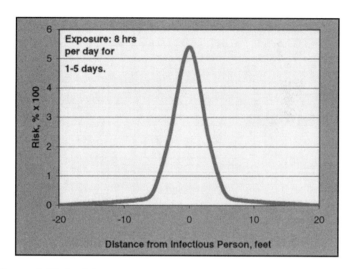

Figure 4. Risk of cold infection from proximity. Risk at zero represents intimate (husband-wife) contact. *Estimated per data from Lidwell.[9]*

continued from page 38

which are sometimes associated with sick building syndrome (SBS). Non-communicable infections are almost entirely due to fungal or actinomycete spores and environmental or agricultural bacteria.

Spores form the most important group of non-communicable diseases. Outdoor spore levels vary with season and climate and can reach very high levels when dry, windy conditions result in disturbance of the soil where fungi grow. Surprisingly, few cases of respiratory infection have ever been attributed to inhalation of outdoor air,[4,5] probably because most people, especially Americans and Europeans, spend over 90 percent of their time indoors.[10] A small proportion of actinomycete infections have occurred outdoors

in agricultural facilities, although most tend to occur inside barns and worksheds.[11,12]

Indoor air spore levels can differ from outdoor air in both concentration and composition of spores. In normal, dry buildings, spore levels tend to be anywhere from 10 to 100 percent of outdoor spore levels[11] and are mostly less than 200 colony forming units (CFU) per cu meter. Problem-free, multi-story office buildings typically have levels that are 10 to 31 percent of the outdoor air[11] levels. The composition of fungal species indoors tends to reflect that of the outdoors.[13] Some fungal species, most notably *Aspergillus* and *Penicillium*, are often found to account for 80 percent of indoor spores.[10]

Spores will germinate and grow in the presence of moisture and nutrients[13] in locations such as basements, drain pans, and on refrigerator coils. As a result of such growth, spores can be generated internally in problem buildings, wet buildings, and certain agricultural facilities at a high enough rate to cause indoor spore levels to exceed outdoor levels. If spore concentrations indoors consistently exceed

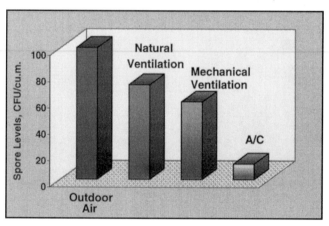

Figure 5. Indoor spore levels by ventilation system type. *From the California Healthy Buildings Study.[11]*

Table 3: Microbial Levels in Indoor and Outdoor Air							
(Suggested Guidelines, Upper Limits, Average or Representative Levels)							
Microbe	Lower Limit CFU/cu.m.	Average Range Low	High	Upper Limit	Qualification	I/O Ratio Low	High	Reference
Indoor Fungal Spores*	50	10	500	150		0.1	0.33	14, 12(ACGIH), 10(CG)
(summer)				500				10(CG)
Outdoor Fungal Spores	100	100	1000	-		-	-	11(CHBS), 10
Actinomycete Spores	0	0	150	240	normal homes	-	-	12(Nevalainen), 10
Outdoor Actino. Spores	0	4	-	-	farmhouses	-	-	12(Heineman)
Bacteria, non-pathogenic	50	0	500	50		0.26	1.1	10, 12, 10(ACGIH)
Outdoor Bacteria	-	179	1083	-		-	-	11(Brickus), 12
Pathogenic Bacteria	0	-	-	0				14(AIHA)
Viruses	0	-	-	0				14(AIHA)

*(when species mix reflects outdoor air)
CG: Canadian Guidelines
ACGIH: American Conference of Government Industrial Hygienists
AIHA: American Industrial Hygiene Association
CHBS: California Healthy Buildings Study

outdoor levels, the building can be inferred to contain an indoor amplifier.[14]

In the California Healthy Buildings Study,[11] naturally ventilated, mechanically ventilated, and air conditioned buildings all had lower indoor spore levels than the outdoors (Fig. 5). However, Fig. 5 may reflect favorable local conditions since many studies have measured much higher levels than these in non-problem buildings.

Table 3 lists the results of various studies that include measurements of outdoor spore levels and typical, average, or representative indoor levels. These levels do not necessarily pose a health threat. Measurements and guidelines vary almost as widely as outdoor levels vary seasonally and geographically.

Microorganisms will take advantage of any opportunity to establish themselves and multiply in a new environment.[4] Niches for microbial growth may be created inadvertently by engineered systems that generate moisture such as humidifiers, evaporative air coolers, cooling coil drain pans, and condensation on ductwork insulation. Amplification may result in airborne concentrations above the outdoors[10] and may reach unhealthy levels.[13] Legionnaire's Disease provides a sentinel example of pathogenic microbial amplification by an engineered system.

Amplifying factors can be controlled through various means, including preventive design through humidity and moisture control. Some other first and second line defensive measures include filtration, the removal of materials that provide nu-

trients, procedural cleaning and maintenance, and the use of biocidal equipment.

Table 4 identifies fungal pathogens that have been found to grow indoors on various surfaces or in HVAC equipment. Unidentified multiple species (spp.) may

Table 4: Fungi That May Grow Indoors				
Airborne Pathogen	Indoor Growth		HVAC Equipment Growth	
	Location	Reference	Location	Reference
Acremonium spp.			humidifier water	Heineman (12)
			HVAC fiberglass insulation	(24)
Alternaria spp.	indoors > outdoors	(2)	cooling systems	(22)
	paint mildew	(26)	refrigerator coils	(25)
	carpet dust	Gravesen (23)	filters	Shata (11), (17)
	floor dust	Hoekstra (23)	filters	Neumeister (10)
			dust in ductwork	Valbjorn (11)
Aspergillus spp.	indoors > outdoors	(2)	evaporative air cooler	(23)
	carpet dust	Gravesen (23)	HVAC fiberglass insulation	(24)
	floor dust	Hoekstra (23)	cooling systems, coils	(22)
			fans, filters	Heineman (12), (17)
			dust in ductwork	Sugawara (10)
Aureobasidium pullulans	moist building materials	Pasanen (23)	filters	Shata (11)
	latex painted surfaces	(26)		
Chaetomium spp.			HVAC fiberglass insulation	(24)
			filters	Heineman (12)
			dust in ductwork	Valbjorn (11)
Cladosporium spp.	wet carpet, wet walls	(21)	evaporative coolers	(22)
	moist building materials	Pasanen (23)	HVAC fiberglass insulation	(24)
	latex painted surfaces	(26)	filters	Shata (11)
	floor dust	Hoekstra (23)	HVAC metal surfaces	(19)
	carpet dust	Gravesen (23)	fans, filters	Heineman (12)
			ductwork dust	Sugawara (10)
Cryptococcus spp.	floor dust	Hoekstra (23)		
Epicoccum spp.	indoors > outdoors	Kemp (16)	fiberglass insulation	Morey (11)
Eurotium herbariorum	gypsum-based finishes	Adan (23)		
Exophiala spp.			humidifier water	Heineman (12)
Fusarium spp.	indoors > outdoors	Fouad (16)	filters	Neumeister (10)
	floor dust	Hoekstra (23)	humidifier water	Heineman (12)
Helminthosporium	indoors > outdoors	Kemp (16)		
Mucor spp.	indoors > outdoors	Kemp (16)	fans, filters	Heineman (12), (17)
	floor dust	Hoekstra (23)	dust in ductwork	Valbjorn (11)
Paecilomyces spp.			humidifier water	Heineman (12)
Penicillium spp.	indoors > outdoors	(2)	air conditioners	(22)
	latex painted surfaces	(26)	evaporative air cooler	(23)
	carpet dust	Gravesen (23)	HVAC ducts	(20)
			filters	Pasanen (12), (17)
			fans, humidifier water	Heineman (12)
Phialophora spp.			humidifier water	Heineman (12)
Phoma spp.	paint mildew	(26)	filters	Neumeister (10)
	floor dust	Hoekstra (23)	humidifier water	Heineman (12)
Rhizopus spp.	floor dust	Hoekstra (23)	fans	Heineman (12)
			filters	Neumeister(10)
			dust in ductwork	Valbjorn(11)
Rhodoturula spp.	wet carpet, wet walls	(21)		
	indoors > outdoors	Kemp (16)		
Scopulariopsis spp.	floor dust	Hoekstra (23)	filters	Heineman (12)
Stachybotris spp.	building materials	Scott (16)	fans, humidifier water	Heineman (12)
	moist building materials	Pasanen (23)		
Trichoderma spp.	indoors	(7)	fans	Heineman (12)
	moist building materials	Pasanen (23)	filters	Neumeister (10)
			ductwork dust	Sugawara (10)
Ulocladium spp.	floor dust	Hoekstra (23)	filters	Neumeister (10)
			humidifier water	Heineman (12)
Wallemia sebi	floor dust	Hoekstra (23)	filters	Shata (11)

not necessarily be pathogenic. Many factors may dictate which pathogens will grow indoors such as climate, indoor materials, degree of human occupancy, hygiene, and moisture levels.[1,8]

Table 5 identifies some pathogenic environmental bacteria that have been found growing indoors or on HVAC equipment. Occasionally, some contagious bacteria disseminated from humans can be found in water, equipment, or in dust, but these are transient occupants and unlikely to grow or survive long outside of human hosts.[1,5]

Nosocomial infections

All respiratory pathogens are potentially nosocomial, but those that occur almost exclusively as nonsocomial infections are listed in Table 1 such as primarily nosocomial respiratory pathogens.

Table 5: Bacteria That May Grow Indoors		
Airborne Pathogen	Location of Growth	Reference
Acinetobacter	potable water	Highsmith (8)
Klebsiella pneumoniae	potable water	Highsmith (8)
Legionella pneumophila	potable water	(4)
	cooling towers	(8)
Micropolyspora faeni	home humidifiers	(21)
Pseudomonas aeruginosa	indoors	Strom (11)
	indoor dust	(1)
	potable water	Highsmith (8)
	evaporative air cooler	(23)
	humidifiers	(25)
Pseudomonas spp.	filters	Martikainen (11)
Serratia Marcescens	potable water	Highsmith (8)
Thermoactinomycetes vulgaris	air conditioners	(25)
	humidifier water	Heineman (12)

The other common nosocomial infections are identified with a purple boxed N in the notes column.

In intensive-care units, almost a third of nosocomial infections are respiratory, but not all of these are airborne since some are transmitted by contact or by intrusive medical equipment.[15] Nosocomial infections can also be airborne but non-respiratory such as when common microbes like *Staphylococcus* settle on open wounds, burns, or medical equipment.

Patients who succumb to nosocomial infections are often those whose natural defenses have been compromised either as a result of disease, medication, injury, or bypassed by intrusive procedures. In cases of immune system deficiency, even a patient's own endogenous flora could cause infection, while normally benign environmental microbes can become pathogenic.

The protection of patients from potential pathogens requires the reduction of microbial contaminants below normal or ambient levels. This is usually accomplished through the use of isolation rooms, HEPA filters, UVGI, and strict hygiene procedures.[15] In the health care environment, particular attention must be paid to the possibility of microbial growth indoors and in the air handling units, even if levels are not a threat to healthy

people. Low-level indoor microbial amplification in health care settings may cause building-related illness (BRI) without actually representing SBS.

Technically, nosocomial infections relate to those who are hospitalized, but health care professionals themselves may be at risk. The Center for Disease Control(CDC) publishes guidelines for control of infections[15] among hospital employees, but appropriate engineering design and maintenance can play a significant role in reducing the risks for medical professionals as well as for patients.

Natural microbial decay

Various environmental factors destroy airborne microbes.[1] Direct sunlight contains lethal levels of ultraviolet radiation. Dehydration renders most microbes inactive, although many spores may survive indefinitely. High temperatures will inactivate all pathogens, some more rapidly than others. Freezing will destroy most pathogens; except that some, especially spores, may be preserved. Oxygen slowly kills most airborne microorganisms through oxidation. Pollution levels that we tolerate our entire lives can be fatal to microorganisms. Plate-out, or adsorption, occurs on all interior building surfaces, but this removal rate tends to be negligible.

Each of these environmental processes reduces pathogen populations according to the following general equation:[1,6]

$$N = N_0 e^{-kt} \qquad (1)$$

where

N = population at time t
N_0 = population at time $t = 0$
k = rate constant for process
$e = 2.718$

The resulting exponential decay curve is known as a survival curve, or death curve. Often, a very small fraction of the microbial population, usually about 0.01 percent, resists chemical or physical inactivation for extended periods of exposure.[1,16]

This relation applies additively to all reduction processes—except that humidity levels will influence the effects of other factors such as ultraviolet germicidal irradiation (UVGI) and heat on a species-dependent basis. In the outdoors, sunlight, temperature extremes, and wind ensure that non-spore microbial populations decay and disperse rapidly, generally within minutes.[1,16] In the indoors, these factors

continued on page 44

continued from page 42

are controlled for human comfort, resulting in airborne microbes surviving longer, sometimes even days.[1,4]

After expulsion by sneezing or coughing, most large droplets will settle out of the air within a matter of minutes. Fig. 6 illustrates this process and is based on fitted data. Many of the micron-sized droplets will rapidly evaporate to droplet nuclei that approach the size of the individual microbe. Micron-sized particles can remain suspended for hours and spread by diffusion or air currents.[8]

Airborne microbes lose viability over time. In the absence of sunlight, the decay rates for each microbial group, based on rates measured in a variety of studies,[16]

Figure 6. Disappearance of airborne sneeze droplets from room air by size. *Based on fitted, normalized data from Duguid.[7]*

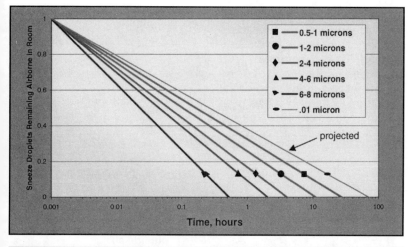

Figure 7. Viability of airborne microbes indoors in absence of sunlight. *Based on averages for each microbial group.[1,16]*

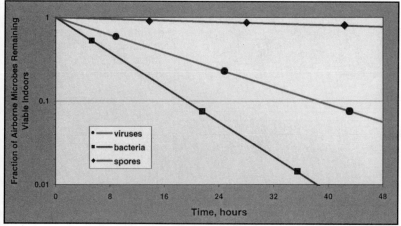

typical air handling unit (AHU). Contagious viruses and bacteria come almost exclusively from humans, and they will appear only in the return air. Spores and environmental bacteria may enter from the outdoors, but once growth (amplification) occurs indoors, they may appear in the return air at higher levels than in the outdoor air. Environmental bacteria are rarely pathogenic for healthy people (Table 1), but they may provide a nutrient source for pathogenic fungi.

Spores can initially enter a building by various routes, including inlet air or infiltration, or they may be brought in with building materials, carpets, clothes, food, pets, or potting soil. In a normal, dry building, the return air will have lower levels of spores than the outdoor air,[11,12] except when snow covers the ground and outdoor spore levels approach zero. When indoor amplifiers are present, the return air could be expected to contain higher levels of spores than the outdoor air, except during dry, windy, summer conditions when outdoor levels of spores can become very high.

Once spores germinate and growth occurs in an AHU or anywhere inside the building, new spores may be generated and appear in the return air. Filters may intercept spores, but moisture may cause them to "grow through" the filter media. Cooling coils can have a pronounced filtering effect on spores,[11,12] but the presence of condensation may also cause microbial growth and amplification[10] downstream of the coils, negating the effect.

Boosting outside air flow may be an option only if the ventilation system is not the source of microbial contamination; in which case, increasing air flow may exacerbate the problem.[11] A fungus problem that is not caused by the ventilation system, such as a leaky roof or wall, requires separate remedial action such as removing the damaged material.[17]

Engineered alternatives

Natural decay mechanisms operate too slowly inside most buildings to prevent secondary infections.[16] Available engineering alternatives include purging with outside air, filtration, UVGI, and isolation through pressurization control. Each of these technologies has advantages and limitations, but optimization for any application is always possible if the microbial IAQ goals are clearly specified.

are shown in Fig. 7. Curiously, bacteria decay faster in air than viruses apparently because they depend more on moisture for their survival than do viruses.

Pathways and dissemination

Fig. 8 illustrates some distinctions between airborne pathogens in relation to a

Pressurization control is commonly used in biohazard facilities and isolation rooms to prevent migration of microbes from one area to another, but inherent costs and operational instability at normal air flow rates limit feasibility for other applications.

Full outside air systems are often used in health care facilities and TB isolation rooms, subject to CDC guidelines.[15] Fig. 9 shows the effect of full purge air flow on the reduction of pathogens in a room with an initial concentration of 100 microbe CFU per cu meter. Comparing this with Fig. 10 shows the results of HEPA filtration at the same recirculation flow rates. The results are practically identical.

The use of HEPA recirculation, of course, carries a lower total energy penalty[2] in hot or cold climates. But in mild or dry climates, high percentages of outside air can prove economical, especially in applications involving evaporative coolers. Hospitals often have commitments to specific guidelines, but other facilities may select and size systems to suit their goals and budgets.

HEPA filters, for example, are not the only choice for controlling microbial IAQ. High or medium efficiency filters are capable of removing airborne pathogens, especially spores, without high operation or replacement costs.[2,16] Overall, particle removal efficiency might be improved by locating medium efficiency filters in the recirculation loop vs. the outside air intakes[16] or even downstream of the cooling coils. But, this choice will depend on each individual system's operating parameters.

Combining purge air with HEPA filtration results in performance that is essentially additive, and cost optimization becomes straightforward. Energy consumption, replacement costs, and microbial IAQ goals will dictate the economic choice for any particular installation.[16] The performance of medium efficiency filters in combination with purge air flow is not directly additive but depends on the filter efficiency vs. particle size curves, the sizes of the pathogens of concern, and the system operating parameters.

UVGI can be an efficient method to use in the right applications such as controlling microbial growth in cooling coils.[18]

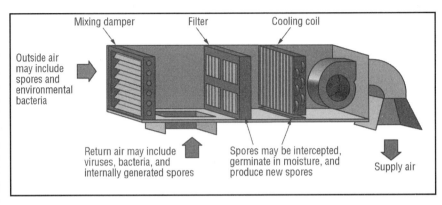

The continuous exposure appears to inhibit fungal growth and may kill the spores as well. In applications involving the disinfection of air streams, the effectiveness of UVGI depends on factors that include air velocity, local air flow patterns, degree of maintenance, characteristic resistance of the microbes, and humidity.[16] A single pass through a UVGI system may have a limited effect, but recirculation, either through stand-alone units or ventilation systems, will result in multiple exposures or chronic dosing.

Figure 8. Sources and pathways of microbial contamination in a typical air handling unit.

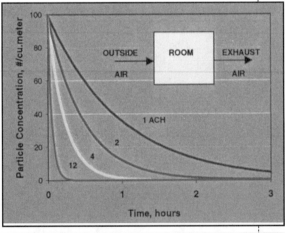

Figure 9. 100 percent outside air: effect of ach on reduction of initial level of room microbial contamination.

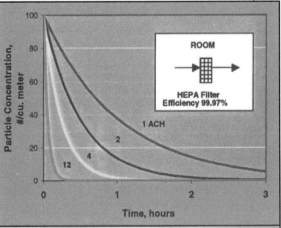

Figure 10. HEPA filter recirculation: effect of flowrate (in ach) on the reduction of initial level of room microbial contamination.

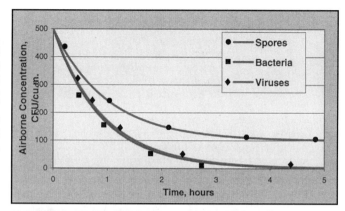

Figure 11. Effects of 25 percent outside air (1 ach) on indoor contaminant levels.[16] Outdoor spore level = 100 cfu per cu meter.

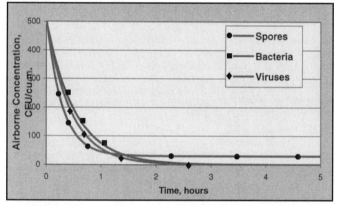

Figure 12. Effect of ASHRAE filter, 80 to 85 percent efficiency on indoor contaminant levels.[16] Recirculation with 25 percent outside air.

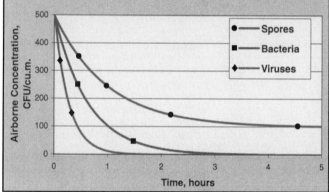

Figure 13. Effect of UVGI on indoor contaminant levels.[16] Recirculation with 25 percent OA. UVGI power mW (W=watt) per sq cm

alistic but provides dramatic differentiation of the effectiveness of pathogen removal.

Fig. 12 shows the effect of an ASHRAE medium efficiency filter (80 to 85 percent dust spot) to the supply air of the model building while maintaining 1 ach of outside air. The filter model describes filter efficiency vs. diameters in accordance with typical vendor performance curves.[16] Spore levels indoors are clearly reduced below outdoor ambient levels. Some reduction of bacteria and viruses can also be noted, but their removal is still dominated by the purging effect of the outside air. The filter used in this analysis provides a baseline for comparison. High efficiency filters, such as the 90 to 95 percent filters used in hospitals,[2] would result in even higher removal rates.

Fig. 13 shows the impact of a UVGI system with 25 μW (W=watt) per sq cm placed in the recirculation loop. The outside air is maintained at 1 ach, but no filters are included. Spores are relatively unaffected by the UVGI, but the viruses are markedly reduced. This model incorporates chronic dosing effects from recirculation with an exposure of 0.2 sec for each pass. The decay rate Equation 1 is applied with known rate constants[16] for a wide cross-section of the microbial species listed in Table 1.

The unusual performance characteristics of each technology have been highlighted in these examples. Inclusion of these characteristics in any evaluation, along with the IAQ design goals, ambient conditions, and internal generation rates, will dictate the choices for any given application—subject only to economic limitations.

Other alternatives

Various current or experimental technologies have the potential for reducing airborne disease transmission or indoor amplification. Biocidal filters can limit or prevent fungal growth on the filter media. Electrostatic filters (i.e., electrets or electrically stimulated filters) are available but have not seen widespread

continued on page 48

Chronic dosing with UVGI can have a major impact on airborne viruses and bacteria.[16]

A graphic comparison of the relative effectiveness of the three main alternatives—outside air purge, filtration, and UVGI—is provided in Fig. 11 through 13. Fig. 11 shows the effect of 1 air changer per hr (ach) of outside air on reduction of room air contaminant concentrations from an initial value. Perfect mixing is assumed, along with 500 CFU per cu meter contamination of each microbial group initially, 100 CFU per cu meter of spores in the outside air, and no internal generation. Natural decay rates from Fig. 7 are incorporated in the model. The scenario of an initially contaminated room may not be re-

continued from page 46

use. Carbon adsorbers have pore sizes too small to remove viruses, but they are effective at removing VOCs produced by some fungi and bacteria.

Other technologies currently under research include low-level ozonation, negative air ionization, and photocatalytic oxidation—a technology that may one day result in a type of light-powered, self-cleaning, microbial filter.

Conclusions

Perfect solutions to the problem of airborne disease transmission do not yet exist, but the available technologies—outside purge air, filtration, and UVGI—can be successfully implemented when their characteristic effects are understood and the goals clearly defined. Whether the application involves improvement of microbial IAQ in an office building or minimizing the risk of infection in an operating room, these technologies can be optimized individually or in combination from a cost or performance standpoint.

Finally, since microbes will never ignore opportunities provided to them, appropriate design, regular surveillance, and maintenance of these technologies in particular, and HVAC systems in general, should always be proactive. **HPAC**

References

1) Mitscherlich, E. and E. H. Marth. Microbial Survival in the Environment. Berlin: Springer-Verlag, 1984.

2) Burroughs, H. E. "Filtration: An investment in IAQ." HPAC Aug. 1997: 55-65.

3) Freeman, B. A. ed. Burrows Textbook of Microbiology. Philadelphia: W. B. Saunders Co., 1985.

4) Ryan, K. J. ed. Sherris Medical Microbiology. Norwalk: Appleton & Lange, 1994.

5) Mandell, G. L. ed. Principles and Practice of Infectious Diseases. New York: Wiley, 1985.

6) Hers, J. F. ed. Airborne Transmission and Airborne Infection. Proc. of VIth International Symposium on Aerobiology. Technical University at Enschede. The Netherlands: Oosthoek Publishing Company, 1973.

7) Duguid, J. P. "The size and the duration of air-carriage of respiratory droplets and droplet-nuclei." Journal of Hygiene 45: 471-479.

8) Kundsin, R. B., ed. (1980). Airborne Contagion, NYAS, New York.

9) Lidwell, O. M. and R. E. O. Williams. "The epidemiology of the common cold." Journal of Hygiene 59 (1961): 309-334.

10) Woods, J. E. ed. Healthy Buildings/IAQ '97. Proc. of ASHRAE Annual IAQ Conference. Washington, DC, 1997.

11) Godish, T. Sick Buildings: Definition, Diagnosis, and Mitigation. Boca Raton: Lewis Publishers, 1995.

12) Samson, R. A., ed. Health Implications of Fungi in Indoor Environments. Amsterdam: Elsevier, 1994.

13) Burge, H. "Bioaerosols: Prevalence and health effects in the indoor environment." Journal of Allerg. Clin. Immunol. May 1990: 687-781.

14) Rao, C. Y. and H. A. Burge. "Review of quantitative standards and guidelines for fungi in indoor air." Journal of Air & Waste Management. Assoc. Sep. 1996: 899-908.

15) Castle, M. and E. Ajemian. Hospital infection control. New York: John Wiley & Sons, 1987.

16) Kowalski, W. J. "Technologies for controlling respiratory disease transmission in indoor environments: Theoretical performance and economics." The Pennsylvania State University.

17) Kemp, S. J., et al. "Filter collection efficiency and growth of microorganisms on filters loaded with outdoor air." ASHRAE Transactions Jan. 1995: 228.

18) Scheir, R. and F. B. Fencl. "Using UVC Technology to Enhance IAQ." HPAC Feb. 1996: 28-29, 85, 87.

Bibliography

19) Ahearn, D. G., et al. "Colonization by Cladosporium spp. of painted metal surfaces associated with heating and air conditioning systems." Journal of Ind. Microbiol Aug. 1991: 277-280.

20) Chang, J. C. S., K. K. Foarde and D. W. VanOsdell. "Assessment of fungal (Penicillium chrysogenum) growth on three HVAC duct materials." Environment International Apr. 1996: 425.

21) Flanningan, et al. Allergenic and toxigenic micro-organisms in houses. Pathogens in the Environment. Oxford: Blackwell Scientific Publications, 1991.

22) Hyvarinen, et al. "Influence of cooling type on airborne viable fungi." Journal of Aerosol Science 26.S1 (1995): s887-s888.

23) Macher, J. M. and J. R. Girman. "Multiplication of microorganisms in an evaporative air cooler and possible indoor air contamination." Environment International 16 (1990): 203-211.

24) Price, D. L., et al. "Colonization of fiberglass insulation used in heating, ventilation, and air conditioning systems." Journal of Ind. Microbiol. 13 (1994): 154-158.

25) Reynolds, S. J., et al. "Elevated airborne concentrations of fungi in residential and office environments." Am. Ind. Hygiene Association Journal 51 (1990): 601-604.

26) Zabel, R. A. and F. Terracina. The role of Aureobasidium pullulans in the disfigurement of latex paint films. Developments in Industrial Microbiology, Society for Industrial Microbiology, Pittsburgh, 1980.

APPENDIX E
LIFE-CYCLE COST ANALYSIS

E.1 LIFE-CYCLE COST ANALYSIS

The life-cycle cost (LCC) method considers all of the cost elements of an investment during its life cycle. The Department of Energy's (DOE) Federal Energy Management Program (FEMP) requires the use of this method to evaluate energy and water conservation investments in federal buildings. The method is described at length in the *Life-Cycle Costing Manual for the Federal Energy Management Program*, NIST Handbook 135 (NIST 1995). The annually published *Energy Price Indices and Discount Factors for LCC Analysis* supplements Handbook 135 (NIST 2002). NIST computer software for life-cycle cost analysis of buildings and building systems is also available.

The LCC method is the ideal economic method to compare HVAC alternatives because these alternatives inherently include energy, water, and operating costs. Adhering to the federal life-cycle costing program presents the advantage of a uniform method for economic analysis of HVAC alternatives with readily available discount factors and price escalation rates, updated annually, for each region in the United States.

The life-cycle cost method is specifically useful in assessing the long-term cost-effectiveness of design alternatives that have different initial investment costs; energy, operating, maintenance, and repair costs; or different lives. Handbook 135 recommends the use of uncertainty assessment and sensitivity analysis, in addition to life-cycle cost calculations.

The life-cycle cost method includes the following cost elements:

- Initial investment cost for each alternative

- Equipment replacement cost and the year of replacement (if replacement occurs within the study period)
- Annual energy costs
- Annual water costs (only if they vary from one alternative to another)
- Annual nonfuel operating, maintenance, and repair costs (OM&R)

To simplify calculations, any of the preceding cost elements can be reduced to only those costs that differ from one alternative to another. For example, if both HVAC alternatives use the same central plant, the costs related to the initial investment and operation of this plant could be excluded from the calculations. But if, for example, the chillers are different from one alternative to another, the costs of the chillers would be included in the calculations.

The calculated present value of each of the annual costs is based upon

- the length of the study period (usually 25 years) and
- the discount rate (either the annually published real DOE discount rate, exclusive of general inflation, or the investor's discount rate).

Present value is found by applying the following factors:

- The single present value (SPV) factor used to calculate the present value of a future cash amount, such as equipment replacement costs, based upon the year of replacement and the selected discount rate;
- The uniform present value (UPV) factors for each of the recurring annual energy costs at a nonconstant escalation rate (based in the FEMP

process upon DOE projections of energy escalation rates, according to the location of the project);

- The UPV factors for annually recurring costs based upon the selected discount factor and the length of study period, applicable to annual non-fuel operating, maintenance, and repair costs (OM&R) and to water consumption and/or disposal.

The summation of all present values for an alternative constitutes the total present value of that alternative. The smaller present value alternative becomes the recommended alternative, unless intangible advantages have to be considered or sensitivity analysis should be performed.

The purpose of an economic analysis is to determine the comparative life-cycle costs of various HVAC system alternatives. Such analysis should provide sufficient data to indicate the most economical and energy-efficient system and to permit a comprehensive review of all computations. The analysis should include and compare total initial capital cost, energy cost, operating cost, system reliability, flexibility, and adaptability of each alternative. Each system alternative considered should satisfy the program requirements completely in terms of flexibility, redundancy, reliability, and ease of maintenance. The total capital cost to provide the program requirements for each alternative should be included as part of the life-cycle cost.

For comparison of systems, a life-cycle cost analysis should run from 15 to 30 years, corresponding to the anticipated useful life of major equipment. Replacement costs should be included for equipment with less than the chosen life cycle. The following are the cost components:

- The escalation rate for fuel or energy costs (oil, gas, coal, electricity, etc.) can be obtained by using the procedures set by the Department of Energy (DOE) in NIST Handbook 135. Alternatively, owners' historical data should be consulted.

- The initial capital cost should include all equipment, auxiliaries, and building-related costs for each complete system. Refer to the *ASHRAE Handbook—HVAC Systems and Equipment*, "Owning and Operating Costs," for a complete list of items to be included in an economic analysis (ASHRAE 2000a).

Energy cost computations should take base loads into consideration. The owner's representative should provide utility usage and rates. Backup computations for items listed in the operating cost should be included in the life-cycle cost report. Computations should be made on a monthly basis, taking into account variations in the heating and cooling loads. Energy usage and cost should be developed using Weather Bureau tapes, or Air Force Manual AFM-88-8, Engineering Weather Data, and the bin method procedure referenced in the latest *ASHRAE Handbook—Fundamentals* (Department of the Air Force 1967; ASHRAE 2001a).

Energy cost computations should consider the energy used by fans and cooling and heating coils, as well as refrigeration plant energy costs that result from the proposed air-conditioning system. The energy analysis should be conducted using a professionally recognized and proven computer program based on hourly calculations.

Total "present" worth is equal to the sum of the first (construction) cost and the present worth of maintenance, replacements, utilities, electricity, and fuel payments for the analysis-life of the project. All of the "present" worth values should be based on appropriate construction schedules.

An equivalent annual cost is often calculated. This is the payment that will amortize the total present worth at the given interest rate using a capital recovery factor (CRF). Taxes or insurance are normally not included in the annual owning cost.

Public Law 95-619 requires that life-cycle cost analyses for federal projects conform to procedures set forth by the Department of Energy. Conducting this type of analysis for other types of projects is highly recommended.

APPENDIX F
VENTILATION STANDARDS
AND CURRENT TRENDS

F.1 INTRODUCTION

The comfort and quality of the environment for an occupant in a building is controlled directly by that building's environmental control system, namely, its ventilation system, whether it is forced, natural, or mixed. Ideally, ventilation systems are designed to maximize human comfort. However, cost and energy consumption constraints are typically imposed, and, as a result, the goal of maximum comfort is usually compromised. Therefore, codes and standards are imposed or recommended for buildings and have been developed in order to protect the health and welfare of occupants. These standards are based on recognized acceptable ranges for environmental characteristics. For example, comfort can be described as follows:

> Thermal comfort is a complex concept that is influenced by a number of parameters and is not always perceived the same by all humans. However, several attempts have been made in order to develop empirical correlations for relating comfort perceptions to specific physiological responses, in a more comprehensive way than the previously presented comfort indices. Among the various models and suggestions for the quantitative estimation of thermal comfort, the most widely used is the one suggested by Fanger. This work has grown to be the most popular way of quantitatively expressing thermal comfort and thermal sensation, known as the Predicted Mean Vote (PMV) Theory and the associated index of Predicted Percent of Dissatisfied (PPD) people. The PMV and PPD indices have been introduced and empirically derived, by Fanger during the 1970's. The method has become since 1984, the basis of the International Standard ISO-7730 and the European Standard EN 27730 (Moderate thermal environments—Determination of the PMV and

PPD indices and specification of the conditions for thermal comfort) for assessing thermal comfort in spaces with average temperatures (ISO 1994).

Energy consumption and reduced operating costs have become dominant factors in the derivation of the codes and standards. Control-system performance evaluation is therefore critical, with life-cycle costs also requiring attention.

However, standards that have focused on these aspects run into problems in their acceptance. Performance-oriented standards have not been widely accepted by contractors and enforcement officials because of increased costs of implementation and liability and barriers in technology transfer. Further, financial decisions based on life-cycle costing have not been accepted by contractors and building developers. These groups have resisted because of a lack of incentives, such as amortization periods and allowance of pass-through of operating costs, and because of the high cost of capital.

F.2 VENTILATION CODES AND STANDARDS

F.2.1 General

The provision of indoor environments in commercial and residential buildings of "comfortable" or "acceptable" thermal quality is an enormous burden on energy consumption. Such provision requires approximately one-third of the total annual energy consumption in buildings (HVAC, lighting, equipment, etc.) in the United States (USDOE 1978) while in the European Union, buildings consume about 40% of the total energy budget (SOEC 1996). An additional 10% may be required to maintain conditions that are acceptable for occupants in industrial facilities (Kusuca 1976). Ventilation systems have been reported to require as much as 50% or 60% of the total energy consumed in buildings (Rohles et al. 1978; Yaglou 1936; Nevins 1976).

Building codes have been adopted and enforced by local, state, and federal government agencies to protect the health, safety, and welfare of the general public. These codes generally take the form of stated minimal acceptable ventilation criteria to be provided by the ventilation system in the buildings. Note that "ventilation air," as used here and elsewhere in this document, refers to outdoor air or recirculated, treated air. During the design phase, compliance with building codes is usually the responsibility of licensed professional engineers and architects. However, after a building has been designed and constructed, responsibility is more vague; the owner or manager usually assumes responsibility for maintaining the quality of the indoor environment, but there is normally no official enforcement.

There are two basic types of standard, the "voluntary" or "consensus standard" and the "mandatory standard."

Consensus standards are those that have been developed and published by authoritative bodies. In the United States, for example, such bodies include the American National Standards Institute (ANSI), the National Fire Protection Association (NFPA), and the American Society for Testing and Materials (ASTM). Other organizations that publish standards for the building industry are the American Society of Heating, Refrigerating and Air-Conditioning Engineers (ASHRAE), the American Society of Mechanical Engineers (ASME), the Illuminating Engineering Society (IES), the American Concrete Institute (ACI), the Air Conditioning and Refrigeration Institute (ARI), and the Sheet Metal and Air Conditioning Contractors National Association (SMACNA).

The standards published by these organizations are usually developed by a consensus method, hence the term "consensus standard." They are usually adopted, after periods of open review, as guidelines of recommended practice or minimal performance criteria by which an organization may govern itself. However, if a voluntary standard is adopted within legal documents, such as government standards or building codes, it may become mandatory.

Standards also are developed in response to state or federal laws. These are known as "mandatory standards" and are developed and promoted in the form of state or federal regulations after they have been subjected to public hearings.

F.2.2 United States

In the United States, regulatory authorities described above in F.2.1 may develop "consensus standards."

U.S. agencies responsible for the development and enforcement of mandatory standards relevant to the building industry include the Department of Housing and Urban Development (HUD), the Department of Health and Human Services (DHHS, formerly the Department of Health, Education, and Welfare, or DHEW), and the Department of Energy (DOE).

In most U.S. states, a Department of Public Health licenses hospitals and other health care facilities. In many cases, especially when federal reimbursement for patient care is provided, hospitals must conform to U.S. Department of Health and Human Services guidelines. These guidelines originally had root in the Hill Burton act passed by Congress after the Second World War in an attempt to provide standards of patient care. The U.S. Department of Health Education and Welfare (HEW) maintained the standards. During the last several years, the American Institute of Architects' Academy of Architecture for Health, with assistance from the U.S. Department of Health and Human Services, has maintained the standards.

F.2.3 Europe

In Europe, the situation is still rather vague. Different national building regulations, codes, and standards are applicable in each member state of the European Union, published by the national professional engineering associations, technical chambers, etc. Some efforts are currently underway to prepare common European standards (European Committee for Standardization, Brussels, Belgium) for the building industry, but these are not yet mandatory.

F.2.4 Other Countries

There is great inconsistency and deficiency in many countries, including some in Asia and Africa and some Latin American countries on standards requirements for health care facilities. It is hoped that this condition will be remedied soon.

F.3 VENTILATION BACKGROUND AND DETAILS

F.3.1 Background

Historically, natural ventilation has been used in the design of buildings. The use of outdoor air for natural ventilation, combined with natural cooling techniques and the use of daylight, have been essential elements of architecture since ancient times.

Classical architecture with H, L, T, or U-shaped floor plans, the use of open courts and limited space depth, maximized windows to facilitate communication of the indoor environment with the outdoors for daylight and natural ventilation. This was common practice even for large commercial buildings until the end of the 19th century (Donaldson and Nagengast 1994).

Naturally ventilated buildings have been common in several parts of the world from the ancient Hellenic architecture to the Arabian wind towers. Natural ventilation was surpassed by mechanical ventilation combined with comfort air conditioning in order to resolve practical problems for the year-round control of the indoor environmental conditions. The possibilities for HVAC in buildings seemed to be trouble-free, until the time that concerns about energy conservation and the sick building syndrome came into play. These problems have generated the need to pay a lot more attention to design options and equipment maintenance and to the development of strict standards and design guidelines that take into consideration all aspects of indoor environmental quality and energy efficiency.

As far back as the 18th Century, ventilation standards have been in place. Studies by Nevins (1976), Klauss et al. (1970), and Arnold and O'Sheridan (1979) showed that ventilation rates increased from 4 cfm per person (1.9 L/s per person) in 1824 to 30 cfm per person (14.2 L/s per person) in 1895. A minimal requirement of 30 cfm per person (14.2 L/s per person) dominated design of ventilation systems during the first quarter of the twentieth century, as evidenced by the fact that in 1925 the codes of 22 states required a minimal ventilation rate of 30 cfm (14.2 L/s) of outdoor air per person (Kusuda 1976). This standard was used until the 1930s when Yaglou et al. (1936) introduced the concept of measuring ventilation rate in terms of cubic feet per minute (L/s) per person to achieve an "odor-free" environment as a function of available airspace per person.

The Yaglou studies have served as a reference for the past 40 years. However, many ventilation codes and standards specify ventilation requirements in terms of room air changes per hour (ACH), rather than exchange rate per person. When ventilation rates are specified in this way, differences in spatial dimensions and occupancy are lost. For example, 5 ACH in a theater with a 20 ft (6.1 m) ceiling height and a sparse occupancy of 100 ft^2 (9.3 m^2) of floor area per person would result in 167 cfm (79 L/s) per person, whereas the same room-air exchange rate and occupancy in a classroom with an 8 ft (2.4 m)

ceiling would mean 67 cfm (32 L/s) per person. However, at full-load occupancies of 10 ft^2 (0.9 m^2) per person in the theater and 20 ft^2 (1.9 m^2) per person in the classroom, 5 ACH would result in 17 cfm (8 L/s) per person in the theater and 13 cfm (6 L/s) per person in the classroom.

The inherent problems associated with specifying air changes per hour have been recognized in some standards for several years. In 1946, the American Standard Building Requirements for Light and Ventilation, A53.1, was published by the American Standards Association (ASA 1946) with primary criteria in cubic feet per minute per square foot of floor area (L/s per square meter) (BOCA 1975). A revision and update of A53.1 was published in 1973 by ASHRAE (as ASHRAE Standard 62-73), with primary criteria in cubic feet per minute per person (L/s per person). The latter standard was adopted by the ANSI (formerly ASA) in 1977 and has been designated ANSI Standard B194.1. For the first time in a ventilation standard, ASHRAE Standard 62-73 provided a quantitative definition of "acceptable outdoor air" and specified conditions under which recirculated air could be used. Both minimal and recommended ventilation rates were specified in the ASHRAE standard to accommodate fuel economy (minimal values) or comfort in odor-free environments (recommended values). Energy savings at design summer and winter conditions resulting from minimal ventilation rates specified in ASHRAE Standard 62-73 were estimated to range from 27% to 81% for various occupied spaces, compared with rates in Standard A53.1.

In 1975, ASHRAE published Standard 90-75, *Energy Conservation in New Building Design* (ASHRAE 1975), to address the need for energy efficient buildings. Based upon this standard, the National Conference of States on Building Codes and Standards, Inc. (NCSBCS), undertook, with the three model-code groups recognized in the United States, to write a model *Code for Energy Conservation in New Building Construction* (BOCA 1977). By 1980, legislation either had been passed or was being considered by 45 states for energy-conservation regulations based on these two documents (Oglesby 1977).

ASHRAE Standard 90-75 was expected to reduce energy requirements in new buildings by 15-60% (Little 1976), but efforts to promote the standard resulted in a conflict with ASHRAE Standard 62-73. Standard 90-75 stated that the "minimum" column in Standard 62-73 for each type of occupancy "shall" be used for design purposes. This statement in Standard 90-75 effectively deleted the "recommended" column in Standard 62-73 and caused serious concerns regarding the possibility of insufficient ventilation in new buildings. For example, when smoking was allowed in a room ventilated at the minimal rate of 5 cfm (2.4 L/s) per person, the carbon monoxide concentrations approached the limits specified by the EPA primary ambient-air quality standards, and particle concentrations exceeded the proposed limits by a factor of 30 to 60 (DHEW 1979; Banks 1978). There is still controversy about what are acceptable concentrations of pollutants and ventilation rates.

In January 1981, ASHRAE adopted Standard 62-1981 in an effort to resolve some of the problems with Standard 90-75 and to reflect newer design requirements, equipment, systems, and instruments. A comparison of Standard 62-1981, Standard 62-73, and the obsolete Standard A53.1 shows that major revisions have been made in an effort to resolve the apparent conflict between operating ventilation control systems for energy savings and operating them for protection of the health and comfort of the occupants. The quality of outdoor air to be used for dilution and control of indoor air pollution has been defined, not only in terms of the EPA primary standards, but also in terms of other recognized guidelines and professional judgment.

Values for minimal and recommended ventilation rates have been replaced with required values for smoking and nonsmoking areas. Nonsmoking areas have proposed values similar to the existing minimal values, and those for smoking areas are similar to or greater than the values currently recommended. A method has been specified that will determine the amount of recirculation air required to compensate for allowable reductions in outdoor air. The amount is determined as a function of air-cleaner efficiency. The operation of mechanical ventilation systems during periods of occupancy is specified as a function of the source of indoor pollutants. An alternative method specifies both objective and subjective criteria for indoor air quality, but the method of achieving control is left to the discretion of the operator. With the advent of performance criteria for indoor pollutant control, conflicts between various codes and standards have become more intensive.

Comparison of ventilation requirements in ASHRAE Standard 62-73 (ASHRAE 1973), ASA Standard A 53.1 (ASA 1946), ANSI/ASHRAE Standard 62-1981 (ASHRAE 1981), and the more recent ANSI/ASHRAE Standard 62-1989 (ASHRAE 1989) challenges the building designer and operator to select a ventilation rate that will meet the require-

ments of all relevant codes and standards. Under these circumstances, the usual procedure has been to select the largest value that would satisfy the requirements of all the codes and standards.

Because of concerns regarding energy consumption and costs, some regulations have been promulgated or proposed that are in direct conflict with those promulgated to protect the health or comfort of occupants. One example was the 1977 Assembly Bill 983 of Wisconsin, "Ventilation Requirements for Public Buildings and Places of Employment." Bill 983 would have eliminated mandatory minimal ventilation requirements specified in the state building code (i.e., 5 cfm per person [2.4 L/s per person]) during the period October 1 to April 1 of each year. Building owners would have been allowed to close or otherwise regulate outside-air intakes to conserve energy during these periods. Bill 983 was passed by the 1977 General Assembly and vetoed by the governor; the veto was overridden by the Senate and sustained by the House. This legislation was reintroduced as a rider to an appropriations bill in the 1979 General Assembly. It was later amended to allow reduced ventilation only through administrative action; in that form, it passed. The state Department of Industry, Labor and Human Relations, previously responsible for ventilation requirements, will administer the law.

Ventilation and control of biologic contamination in medical facilities, especially in some hospital treatment areas, has been the subject of much research since the middle of the nineteenth century (Banks 1978; Lieser 1975). Since 1969, regulations have allowed recirculation in sensitive areas such as operating rooms (OR). In this kind of installation, at least, two air filters are required, namely, a prefilter and a final filter, rated at 25% and 90% efficiency, respectively, according to ASHRAE Standard 52-76 (1976). The filters must be properly maintained to secure their optimum performance. Each space in which inhalation anesthetic agents are administered must also be equipped with a separate scavenging system for exhausting waste anesthetic gases.

Studies have shown that 80-90% of bacterial contamination found in a wound comes from the ambient air (Howorth 1985). Proper ventilation is necessary to (1) remove anesthetic gases and odors released during an operation, which may permanently or temporarily disturb the occupants; (2) reduce bacteria, viruses, and dust concentration to acceptable levels, so that the indoor air satisfies the aseptic levels in accordance with health guidelines for the patients and space occupants; and (3) provide optimum and comfortable working conditions for the occupants to facilitate their demanding work during an operation.

Airborne contaminants are usually attached to dust particles or water molecules. Studies have shown that 99.9% of all bacteria present in a hospital are removed by 90-95% efficient filters. This is because bacteria are typically present in colony forming units that are larger than 1 mm. Viruses are more difficult to control since airborne infective viruses are much less than 1 mm in size.

The number of air changes per hour must be at least 20, to maintain the OR at a positive pressure, while the outdoor air requirements for acceptable indoor air quality must be at least 51 m^3/h (14.2 L/s) per person according to ASHRAE Standard 62. Special requirements and pressure relationships may determine different minimum ventilation rates and filter efficiencies (Balaras et al. 2002). Procedures generating specific indoor contaminants may also require higher air-change rates. The surgical suite is maintained at a positive pressure in relation to the other OR secondary use spaces. This minimizes the chance of air entering into the surgical suite from the more contaminated spaces. Zone pressurization introduces specific control requirements that can be accomplished by different methodologies, such as flow tracking and differential space pressurization.

The indoor air flow patterns in the surgical suite must ensure that the air masses are directed from the clean to the less clean zones and that there are no pockets where the air can be trapped. The main air flow pattern should not encounter any obstacles, especially in the direction toward the main pollution sources around the operating table (i.e., medical staff and patient). The air velocity must be maintained at low levels to avoid drafts and turbulence that will cause air mixing and the dispersion of bacteria and airborne particles. Also, there is the danger that higher velocity flows could cause impingement on the wound site (Lewis 1993).

The ventilation system must operate continuously during surgery and even when the OR is not being used but possibly at a reduced ventilation rate. This is necessary to maintain continuous aseptic indoor conditions and stand-by operation. However, depending on the ventilation system, implementing a proper control strategy during the off-use hours can reduce the total air change rate and thus reduce energy consumption (Woods et al. 1986). The airflow can be reduced to 30% of the full-load conditions during off-use hours.

F.3.2 European Health Care Ventilation Standards Details

The European standards for hospital ORs differ in the various member states. There are usually two distinct categories of operating rooms, depending on the nature of the surgeries performed, namely, the "low risk" ORs for routine and low risk surgeries and the "high risk" ORs for demanding surgeries (i.e., orthopedic, heart, etc.). In general, the ventilation requirements for the low risk ORs do not differ significantly. However, there can be significant differences for the high risk class. For example, according to the German Standard DIN 1946 (1999), the recommended rates are 60 m^3 per m^2 per h (1.6 L/s per ft^2), if the room height is 3.0 m (9.8 ft), or else 20 ACH. However, regulations in other countries, such as France, Switzerland, and the U.K., recommend much higher ventilation rates with laminar air flow supply. Most of the other European countries follow the German standard.

F.3.3 U.S. Health Care Ventilation Standards—Details

Ventilation standards promulgated by the AIA Guidelines and by ASHRAE have been different. An attempt was made during the work of the SP 91 Committee in preparing this manual to understand the differences between the two standards and to incorporate CFD (computational fluid dynamics) work done by Memarzadeh and Manning (2000). Table F-1 illustrates the differences between the two and the attempt to reach common ground.

Table F-1 presents criteria for general pressure relationships and ventilation of certain hospital areas from two published documents: ASHRAE Applications Handbook (1999a) and AIA Guidelines (2001). Relative humidity and space temperature criteria for ASHRAE in Table F-1 were also drawn from the Handbook. The table also presents a compilation of "best practice" criteria in design application. The "best practice" criteria are summarized in Table 4-1.

Tables 4-1 and F-1 are in a consistent format. To provide for this, some functional space nomenclature may be altered or located differently than in the source tables.

F.4 AIR DIFFUSION CRITERIA

In general, air is supplied to ventilate an enclosed space (i.e., a room or various zones in a building) for two main reasons:

• *To maintain acceptable oxygen concentration and dilution and removal of carbon dioxide and other contaminants for safety of the occupants.* However, it should be noted that supplying the specified or mandated rates for ventilation does

Table F-1. Comparison of Engineering Best Practice with *AIA Guidelines** and *ASHRAE Handbook***
(For a larger version of this table see insert.)

Function Space	Pressure Relationship to Adjacent Areas (a) (2)			Minimum Air Changes of Outdoor Air per Hour (b) (3)			Minimum Total Air Changes per Hour (c) (4) (5)			All Air Exhausted Directly to Outdoors (6)		
	Manual	Handbook	AIA (1)	Manual	Handbook	AIA (1)	Manual	Handbook	AIA (1)	Manual	Handbook	AIA (1)
Surgery And Critical Care												
Operating Room (all outdoor air system)		P	—		15	—		15	—		Yes	—
Operating Room (recirculating air system)	P	P	—	5	5	—	25	25	—	—	Optional	—
Operating/surgical cystoscopic rooms (10), (11)	P	—	Out	5	—	3	25	—	15	—	—	—
Delivery Room (all outdoor air system)		P	—		15	—		15	—		Optional	—
Delivery Room (recirculating air system)		P	—		5	—		25	—		Optional	—
Delivery Room (10)	P	—	Out	5	—	3	25	—	15	—	—	—
Recovery Room	—	E	—	2	2	2	6	6	6	—	Optional	—
Critical and Intensive Care	—	—	—	2	—	2	6	—	6	—	—	—
Newborn Intensive Care	—	—	—	2	—	2	6	—	6	—	—	—
Treatment Room (13)	—	—	—	—	—	—	6	—	6	—	—	—
Nursery Suite	P	P	—	5	5	—	12	12	—	—	Optional	—
Trauma Room (f) (13)		P	Out		5	3	12	12	15		Optional	—
Trauma Room (crisis or shock) (f) (13a)	P			3			15			Yes		
Trauma Room (conventional ED or treatment) (f) (13a)	P			2			6			—		
Anesthesia Storage (see code requirements)		±	—		Optional	—		8	—		Yes	—
Anesthesia Gas Storage	N	—	In	—	—	—	8	—	8	Yes	—	Yes
Endoscopy (11)	N	—	In	2	—	2	6	—	6	—	—	—
Bronchoscopy	N	—	In	2	—	2	12	—	12	Yes	—	Yes
ER Waiting Rooms	N	—	In	2	—	2	12	—	12	Yes	—	Yes (14), (15)
Triage	N	—	In	2	—	2	12	—	12	Yes	—	Yes (14)
Radiology Waiting Rooms	N	—	In	2	—	2	12	—	12	Yes	—	Yes (14), (15)
Class A Operating (procedure) Room	N	—	Out	3	—	3	15	—	15	—	—	—
Nursing												
Patient Room	—	±	—	2	2	2	6	4	6 (16)	—	Optional	—
Toilet Room (g)	N	N	In	Optional	Optional	—	10	10	10	Yes	Yes	Yes
Intensive Care		P	—		2	—		6	—		Optional	—
Newborn Nursery Suite	—	—	—	2	—	2	6	—	6	—	—	—
Protective Isolation (i)		P	—		2	—		15	—		Yes	—
Infectious Isolation (h)		±	—		2	—		6	—		Yes	—
Protective Environment Room (11), (17)	P	—	Out	2	—	2	12	—	12	—	—	—
Airborne Infection Isolation Room (11), (18)	N	—	In	2	—	2	12	—	12	Yes	—	Yes (15)
Isolation Alcove or Anteroom (17), (18)	P/N	±	In/Out	2	2	—	10	10	10	Yes	Yes	Yes
Labor/Delivery/Recovery	—	—	—	—	—	2	—	—	6 (16)	—	—	—
Labor/Delivery/Recovery/Postpartum	—	—	—	—	—	2	—	—	6 (16)	—	—	—
Labor/Delivery/Recovery/Postpartum (LDRP) (16)	—	E	—	2	2	—	6	4	—	—	Optional	—
Patient Corridor	—	E	—	2	2	—	4	4	2	—	Optional	—
Public Corridor	N			2			2					
Ancillary												
Radiology (19) x-ray (surgery and critical care)		P	—		3	—		15	—		Optional	—
Radiology (19) x-ray (diagnostic and treatment)	—	±	—	2	2	—	6	6	—	—	Optional	—
Radiology (19) x-ray (surgery/critical care and catherization)	P	—	Out	3	—	3	15	—	15	—	—	—
Radiology (19) Darkroom	N	N	In	2	2	2	10	10	10	Yes	Yes (j)	Yes
Laboratory, general (19)	N	N	—	2	2	—	6	6	6	Yes	Yes	—
Laboratory, bacteriology	N	N	—	2	2	—	6	6	—	Yes	Yes	—
Laboratory, biochemistry (19)	P	P	Out	2	2	—	6	6	6	Optional	Optional	—
Laboratory, cytology	N	N	In	2	2	—	6	6	6	Yes	Yes	Yes
Laboratory, glasswashing	N	N	In	Optional	Optional	—	10	10	10	Yes	Yes	Yes
Laboratory, histology	N	N	In	2	2	—	6	6	6	Yes	Yes	Yes
Microbiology (19)	N	—	In	—	—	—	6	—	6	Yes	—	Yes
Laboratory, nuclear medicine	N	N	In	2	2	—	6	6	6	Yes	Yes	Yes
Laboratory, pathology	N	N	In	2	2	—	6	6	6	Yes	Yes	Yes
Laboratory, serology	P	P	Out	2	2	—	6	6	6	Yes	Optional	—
Laboratory, sterilizing	N	N	In	Optional	Optional	—	10	10	10	Yes	Yes	Yes
Laboratory, media transfer	P	P	—	2	2	—	4	4	—	Optional	Optional	—
Autopsy		N	—		2	—		12	—		Yes	—
Autopsy Room (11)	N	—	In	2	—	—	12	—	12	Yes	—	Yes
Nonrefrigerated Body-Holding Room (k)	N	N	In	Optional	Optional	—	10	10	10	Yes	Yes	Yes
Pharmacy	P	P	Out	2	2	—	4	4	4	—	Optional	—
Administration												
Admitting and Waiting Rooms	N	N	—	2	2	—	6	6	—	Yes	Yes	—
Diagnostic And Treatment												
Bronchoscopy, sputum collection, and pentamidine administration	N	N	—	2	2	—	12	10	—	Yes	Yes	—
Examination Room	—	±	—	2	2	—	6	6	6	—	Optional	—
Medication Room	P	P	Out	2	2	—	4	4	4	—	Optional	—
Treatment Room	—	±	—	2	2	—	6	6	6	—	Optional	—
Physical Therapy and Hydrotherapy	N	N	In	2	2	—	6	6	6	—	Optional	—
Soiled Workroom or Soiled Holding	N	N	In	2	2	—	10	10	10	Yes	Yes	Yes
Clean Workroom or Clean Holding	P	P	Out	2	2	—	4	4	4	—	Optional	—
Sterilizing And Supply												
ETO-Sterilzer Room	N	—	In	—	—	—	10	—	10	Yes	—	Yes
Sterilizer Equipment Room	N	N	In	—	Optional	—	10	10	10	Yes	Yes	Yes
Central Medical and Surgical Supply												
Soiled or Decontamination Room	N	N	In	2	2	—	6	6	6	Yes	Yes	Yes
Clean Workroom	P	—	Out	2	—	—	4	—	4	—	—	—
Sterile Storage	P	—	Out	2	—	—	4	—	4	—	—	—
Clean Workroom and Sterile Storage		P	—		2	—		4	—		Optional	—
Equipment Storage		±	—		2 (Optional)	—		2	—		Optional	
Service												
Food Preparation Center (l) (20)	—	±	—	2	2	—	10	10	10	Yes	Yes	—
Warewashing	N	N	In	Optional	Optional	—	10	10	10	Yes	Yes	Yes
Dietary Day Storage	—	±	In	Optional	Optional	—	2	2	2	—	Optional	—
Laundry, general	N	N	—	2	2	—	10	10	10	Yes	Yes	Yes
Soiled Linen Sorting and Storage	N	N	In	Optional	Optional	—	10	10	10	Yes	Yes	Yes
Clean Linen Storage	P	P	Out	2 (Optional)	2 (Optional)	—	2	2	2	—	Optional	—
Linen and Trash Chute Room	N	N	—	Optional	Optional	—	10	10	—	Yes	Yes	—
Soiled Linen and Trash Chute Room	—	—	In	—	—	—	—	—	10	—	—	Yes
Bedpan Room	N	N	In	Optional	Optional	—	10	10	10	Yes	Yes	Yes
Bathroom	N	N	In	Optional	Optional	—	10	10	10	Yes	Optional*	—
Janitor's Closet	N	N	In	Optional	Optional	—	10	10	10	Yes	Optional	Yes

Table F-1. Comparison of Engineering Best Practice with *AIA Guidelines** and *ASHRAE Handbook*** (Continued)
(For a larger version of this table see insert.)

Function Space	Air Recirculated Within Room Units (d) (7)			Relative Humidity (8) (%)			Design Temperature (9) (°F/°C)			Proposed Comments
	Manual	Handbook	AIA (1)	Manual	Handbook	AIA (1)	Manual	Handbook	AIA (1)	
Surgery And Critical Care										
Operating Room (all outdoor air system)		No	—		45-55	—		62-80	—	
Operating Room (recirculating air system)	No	No	—	30-60			68-75			A1
Operating/surgical cystoscopic rooms (10), (11)	No		No	30-60		30-60	68-75		68-73 (20-23) (12)	A1
Delivery Room (all outdoor air system)		No	—		45-55	—		62-80	—	
Delivery Room (recirculating air system)		No	—							
Delivery Room (10)	No	—	No	30-60		30-60	68-75		68-73 (20-23)	B1
Recovery Room	No	No	No	30-60	45-55	30-60	70-75	75	70-75 (21-24)	C1
Critical and Intensive Care	No	—	No	30-60		30-60	70-75		70-75 (21-24)	C2
Newborn Intensive Care	No	—	No	30-60		30-60	72-78		72-78 (22-26)	C2
Treatment Room (13)	—	—	—	30-60		—	70-75		75 (24)	C2
Nursery Suite	No	No	—	30-60	30-60	—	75-80	75-80		D1
Trauma Room (f) (13)		No	No		45-55	30-60		62-80	70-75 (21-24)	
Trauma Room (crisis or shock) (f) (13a)	Yes			30-60			70-75			B2
Trauma Room (conventional ED or treatment) (f) (13a)	No			30-60			70-75			B2
Anesthesia Storage (see code requirements)		No	—						—	
Anesthesia Gas Storage	—	—	—	—		—	—		—	C3
Endoscopy (11)	No	—	No	30-60		30-60	68-73		68-73 (20-23)	C2
Bronchoscopy	No	—	No	30-60		30-60	68-73		68-73 (20-23)	C2
ER Waiting Rooms	—	—	—	30-60		—	70-75		70-75 (21-24)	C2
Triage	—	—	—	—		—	70-75		70-75 (21-24)	C2
Radiology Waiting Rooms	—	—	—	—		—	70-75		70-75 (21-24)	C2
Class A Operating (procedure) Room	No	—	No	30-60		30-60	70-75		70-75 (21-24)	A4
Nursing										
Patient Room	—	Optional	—	30-60	30 (winter), 50 (summer)	—	70-75	75	70-75 (21-24)	B3
Toilet Room (g)	No	No	—	—		—	—		—	C3
Intensive Care		No	—		30-60	—		75-80		
Newborn Nursery Suite	No	—	No	30-60		30-60	72-78		72-78 (22-26)	C2
Protective Isolation (i)		Optional	—			—			—	
Infectious Isolation (h)		No	—		30 (winter), 50 (summer)	—		75	—	
Protective Environment Room (11), (17)	No	—	No	—		—	70-75		75 (24)	C2
Airborne Infection Isolation Room (11), (18)	No	—	No	—		—	70-75		75 (24)	C2
Isolation Alcove or Anteroom (17), (18)	No	No	No	—		—	—		—	D1
Labor/Delivery/Recovery		—	—			—			70-75 (21-24)	
Labor/Delivery/Recovery/Postpartum		—	—			—			70-75 (21-24)	
Labor/Delivery/Recovery/Postpartum (LDRP) (16)	—	Optional	—	30-60	30 (winter), 50 (summer)	—	70-75	75	—	A2
Patient Corridor	—	Optional	—	—		—	—		—	D2
Public Corridor	—		—	—			—			
Ancilliary										
Radiology (19) x-ray (surgery and critical care)		No	—			—			—	
Radiology (19) x-ray (diagnostic and treatment)	—	Optional	—	30-60	40-50	—	72-78	78-80	75 (24)	D2
Radiology (19) x-ray (surgery/critical care and catherization)	No	—	No	30-60		30-60	70-75		70-75 (21-24)	C2
Radiology (19) Darkroom	No	No	No	—		—	—		—	D2
Laboratory, general (19)	No	No	—	30-60	Comfort Range	—	70-75	Comfort Range	75 (24)	D2
Laboratory, bacteriology	No	No	—	30-60	Comfort Range	—	70-75	Comfort Range	—	D2
Laboratory, biochemistry (19)	No	No	No	30-60	Comfort Range	—	70-75	Comfort Range	75 (24)	D2
Laboratory, cytology	No	No	No	30-60	Comfort Range	—	70-75	Comfort Range	75 (24)	D3
Laboratory, glasswashing	—	Optional	—	—	Comfort Range	—	—	Comfort Range	—	D3
Laboratory, histology	No	No	No	30-60	Comfort Range	—	70-75	Comfort Range	75 (24)	C3
Microbiology (19)	No	—	No	30-60		—	70-75		75 (24)	C4
Laboratory, nuclear medicine	No	No	No	30-60	Comfort Range	—	70-75		75 (24)	C5
Laboratory, pathology	No	No	No	30-60	Comfort Range	—	70-75		75 (24)	C4
Laboratory, serology	No	No	No	30-60	Comfort Range	—	70-75		75 (24)	C4
Laboratory, sterilizing	No	No	—	30-60	Comfort Range	—	70-75		—	C4
Laboratory, media transfer	No	No	—	30-60	Comfort Range	—	70-75		—	D2
Autopsy		No	—			—			—	
Autopsy Room (11)	No	—	No	—		—	—		—	C4
Nonrefrigerated Body-Holding Room (k)	No	No	—	—		—	70		70 (21)	C3
Pharmacy	—	Optional	—	30-60		—	70-75		—	C4
Administration										
Admitting and Waiting Rooms	—	Optional	—	30-60		—	70-75		—	D4
Diagnostic And Treatment										
Bronchoscopy, sputum collection, and pentamidine administration	—	Optional	—	30-60		—	70-75		—	D4
Examination Room	—	Optional	—	30-60		—	70-75		75 (24)	C4
Medication Room	—	Optional	—	30-60		—	70-75		—	C4
Treatment Room	—	Optional	—	30-60	30 (winter), 50 (summer)	—	70-75	75	75 (24)	C6
Physical Therapy and Hydrotherapy	—	Optional	—	30-60	Comfort Range	—	72-80	Comfort Range/up to 80	75 (24)	C4
Soiled Workroom or Soiled Holding	No	No	No	30-60	Comfort Range	—	72-78	Comfort Range	—	D3
Clean Workroom or Clean Holding	—	Optional	—	—		—	—		—	C3
Sterilizing And Supply										
ETO-Sterilzer Room	No	—	No	—		30-60	—		75 (24)	C5
Sterilzer Equipment Room	No	No	—	—		—	—		—	C4
Central Medical and Surgical Supply										
Soiled or Decontamination Room	No	No	No	30-60	Comfort Range	—	72-78	Comfort Range	68-73 (20-23)	D5
Clean Workroom	No	—	No	30-60		30-60	72-78		75 (24)	D8
Sterile Storage	—	—	—	30-60		(Max) 70	72-78		—	D7
Clean Workroom and Sterile Storage		Optional	—		Under 50	—		Comfort Range		
Equipment Storage		Optional	—	—		—				
Service										
Food Preparation Center (l) (20)	No	No	No	—		—	—		—	C3
Warewashing	No	No	No	—		—	—		—	C3
Dietary Day Storage	No	No	—	—		—	—		—	C7
Laundry, general	No	No	—	—		—	—		—	D3
Soiled Linen Sorting and Storage	No	No	No	—		—	—		—	C2
Clean Linen Storage	—	Optional	—	—		—	—		—	C3
Linen and Trash Chute Room	No	No	—	—		—	—		—	C2
Soiled Linen and Trash Chute Room	—	—	No	—		—	—		—	D2
Bedpan Room	No	No	—	—		—	—		—	C3
Bathroom	No	No	—	—		—	72-78		75 (24)	C8
Janitor's Closet	No	No	No	—		—	—		—	D3

* AIA Guidelines—*Guidelines for Design and Construction of Hospital and Health Care Facilities*, Chapter 7, Table 7.2, American Institute of Architects Academy, 2001.
** ASHRAE Handbook—*1999 ASHRAE Handbook—HVAC Applications*, Chapter 7, Table 3.

Notes to Table F-1, I

I. 1999 ASHRAE Handbook table references with some clarifications

P = Positive
N = Negative
± = Continuous directional control not required

(a) Where continuous directional control is not required, variations should be minimized, and in no case should a lack of directional control allow the spread of infection from one area to another. Boundaries between functional areas (wards or departments) should have directional control. Lewis (1998) describes methods for maintaining directional control by applying air-tracking controls.

(b) Ventilation in accordance with ASHRAE Standard 62, *Ventilation for Acceptable Indoor Air Quality*, should be used for areas for which specific ventilation rates are not given. Where a higher outdoor air requirement is called for in Standard 62 than in Table 3 (*1999 ASHRAE Handbook—HVAC*), the higher value should be used.

(c) Total air changes indicated should be either supplied or, where required, exhausted.

(d) Recirculating HEPA filter units used for infection control (without heating or cooling coils) are acceptable.

(e) For operating rooms, 100% outside air should be used only when codes require it and only if heat recovery devices are used.

(f) The term "trauma/shock room" as used here is the entry area to the emergency room used for general initial treatment and stabilization of accident victims. The operating room within the Emergency Department that is routinely used for emergency surgery should be treated as an operating room.

(g) See section on Patient Rooms for discussion on design of central toilet exhaust systems.

(h) The Airborne Infection (infectious) isolation rooms described in this table are those that might be used for infectious patients in the average community hospital. The rooms are negatively pressurized. Some isolation rooms may have a separate anteroom. Refer to the discussion in the chapter for more detailed information. Where highly infectious respirable diseases such as tuberculosis are to be isolated, increased air change rates should be considered.

(i) Protective Environment isolation rooms are those used for immunosuppressed patients. The room is positively pressurized to protect the patient. Anterooms are generally required and should be negatively pressurized with respect to the patient room.

(j) All air need not be exhausted if darkroom equipment has scavenging exhaust duct attached and meets ventilation standards on NIOSH, OSHA, and local employee exposure limits.

(k) The nonrefrigerated body-holding room is only for facilities that do not perform autopsies on-site and use the space for short periods while waiting for the body to be transferred.

(l) Food preparation centers should have an excess of air supply for positive pressure when hoods are not in operation. The number of air changes may be reduced or varied for odor control when the space is not in use. Minimum total air changes per hour should be that required to provide proper makeup air to kitchen exhaust systems. See Chapter 30 (*1999 ASHRAE Handbook*), "Kitchen Ventilation."

Notes to Table F-1, II

II. 2001 AIA Guidelines table references with some clarifications

(1) The ventilation rates in this table cover ventilation for comfort, as well as for asepsis and odor control in areas of acute care hospitals that directly affect patient care and are determined based on health care facilities being predominantly "No Smoking" facilities. Where smoking may be allowed, ventilation rates will need adjustments. Areas where specific ventilation rates are not given in the table shall be ventilated in accordance with ASHRAE Standard 62, *Ventilation for Acceptable Indoor Air Quality*, and *ASHRAE Handbook—HVAC Applications*. Specialized patient care areas, including organ transplant units, burn units, specialty procedure rooms, etc., shall have additional ventilation provisions for air quality control as may be appropriate. OSHA standards and/or NIOSH criteria require special ventilation requirements for employee health and safety within health care facilities.

(2) Design of the ventilation system shall provide air movement that is generally from clean to less clean areas. If any form of variable air volume or load shedding system is used for energy conservation, it must not compromise the corridor-to-room pressure balancing relationships or the minimum air changes required by the table.

(3) To satisfy exhaust needs, replacement air from the outside is necessary. Table 7.2 (2001 AIA Guidelines) does not attempt to describe specific amounts of outside air to be supplied to individual spaces except for certain areas such as those listed. Distribution of the outside air, added to the system to balance required exhaust, shall be as required by good engineering practice. Minimum outside air quantities shall remain constant while the system is in operation.

(4) Number of air changes may be reduced when the room is unoccupied if provisions are made to ensure that the number of air changes indicated is reestablished any time the space is being utilized. Adjustments shall include provisions so that the direction of air movement shall remain the same when the number of air changes is reduced. Areas not indicated as having continuous directional control may have ventilation systems shut down when space is unoccupied and ventilation is not otherwise needed, if the maximum infiltration or exfiltration permitted in Note 2 is not exceeded and if adjacent pressure balancing relationships are not compromised. Air quantity calculations must account for filter loading such that the indicated air change rates are provided up until the time of filter change-out.

(5) Air change requirements indicated are minimum values. Higher values should be used when required to maintain indicated room conditions (temperature and humidity), based on the cooling load of the space (lights, equipment, people, exterior walls and windows, etc.). Certain operating rooms may require lower or higher temperature or humidity conditions.

(6) Air from areas with contamination and/or odor problems shall be exhausted to the outside and not recirculated to other areas. Note that individual circumstances may require special consideration for air exhaust to the outside, e.g., in intensive care units, in which patients with pulmonary infection are treated, and rooms for burn patients.

(7) "Air Recirculated within Room Units" refers to those local units that are used primarily for heating and cooling of air and not disinfection of air. Because of cleaning difficulty and potential for buildup of contamination, recirculating room units shall not be used in areas marked "No." However, for airborne infection control, air may be recirculated within individual isolation rooms if HEPA filters are used. Isolation and intensive care unit rooms may be ventilated by reheat induction units in which only the primary air supplied from a central system passes through the reheat unit. Gravity-type heating or cooling units, such as radiators or convectors, shall not be used in operating rooms and other special care areas. See Appendix A (2001 AIA Guidelines) for a description of recirculation units to be used in isolation rooms. Recirculating devices with HEPA filters may have potential uses in existing facilities as interim, supplemental environmental controls to meet requirements for the control of airborne infectious agents. Limitations in design must be recognized. The design of either portable or fixed systems should prevent stagnation and short-circuiting of airflow. The supply and exhaust locations should direct clean air to areas where health care workers are likely to work, across the infectious source, and then to the exhaust, so that the health care worker is not in position between the infectious source and the exhaust location. The design of such systems should also allow for easy access for scheduled preventive maintenance and cleaning.

(8) The ranges listed are the minimum and maximum limits where control is specifically needed. The maximum and minimum limits are not intended to be independent of a space's associated temperature. The humidity is expected to be at the higher end of the range when the temperature is also at the higher end, and vice versa.

(9) Where temperature ranges are indicated, the systems shall be capable of maintaining the rooms at any point within the range during normal operation. A single figure indicates a heating or cooling capacity of at least the indicated temperature. This is usually applicable when patients may be undressed and require a warmer environment. Nothing in these guidelines shall be construed as precluding the use of temperatures lower than those noted when the patients' comfort and medical conditions make lower temperatures desirable. Unoccupied areas such as storage rooms shall have temperatures appropriate for the function intended.

(10) National Institute for Occupational Safety and Health (NIOSH) Criteria Documents regarding Occupational Exposure to Waste Anesthetic Gases and Vapors, and Control of Occupational Exposure to Nitrous Oxide indicate a need for both local exhaust (scavenging) systems and general ventilation of the areas in which the respective gases are utilized.

(11) Differential pressure shall be a minimum of 0.01 in. w.g. (2.5 Pa). If alarms are installed, allowances shall be made to prevent nuisance alarms of monitoring devices.

Notes to Table F-1, II (Continued)

> The verification of airflow direction can include a simple visual method such as smoke trail, ball-in-tube, or flutter-strip. These devices will require a minimum differential air pressure to indicate airflow direction.
>
> (12) Some surgeons may require room temperatures that are outside of the indicated range. All operating room design conditions shall be developed in consultation with surgeons, anesthesiologists, and nursing staff.
>
> (13) The note in AIA Guidelines is clarified. **(13a)** The term trauma room as used here is the operating room space in the emergency department or other trauma reception area that is used for emergency surgery. **(13b)** The first aid room and/or "emergency room" used for initial treatment of accident victims may be ventilated as noted for the "treatment room." Treatment rooms used for bronchoscopy shall be treated as bronchoscopy rooms. Treatment rooms used for cryosurgery procedures with nitrous oxide shall contain provisions for exhausting waste gases.
>
> (14) In a ventilation system that recirculates air, HEPA filters can be used in lieu of exhausting the air from these spaces to the outside. In this application, the return air shall be passed through the HEPA filters before it is introduced into any other spaces.
>
> (15) If it is not practical to exhaust the air from the airborne infection isolation room to the outside, the air may be returned through HEPA filters to the air-handling system exclusively serving the isolation room.
>
> (16) Total air changes per room for patient rooms, labor/delivery/recovery rooms, and labor/delivery/recovery/postpartum rooms may be reduced to 4 when supplemental heating and/or cooling systems (radiant heating and cooling, baseboard heating, etc.) are used.
>
> (17) The protective environment airflow design specifications protect the patient from common environmental airborne infectious microbes (i.e., *Aspergillus* spores). These special ventilation areas shall be designed to provide directed airflow from the cleanest patient area to less clean areas. These rooms shall be protected with HEPA filters at 99.97 percent efficiency for 0.3 μm sized particle in the supply airstream. These interrupting filters protect patient rooms from maintenance-derived release of environmental microbes from the ventilation system components. Recirculation HEPA filters can be used to increase the equivalent room air exchanges. Constant volume airflow is required for consistent ventilation for the protected environment. If the facility determines that airborne infection isolation is necessary for protective environment patients, an anteroom should be provided. Rooms with reversible airflow provisions for the purpose of switching between protective environment and airborne infection isolation functions are not acceptable.
>
> (18) The infectious disease isolation room described in these guidelines is to be used for isolating the airborne spread of infectious diseases, such as measles, varicella, or tuberculosis. The design of airborne infection isolation (AII) rooms should include the provision for normal patient care during periods not requiring isolation precautions. Supplemental recirculating devices may be used in the patient room, to increase the equivalent room air exchanges; however, such recirculating devices do not provide the outside air requirements. Air may be recirculated within individual isolation rooms if HEPA filters are used. Rooms with reversible airflow provisions for the purpose of switching between protective environment and AII functions are not acceptable.
>
> (19) When required, appropriate hoods and exhaust devices for the removal of noxious gases or chemical vapors shall be provided (see Section 7.31.D14 and 7.31.D15, 2001 AIA Guidelines, and NFPA 99).
>
> (20) Food preparation centers shall have ventilation systems whose air supply mechanisms are interfaced appropriately with exhaust hood controls or relief vents so that exfiltration or infiltration to or from exit corridors does not compromise the exit corridor restrictions of NFPA 90A, the pressure requirements of NFPA 96, or the maximum defined in the table. The number of air changes may be reduced or varied to any extent required for odor control when the space is not in use. See Section 7.31.D1.p., 2001 AIA Guidelines.

Notes to Table F-1, III

III. Notes

A1   The operating room ventilation rates are different between the 2001 *AIA Guidelines for Design and Construction of Hospital and Health Care Facilities* (2001 AIA Guidelines) and *1999 ASHRAE Handbook—HVAC Applications* (1999 ASHRAE Handbook). Consider if the surgery performed is minor or major. No reduction of ventilation rate is suggested even when 100% outside air is used. Ventilation rate recommendation based upon 1999 ASHRAE Handbook. Special temperature and humidity conditions in certain situations may be required. The temperature setpoint should be able to be adjusted by surgical staff over a range of 62 to 80°F (17 to 27°C). It should also be noted that 64 to 72°F (18 to 22°C) is the usual temperature range for ORs unless special circumstances exist, and 45-45% humidity is a preferable target but 30-60% is an acceptable range.

      The required air change rates are also a function of space temperature setpoint, supply air temperature, sensible and latent heat load in the space. Appendix I describes the recent research on this subject and describes different ventilation system performances at different ACH. Continued use of 25 ACH (as recommended in ASHRAE Handbook—Applications) provides a safety margin to accommodate cooling load in modern operating rooms generated due to increasing use of electronic equipment during surgery, which generates large sensible heat load.

      The designer should review the type of clinical activity and severity of the surgery performed before selecting the appropriate ventilation rates, temperature, and humidity conditions.

A2   The labor/delivery/recovery/postpartum ventilation rates are different between the 2001 AIA Guidelines and 1999 ASHRAE Handbook. The designer should review the type of clinical activity and severity of the surgery performed before selecting the appropriate ventilation rates.

      Ventilation rate recommendation based upon 2001 AIA Guidelines. Temperature and humidity is from 1999 ASHRAE Handbook. The design temperature is shown to have range.

A3   The Protective or Infectious Isolation room ventilation rates are different between the 2001 AIA Guidelines and 1999 ASHRAE Handbook. The designer should review the type of clinical activity and severity of the surgery performed before selecting the appropriate ventilation rates: recommendation based upon 2001 AIA Guidelines, recommendation based upon 1999 ASHRAE Handbook.

A4   New category added to account for operating rooms in day surgery application.

B1   The delivery room ventilation rates are different between the new 2001 AIA Guidelines and 1999 ASHRAE Handbook. The designer should review the type of clinical activity and severity of the surgery performed before selecting the appropriate ventilation rates. Ventilation rate recommendation are based upon 1999 ASHRAE Handbook. 2001 AIA Guidelines for temperature and humidity conditions are adopted.

B2   The trauma room ventilation rates are different between the 1999 ASHRAE Handbook and the 2001 AIA Guidelines. The designer should review the type of clinical activity and severity of the surgery performed before selecting the appropriate ventilation rates. Consider if the surgery performed is minor or major

      Ventilation rate recommendation is based upon 1999 ASHRAE Handbook. Temperature and humidity requirements are also based upon 1999 ASHRAE Handbook.

B3   2001 AIA Guidelines and 1999 ASHRAE Handbook standards are different. However, recent 1999 ASHRAE Handbook published research was used to determine ventilation rates in the new 2001 AIA Guidelines. Humidity and temperature recommendations are based upon 1999 ASHRAE Handbook. Space temperature design range is defined.

C1   Similar standards between 2001 AIA Guidelines and 1999 ASHRAE Handbook. No pressure difference between recommendation is made. The relative humidity requirement is more restrictive in 1999 ASHRAE Handbook and as a design guide it is recommended. The design guide is more restricted for space temperature as well.

C2   Only defined in 2001 AIA Guidelines. Same condition adapted for best practices.

C3   Similar standards between 2001 AIA Guidelines and 1999 ASHRAE Handbook.

C4   Similarly between 2001 AIA Guidelines and 1999 ASHRAE Handbook. Wider temperature is recommended and humidity ranges are also specified.

C5   Mostly defined in 2001 AIA Guidelines. New humidity and temperature ranges are also specified.

C6   In Treatment Room similar standard between 1999 ASHRAE Handbook and 2001 AIA Guidelines. However, 1999 ASHRAE Handbook temperature and humidity range is adopted. A range is provided for temperature setting.

C7   Similarity between 1999 ASHRAE Handbook and 2001 AIA Guidelines. However, 2001 AIA Guidelines recommendation that space be negative is not adopted.

C8   Similar between 2001 AIA Guidelines and 1999 ASHRAE Handbook. Toilet is exhausted directly outdoors.

Notes to Table F-1, III (Continued)

D1   Only defined in 1999 ASHRAE Handbook. The pressure with respect to adjacent space may be positive or negative depending upon the type of anteroom.

D2   Only defined in 1999 ASHRAE Handbook.

D3   Similar standards between 2001 AIA Guidelines and 1999 ASHRAE Handbook. One has more details. Recommendation based upon 1999 ASHRAE Handbook.

D4   Defined in 1999 ASHRAE Handbook. Humidity and design temperature added.

D5   Some similarities between 1999 ASHRAE Handbook and 2001 AIA Guidelines. However, 2001 AIA Guidelines has no humidity recommendation and has a lower temperature range. 2001 AIA Guidelines suggests 68-73°F (20-23°C), which appears too restrictive.

D6   Defined by 2001 AIA Guidelines. Minimum outside air is added.

D7   Similar between 2001 AIA Guidelines and 1999 ASHRAE Handbook. Humidity levels are adopted from 1999 ASHRAE Handbook. Specific temperature range is provided.

not guarantee adequate dilution or removal of contaminants if the air is not uniformly diffused throughout the occupied space. In particular, the further the airflow pattern differs from a "plug" or "piston" flow, the worse the dilution of the contaminant.

- *To provide a thermally controlled environment that is acceptable to the occupants.* An acceptable thermal environment has been defined as one in which at least 80% of the occupants, clothed normally and engaged in sedentary or near-sedentary activities, would express thermal comfort, which is defined as "that condition of mind which expresses satisfaction with the thermal environment" (ASHRAE 1974). This criterion is typically calculated using the Fanger index, Predicted Percentage Dissatisfied (PPD), which is calculated in conjunction with another index, namely, Predicted Mean Vote (PMV). These indices are dependent on many factors: the activity and typical clothing of the occupants and the combination of air temperature, mean radiant temperature, relative humidity, and air velocity. Therefore, all these factors must be appropriate for the occupants to feel comfortable.

Conventionally, air diffusion control has been designed and installed to meet the criteria for thermal comfort, with the assumption that the air-quality criteria will be met simultaneously.

F.5   NEW TREND IN VENTILATION SYSTEM DESIGN

In general, the design of air inlet and outlet and overall air distribution from ventilation systems has largely relied on the experience of the design engineer and rules of thumb. Although this approach has proved successful, such designs have traditionally carried significant safety margins to allow for the

inevitable uncertainty associated with the complexity of air movement. Furthermore, the increasing cost of equipment and energy, combined with the growing emphasis on environmentally friendly design and operation, has forced designers to consider alternative means of designing ventilation systems, which utilize computational or analytical techniques.

One such technique is based on computational fluid dynamics, known as CFD. The technique of CFD presumes that the equations that govern the physical behavior of a flow/thermal system are known, in the form of the Navier-Stokes, thermal energy, and/or species equations, with the appropriate equation of state. The equations require the conservation, both locally and globally, of mass, momentum, thermal energy, and species concentration. The general form of the equations can be written as:

$$\frac{\partial}{\partial t}(\rho\varphi) + div(\rho\vec{V}\varphi - \Gamma_\varphi \, grad\varphi) = S_\varphi \qquad (1)$$

Transient + Convection − Diffusion = Source

where

ρ =   density

$\vec{V}$ =   velocity vector

φ =   dependent variable

Γ_φ =   exchange coefficient (laminar + turbulent)

S_φ =   source or sink

The equations are partial differential equations (PDEs). The dependent variables to be calculated are the velocity components (u, v, w), pressure (P), temperature (T), and some scalar (F), and the independent variables are the space coordinates (x, y, z) and time (t). To solve the equations, initial and boundary conditions must be specified around the boundary of the system (domain). Because the equations are highly nonlinear, they are not solvable by explicit, closed-form analytical methods. Approximate (numerical) methods, such as the finite difference method, finite volume method, or the finite element method, are typically used for solving the equations.

In all these approaches, the domain is discretized (divided) into cells or elements and nodal points are defined. Upon solution of the equations, the values of the dependent variables (u, v, w, P, T, F) are specified at each node, and derived quantities such as vorticity and stream function may also be obtained. In addition, surface film coefficients (h) or shear stress (drag) may be calculated and used for further design analysis.

From the three options for the numerical solution, the finite volume and finite element methods are currently the most popular. In finite volume, fluxes are balanced across all cells of a control volume, ensuring the local and global conservation implicit in the physical process being modeled. Flux balance is not necessarily conserved in a finite element framework, but the computational grid resulting from discretization is, by default, irregular (unstructured) and the procedure is suitable for problems with complicated geometries and boundary conditions and for coupled analysis, such as fluid-structure interaction.

The CFD technique, however, has far more applications than building services. Typical questions that can be answered by CFD are:

- Where should the flow inlets and/or outlets be located?
- What kinds of velocities are expected at a specified portion of the system?
- What does the flow pattern look like?
- What is the heat transfer coefficient (or Nusselt number) on a specified portion of the system surface?
- What is the temperature distribution in a specified portion of the system?
- What is the drag on a specified portion of the system surface?
- What is the time response of the system with respect to heat transfer and flow development?
- How is a species or chemical reactant or product transported by fluid flow?

Some of the advantages of a CFD analysis over experimental data, include:

- The ability to simulate realistic systems.
- The ability to set precise and ideal conditions on the boundary of a CFD model.
- Avoidance of problems related to the intrusion by the measuring device. For example, CFD may discover significant flow features that otherwise couldn't be revealed with physical experiments.
- The cost for a CFD analysis is less compared to the cost of performing experiments.
- The ability to consider "hostile" environments. For CFD, it is never too toxic, too hot, or too fast. Parametric studies are easily performed with CFD.
- The quick and systematic screening of a large number of design concepts, before a prototype of the design is ever built.
- Detailed local information as well as surface information. Typically, physical tests provide data only at selected points; an alternative technique must be used to obtain surface information.

A disadvantage of the use of CFD is that the codes are not "black boxes" and a clear and comprehensive understanding of the fluid mechanics and heat transfer phenomena is necessary. Training and experience in the use of CFD software is necessary in order to be able to properly use this kind of tool and to be able to interpret the results correctly. CFD is particularly prone to the adage "garbage in, garbage out."

Furthermore, it should be noted that CFD is NOT trouble-free nor will it replace physical experiments. For certain problems, the boundary and initial conditions are not known or the physics may not be understood to a point where users can be confident that they have taken every factor into account after creating a CFD model.

Moreover, turbulence, chemical reaction, radiation, and two-phase systems (such as boiling, condensation, and multiphase flow through a pipe) are very challenging as the equations to build a CFD model are not well understood. For these cases, empiricism will continue to be the feasible method to generate engineering design data.

For all practical purposes, CFD does not replace physical experiments, but it can significantly reduce the amount of experimental work that engineers do. A typical approach that seems to be working for the automobile industry is to perform laboratory-scale experiments and model them with CFD in order to validate that CFD is predicting acceptably accurate solutions. The engineer may then scale up the model computationally, as this is significantly cheaper and faster than doing so in the real world.

Upon experimental validation of a specific CFD model, one can study different configurations without building excessive numbers of physical models. Thus, when CFD works, the number of prototypes is reduced, cutting manufacturing costs and reducing overall time to market. This leads to a quicker turn-around in the design cycle. The result is the avoidance of the need to divert significant amounts of time and resources to building and evaluating prototypes.

Ongoing work has been undertaken by numerous organizations (and mainly the by the National Institutes of Health [NIH] in Bethesda, Maryland) to demonstrate the use of CFD, also known as airflow modeling, to assess the performance of the ventilation system as applied to building services and validate the results with empirical data. The work (Memarzadeh 1996, 1998; Memarzadeh and Jiang 2000; Memarzedeh and Manning 2000) has used CFD to tackle the design of ventilation systems in a variety of different built environments.

In Memarzadeh (1996), CFD was used to consider laboratory ventilation system design such that hood containment was optimized. Over 100 alternative designs were considered to derive applicable guidelines, which would have been a massive undertaking experimentally. Similarly, Memarzadeh (1998), in a study that considered appropriate animal research facility ventilation design, considered over 100 different design scenarios. In this case, a minimum cfm (L/s) per animal body weight was determined using CFD, a value which has been subsequently confirmed experimentally.

In the case of Memarzadeh and Jiang (2000) and Memarzadeh and Manning (2000), the results of the study were used to help confirm or modify standards in health care facilities (AIA 2001). Memarzadeh and Jiang (2000) concluded that 10 total ACH was the recommended ventilation rate, as higher rates of ventilation did not decrease exposure in the room. As

this value was close to the CDC value (1994) of 12 ACH, the higher value was retained. Memarzadeh and Manning (2000) concluded that 6 ACH and 4 ACH (if baseboard heating is provided) are the minimum ventilation rates required to provide satisfactory patient comfort. The analysis also showed that the previously recommended ventilation rate of 2 ACH would result in a "stuffy" room. In both of these studies, analysis algorithms were incorporated to the "standard" airflow modeling analysis to provide the necessary information: in the former case, a particle tracking routine was developed, while comfort and uniformity index calculators, such as the Fanger indices mentioned earlier, were added in the latter case.

F.6 CONCLUSIONS

This paper has outlined a brief history of the changing standards in ventilation systems in the built environment, in particular those that relate to comfort and air quality. The standards have been successively refined, with criteria such as ACH scrutinized carefully, as they directly impact the energy consumption and operating costs for the ventilation system.

Recently, the technique of airflow modeling, in the shape of computational fluid dynamics (CFD), has been utilized to consider ventilation systems in a wide range of applications, and the relevance of the appropriate standard for that application has been readily considered. The implementation of airflow modeling has already had an impact on standards, and this trend is likely to continue.

APPENDIX G
POWER QUALITY ISSUES

G.1 EMERGENCY POWER

G.1.1 Overview

Hospitals are critical facilities that must continue to operate during power outages. The main electrical service to a hospital building should be as reliable as possible. Because of the high cost of emergency power generation, only certain elements of an HVAC system need to be served by the emergency power supply system (EPSS). A reliable distribution system is an essential component of the emergency power supply system. In order to ensure that emergency power systems are installed in a reliable manner, the National Electrical Code (NFPA 70) requires that all parts of the EPSS be clearly labeled and wired completely independent of all other wiring systems. This is to prevent concurrent failure of both normal and emergency power in case of a fire or other emergency condition. The following are guidelines regarding which areas and systems should be served from an emergency power source.

G.1.2 Hospital Heating and Ventilation Systems on Emergency Power

The two main NFPA codes dealing solely with electrical design, construction, and installation criteria for health care facilities are Article 517 of NFPA 70 "The National Electrical Code" and Chapter 3 of NFPA 99 "Standard for Health Care Facilities" (NFPA 2002a, 2002b). Both of these NFPA documents dictate minimum requirements for heating and ventilation systems on emergency power in a hospital.

According to NFPA 99 (Chapter 3) and NFPA 70 (Article 517), the following hospital heating and ventilating loads should be fed from emergency power.

Table G-1. Emergency Power for Hospital HVAC Systems

Area	Emergency Heating Required	Emergency Ventilation Required
Operating suite, including operating rooms, recovery rooms, etc.	✓	✓
Birthing rooms, delivery rooms	✓	✓
Intensive care	✓	✓
Nursery	✓	✓
Dietary and food preparation areas		✓*
General patient rooms	✓**	
Infection/Isolation rooms	✓**	✓
Sterilization areas		
Emergency suites and trauma rooms	✓	
Laboratory fume exhaust hoods		✓
Hyperbaric facilities		✓

Table G-1. Emergency Power for Hospital HVAC Systems (Continued)

Hypobaric facilities		✓
Nuclear medicine (areas where radioactive material is used)		✓
Ethylene oxide and anesthesia gas evacuation		✓
Coronary care areas	✓	✓

Notes:
*Kitchen hood supply and/or exhaust, if required, to operate during a fire under the hood.
**Heating in general patient rooms is not required in the following situations: (1) the outside design temperature is above +20°F (−6.7°C); (2) the outside design temperature is below +20°F (−6.7°C) and selected rooms with emergency heating are provided for confined patients; or (3) the facility is served from a dual (redundant) source of normal power.

G.1.3 Additional Equipment on Emergency Power

In addition to the above, the following equipment and systems should be considered for service by emergency power:

- Boiler plant, including boilers, boiler feed pumps, condensate transfer pumps, condensate pumps, fuel oil pumps, combustion air handlers, hot water circulation pumps, and boiler room control panels and control compressed air.
- Critical areas, such as operating suites, should have access to mechanical cooling during a prolonged power outage. This is especially true in areas of the country subject to hot, humid climates. Air-handling systems serving these areas should have a backup chiller on emergency power that can be switched on and isolated from the central chilled water plant during a prolonged power outage. The hospital engineering staff and designers should perform a risk assessment for inclusion of cooling capabilities on the emergency power systems. Many facilities currently lack adequate capacity for even basic code requirements. Provisions for cooling on emergency power must include chilled water pumping systems, cooling towers, control systems, etc. Significant expense may be required to provide reliable emergency power to a portion of the chilled water plant. Additional generator capacity, electrical distribution, and transfer switches in usually tight footprints are typically required. Hybrid (gas fired, steam absorption, electric) plant solutions are a consideration to provide an emergency power provision that does not require as much generator capacity.
- Domestic hot water that serves dietary and patient care areas.
- Domestic water booster pumps.
- Chilled water pumps should be on emergency power where the volume of water in the piping can act as a storage system, offering some assistance with mechanical cooling for a period of time. In many cases the chilled water plant is manually back-fed with emergency power so that chillers, towers, pumps, etc., can be selectively operated manually if the generation plant has sufficient spare capacity.
- Other systems whose function is necessary for safe operation of the building or facilities during an extended electrical outage.

G.2 VARIABLE FREQUENCY DRIVES

G.2.1 Specifying Variable Frequency Drives for Hospitals and Clinics

Prevalent use of variable frequency drives (VFDs) can cause power quality problems that interfere with sensitive electrical equipment used in health care facilities. In general, the power quality problems are caused by electrical harmonic distortion, which the solid state VFDs inject on the power system.

Harmonics are defined as "sinusoidal voltages or currents having frequencies that are integer multiples of the frequency at which the supply system is designed to operate." Most power systems are designed to operate at 60 Hz, which is referred to as the *fundamental frequency*. Since harmonics are periodic disturbances occurring in intervals of the fundamental frequency, they are broken down and identified in waveforms that are multiples of the fundamental frequency. Thus a third harmonic component of a voltage with a fundamental frequency of 60 Hz would be a (3)*(60) Hz or a 180 Hz wave.

Harmonic voltages and currents are generated by solid state (nonlinear) electrical equipment such as rectifiers, most lighting, computer power supplies, battery chargers, and VFDs.

Harmonic distortion has been recognized in the industry for the last 40 years. But before the recent proliferation of static power rectifiers, nonlinear elements in a building electrical circuit were generally minimal, and their effects were small and usually overlooked. With the advent of more and more sensitive electronic equipment and the increased use of nonlinear equipment, the effects of harmonic distortion can no longer remain unaddressed.

As nonlinear current flows through the electrical distribution system, it induces voltage distortion. When distorted voltage is delivered to equipment designed for a sinusoidal voltage, the result can often be overheating or malfunction. In addition, the unbalanced nature of harmonic currents will cause increased neutral currents, which can cause the wiring in motors and transformers to significantly overheat.

G.2.2 Application Considerations for VFDs

Variable frequency drives (VFDs) inject harmonic currents into the power system due to the nonlinear nature of switching in electronic power devices. The harmonic current combined with the system impedance frequency response characteristic can create harmonic voltage distortion. The harmonic voltages and currents can cause spurious operation of relays and controls, capacitor failures, motor and transformer overheating, and increased power system losses. These problems can also be compounded by the application of power factor correction capacitors (especially on low-voltage systems), which can create resonance conditions that magnify the harmonic distortion levels.

Several concerns associated with harmonic distortion levels need to be addressed in the project specifications. This will avoid significant harmonic-related problems with both the VFD equipment and the controlled operations. These concerns include the following:

- Harmonic distortion on both the supply side and motor side of the drive.
- Equipment derating due to harmonic distortion produced by VFDs.
- Audible noise caused by high-frequency (several kilohertz) components in the current and voltage.
- Harmonic filter design and specification.
- Harmonic distortion that is destructive to emergency generators. The harmonic analysis of the system must include an analysis of the negative effects of harmonics on the emergency power system.

Nuisance Tripping Concerns

A three-phase VFD system consists of three basic components (rectifier, dc link, and inverter) and a control system. The rectifier converts the three-phase 60-Hz ac input to a dc signal. Depending upon the system, an inductor, a capacitor, or a combination of these components smoothes the dc signal (reduces voltage ripple) in the dc link. The inverter circuit converts the dc signal into a variable-frequency ac voltage to control the speed of the induction motor. A voltage-source inverter (VSI) drive is often considered for this application, and concerns regarding this particular device will be outlined.

These drives (the most common types up to 300 hp) use a large capacitor in the dc link to provide a relatively consistent dc voltage to the inverter. The inverter then chops this dc voltage to provide a variable-frequency ac voltage for the motor. VSI drives can be purchased off the shelf and employ pulse-width-modulation (PWM) techniques to improve the quality of the output voltage waveform. However, there is a concern regarding nuisance tripping due to capacitor switching transients. Small VFDs have a VSI rectifier (ac to dc) and use a PWM inverter (dc to ac) to supply the motor. This design requires a dc capacitor to smooth the dc link voltage. The controls for this type of drive have protection for dc overvoltages and undervoltages with narrow thresholds. It is not uncommon for the dc overvoltage control to cause tripping of the drive whenever the dc voltage exceeds 1.17 per unit (for this particular application, 760 volts for a 480-volt application). Since the dc capacitor is connected alternately across each of the three phases, drives of this type can be extremely sensitive to overvoltages on the ac power side.

One event of particular concern is capacitor switching on the system. Voltage switching transients result in a surge of current into the dc link capacitor at a relatively low frequency (300-800 Hz). This current surge charges the dc link capacitor, causing an overvoltage to occur (through Ohm's law). The overvoltage (not necessarily magnified) exceeds the voltage tolerance thresholds associated with the overvoltage protection, which most likely will trip the VFD out of service. This is called nuisance tripping because the situation can occur day after day, often at the same time.

Several methods are available to ameliorate such tripping; some are simple and some costly. Use of a harmonic filter to reduce overvoltages, an expensive alternative, is effective in protecting drives from component failure but may not completely eliminate nuisance tripping of small drives. The most effective (and inexpensive) way to eliminate nuisance tripping of small drives is to isolate them from the power system with series inductors (chokes). With a concomitant voltage drop across the inductor, the series inductance of the choke(s) reduce(s) the current surge into the VFD, thereby limiting the dc overvoltage. The most important issue regarding this method is that the designer should determine the precise inductor size for each VFD; this requires a detailed transient simulation that takes into account capacitor size, transformer size, etc. The choke size must be selected carefully. If the choke has too much impedance, it can increase harmonic distortion levels and notching transients at the drive terminals. Chokes for this application are commercially available in sizes from 1.5% to 5% of the VFD impedance at various hp ratings. A size of 3% is sufficient to avoid nuisance tripping due to capacitor switching operations. Standard isolation transformers serve the same purpose.

Voltage Sag Concerns

Despite the many advantages provided by VFDs, the concern for nuisance tripping during voltage sag conditions remains. This power quality concern involves the control sensitivity to short-duration voltage sags and momentary interruptions. Actually, many different kinds of controls and even motor contactors are sensitive to these voltage sags. Voltage sags caused by faults on the power system represent one of the most important problems that can be experienced by the sensitive loads (equipment used in a clinical setting).

Whenever there is a fault on the transmission or distribution system serving a facility (faults cannot be completely avoided regardless of the system design), there will be either a voltage sag or an interruption. If the fault occurs on a parallel distribution feeder circuit or on the transmission system, there will be a voltage sag that lasts until the fault is cleared by some protective device (typically 3-30 cycles depending on the fault location). A method of predicting the likelihood of faults in a certain region along with knowledge of equipment sensitivity can be used to determine an "area of vulnerability." A combination of computer short-circuit simulations and lightning susceptibility analysis should be used to determine the affected area. The VFD controls should be designed to handle these voltage sag conditions without tripping. Ride-through capability is seldom mentioned in project specifications. This is an important consideration when VFDs are applied in critical facilities, such as hospitals and clinics, where nuisance tripping can cause significant problems. The designer should evaluate the level of sensitivity of the controls to voltage sags. If such concern exists he/she should consider applying power conditioning to the controls themselves. Ferroresonant transformers can handle voltage sags down to approximately 60% of the nominal voltage. This is sufficient to handle virtually all voltage sags caused by single line-to-ground faults on the power system. If additional protection is needed, the controls can be protected with an uninterruptible power supply (UPS) system, which can handle complete interruptions in the input signal.

Transient Overvoltage Concerns

Transient overvoltages occur in connection with capacitor switching. Each time a capacitor is energized, a transient voltage oscillation occurs between the capacitor and the power system inductance. The result is a transient overvoltage that can be as high as 2.0 per unit (of the normal voltage) at the capacitor location. The magnitude is usually less than 2.0 per unit due to dampening provided by system loads and losses.

The transient overvoltages caused by capacitor energizing are generally not a concern to electric utilities because their magnitude is usually below the level at which surge protective devices operate (1.5-2.0 per unit). However, these transients can be magnified at a facility if the facility has low-voltage capacitor banks for (displacement) power factor correction. The designer should check for this situation. When the frequency of a transient overvoltage matches the series-resonant frequency of a facility's transformer coupled with the utility capacitor(s), a low-impedance, high-current (at the resonant frequency) condition results. When the resonant-frequency current completes its path to ground through the capacitor, the voltage experiences a "boost" to the ground-reference voltage.

The magnification of capacitor switching transients is most severe when the capacitor switched on the higher voltage system is much larger (kVAR) than the capacitor at the low-voltage bus. Generally, this situation occurs most frequently for substation switching. The frequency of oscillation that occurs when the high-voltage capacitor is energized is close to the resonant frequency formed by the step-down transformer in series with the low-voltage capacitor. There is little resistive load on the low-voltage system to provide dampening of the transient, as is usually the case with industrial plants (motors do not provide significant damping of these transients). It is not uncommon for magnified transients at low-voltage capacitors to range from 3.0 to 4.0 per unit. These transients have significant energy associated with them and are likely to cause failure of protective devices, metal oxide varistors (MOVs), electronic components (silicon-controlled rectifiers, etc.), and capacitors. VFDs are particularly susceptible to these transients because of the relatively low peak-inverse voltage ratings of the semiconductor switches and the low-energy ratings of the MOVs used to protect the VFD power electronics.

The following should be evaluated, and identified in the specifications, to control such magnified transient overvoltages:

- Using vacuum switches with synchronous closing control to energize a capacitor bank and control capacitor switching transient.
- Providing high-energy MOV protection on 480-volt buses. The energy capability of these arresters should be at least 1 kJ.
- Using tuned filters for power factor correction instead of just shunt capacitor banks. (Tuned filters change the frequency response of the circuit and usually prevent magnification problems. This solution combines power factor correction, harmonic control, and transient control.)

EMI and RFI Concerns

IEEE Standard 519, *Recommended Practices and Requirements for Harmonic Control in Electric Power Systems*, recommends limits for voltage distortion and harmonic current resulting from nonlinear loads (IEEE 1992). The IEEE standard, however, is not intended to cover the effects of radio frequency (RF) interference. As a result, specifications will occasionally refer to FCC Rules and Regulations, Volume 2, Part 15, Subpart J, Class A (referred to as "FCC rule") to establish limits on electromagnetic emissions for VFDs.

The "FCC rule" was published in October 1982 primarily for computing devices. Computers will generate RF energy and possibly cause interference with nearby equipment. Generally, the rule sets conducted and radiated RF limits for electronic devices using timing signals or digital techniques with pulse rates in excess of 10,000 pulses per second. Technically speaking, VFDs with high-frequency timing circuits conform to this description, although they are not intended as a computing device described in the "FCC rule." The primary and more significant source of electromagnetic interference (EMI) from a VFD stems from the power circuits, and in this respect, drives become an incidental radiation device. The only requirement for incidental radiation devices in the "FCC rule" is that they shall be operated so that the RF energy emitted does not cause harmful interference. If so, the operator must eliminate the interference.

All VFDs, regardless of the manufacturer, will produce electromagnetic emissions to some degree. These emissions are primarily due to the steep wave fronts and very rapid switching of power semiconductors in the VFD. Typically this occurs when transistors, GTOs or other "fast devices" are gated on and off in dc chopper circuits and inverter power circuits for PWM, current source, and six-step drives. Conductors to the VFDs and motor can act as an antenna and radiate the RF energy into the media. Therefore, it is possible for RF to be induced into nearby antennas and other conductors and be carried to the loads in other circuits. Holding a portable AM radio near a power outlet in close proximity to an EMI source can be evidence of this situation.

DDC control systems, telecommunication services, and other electronic equipment utilizing very high frequencies may experience noise interference or malfunctions when subject to EM/RF energy. Specifications should clearly outline the corrective measures required. The first and foremost corrective measure to avoid problems associated with EMI is proper routing of drive conductors in separate metallic conduits, even separate raceways if practical, and as remote as possible from any other conductors or suspect equipment. This will usually be sufficient to avoid EMI problems.

EM/RF filters can be engineered to trap or inhibit high-frequency emissions into power system conductors. Due to the nature of EMI, however, the effectiveness of any filter is highly sensitive to where it is installed. Further, it is not ensured that a filter will correct a given problem even though it may meet FCC limits. Most manufacturers will include this footnote with their literature. "Filters are expensive and usually require additional space. It is recommended that they be furnished only when they are specifically required to avoid or solve a problem after exhausting all proper installation methods. In addition, filters are an additional component and must be considered in the overall reliability of a power system." To contain RF radiation through the media from VFD, complete shielding using a metallic enclosure is required. This approach will usually contain most of the radiated RF within a reasonable distance.

APPENDIX H
SAMPLE CONTROL STRATEGIES

H.1 SEQUENCE OF OPERATION OF 100% OUTSIDE AIR-HANDLING UNIT WITH TWO SUPPLY FANS, A COMMON EXHAUST FAN, AND A HOT WATER RUN-AROUND LOOP HEAT RECOVERY SYSTEM
(See Figure H-1)

Start-Up Mode

The air-handling system shall be automatically started or stopped by EMS (energy management system) whenever the H-O-A (Hand-Off-Auto switch) is in the auto position and manually started or stopped by the hand position.

The air-handling unit consists of two supply fans and a common exhaust fan. If the outside air temperature is less than 45°F (7°C) (adjustable), the preheat valve shall open to outside air one minute before the unit fan(s) starts. Once the fan status is proven, the preheat valve shall slowly close and control as defined in the "Temperature Control" section following. Upon a signal to start the unit, the supply and exhaust isolation dampers as well as the outside air damper shall open before the fans start. Isolation damper end-switches shall prove that damper is open and allow the fan(s) to start through hardwired interlocks.

On a command to shut down a fan, hardwired time delay relays shall prevent the isolation damper from closing for 30 seconds (adjustable), once the fan shuts off. This shall prevent a buildup of pressure as the fan spins down, preventing the fan's high static limit from tripping.

Fan Speed Control

Supply and exhaust airflow stations shall input cfm (L/s, typical) air volume data to the EMS system. During the start-up mode, supply fan(s) shall slowly ramp up to speed in tandem to maintain the setpoint of the supply air static pressure located two-thirds downstream of the main ductwork. If a single supply fan fails, the remaining fan shall compensate by increasing speed to maintain the setpoint.

Restart of the failed fan shall be initiated through the EMS front-end system. Upon initiating the restart, the remaining operating fan shall ramp down to minimum speed. Once the operating fan reaches minimum speed, a start signal shall be given to the restart fan. Both fans shall then be ramped up in speed until they synchronize with the master static loop. If the restarted fan fails to start, its isolation damper shall close and the failure shall be indicated at the EMS front end. The operating fan shall ramp up alone and synchronize with the duct static control.

Temperature Control

The discharge temperature is maintained by sequencing the speed of the heat recovery pump, modulating preheat valve, and chilled water valve in sequence. As the discharge air temperature rises, the heat recovery pump shall ramp down toward the minimum speed. If the temperature continues to rise, the preheat valve shall modulate closed. As the discharge temperature rises further, the chilled water valve shall modulate open. The reverse shall occur when the discharge temperature decreases. The chilled water valve shall not open when the heat recovery pump is operating in the heating mode or when the preheat valve is open.

The heat recovery pump shall start when the outside air temperature is greater than the exhaust air temperature +5°F (2.8°C) (adjustable) or when the

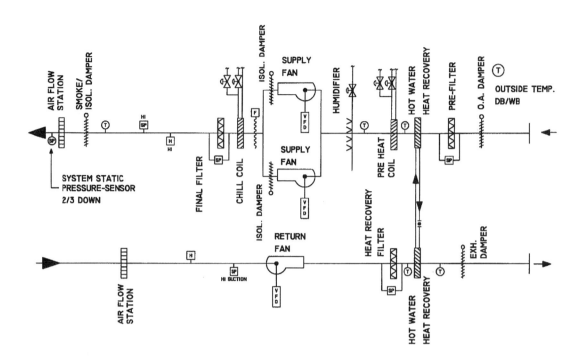

Figure H-1   Air-handling unit with return fan and air side economizer.

outside air temperature falls 3.0°F (1.7°C) (adjustable) below the setpoint of the preheat air temperature.

Central Humidification

The humidifier shall be modulated to maintain exhaust air relative humidity. As the humidity of the exhaust air increases, the humidifier valve shall modulate closed. The reverse shall occur when the humidity of the exhaust air decreases. A high-limit humidistat shall limit the signal to the humidifier if the humidity of the supply air exceeds 90% (hardware adjustable) The humidifier valve shall remain closed whenever the chilled water coil is being used. Upon loss of airflow, a panel-mounted static pressure switch shall close the humidifier control valve.

Safeties

All AHU safety devices are hardwired and independent of the EMS system. These devices shall shut down equipment through hardwired interlocks and provide alarm status to the operator through the EMS front end.

Freeze Protection

A manual-reset low-limit thermostat installed at the discharge of the fan shall disable the supply and exhaust fans and close the outside and isolation dampers, and the chilled water valve shall open fully when it senses a temperature of 38°F (3°C) (adjustable). Preheat valve shall modulate to maintain DAT setpoint to prevent overheating.

Duct Static

A manual-reset, discharge-air, high static safety located before the supply air isolation/smoke damper shall disable both supply fans and input to the DDC system upon sensing a static pressure higher than the normal operating set point.

A manual-reset, outside air intake, low-static safety shall disable both supply fans and input to the DDC system upon sensing a static pressure lower than the normal operating set point.

A manual-reset, exhaust-air, low-static safety located before the exhaust fan shall disable the fan and input to the DDC system upon sensing a static pressure lower than the normal operating setpoint.

Humidity High Limit

A discharge-air, autoreset, high-limit humidity control shall close the humidifier valve and input to the DDC system upon sensing a supply air humidity of 90% (adjustable).

Duct Smoke Detection

Smoke detectors located at the supply air discharge plenum and exhaust ducts shall initiate the duct smoke sequence as follows:

Supply Air Smoke Alarm

When the supply fan smoke detector detects smoke, the supply fans shall be disabled through hardwired interlocks and the supply air smoke damper and outside air damper shall close through hardwired interlocks. All of the control functions of the air-handling unit shall return to the normal condition when the smoke detector is manually reset.

Comments

- DDC controls can provide more flexibility and tighter control than pneumatic controls. DDC control is an excellent tool for trending data and troubleshooting.

- Two supply fan systems can provide system redundancy for critical care area such as operating rooms and intensive care units.

- System design can be based on return air, not 100% outside air.

- Activating the preheat control valve before the fan starts can prevent the freezestat from tripping during start-up

- The heat recovery system can be another type such as an air-to-air heat exchanger, heat pipes, or desiccant type heat exchanger.

- Nuisance and freezestat tripping of the freezestat can be avoided by locating chilled water coils downstream of the supply fan.

- To prevent the humidifier from wetting the system's final filter, the distance between the steam humidifier grid and the final filters should be as long as possible.

- Safeties can also be installed through software, but hardwired interlocks are more reliable because they eliminate operator and software errors.

H.2 SEQUENCE OF OPERATION OF 100% OUTSIDE AIR-HANDLING UNIT WITH EXHAUST FAN AND HOT WATER RUN-AROUND LOOP HEAT RECOVERY SYSTEM (See Figure H-2)

Start-Up Mode

The air-handling system shall be automatically started or stopped by the EMS or whenever the H-O-A switch is in the auto position and manually started or stopped by the hand position.

The air-handling system consists of a supply fan and an exhaust fan. If the outside air temperature is less than 45°F (7°C) (adjustable), the preheat valve shall open to the outside air one minute before the unit fan(s) starts. Once the fan status is proven, the preheat valve shall close slowly and control as defined in the "Temperature Control" section following. Upon a signal to start the unit, the supply and exhaust isolation dampers as well as the outside air damper shall open before the fans start. Isolation damper end-switches shall prove that damper is open

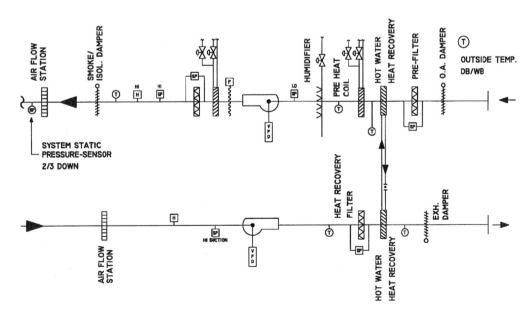

Figure H-2   One hundred percent outside air-handling unit with exhaust fan and heat recovery system.

and allow the fan(s) to start through hardwired interlocks.

On a command to shut down a fan, hardwired time delay relays shall prevent the isolation damper from closing for 30 seconds (adjustable) once the fan shuts off. This shall prevent a buildup of pressure as the fan spins down and prevent the fan's high static limit from tripping.

Fan Speed Control

Supply and exhaust airflow stations shall input cfm (L/s, typical) air volume data to the EMS system. During the start-up mode, the supply fan shall slowly ramp up to speed in tandem to maintain the setpoint of the supply air static pressure located two-thirds downstream of the main ductwork.

Restart of the failed fan shall be initiated through the EMS front-end system. Upon initiating the restart, the system shall start in the sequence outlined in the start-up mode.

Temperature Control

The discharge temperature is maintained by sequencing the speed of the heat recovery pump, modulating preheat valve, and chilled water valve in sequence. As the discharge air temperature rises, the heat recovery pump shall ramp down toward the minimum speed. If the temperature continues to rise, the preheat valve shall modulate closed. As the discharge temperature rises further, the chilled water valve shall modulate open. The reverse shall occur with a decrease in discharge temperature. The chilled water valve shall not open when the heat recovery pump is operating in heating mode or when the preheat valve is open.

The heat recovery valve shall open, and the pump shall start when the outside air temperature is higher than the exhaust air temperature +5°F (2.8°C) (adjustable) or when the outside air temperature falls 3°F (1.7°C) (adjustable) below the setpoint of the preheat air temperature.

Central Humidification

The humidifier shall be modulated to maintain exhaust air humidity. As the humidity of the exhaust air increases, the humidifier shall modulate closed. The reverse shall occur when the humidity of the exhaust air decreases. A high-limit humidistat shall limit the signal to the humidifier if the humidity of the supply air exceeds 90% (hardware adjustable). The humidifier valve shall remain closed whenever chilled water coil is being used. Upon loss of airflow,

a panel-mounted static pressure switch shall close the humidifier control valve.

Safeties

All AHU safety devices are hardwired and independent of the EMS system. These devices shall shut down equipment through hardwired interlocks and provide alarm status to the operator through the EMS front end.

Freeze Protection

A manual-reset, low-limit thermostat installed at the discharge of the fan shall disable the supply and exhaust fans and close the outside and isolation dampers, and the chilled water valve shall open fully when it senses a temperature of 38°F (3°C) (adjustable). The preheat coil valve shall modulate to discharge air temperature (DAT) setpoint to prevent overheating.

Duct Static

A manual-reset, discharge-air, high-static safety located before the supply air isolation/smoke damper shall disable both supply fans and input to the DDC system when it senses a static pressure higher than the normal operating setpoint.

A manual-reset, outside air intake, low-static safety shall disable both supply fans and input to the DDC system when it senses a static pressure lower than the normal operating setpoint.

A manual-reset, exhaust-air, low-static safety located before the exhaust fan shall disable the fan and input to the DDC system when it senses a static pressure lower than the normal operating setpoint.

Humidity High Limit

A discharge-air, autoreset, high-limit humidity control shall close the humidifier valve and input to the DDC system upon sensing a supply air humidity of 90% (adjustable).

Supply Air Smoke Alarm

When the supply fan smoke detector detects smoke, the supply fan shall be disabled through hardwired interlocks and the supply air smoke damper and outside air damper shall close through hardwired interlocks.

All of the control functions of the air-handling unit shall return to the normal condition when the smoke detector is manually reset.

Comments

- DDC control can provide more flexibility and tighter control than pneumatic control.

DDC is an excellent tool for trending data and troubleshooting.

- Activating the preheat valve before the supply fan starts will help prevent the freezestat from tripping during start-up

- The heat recovery system can also be another type such as an air-to-air heat exchanger, heat pipe, or desiccant type heat recovery.

- Premature tripping of freezestat can be avoided by locating the chilled water coil downstream of the supply fan.

- To prevent the humidifier from wetting the system's final filter, the distance between the steam humidifier grid and the final filters should be as long as possible.

- Safeties can also be installed through software, but hardwired interlocks are more reliable because they eliminate operator and software errors.

H.3 SEQUENCE OF OPERATION OF 100% OUTSIDE AIR-HANDLING UNIT WITH FACE AND BYPASS AND EXHAUST FAN

Start-Up Mode

The air-handling system shall be automatically started or stopped by the EMS or whenever the H-O-A switch is in the auto position and manually started or stopped by the hand position.

The air-handling system consists of a supply fan and an exhaust fan. If the outside air temperature is less than 40°F (4°C) (adjustable), the preheat valve shall open under control before the unit fan(s) starts. Once the fan status is proven, the face and bypass dampers shall modulate and control as defined in the "Temperature Control" section that follows. Upon a signal to start the unit, the supply and exhaust isolation dampers as well as the outside air damper shall open before the fans start. Damper end-switches shall prove that damper is open and allow the fan(s) to start through hardwired interlocks.

On a command to shut down a fan, hardwired time delay relays shall prevent the isolation damper from closing for 30 seconds (adjustable), once the fan shuts off. This shall prevent a buildup of pressure as the fan spins down and prevent the fan's high static limit from tripping.

Fan Speed Control

Supply and exhaust airflow stations shall input cfm (L/s, typical) air volume data to the EMS system. During the start-up mode, the supply fan shall slowly ramp up to speed to maintain the setpoint of the supply air static pressure located two-thirds downstream of the main ductwork. In a dual fan situation, if a supply fan fails, the remaining fan shall also shut down.

Restart of the failed fan shall be initiated through the EMS front-end system. Upon initiating the restart, the system shall start under the sequence outlined in the start-up mode.

Temperature Control

The discharge air temperature is maintained by operating the heating control valves, face and bypass dampers, and chilled water control valves in sequence. Whenever the outside air temperature is less than 40°F (4°C), the heating control valves shall modulate to fully open positions, and the face and bypass dampers shall modulate to maintain the setpoint of the discharge air temperature. When the outside air temperature is higher than 40°F (4°C) and the temperature of the outside air is equal to the setpoint of the discharge air temperature, the face damper shall be opened fully and the bypass damper shall be fully closed. When the outside air temperature is higher than the setpoint of the discharge air temperature, the face damper shall open fully, the bypass damper shall be closed, the heating control shall be fully closed, and the chilled water control valves shall modulate to maintain the setpoint of the discharge air temperature.

Central Humidification

The humidifier shall be modulated to maintain exhaust air relative humidity. As the humidity of the exhaust air increases, the humidifier valve shall modulate closed. The reverse shall occur when the humidity of the exhaust air decreases. A high-limit humidistat shall limit the signal to the humidifier if the humidity of the supply air exceeds 90% (hardware adjustable). The humidifier valve shall remain closed whenever the chilled water coil is being used. Upon loss of airflow, a panel-mounted static pressure switch shall close the humidifier control valve.

Safeties

All AHU safety devices are hardwired and independent of the EMS system. These devices shall shut down equipment through hardwired interlocks and provide alarm status to the operator through the EMS front end.

Freeze Protection

A manual-reset, low-limit thermostat installed at the cooling coil section shall disable the supply and exhaust fans and close the outside and isolation dampers, and the chilled water valve shall open fully when it senses a temperature of 38°F (3°C) (adjustable). Heating valves could go wide open with the face damper closed.

Duct Static

A manual-reset, discharge-air, high-static safety located before the supply air isolation/smoke damper shall disable both supply fans and input to the DDC system upon sensing a static pressure higher than the normal operating setpoint.

A manual-reset, outside air intake, low-static safety shall disable both supply fans and input to the DDC system upon sensing a static pressure lower than the normal operating setpoint.

A manual-reset, exhaust air, low-static safety located before each exhaust fan shall disable the corresponding fan and input to the DDC system upon sensing a static pressure lower than the normal operating setpoint.

Humidity High Limit

A discharge-air, autoreset, high-limit humidity control shall close the humidifier valve and input to the DDC system upon sensing a supply air humidity of 90% (adjustable).

Supply Air Smoke Alarm

When the supply fan smoke detector detects smoke, the supply fans shall be disabled through hardwired interlocks and the supply air smoke damper and outside air damper shall close through hardwired interlocks.

All of the control functions of the air-handling unit shall return to the normal condition when the smoke detector is manually reset.

Comments

- DDC control can provide more flexibility and tighter control than pneumatic control. DDC control is an excellent tool for trending data and troubleshooting.
- The fan's control sequence is based on VFDs. With today's technology, a first-cost VFD option is preferable to a variable pitch fan.
- Activating the preheat valve before the supply fan starts will help prevent the freezestat from tripping during start-up.

- Premature tripping of the freezestat can be avoided by locating the chilled water coil downstream of the supply fan.
- To prevent the humidifier from wetting the system's final filter, the distance between the steam humidifier grid and the final filters should be as long as possible.
- The preheat coil must be sized to heat the outside air from the outdoor air design temperature to the design setpoint of the discharge air temperature.
- The face and bypass dampers require periodic maintenance to perform properly. Consider alternatives where regular maintenance is uncertain.
- Safeties can also be installed through software, but hardware interlocks are more reliable because they eliminate operator and software errors.

H.4 SEQUENCE OF OPERATION OF AIR-HANDLING UNIT WITH RETURN AIR FAN AND AIR-SIDE ECONOMIZER (See Figure H-3)

Start-Up Mode

The air-handling system shall be automatically started or stopped by the EMS or whenever the H-O-A switch is in the auto position and manually started or stopped by the hand position.

It is preferable to start return fan first to warm up unit before starting supply fan. Upon a signal to start the unit, the supply fan smoke/isolation damper and the return air damper shall open, and the exhaust air damper and economizer air damper shall close before the fans start. The supply fan smoke/isolation damper end-switches shall prove that dampers are open and allow the fan(s) to start through hardwired interlocks. After supply fan and return have met the static pressure requirement of the system, the minimum outside air damper shall open, and the EMS shall modulate dampers, heating valves, and chilled water valves in sequence to maintain the predetermined setpoint of the discharge air temperature.

On a command to shut down a fan, hardwired time delay relays shall prevent the isolation damper from closing for 30 seconds (adjustable), once the fan shuts off. This shall prevent a buildup of pressure as the fan spins down and prevent the fan's high static limit from tripping.

Fan Speed Control

The supply and return airflow stations shall input cfm (L/s, typical) air volume data to the EMS

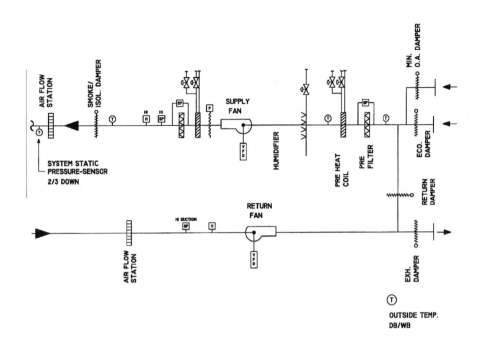

Figure H-3   One hundred percent outside air-handling unit with two supply fans, and a common exhaust fan and hot water run around loop heat recover.

system. During the start-up mode, both the supply fan and return shall slowly ramp up to speed in tandem to maintain the setpoint of the supply air static pressure located two-thirds downstream of the main ductwork. The return fan shall modulate to maintain a predetermined minimum outside air cfm volume (based on supply and return cfm measurement. In a dual fan situation, if a supply or return fan fails, the remaining fan shall also shut down.

Restart of the failed fan shall be initiated through the EMS system. Upon initiating the restart, the system shall start in the sequence outlined in the start-up mode.

Temperature Control

The discharge temperature is maintained by modulating the preheat valves, economizer dampers, and the chilled water valves in sequence. As the discharge air temperature rises, the preheat valves shall modulate closed. If the temperature continues to rise, the economizer dampers shall modulate open to the outside air if the unit is in the economizer mode. If the economizer dampers are fully open and the temperature continues to rise, the chilled water valves shall modulate open. The reverse shall occur when the discharge temperature decreases.

The economizer mode shall be determined by comparing the enthalpy of the return air with the enthalpy of the outside air. If the enthalpy of the outside air is less than the enthalpy of the return air, the unit shall be in the economizer mode, and the dampers shall modulate, as required, to maintain the discharge air temperature. If the enthalpy of the outside air is greater than the enthalpy of the return air, then the economizer mode shall be switched off, and the minimum outside air damper shall remain open for the minimum outside air requirement.

Central Humidification

The humidifier shall be modulated to maintain exhaust air relative humidity. As the humidity of the exhaust air increases, the humidifier valve shall modulate closed. The reverse shall occur when the humidity of the exhaust air decreases. A high-limit humidistat shall limit the signal to the humidifier if the humidity of the supply air exceeds 90% (hardware adjustable). The humidifier valve shall remain closed whenever the chilled water coil is being used. Upon loss of airflow, a panel-mounted static pressure switch shall close the humidifier control valve.

Safeties

All AHU safety devices are hardwired and independent of the EMS system. These devices shall shut down equipment through hardwired interlocks and provide alarm status to the operator through the EMS front end.

Freeze Protection

A manual-reset, low-limit thermostat installed at the discharge of the fan shall disable the supply and exhaust fans and close the outside and isolation dampers, and the chilled water valve shall open fully when it senses a temperature of 38°F (3°C) (adjustable). Preheat valve shall modulate to maintain DAT setpoint to prevent overheating.

Duct Static

A manual-reset, discharge-air, high-static safety located before the supply air isolation/smoke damper shall disable supply fan and input to the DDC system when it senses a static pressure higher than the normal operating setpoint.

A manual-reset, outside air intake, low-static safety shall disable the supply fan and input to the DDC system when it senses a static pressure lower than the normal operating setpoint.

A manual-reset, exhaust-air, low-static safety located before the return fan shall disable the fan and input to the DDC system when it senses a static pressure lower than the normal operating setpoint.

Humidity High Limit

A discharge-air, autoreset, high-limit humidity control shall close the humidifier valve and input to the DDC system when it senses a supply air humidity of 90% (adjustable).

Supply Air Smoke Alarm

When the supply fan smoke detector detects smoke, the supply air smoke/isolation damper shall close through hardwired interlocks. The outside air damper and return air and supply fans shall be disabled through hardwired interlocks. For units with capacity 15,000 cfm (7080 L/s) or more, according to NFPA, return air smoke detectors and dampers are required. Upon sensing smoke in the return airstream, the return fan and return air dampers shall be shut down or fan shall continue to operate with unit dampers positioned to exhaust smoke out of the building, if designed as a part of the smoke control system.

All of the control functions of the air-handling unit shall return to the normal condition when the smoke detector is manually reset.

Notes

- DDC control can provide more flexibility and a tighter control loop than pneumatic control.
- Premature tripping of the freezestat can be avoided by locating the chilled water coils downstream from the supply fan.
- To prevent the humidifier from wetting the system's final filter, the distance between the steam humidifier grid and the final filters should be as long as possible.
- Safeties can also be installed through software, but hardwired interlocks are more reliable because they eliminate operator and software errors.

H.5 SEQUENCE OF OPERATION OF HOT DECK AND COLD DECK AIR-HANDLING UNIT WITH RETURN AIR FAN AND AIR-SIDE ECONOMIZER (DEHUMIDIFICATION AND COOLING OF ALL SUPPLY AIR WITH REHEAT FOR HOT STREAM)

Start-Up Mode

The air-handling system shall be automatically started or stopped by the EMS or whenever the H-O-A switch is in the auto position and manually started or stopped by the hand position.

Upon a signal to start the unit, the hot deck and cold deck supply fan smoke/isolation damper and the return air damper shall open, and the exhaust air damper and economizer air damper shall close before the fans start. Hot deck and cold deck supply fan smoke/isolation end-switches shall prove that damper is open and allow the fan(s) to start through hardwired interlocks. After the supply fan and the return fan have met the static pressure requirement of the system, the minimum outside air damper shall open, and the EMS shall modulate dampers, preheating valves, reheat valves, and chilled water valves in sequence to maintain the predetermined setpoint of the discharge air temperature.

On a command to shut down a fan, hardwired time delay relays shall prevent the isolation damper from closing for 30 seconds (adjustable), once the fan shuts off. This shall prevent a buildup of pressure as the fan spins down and prevent the fan's high-static limit from tripping.

Fan Speed Control

The supply and return airflow stations shall input cfm (L/s, typical) air volume data to the EMS system. The EMS shall monitor static pressure sensors in each of the hot and cold deck risers located two-thirds downstream of the unit. During the start-up mode, the supply fan shall slowly ramp up to required speed to maintain the setpoint of the supply air static pressure based on the lower of the two sensors. The return fan shall modulate in tandem to maintain a predetermined minimum outside air cfm volume (based on supply and return cfm measurements. In a dual fan situation, if a supply or return fan fails, the remaining fan shall also shut down.

Restart of the failed fan shall be initiated through the EMS system. Upon initiating the restart, the system shall start in the sequence outlined in the start-up mode.

Temperature Control

The cold deck discharge temperature is maintained by modulating the preheat valves, economizer dampers, and the chilled water valves in sequence. As the cold deck discharge air temperature rises, the preheat valves shall modulate closed. If the temperature continues to rise, the economizer dampers shall modulate open to the outside air if the unit is in the economizer mode. If the economizer dampers are fully open and the temperature continues to rise, the chilled water valves shall modulate open. The reverse shall occur when the cold deck discharge temperature decreases.

The economizer mode shall be determined by comparing the enthalpy of the return air with the enthalpy of the outside air. If the enthalpy of the outside air is less than the enthalpy of the return air, the unit shall be in the economizer mode, and the dampers shall modulate, as required, to maintain the discharge air temperature. If the enthalpy of the outside air is greater than the enthalpy of the return air, then the economizer mode shall be switched off, and the minimum outside air damper shall remain open for the minimum outside air requirement.

The hot deck discharge temperature is maintained by modulating the reheat valves. The hot deck discharge temperature shall be linearly reset based on the outside air temperature.

Central Humidification

The humidifier shall be modulated to maintain exhaust air relative humidity. As the humidity of the exhaust air increases, the humidifier valve shall modulate closed. The reverse shall occur when the humidity of the exhaust air decreases. A high-limit humidistat shall limit the signal to the humidifier if the humidity of the supply air exceeds 90% (hard-ware adjustable). The humidifier valve shall remain closed whenever the chilled water coil is being used. Upon loss of airflow, a panel-mounted static pressure switch shall close the humidifier control valve.

Safeties

All AHU safety devices are hardwired and independent of the EMS system. These devices shall shut down equipment through hardwired interlocks and provide alarm status to the operator through the EMS front end.

Freeze Protection

A manual-reset, low-limit thermostat installed at the discharge of the fan shall disable the supply and return fans and close the outside and isolation dampers, and the chilled water valve shall open fully when it senses a temperature of 38°F (3°C) (adjustable). Preheat valve shall modulate to maintain DAT setpoint to prevent overheating.

Duct Static

A manual-reset, discharge-air, high-static safety located before the hot deck and cold deck supply air isolation/smoke dampers shall disable the supply fan and input to the DDC system when it senses a static pressure higher than the normal operating setpoint.

A manual-reset, outside air intake, low-static safety shall disable the supply fan and input to the DDC system when it senses a static pressure lower than the normal operating setpoint.

A manual-reset, return-air, low-static safety located before the return fan shall disable the corresponding fan and input to the DDC system when it senses a static pressure lower than normal operating setpoint.

Humidity High Limit

A discharge-air, autoreset, high-limit humidity control shall close the humidifier valve and input to the DDC system upon sensing a supply air humidity of 90% (adjustable).

Supply Air Smoke Alarm

When the supply fan smoke detector detects smoke, the hot deck and cold deck supply air smoke/isolation dampers shall close through hardwired interlocks. The outside air damper and return air and supply fans shall be disabled through hardwired interlocks.

All of the control functions of the air-handling unit shall return to the normal condition when the smoke detector is manually reset.

Notes

- DDC control can provide more flexibility and tighter control loop than pneumatic control. DDC control is an excellent tool for trending data and troubleshooting.
- Premature tripping of the freezestat can be avoided by locating the chilled water coils downstream from the supply fan.
- To prevent the humidifier from wetting the system's final filter, the distance between the steam humidifier grid and the final filters should be as long as possible.
- Safeties can also be installed through software, but hardwired interlocks are more reliable because they eliminate operator and software errors.

- Hot deck reheat and duct must be sized for maximum heating and reheat load that exists when no cooling is required.
- The control of dehumidification and cooling of all supply air with a hot stream dual air system is simple, but the economy is poor because cooling is canceled by reheat at hot/cold deck terminal unit controls.
- Either high or low velocity duct distribution may be used for a dual-duct system.
- Dual air systems require careful control of reheat and positive tightness of hot/cold deck terminal mixing dampers to function satisfactorily. Also, the distribution systems are subject to instability due to the terminal unit proportioning dampers.

APPENDIX I
OPERATING ROOM AIR DISTRIBUTION

The following paper, "Comparison of Operating Room Ventilation Systems in the Protection of the Surgical site" by Farhad Memarzadeh, P.E., Ph.D., and Andrew P. Manning, Ph.D., is from *ASHRAE Transactions* 108(2).

Comparison of Operating Room Ventilation Systems in the Protection of the Surgical Site

Farhad Memarzadeh, P.E., Ph.D.
Member ASHRAE

Andrew P. Manning, Ph.D.
Associate Member ASHRAE

ABSTRACT

This paper uses airflow modeling and particle-tracking methodologies to compare the risk of contaminant deposition on an operating room (OR) surgical site and back table for different ventilation systems. The ventilation system designs considered incorporated commonly used diffuser types, in particular, conventional, laminar, nonaspirating, and displacement diffuser types. Further, a range of different air change rates were considered, from 15 to 150 ACH. The room equipment layout and distribution was agreed upon by a panel of physicians and engineers as being representative of a typical newly designed operating room. The type of particle considered in this study was a squame, or skin scale, which is around 10 microns in size. Particles were released from three locations in the room, which represented likely sources of generation, and tracked to determine whether they would impinge on either the surgical site or a back table. The results were tabulated such that the lowest percentage of impacts would indicate the most appropriate ventilation system. The results show that ventilation systems that provide laminar flow conditions are the best choice, although some care needs too be taken in their design. A face velocity of around 30 to 35 fpm (0.15m/s to 0.18m/s) is sufficient from the laminar diffuser array, provided that the size of the diffuser array is appropriate.

INTRODUCTION

The risk of postoperative infection is present in all surgical procedures, but it can be particularly serious in certain operations, for example, joint replacement. There are several factors that could affect such infection, namely, patient factors (i.e., susceptibility to infection), surgical field factors (i.e., the thermal plume from the site), room factors (i.e., cleanliness of the OR), and HVAC factors (i.e., air change rate [ACH] and direction of airflow). Figure 1 shows sources, routes, and interactions of many of the factors.

In terms of the bacteria that cause infection, it is agreed in the literature that the primary source of such bacteria are squames, or skin scales or particles, Woods et al. (1986). These particles are of the order of 10 microns in diameter and are shed from exposed regions of skin, both from the surgical staff and also by the patient. Therefore, in this study, only this source of contaminant is considered.

There are standards suggested for air-conditioning systems for operating theaters in different countries. The standard for operating room design in Germany, for example, is DIN 1946/4, which had its latest revision in 1999. This stan-

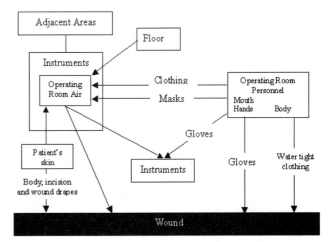

Figure 1 *Source and routes of infection in the operating room (Lewis 1993).*

Farhad Memarzadeh is the chief of technical resources at the National Institute of Health, Bethesda, Md. **Andrew P. Manning** is the director of engineering at Flomerics, Inc., Southboro, Mass.

dard contains some specific details for the design of the OR. The supply air discharge temperature should be set such that the return air temperature at the room is between 71.6°F (22°C) and 78.8°F (26°C). The standard defines a reference supply airflow rate of 1413 cfm (0.67 m³/s). The actual amount to be supplied to the room, however, is defined using the following two factors:

- relative airborne microorganism concentration, ε_s, and
- contamination factor or ratio in the protected area, μ_s.

The value of ε_s is calculated from

$$\varepsilon_s = \mu_s \frac{\dot{V}_{ZU}^*}{\dot{V}_{ZU}}, \tag{1}$$

where

$\mu_s = k_s / k_R$ = contamination factor in the protected area,

k_R = average airborne microorganism concentration in the room at $\dot{V}_{ZU}$,

ks = average airborne microorganism concentration in the protected area,

$\dot{V}_{ZU}^*$ = reference supply airflow volume flow rate (1413 cfm [0.67 m³/s]),

$\dot{V}_{ZU}$ = actual supply air volume flow rate.

For the relative airborne microorganism concentration, which is regarded as a measure of the given hygienic quality of the air, the limiting value, ε_{szul}, is specified relative to the minimum requisite supply air volume flow rate, $\dot{V}_{ZU\,min}$, by the following equation:

$$\dot{V}_{ZU\,min} = \dot{V}_{ZU}^* \frac{\mu_s}{\varepsilon_{szul}} \tag{2}$$

The value of ε_{szul} is evaluated on the type of OR and the type of surgery performed in it. In particular, the code identifies two types of OR:

- Type A operating theatres require displacement flow systems, namely, laminar flow systems. Type A operating theatres require especially high levels of sterility, for example, transplantations, cardiac surgery, joint prosthetics, alloplasty. Here, the value of ε_{szul} is taken as two-thirds.
- Type B operating theatres require mix flow or displacement flow systems. Type B operating theatres require high levels of sterility. Here, the value of ε_{szul} is taken as 1.

However, since under any given operating conditions, μ_s is not only a function of the air distribution system but also a number of other parameters—in particular, of the supply airflow rate itself—the minimum airflow rate for the OR can only be determined by experiment. The experimental procedure is defined by DIN 4799 (1990), which specifies that the

OR floor area has to be between 25 and 60 m², and the ceiling height has to be at least 3 m.

The *1999 ASHRAE Handbook* suggests that

the delivery of air from the ceiling, with a downward movement to several exhaust inlets located on opposite walls, is probably the most effective air movement pattern for maintaining the concentration at an acceptable level.

The handbook suggests that the temperature range should be between 62°F (16.67°C) and 80°F (26.67°C), and that positive pressurization should be maintained. It also suggests that the air should be supplied at the ceiling and exhausted or returned from at least two locations near the floor. It suggests that supply diffusers should be of the unidirectional type, and that high-induction ceiling or side-wall diffusers should be avoided. The suggested ACH is 15 ACH for systems that use all outdoor air and 25 ACH for recirculating air systems.

Some studies have been published that consider the relative merits of different systems. However, studies such as Lidwell (1988) and Schmidt (1987) do not include specific system design data for these systems, so it is difficult to establish definitive recommendations for the actual design of the ventilation system. Further, there are conflicting data regarding the system that is generally recognized as the cleanest type of system. In particular, while laminar flow systems are recognized in providing lower general concentration levels in the room, they are sometimes blamed for higher infection rates than more conventional systems, for example, Salvati et al. (1982). The theory put forward by Lewis (1993) is that laminar flow systems cause impingement on the wound site. However, this seems to be based on the use of high laminar flow velocities at supply: Schmidt (1987) defines a laminar system as having velocities of at least 90 fpm (0.45m/s).

The studies mentioned above were experiment-based. However, an alternative technique, computational fluid dynamics (CFD) (sometimes known as airflow modeling), has been proven to be very powerful and efficient in research projects involving parametric study on room airflow and contaminant dispersion (Ziang et al. 1995; Haghighat et al. 1994). In addition, the output of the CFD simulation can be presented in many ways, for example, with the useful details of field distributions, as well as overviews on the effects of parameters involved. Therefore, CFD is employed as a main approach in this study.

The only CFD study identified in this literature search that addressed contamination control in an operating room was Lo (1997). However, this study made two assumptions, which would make the conclusions less useful. In particular, the study only considered an isothermal operating room and, secondly, the contaminant was considered as a concentration. Therefore, in the former case, the effect of significant thermal plumes in the room was ignored. In the latter case, the assumption that the particles in the room can be considered to follow the Brownian motion of the airflow is strictly applicable to particles, which are 1 micron or less in diameter (Crowe et. al

1998). While bacteria and viruses do conform to this criteria, as noted above, bacteria are usually transported in operating rooms by squames, which are considerably bigger (in the range of 10 microns) and so do not necessarily follow Brownian motion. For this reason, concentration sources were not used in this study. A further reason was that the use of concentration would make the question of impact of the particles on the surgical site more difficult to determine.

In the study documented here, airflow modeling is used to consider the dispersion of squame-sized particles in various ventilation system design operating rooms. The particle tracking routine was previously developed for use in Memarzadeh (2000). In order to establish the relative ranking of the different systems, two target areas of concern are considered: the surgical site and back table. The reason for the latter target is that squames that strike this surface are likely to directly contaminate instruments.

PURPOSE OF STUDY

The main purposes of the study presented in this paper are to

- use advanced numerical modeling and empirical data to evaluate the effects of some of the room parameters, such as

  - ventilation flow rate,
  - diffuser type and location,
  - supply temperature, and
  - exhaust location,

  on minimizing the risk of contamination of an operating room surgical site and a back table from specific particulate sources;

- evaluate the same parameters to determine which ventilation systems evacuate the room of particles most effectively; and
- provide an architectural/engineering tool for good design practice that is generally applicable to conventional operating room use.

METHODOLOGY

Airflow Modeling

Airflow modeling based on computational fluid dynamics (CFD), which solves the fundamental conservation equations for mass, momentum, and energy in the form of the Navier-Stokes equations, is now well established.

$$\frac{\partial}{\partial t}(\rho\varphi) + div(\rho \vec{V}\varphi - \Gamma_\varphi grad\ \varphi) = S_\varphi \qquad (3)$$

Transient + Convection – Diffusion = Source

where

ρ = density
$\vec{V}$ = velocity vector

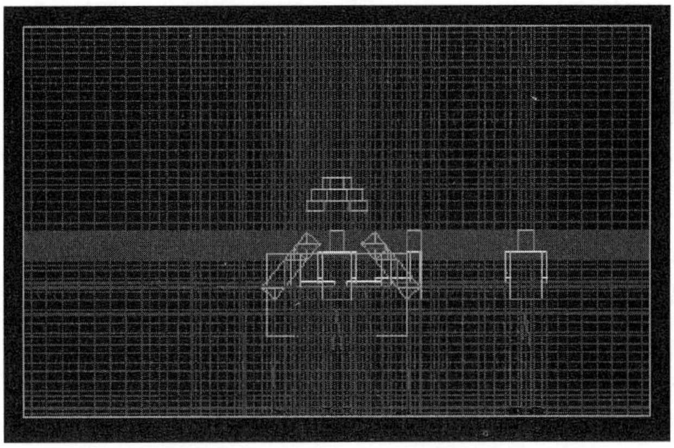

Figure 2 *Geometric model of operating room and superimposed grid of cells for calculation.*

φ = dependent variable
Γ_φ = exchange coefficient (laminar + turbulent)
S_φ = source or sink

Airflow modeling solves the set of Navier Stokes equations by superimposing a grid of many tens or even hundreds of thousands of cells that describe the physical geometry, heat and contamination sources, and air itself. Figure 2 shows one of the operating room case geometries and the corresponding space discretization, subdividing the operating room into cells. In this study, a finite-volume approach was used to consider the discretization and solution of the equations.

The simultaneous equations thus formed are solved iteratively for each one of these cells to produce a solution that satisfies the conservation laws for mass, momentum, and energy. As a result, the flow can then be traced in any part of the room, simultaneously coloring the air according to another parameter such as temperature.

The particle-tracking algorithm was based on the k-ε turbulence model. Further, the k-ε turbulence model represented the most appropriate choice of model because of its extensive use in other applications. No other turbulence model has been developed that is as universally accepted as the k-ε turbulence model.

Validation of Numerical Modeling and Analysis

The 1998 publication, *Ventilation Design Handbook on Animal Research Facilities Using Static Microisolators* (Memarzadeh 1998), by the National Institutes of Health provided the most extensive empirical validation to date. The methodology and the results generated in the 1998 publication were peer reviewed by numerous entities, such as Harvard University, etc. In order to analyze the ventilation performance of different settings, numerical methods based on computational fluid dynamics were used to create computer simulations of more than 160 different room configurations. The performance of this approach was successfully verified by comparison with an extensive set of experimental measurements. A total of 12.9 million experimental (empirical) data values were collected to confirm the methodology. The average error between the experimental and computational values was 14.36% for temperature and velocities, while the equivalent value for concentrations was 14.50%.

To forward this research, several meetings were held to solicit project input and feedback from the participants. There were more than 55 international experts in all facets of the animal care and use community, including scientists, veterinarians, engineers, animal facility managers, and cage and rack manufacturers. The prepublication project report underwent peer review by a ten-member panel from the participant group, selected for their expertise in pertinent areas. Their comments were adopted and incorporated in the final report.

The results from the 1998 publication were also reviewed by several ASHRAE technical committees and were cited in the *1999 ASHRAE Handbook—Applications* and the *2001 ASHRAE Handbook—Fundamentals*.

Simulation of Contaminant Particles

The basic assumption in this study is that the squames can be simulated as particles being released from several sources surrounding the occupant. These particles are then tracked for a certain period of time in the room. The methodology is similar to that employed previously in Memarzadeh and Jiang (2000), where tuberculosis carrying droplets were released from around the patient in an isolation room to simulate coughs, and were subsequently tracked. Since the airflow in a ventilated room is turbulent, the squames are transported not only by convection of the airflow but also by the turbulent diffusion. The squames are light enough and in small enough quantities that they can be considered not to exert an influence on airflow. Therefore, from the output of the CFD simulation, the distributions of air velocities and the turbulent parameters can be directly applied to predict the path of the airborne squames in convection and diffusion processes.

Particle Trajectories

The methodology for predicting turbulent particle dispersion used in this study was originally laid out by Gosman and Ioannides (1981) and validated by Ormancey and Martinon (1984), Shuen et al. (1983), and Chen and Crowe (1984). Experimental validation data were obtained from Snyder and Lumley (1971). Turbulence was incorporated into the Stochastic model via the k-ε turbulence model (Alani et al. 1998).

The particle trajectories are obtained by integrating the equation of motion in three coordinates:

$$m_p \frac{du_p}{dt} = \frac{1}{2} C_D A_p \rho (u - u_p) \sqrt{(u - u_p)^2 + (v - v_p)^2 + (w - w_p)^2} + m_p g_x$$

(4a)

$$m_p \frac{dv_p}{dt} = \frac{1}{2} C_D A_p \rho (v - v_p) \sqrt{(u - u_p)^2 + (v - v_p)^2 + (w - w_p)^2} + m_p g_y$$

(4b)

$$m_p \frac{dw_p}{dt} = \frac{1}{2} C_D A_p \rho (w - w_p) \sqrt{(u - u_p)^2 + (v - v_p)^2 + (w - w_p)^2} + m_p g_z$$

(4c)

$$\frac{dx_p}{dt} = u_p$$

(5a)

$$\frac{dy_p}{dt} = v_p$$

(5b)

$$\frac{dz_p}{dt} = w_p$$

(5c)

where

u, v, w	=	instantaneous velocities of air in x, y, and z directions
u_p, v_p, w_p	=	particle velocity in x, y, and z directions
x_p, y_p, z_p	=	particle moving in x, y and z direction
g_x, g_y, g_z	=	gravity in x, y, and z directions
A_p	=	cross-sectional area of the particle
m_p	=	mass of the particle
ρ	=	density of the particle
C_D	=	drag coefficient
dt	=	time interval

$$C_D = \frac{24}{\text{Re}} \left(1 + \frac{3}{16} \text{Re} \right)^{0.5} \qquad \text{for Re} \leq 560 \qquad (6)$$

and

$$C_D = 0.44 \qquad \text{for Re} > 560 \qquad (7)$$

The Reynolds number of the particle is based on the relative velocity between particle and air.

In laminar flow, particles released from a point source with the same weight would initially follow the airstream in the same path and then fall under the effect of gravity. Unlike laminar flow, the random nature of turbulence indicates that the particles released from the same point source will be randomly affected by turbulent eddies. As a result, they will be diffused away from the streamline at different fluctuating levels. In order to model the turbulent diffusion, the instantaneous fluid velocities in the three Cartesian directions—u, v, and w—are decomposed into the mean velocity component and the turbulent fluctuating component as

$$u = \bar{u} + u', \qquad v = \bar{v} + v', \qquad w = \bar{w} + w',$$

where $\bar{u}$ and u' are the mean and fluctuating components in x-direction. The same applies for y- and z-directions. The stochastic approach prescribes the use of a random number generator algorithm, which, in this case, is taken from Press et al. (1992) to model the fluctuating velocity. It is achieved by using a random sampling of a Gaussian distribution with a mean of zero and a standard deviation of unity. Assuming isotropic turbulence, the instantaneous velocities of air are then calculated from kinetic energy of turbulence:

$$u = \bar{u} + N\alpha \quad (8a)$$

$$v = \bar{v} + N\alpha \quad (8b)$$

$$w = \bar{w} + N\alpha \quad (8c)$$

where N is the pseudo-random number, ranging from 0 to 1, with

$$\alpha = \left(\frac{2k}{3}\right)^{0.5}, \quad (9)$$

where k is the turbulent kinetic energy.

The mean velocities, which are the direct output of CFD, determine the convection of the particles along the streamline, while the turbulent fluctuating velocity, $N\alpha$, contributes to the turbulent diffusion of the particle.

Particle Interaction Time

With the velocities known, the only component needed for calculating the trajectory is the time interval (t_{int}) over which the particle interacts with the turbulent flow field. The concept of turbulence being composed of eddies is employed here. Before determining the interaction time, two important time scales need to be introduced: the eddy's time scale and the particle transient time scale.

The eddy's time scale is the lifetime of an eddy, defined as

$$t_e = \left(\frac{l_e}{|N\alpha|}\right) \quad (10)$$

where

$$l_e = \frac{C_\mu k^{\frac{3}{2}}}{\varepsilon}, \quad (11)$$

l_e = dissipation length scale of the eddy,

k = turbulent kinetic energy,

ε = dissipation rate of turbulent kinetic energy,

C_μ = constant in the turbulence model.

The transient time scale for the particle to pass through the eddy, t_r, is estimated as

$$t_r = -\tau \ln\left\{1.0 - \frac{l_e}{\tau\left|(\sqrt{\bar{u}^2 + \bar{v}^2 + \bar{w}^2}) - (\sqrt{(u_p)^2 + (v_p)^2 + (w_p)^2})\right|}\right\} \quad (12)$$

and

$$\tau = \frac{\frac{4}{3}\rho_p D}{\left\{\rho C_D \left|(\sqrt{\bar{u}^2 + \bar{v}^2 + \bar{w}^2}) - (\sqrt{(u_p)^2 + (v_p)^2 + (w_p)^2})\right|\right\}}, \quad (13)$$

where τ is the particle relaxation time, indicating the time required for a particle starting from rest to reach 63% of the flowing stream velocity. The variable D is the diameter of the particle.

The interaction time is determined by the relative importance of the two events. If the particle moves slowly relative to the gas, it will remain in the eddy during the whole lifetime of the eddy, t_e. If the relative velocity between the particle and the gas is appreciable, the particle will transverse the eddy in its transient time, t_r. Therefore, the interaction time is the minimum of the two:

$$t_{int} = \min(t_e, t_r) \quad (14)$$

Particle Outcomes

The methodology was refined to consider different particle outcomes, namely:

- the particle is vented from the room via ventilation and

- the particle hits one of the two designated targets, namely, the surgical site (defined later) or the top surface of the back table.

Particles that are neither vented nor strike the target are assumed to remain in the room when the overall particle tracking time limit is reached.

Testing of Particle Tracking and Target Detection Methodology

A simple test configuration was defined to confirm that the particle tracking methodology was functioning as intended. There are many aspects to be investigated, including inertial, gravitational, and slip effects, but, in particular, the simulation sample here was intended to test that the target detection methodology worked correctly. The test was specified to incorporate typical flow and blockage effects present in the operating room, in particular, an inlet (supply), openings (vents), a block in the flow path (internal geometry and obstructions), and a specific target.

The test configuration had dimensions of 20 in. × 20 in. × 40 in. (0.5 m × 0.5 m × 1.0 m). It contained a 20 in. × 20 in. (0.5 m × 0.5 m) supply at one end, through which the flow rate was varied, and an opening of half that size at the other end. The opening was defined as representing atmospheric conditions: no flow rate was defined through the openings. There were two blocks, of dimensions 20 in. × 10 in. × 20 in. (0.5 m × 0.25 m × 0.5 m) and 8 in. × 4 in. × 20 in. (0.2 m × 0.1 m × 0.5 m), which were included to represent typical obstruction. A target of dimension 6 in. × 20 in. (0.15 m × 0.5 m) was also included.

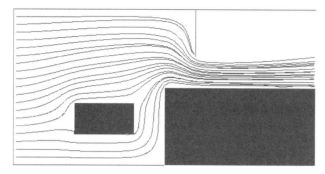

Figure 3 *Result of particle target test case.*

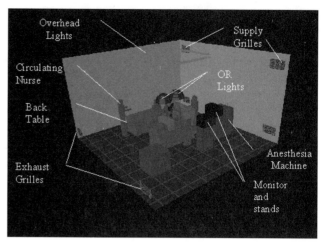

Figure 4 *Layout of baseline operating room—Mayo stand view.*

In the tests, 20 particles were released with even spacing across the center of the inlet supply. The test particles were 10 mm in diameter, with a density of 1000 kg/m³. A flow rate of 1060 cfm (0.5m³/s) was considered. Different coordinate orientations were considered to evaluate whether coordinate biasing existed. In particular, the configuration was considered with the supply in the positive and negative x, y, and z directions, respectively. Therefore, six cases were run to test the particle tracking methodology.

The results of a typical case are shown in Figure 3, in particular, the positive *x*. The blue lines represent the particle tracks. The figure clearly shows that the target stops two particles and that the rest of the particles exit correctly through the end opening.

These features are also exhibited by all the other cases. Based on the results from these tests, the particle tracking methodology can be seen to be working correctly.

Calculation Procedure

The calculation procedure was as follows:

- Compute the field distribution of fluid velocity, temperature, and turbulent parameters.

- Specify the source locations from where a specified number of particles are released. Note that the particles are not continuously released: they are released from the source locations only at the start of the analysis time period (i.e., $t = 0$ s).

- Perform computational analysis to calculate trajectory for each particle for up to 3600 s from initial release. The output of the analysis includes
    - the percentage of particles that are vented from the room via ventilation, varying with time, and
    - the percentage of particles that strike a designated target in the room, in particular, either the surgical site or the top surface of the back table, at the end of the overall time period (3600 s). Note that this quantity was not measured with time because of the small number of particles that actually hit the targets.

OUTLINE OF BASELINE MODEL

A typical operating room layout in terms of the number of surgical staff, lights, machinery, tables, and patient was considered for the baseline model for the CFD simulations. The general features of the baseline room are given in Figure 4 and Table 1 and are listed below.

A panel of physicians and engineers agreed upon the layout of the room during the initial stages of the study. Items such as gas columns were not included with the belief that they obstruct the free movement of large equipment in operating rooms, limit the placement and position of the operating table, and are difficult to keep clean. Also, the panel believes operating rooms should be going more toward connection of gas lines at the ceiling, since such lines would not provide significant blockage to airflow. Other significant items of equipment, for example, a C-arm, were not included in this study, as the panel felt that they did not constitute "typical" equipment. It is recognized that such items may influence the airflow and temperature distribution in the OR, and that they should be considered in future studies.

Description in Brief

Room

- 20 ft × 20 ft × 12 ft (6.1 m × 6.1 m × 3.66 m) high
- Five surgical staff members
- One patient
- One back table
- One anesthesia machine
- Two monitors (and stands)
- One inactive machine
- Two surgical lights
- Dimensions of internal blockages are given in Table 1.

TABLE 1
Dimensions and Heat Dissipations of Major Items in Operating Room

Item	Dimensions	Heat Dissipation
Operating table	30 in. wide × 30 in. high × 72 in. long	None—operating table only operates intermittently
Surgical lights (×2)	2 ft diameter × 1 ft hemisphere	150 W each
Surgical staff	Height assumed as 5 ft 9 in. Two of the staff are leaning over surgery site	100 W each
Anesthesia machine	30 in. × 30 in. × 48 in. high	200 W
Machine1	30 in. × 30 in. × 30 in. high	None—represents blockage only or intermittently operating machinery
Mayo stand	10 in. × 30 in., located 8 in. above patient level	None
Back table	30 in. × 30 in. high × 60 in. long	None
Monitor and stand (×2)	Stand: 12 in. × 24 in. × 40 in. high Monitor: 16 in. × 18 in. × 10 in. high	Monitors dissipate 200 W each
Patient	With drape, patient covers most of table	Exposed head dissipates 46 W (70% of 65 W); Surgery site is 1 ft × 1 ft area with surface temperature = 100°F
Overhead lights (×4)	6 ft × 1 ft	180 W each

Supply

- Two supply grilles each providing 750 cfm (0.35 m³/s) for a total of 18.75 ACH
- 24 in. × 14 in. (0.61 m × 0.36 m) grilles
- Supply discharge temperature, 67.5°F (19.7°C), set such that the exhaust air temperature was 72°F (22.2°C)

Exhaust

- Four exhaust grilles each extracting 375 cfm (0.17 m³/s)
- 24 in. × 14 in. (0.61 m × 0.36 m) grilles

Heat Sources

- Heat sources were those that could be considered constant, not intermittent, sources
- Total cooling load, 2166W (see Table 1)

Model Considerations

Several different ventilation systems were considered in this study. The different ventilation systems considered, which are listed in Table 2, are intended to replicate approximately those outlined in Schmidt (1987). Cases 1 and 10 use conventional grilles as the basis of the ventilation system, which provide jets at a (relatively) high velocity at discrete locations in the room. Cases 2, 3, 4, 5, 6, 7, and 9 all provide variations on a laminar flow type ventilation system, which aim to provide vertically downward flow conditions. The changes between the cases are typically associated with differences in diffuser array size. The systems in these cases avoided the higher velocities typically associated with them, namely, 90 fpm (0.45 m/s) to determine if the laminar flow concept could

be made to work practically. Further, Cases 3 and 4 are based on the DIN 1946/4 (1999) standard, while Cases 5 and 6 consider low level only and high level only exhaust systems, respectively. Case 8 considered upward displacement units, which aim to provide low-velocity flow at low level, with exhausts placed at high level. Finally, Case 11 was suggested by Milton Goldman, who presented a summary of operating room contamination issues at a recent ASHRAE meeting (Goldman 2000). In this concept, a U-shaped array of laminar flow diffusers above the table was used in combination with a nozzle that provides air horizontally along the length of the table toward the anesthesia screen. The intention of the nozzle flow is to sweep away contaminants from the surgical site up toward an exhaust located in the ceiling.

The various diffuser types considered in this project were all modeled using a combination of several boundary conditions, which were validated prior to the room parametric study. Great care was taken with regard to the correct representation of the diffusers in the room, as well as the numerical grid used. The numerical diffuser models were validated against available manufacturers' data to ensure that throw characteristics were matched accurately. This was performed for all the diffuser types (conventional grille, laminar flow, nonaspirating, displacement) and for an appropriate range of flow rates.

The number of grid cells used in these cases was of the order of 600,000 cells. Grid dependency tests were performed to ensure that the results were appropriate and would not vary on increasing the grid density. In particular, attention in the tests was directed at the areas containing the main flow or heat sources in the room, for example, the diffusers and close to the surgical site and back table. Grid was added appropriately in these regions and their surroundings until grid independence was achieved.

TABLE 2
Details of Cases Considered in Study

Case	System	Diffuser Details	Volume Flow Rate, cfm (m³/s)	ACH	Supply Temp. to Maintain 72°F (22.2°C) °F (°C)	Supply Velocity, fpm (m/s)	Notes	Diffuser Types Used in Cases
1	Conventional	Supply and exhaust grilles: 24 in. × 14 in. (0.61 m × 0.36 m)	1500 (0.71)	18.75	67.5 (19.7)	321.43 (1.63)	Air is supplied at high level (one side), exhausted at low level (two sides)	Conventional (supply and exhaust)
2	Laminar	Entire ceiling has laminar flow supplies (20 ft × 20 ft [6.10 m × 6.10 m]); Exhausts are 14 in. × 20 ft (0.36 m × 6.10 m)	12000 (5.66)	150	71.5 (21.9)	30 (0.15)	Exhaust grilles are located at low level (two sides)	Laminar (supply) Conventional (exhaust)
3	Laminar	Array of supply grilles immediately above table (4 ft × 8 ft [1.22 m × 2.44 m])	1200 (0.57)	15	66.2 (19.0)	37.5 (0.19)	Exhaust grilles are located on one side and high and low level	Laminar (supply) Conventional (exhaust)
4	Laminar (mixed level exhausts)	Array of supply grilles immediately above table (6 ft × 8 ft [1.83 m × 2.44 m])	1600 (0.76)	20	67.6 (19.8)	33.3 (0.17)	Exhaust grilles are located on one side and high and low level	Laminar (supply) Conventional (exhaust)
5	Laminar (low level exhausts)	Array of supply grilles immediately above table (6 ft × 8 ft [1.83 m × 2.44 m])	1600 (0.76)	20	67.6 (19.8)	33.3 (0.17)	Exhaust grilles are located on one side at low level	Laminar (supply) Conventional (exhaust)
6	Laminar (high level exhausts)	Array of supply grilles immediately above table (6 ft × 8 ft [1.83 m × 2.44 m])	1600 (0.76)	20	67.6 (19.8)	33.3 (0.17)	Exhaust grilles are located on one side at high level	Laminar (supply) Conventional (exhaust)
7	Unidirectional flow with curtains	Array of supply grilles immediately above operating table (10 ft × 12 ft [3.05 m × 3.66 m]); Exhaust grilles: 24 in. × 14 in. [0.61 m × 0.36 m]	3000 (1.42)	37.25	69.7 (20.9)	25 (0.13)	Curtains on all four sides, 10 ft × 12 ft × 5 ft (3.05 m × 3.66 m × 1.52 m) high (extends to ceiling) Air is exhausted on one side at high and low levels	Laminar (supply) Conventional (exhaust)
8	Upward displacement	Displacement supply diffusers: 6 ft × 30 in. × 60 in. (0.15 m × 0.76 m × 1.52 m) Exhaust grilles: 24 in. × 14 in. (0.61 m × 0.36 m)	3000 (1.42)	37.25	69.7 (20.9)	30 (0.15)	Exhaust grilles are located on bottom of 1 ft × 1 ft × 2 ft (0.3 m × 0.3 m × 0.61 m) stubs	Upward displacement (supply) Conventional (exhaust)
9	Non-aspirating diffusers	Array of supply grilles immediately above operating table (8 ft × 8 ft [2.44 m × 2.44 m]); Exhaust grilles: 24 in. × 14 in. (0.61 m × 0.36 m)	2000 (0.94)	25	68.5 (20.3)	31.25 (0.16)	Air is exhausted at low level, 1 ft (0.3 m) from floor	Nonaspirating (supply) Conventional (exhaust)
10	Low supply/ high exhaust	Supply and exhaust grilles: 24 in. × 14 in. (0.61 m × 0.36 m)	1500 (0.71)	18.75	67.5 (19.7)	321.43 (1.63)	Air is supplied at low level (two side), exhausted at high level (two sides)	Conventional (supply and exhaust)
11	Goldman concept	U-shaped array of supply grilles immediately above operating table (6 used) Nozzles: 3 in. (7.62e-2 m) dia. Exhaust grilles: 24 in. × 14 in. (0.61 m × 0.36 m)	1520 (0.72) (1500(0.71) through array, 20 (0.01) through nozzle)	19	67.5 (19.7)	31.25 (0.16) & 320 (1.63)	Nozzle is provided via chimney and is located 5 ft (1.52 m) above floor level Air is exhausted at low level on two sides, and a ceiling level immediately above patient	Laminar (Supply) Conventional (Exhaust)

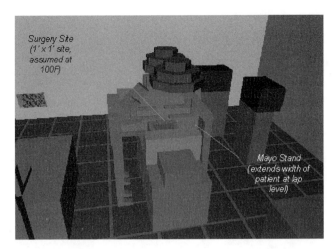

Figure 5 *Surgical site and Mayo Stand.*

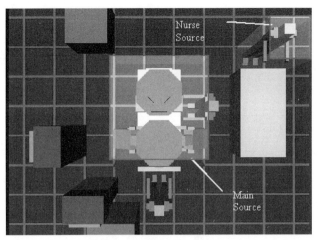

Figure 6 *Location of Main and Nurse particle release sources—plan view.*

Contamination Consideration

The source of contaminants considered in this study was squames. Squames are cells that are released from exposed regions of the surgery staff (for example, neck, face, etc.) and are the primary transport mechanism for bacteria in the OR. They are approximately 25 microns (μm) by 3 to 5 microns thick. Approximately 1.15×10^6 to 0.9 to 10^8 are generated during a typical (2 to 4 hours) procedure (Synder 1996). In this study, the particles would be tracked to see how many of these particles hit the back table (shown in Figure 4) or the surgical site. For the purposes of this study, the surgical site was considered as a 1 ft $\times$ 1 ft (0.3 m $\times$ 0.3 m) square where the surface temperature was 100°F (37.78°C); it is shown in Figure 5.

Obviously, keeping track of so many particles in the study would not be feasible. Therefore, a representative number of particles were introduced from three arrays of sources. The locations of the sources, designated as *Main*, *Nurse*, and *Surgery*, are shown in Figures 6 and 7. The *Main* source was intended to represent the general volume that the squames could be released from as the surgical staff passed around the table. Particles from this source were released in a 3 $\times$ 3 $\times$ 3 pattern. The *Nurse* source was intended to represent the general volume that the squames could be released from the circulating nurse. Particles from this source were released in a 2 $\times$ 2 $\times$ 2 pattern. Finally, the *Surgery* source was intended to represent the general volume that the squames could be released from as the surgical staff leaned over the surgical site. Because the particles could readily pass to the instruments at this point, the *Surgery* source/top surface of back table target analysis was not performed in this study. The sizes of the sources are shown in Table 3.

A number of tests were performed to determine how many particles were released from each point such that the analysis did not change. It was found necessary to release 500 particles from each of the source locations to ensure that the results were consistent.

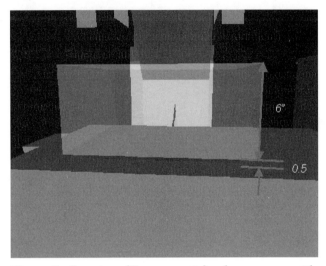

Figure 7 *Location of Surgery particle release source—side view.*

RESULTS

The results are presented in both graphical and tabulated format for the different ventilation systems. There are three potential particle outcomes:

- The particle vents from the room via exhaust grilles. In this case, the particle tracking analysis is stopped.
- The particle strikes the surgical site or top surface of back table. In this case, the particle tracking analysis is stopped.
- The particle remains in the room at the time where particle tracking is stopped (3600 s).

The results are considered for two of the outcomes, namely the particle is vented via ventilation and the particle strikes a designated target, in terms of percentages of total particles released. The other outcome is a trivial calculation, namely:

TABLE 3
Details of Particle Sources

Source	Physical Size	Particle Array	Position
Main	54 in. × 58 in. × 24 in. (1.37 m × 1.47 m × 0.61 m)	3 × 3 × 3 (13500 particles)	Centered over bed Extends from anesthesia screen to end of bed Begins at 4 ft (1.22 m AFF)
Nurse	24 in. × 24 in. × 72 in. (0.61 m × 0.61 m × 0.83 m)	2 × 2 × 2 (4000 particles)	Centered over circulating nurse Begins at floor level
Surgery	14 in. × 14 in. × 6 in. (0.36 m × 0.36 m × 0.15 m)	3 × 3 × 3 (13500 particles)	Centered over surgery site Begins at 0.5 in. (1.27e-2 m) above surgery site

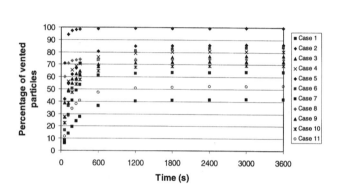

Figure 8 *Percentage of particles vented from room via ventilation: Main source.*

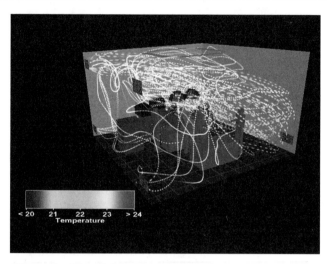

Figure 9 *Flow field pattern in Case 1.*

Percentage of particle remaining in room at end of particle tracking analysis = 100 – ((Percentage of particles vented from room at end of particle tracking analysis) + (Percentage of particles that strike surgical site or top surface of back table))

In terms of the particles that remain in the room, the analysis shows that the particles either become trapped in recirculation regions (which they may exit after very long time periods) or fall by gravity to the floor in low-velocity flow regions.

Percentage of Particles Removed by Ventilation Varying with Time

Figure 8 shows the percentage of particles vented from the room via ventilation from the *Main* sources. The *Nurse* and *Surgery* source equivalents are similar. Further, the percentages of particles vented from the room via ventilation at the end of the tracking period, 3600 s, are given in Table 4.

The plots and table show that there is a wide range in the level of effectiveness in removing the particles via ventilation. This is an expected result, but there are interesting points to be drawn from the results. First, cases that have the same ACH show marked differences in terms of the percentage of particles removed via ventilation. For example, Case 10 demonstrates a more effective removal of particles than Case 1. The reason in this example is that the ventilation system in Case 1

TABLE 4
Percentage of Particles Vented
from Room After One Hour

Case	System	ACH	Percentage of Particles Vented from Room After One Hour		
			Main	**Nurse**	**Surgical**
1	Conventional	18.75	41.9	49.7	46.0
2	Laminar	150	99.4	98.4	94.8
3	Laminar	15	77.3	49.7	73.3
4	Laminar (mixed)	20	80.4	54.2	86.7
5	Laminar (low only)	20	85.9	60.8	86.0
6	Laminar (high only)	20	83.8	72.1	80.1
7	Unidirectional flow with curtains	37.25	63.5	65.0	64.9
8	Upward displacement	37.25	74.3	77.4	44.3
9	Non-aspirating diffusers	25	72.4	74.1	60.7
10	Low supply/high exhaust	18.75	69.2	81.8	73.8
11	Goldman concept	19	52.2	48.2	44.7

results in the formation of two large recirculations in the room where particles can become trapped (Figure 9), whereas, in Case 10, the ventilation system works with the thermal plume in the center of the room in driving the particles up to the high level exhausts (Figure 10). Secondly, taking Cases 3, 4, 5, 6, and 9 as a group that adopts the same general approach to ventilation, the percentage vented becomes more uniform in terms of particle release location, though not necessarily in terms of magnitude, as the ACH is increased and the size of the supply array becomes bigger. The reason for this is that, for the smaller laminar arrays, the areas outside the direct influence of the supply have very low velocity flow fields. Here the particles tend to drop via gravity to the floor level and remain in the room when the particle time limit is reached.

Percentage of Particles That Hit Surgical Site or Top Surface of Back Table

Table 5 shows the percentage of particles that strike the surgical site or back table targets from the *Main*, *Nurse*, and *Surgery* sources. As with the consideration of the vented out particles, there are several interesting points to be made.

First, the percentages of particles that hit the surgical site from the *Main* or *Nurse* sites are low, in particular, less than 1%. This is because of the relative dominance of the thermal plume caused by the surgical site. For example, Figure 11 shows such a plume for Case 2. It is only when the particles are released close to the site, in particular, the *Surgery* source, that the percentage becomes significant. Second, ACH is not as significant in the *Surgery* source/surgical site analysis as

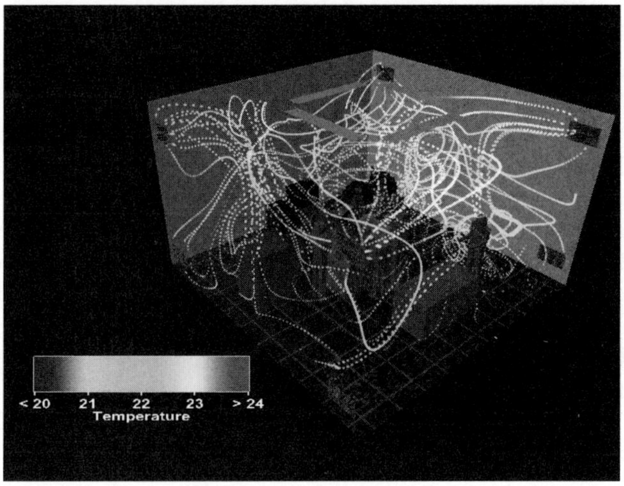

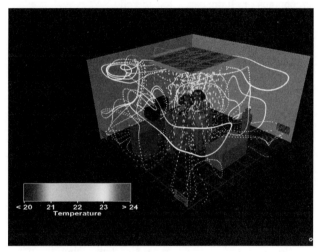

Figure 10 *Flow field pattern in Case 10.*

Figure 11 *Flow field pattern in Case 9.*

TABLE 5
Percentage of Particles that Hit Surgical Site or Back Table

Case	System	ACH	Percentage of Particles that Hit Surgical Site			Percentage of Particles that Hit Back Table	
			Main	Nurse	Close	Main	Nurse
1	Conventional	18.75	0.2	0.3	4.7	1.4	2.4
2	Laminar	150	0.0	0.0	4.2	0.1	0.0
3	Laminar	15	0.2	0.0	4.1	0.1	0.6
4	Laminar (Mixed)	20	0.0	0.0	1.9	0.2	0.3
5	Laminar (Low Only)	20	0.0	0.0	2.1	0.0	0.2
6	Laminar (High Only)	20	0.0	0.0	2.7	0.2	0.2
7	Unidirectional flow with curtains	37.25	0.5	0.0	5.2	2.4	0.2
8	Upward Displacement	37.25	0.0	0.1	3.4	0.0	0.0
9	Non-aspirating diffusers	25	0.0	0.0	2.1	0.1	0.2
10	Low supply/ High exhaust	18.75	0.0	0.0	6.9	0.2	0.9
11	Goldman Concept	19	0.1	0.2	4.6	1.1	9.8

design of the ventilation system. In particular, a lower percentage of particles hit the site in Case 4, which has an ACH of 20, than Case 2, which has an ACH of 150. Third, with the exception of Case 11, the percentage of particles that hit the back table from the *Main* or *Nurse* sites are relatively low. While there is no thermal plume preventing the particles from hitting the table, the particles only strike the target if they enter a region of low velocity flow, where the particles settle by gravity, or they are blown directly onto the table, which is the case in the high *Nurse* source value of 9.8%. The results shown for Cases 4, 5, and 6 indicate that a mixture of exhaust location levels is better than low or high only. Finally, the cases that can be placed together in a laminar flow type group, namely, Cases 2, 3, 4, 5, 6, and 9, do not show higher strike rates than the other systems. In fact, Cases 4 and 9 represent the lowest strike percentages of all the cases considered.

CONCLUSIONS AND DISCUSSION

From the above results, the study showed:

- Cases that have the same ACH show marked differences in terms of the percentage of particles removed via ventilation.
- The practice of increasing ACH to high levels results in excellent removal of particles via ventilation, but it does not necessarily mean that the percentage of particles that strike surfaces of concern will continue to decrease.
- The percentages of particles that hit the surgical site from the *Main* or *Nurse* sites are low, less than 1%. This is because of the relative dominance of the thermal plume caused by the surgical site. Only when the particles are released close to the site, in particular the *Surgery* source, does the percentage become significant.
- ACH is not as significant in the *Surgery* source/surgical site analysis as design of the ventilation system. In particular, a lower percentage of particles hit the site in a case that has an ACH of 20 than one that has an ACH of 150.
- In a system that provides a laminar flow regime, a mixture of exhaust location levels works better than either low or high level locations only. However, the difference is not significant enough that the low or high level location systems are not viable options.
- Systems that provide laminar flow regimes represent the best option for an operating room in terms of contamination control, as they result in the smallest percentage of particles impacting the surgical site. However, care needs to be taken in the sizing of the laminar flow array. A face velocity of around 30 to 35 fpm (0.15 to 0.18 m/s) is sufficient from the laminar diffuser array, provided that the array size itself is set correctly.

To expand on the issue of diffuser array size, it appears that the main factor in the design of the ventilation system is the control of the central region of the operating room. In

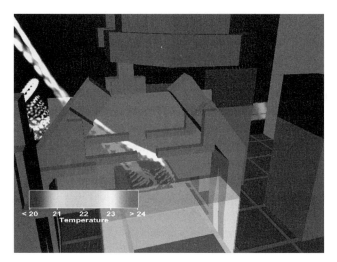

Figure 12 *Thermal plume from surgical site in Case 2 (laminar design).*

particular, the operating lights and surgical staff represent a large heat density in the middle of the room. Particulates could get caught in buoyant plumes created by these heat-dissipating objects, at which point control of them is lost. However, if a laminar flow type system is employed, the particles are instead driven by the flow to be exhausted. Ideally then, the array size should be large enough to cover the main heat-dissipating objects. This is illustrated in Figure 11, which shows the flow field for Case 9.

Further, another factor is the thermal plume created by the surgical site, shown for Case 2 in Figure 12. Provided that the laminar flow regime is not strong enough such that the particles are impinged on the surgical site against the thermal plume, a danger highlighted by Lewis (1993), then the plume should be sufficient to protect the surgical site.

REFERENCES

Alani A., D. Dixon-Hardy, and M. Seymour. 1998. Contaminants transport modelling. EngD in Environmental Technology Conference.

ASHRAE. 1999. *1999 ASHRAE Handbook—Applications.* Atlanta: American Society of Heating, Refrigerating and Air-Conditioning Engineers, Inc.

Chen, P-P., and C.T. Crowe. 1984. *On the Monte-Carlo method for modelling particle dispersion in turbulence gas-solid flows.* ASME-FED 10, 37 – 42.

Crowe, C., M. Sommerfield, and Y. Tsuji. 1998. *Multiphase flows with droplets and particles.* CRC Press.

DIN. 1999. DIN 1946/4, *Heating, ventilation and air conditioning: HVAC systems in hospitals.*

DIN. 1990. DIN 4799, *Luftfuhrungssyteme fur Operationsraume.*

Goldman, M. 2000. Operating room airflow and distribution. ASHRAE 2000 Winter Meeting, Dallas.

Gosman, D., and E. Ioannides. 1981. *Aspects of computer simulation of liquid-fuelled combustors*. AIAA 19th Aerospace Science Meeting 81-0323, 1 – 10.

Haghighat, F., Z. Jiang, and Y. Zhang. 1994. Impact of ventilation rate and partition layout on VOC emission rate: Time-dependent contaminant removal. *International Journal of Indoor Air Quality and Climate* 4: 276-283.

Lewis, J.R. 1993. Operating room air distribution effectiveness. *ASHRAE Transactions* 99(2): 1191-1200.

Lidwell, O.M. 1988. Air, antibiotics and sepsis in replacement joints. *Journal of Hospital Infection* 11 (Supplement C): 18-40.

Lo, L-M. 1997. Numerical studies of airflow movement and contaminant transport in hospital operating rooms. M.Sc thesis, University of Minnesota.

Memarzadeh, F. 2000. *Assessing the efficacy of ultraviolet germicidal irradiation and ventilation in removing mycobacterium tuberculosis*. National Institutes of Health, Office of the Director, Bethesda, Md.

Memarzadeh, F. 1998. *Ventilation design handbook on animal research facilities using static microisolators*. National Institutes of Health, Office of the Director, Bethesda, Md.

Memarzadeh, F., and Z. Ziang. 2000. Methodology for minimizing risk from airborne organisms in hospital isolation rooms. *ASHRAE Transactions*.

Ormancey, A., and J. Martinon. 1984. Prediction of particle dispersion in turbulent flow. *PhysicoChemical Hydrodynamics* 5: 229 – 224.

Press, W.H., S.A. Teukolsky, W.T. Vetterling, and B.P. Flannary. 1992. *Numerical recipes in FORTRAN*, 2d ed. Cambridge: Cambridge University Press.

Salvati, E.A., R.P. Robinson, S.M. Zeno, B.L. Koslin, B.D. Brause, and P.D. Wilson. 1982. Infection rates after 3175 total hip and total knee replacements performed with and without a horizontal unidirectional filtered airflow system. *Journal of Bone and Joint Surgery, Inc.* 64A(4): 525-535.

Schmidt, P. 1987. Air control in operating theatres. *Heizung Luftung Haus Technik* 38(3): 145-153.

Shuen, J-S., L-D. Chen, and G.M. Faeth. 1983. Evaluation of a stochastic model of particle dispersion in a turbulent round jet. *AIChE Journal* 29: 167-170.

Snyder, O.P. 1996. A 'safe hands' wash program for retail food operations. Hospitality Institute of Technology and Management, St. Paul, Minnesota.

Snyder, W.H., and J.L. Lumley. 1971. Some measurement of particle velocity autocorrelation functions in turbulent flow. *J. Fluid Mechanics* 48: 41-71.

Woods, J.E., D.T. Braymen, R.W. Rasmussen, P.E. Reynolds, and G.M. Montag. 1986. Ventilation requirements in hospital operating rooms—Part I: Control of airborne particles. *ASHRAE Transactions* 92(2).

Ziang, Z., Q. Chen, and F. Haghighat. 1995. Airflow and air quality in large enclosures. *ASME Journal of Solar Energy Engineering* 117: 114-122.

DISCUSSION

Anand Seth, Director of Utilities and Engineering, Partners Health Care Systems, Boston, Mass.: Excellent work. It has been a long time since such work was done. If the internal load is higher, would we recommend lower supply air temperature?

Farhad Memarzadeh: If the governing standard dictated that the same exhaust temperature was required, then the supply air temperature would automatically be decreased. In a general response, the important issue is control of the central thermal plume. Control would be lost, at least to some extent, if the supply temperature was not decreased accordingly with load.

Leon Kloostra, Chief Engineer, Titus, Richardson, Tex.: (1) What effect will OR lights mounted directly above the OR table give us? (2) Will airborne infection increase even with the best airflow design with the light mounted directly over the OR table?

Memarzadeh: (1) The OR lights would still be part of the central thermal plume. They would have to be moved outside of the central region to have a significant impact. (2) There may be some impact to the infection rate, but it will be somewhat dependant on the way the flow reacts to the new interaction between the OR lights and other objects in their proximity. The effect may be adverse or beneficial.

Nicholas Smilanich, President, Sensor Development Corporation, Rock River, Ohio: (1) Would model apply to VOC's distribution? (2) Would the model apply to fungus and mold also?

Memarzadeh: (1) In the case of VOCs, it is very unlikely that the surgical site would be affected. Further, there would be no deposition of VOCs in the room. (2) In the case of fungus and mold, the two have a wide range of sizes. For example, Pencillium is 3 to 5 microns, Stemphylium up to 75 microns. Here the model will be applicable up to a certain level, then larger sizes will be more susceptible to impingement into the surgical site, and deposition within the room. Smaller particle sizes will be less susceptible.

Scott M. Fanning, P.E., Principal, Fanning, Fanning and Associates, Inc., Lubbock, Tex.: It appeared from the presentation that low return was preferred in limiting infection at the wound site. Please elaborate on the number and location of return air grilles for optimum asepsis control.

Memarzadeh: The lowest infection rate of the surgical site actually occurs for a mixture of high and low exhausts, rather than low only, though the difference is relatively small. As far as optimal placement and number is concerned, further cases would need to be run to determine these values, as the sample number with regards to this aspect is insufficient in this study.

REFERENCES

ACGIH. 1995. *Industrial Ventilation, A Manual of Recommended Practice*, 22nd ed., Appendix A. Cincinnati: American Conference of Governmental Industrial Hygienists.

ACGIH. 1988. *Industrial Ventilation, A Manual of Recommended Practice*, 20th ed. Cincinnati: American Conference of Governmental Industrial Hygienists.

AIA. 2001. *Guidelines for Design and Construction of Hospitals and Health Care Facilities.* Washington, D.C.: American Institute of Architects.

AIA. 1996-97. *Guidelines for Design and Construction of Hospital and Health Care Facilities*, Section 1.4, Provisions for Disasters. Washington, D.C.: American Institute of Architects.

AHA. 1985. Steam Purity: Resolving Observed Problems (catalog number 031801). Chicago: American Society for Hospital Central Service Personnel of the American Hospital Association.

AMCA. 1990. *AMCA 201-90, Fans and Fan Systems.* Arlington Heights, Ill.: Air Movement and Control Association International, Inc.

American College of Surgeons. 1996. *Guidelines for Optimal Office-Based Surgery*, 2d ed. Chicago: ACS.

American College of Surgeons. 1976. Definition of Surgical Microbiologic Clean Air. *Bulletin of American College of Surgeons* 61: 19–21.

ARI. 1999a. *ARI 430-99, Central Station Air Handling Units.* Arlington, Va.: Air-Conditioning and Refrigeration Institute.

ARI. 1999b. *ARI 700-99, Specification for Fluorocarbon Refrigerants.* Arlington, Va.: Air-Conditioning and Refrigeration Institute.

Arthur D. Little, Inc. 1976. Impact Assessment of ASHRAE Standard 90-75, Energy Conservation and New Building Design. Federal Energy Administration, Washington, D.C. (Available from National Technical Information Service, Springfield, Va., as PB-252 639.)

ASA. 1946. *American Standard Building Requirements for Light and Ventilation* (A 53.1). New York: American Standards Association.

ASHE. 1993, 1994. *Facilities Engineering; Management Series.* Chicago: American Society for Healthcare Engineering.

ASHRAE. 2003. *Guideline 16-2003, Selecting Outdoor, Return, and Relief Dampers for Air-Side Economizer Systems.* Atlanta: American Society of Heating, Refrigerating and Air-Conditioning Engineers, Inc.

ASHRAE. 2001a. *2001 ASHRAE Handbook—Fundamentals.* Atlanta: American Society of Heating, Refrigerating and Air-Conditioning Engineers, Inc.

ASHRAE. 2001b. *ANSI/ASHRAE Standard 15-2001, Safety Standard for Refrigeration Systems.* Atlanta: American Society of Heating, Refrigerating and Air-Conditioning Engineers, Inc.

ASHRAE. 2001c. *ANSI/ASHRAE Standard 62-2001, Ventilation for Acceptable Indoor Air Quality.* Atlanta: American Society of Heating, Refrigerating and Air-Conditioning Engineers, Inc.

ASHRAE. 2001d. *ANSI/ASHRAE/IESNA Standard 90.1-2001, Energy Standard for Buildings Except Low-Rise Residential Buildings*. Atlanta: American Society of Heating, Refrigerating and Air-Conditioning Engineers, Inc.

ASHRAE. 2000a. *2000 ASHRAE Handbook—HVAC Systems and Equipment*. Atlanta: American Society of Heating, Refrigerating and Air-Conditioning Engineers, Inc.

ASHRAE. 2000b. *ASHRAE Guideline 12, Minimizing the Risk of Legionellosis Associated with Building Water Systems*. Atlanta: American Society of Heating, Refrigerating and Air-Conditioning Engineers, Inc.

ASHRAE. 1999a. *1999 ASHRAE Handbook—HVAC Applications*. Atlanta: American Society of Heating, Refrigerating and Air-Conditioning Engineers, Inc.

ASHRAE. 1999b. *Standard 52.2, Method of Testing General Ventilation Air-Cleaning Devices for Removal Efficiency by Particle Size*. Atlanta: American Society of Heating, Refrigerating and Air-Conditioning Engineers, Inc.

ASHRAE. 1996. *ASHRAE Guideline 1-1996, The HVAC Commissioning Process*. Atlanta: American Society of Heating, Refrigerating and Air-Conditioning Engineers, Inc.

ASHRAE. 1993. *Air-Conditioning Systems Design Manual*. Atlanta: American Society of Heating, Refrigerating and Air-Conditioning Engineers, Inc.

ASHRAE. 1992. *Standard 52.1, Gravimetric and Dust-Spot Procedures for Testing Air-Cleaning Devices Used in General Ventilation for Removing Particulate Matter*. Atlanta: American Society of Heating, Refrigerating and Air-Conditioning Engineers, Inc.

ASHRAE. 1991. *Terminology of HVAC&R*. Atlanta: American Society of Heating, Refrigerating and Air-Conditioning Engineers, Inc.

ASHRAE. 1981. *ASHRAE Standard 62-1981, Ventilation for Acceptable Indoor Air Quality*. Atlanta: American Society of Heating, Refrigerating and Air-Conditioning Engineers, Inc.

ASHRAE. 1977. *ASHRAE Standard 90-75, Energy Conservation in New Building Design* (Section 12). New York: American Society of Heating, Refrigerating and Air-Conditioning Engineers, Inc.

ASHRAE. 1976. *ASHRAE Standard 52-76, Method of Testing Air-Cleaning Devices Used in General Ventilation for Removing Particulate Matter*. New York: American Society of Heating, Refrigerating and Air-Conditioning Engineers, Inc.

ASHRAE. 1974. *ASHRAE Standard 55-74, Thermal Environmental Conditions for Human Occupancy*. New York: American Society of Heating, Refrigerating and Air-Conditioning Engineers, Inc.

ASPE. 1994. *ASPE Data Book*, Chapter 28, Water Treatment. Westlake, Calif.: American Society of Plumbing Engineers.

ASTM. 2000. *D1356-00a, Standard Terminology Relating to Sampling and Analysis of Atmospheres*. West Conshohocken, Penn.: ASTM International.

Balaras, C.A., et al. 2002. HVAC systems and indoor conditions in hellenic hospital operating rooms. *ASHRAE Transactions* 108(2): 23-37.

Banks, R.S. (ed.). 1978. Hospital ventilation standards and energy conservation. *Proceedings of the 1978 International Working Conference*. Lawrence Berkeley Laboratory, Berkeley, Calif.

Bartley, J.M. 2000. *APIC State-of-the-Art Report: The Role of Infection Control During Construction in Healthcare Facilities*. Washington, D.C.: Association for Professionals in Infection Control and Epidemiology, Inc.

BOCA. 1977. *Model Code for Energy Conservation in New Building Construction*. Building Officials and Code Administrators International, Inc. (BOCA), International Conference of Building Officials (ICBO), National Conference of States on Building Codes and Standards, Inc. (NCSBCS), and Southern Building Code Congress International, Inc. (SBCCI) for U.S. Department of Energy, Washington, D.C. (Available from National Technical Information Service, Springfield, Va., as SAN/1230-l.)

BOCA. 1975. *The BOCA Basic Building Code*, 6th ed. Chicago: Building Officials and Code Administrators International, Inc.

Bregande, B. 1974. Major Issues in Construction and Design. In *Ambulatory Surgical Centers: Development and Management*. T.T. Donovan, ed., pp. 47–57. Germantown, Md: Aspen Systems Corp.

Brosseau, L.M., et al. 2000a. Methods and criteria for cleaning contaminated ducts and air-handling equipment. *ASHRAE Transactions* 106(1): 188-199.

Brosseau, L.M. et al. 2000b. Duct cleaning: A review of associated health effects and results of company and expert survey. *ASHRAE Transactions* 106(1): 180-187.

Butkus, A. S., D. L. Doyle, J. O'Brien Gibbons, and L.V. Wilson. 1999. *Grumman/Butkus Bulletin* (September).

Carlson, N.G., and A.J. Streifel. 1996. Quality Assurance Methods Used During Remediation of Fiberglass Lined Duct Work with Fungal Contamination. Presented at the American Industrial Hygiene Conference and Exposition (Washington, D.C.). Unpublished.

Carrier. 1997. *Light and Heavy Commercial Products and Systems Catalog.* Carrier Corporation, Syracuse, N.Y.

CDC. 2001. Draft Guideline for Environmental Infection Control in Healthcare Facilities. Atlanta: Centers for Disease Control and Prevention.

CDC. 1999. *Biosafety in Microbiological and Biomedical Laboratories,* 4th ed. Washington, D.C.: National Institutes of Health and Centers for Disease Control and Prevention.

CDC. 1999. *Bioterrorism Readiness Plan: A Template for Healthcare Facilities.* Atlanta: Centers for Disease Control and Prevention.

CDC. 1994. Guidelines for Preventing the Transmission of Mycobacterium Tuberculosis in Health-Care Facilities. *MMWR Recommendations and Reports* 43(RR-13), October 28. U.S. Department of Health and Human Services, Public Health Service. Atlanta: Centers for Disease Control and Prevention.

CDC. 1994. Guidelines for Preventing Transmission of Mycobacterium Tuberculosis in Health-Care Settings. *Morbidity Mortality Weekly Report* 43 (RR-13). Atlanta: Centers for Disease Control and Prevention.

Coogan, J.J. 1996. Effects of surrounding spaces on rooms pressurized by differential flow control. *ASHRAE Transactions* 102(1): 18-25.

Davis, J.R. 1998. Avoiding litigation arising from IAQ complaints. *Heating/Piping/Air Conditioning* 70(10): 89–92.

Department of the Air Force. 1967. *Facility Design and Planning: Engineering Weather Data* (AFM-88-8). Washington, D.C.

DHEW. 1979. *Minimum Requirements of Construction and Equipment for Hospital and Medical Facilities* (DHEW Publication No. (BRA) 79-14500). Washington, D.C.: U.S. Department of Health, Education, and Welfare, Health Resources Administration,

DIN. 1999. DIN 1946/4, *Ventilation and Air Conditioning—Part 4: Ventilation in Hospitals.* Berlin: Deutsches Institut fur Normung.

Donaldson, B., and B. Nagengast. 1994 *Heat and Cold: Mastering the Great Indoors.* Atlanta: American Society of Heating, Refrigerating and Air-Conditioning Engineers, Inc.

Dorland's Illustrated Medical Dictionary, 29th ed. 2000. Philadelphia: W.B. Saunders Co.

Dupont, P. 1999. Air Distribution Systems. In *A Practical Guide to Ventilation Practices and Systems for Existing Buildings. HPAC Engineering Supplement—Contracting Business,* April/May.

DuPont, P. 2000. Chilled Water Plants, Chapter 5.4. In *Handbook of Facilities Engineering and Management for Institutional, Commercial and Industrial Buildings,* A. Seth et al. (eds.) New York: McGraw-Hill.

Edgerton, S.A., D.V. Kenny, and D.W. Joseph. 1989. Determination of amines in the indoor air from steam humidification. *Environmental Science & Technology* 23(4).

Elovitz, K.E. 1993. Should engineers notify occupants about chemicals in steam? *Consulting-Specifying Engineer* (September).

Farnsworth Group. 2001. Energy Analysis: Genesis Health Care Facility East and West Campus, Davenport, IA. St. Louis: Farnsworth Group.

FEMA. 1984. *Hospital Emergency Department Management of Radiation Accidents.* Washington, D.C.: Federal Emergency Management Agency.

Ferguson, K. 2000. Chapter 9.6 in *Handbook of Facilities Engineering and Management for Commercial, Institutional and Industrial Buildings,* A. Seth et al. (eds.). New York: McGraw-Hill.

Garay, P.N., and F.M. Cohn. 1992. *High-Quality Industrial Water Management Manual.* Lilburn, Ga.: The Fairmont Press.

Garner, J.S. 1996. Guideline for isolation precautions in hospitals. *Infection Control & Hospital Epidemiology* 17(1): 53–80.

Grattan, D.A., M.E. Koutek, and S.A. Russum. 1989. Amine levels in steam-humidified room air. *Engineered Systems* (September/October).

Hakbaz, M., and M. Martyak. 2000. *Healthcare Facilities Management Series: Unleashing the Potential of the Facility Condition Assessment Using Web Technology.* Chicago: American Society for Healthcare Engineering.

Hambraeus, A. 1988. Aerobiology in the operating room—A review. *Journal of Hospital Infection.*

Harteen, B.T., S. Blake, and W. Hughes. 2000. Chapters 7.1.1 and 7.1.2 in *Handbook of Facilities Engineering and Management for Commercial, Institutional and Industrial Buildings*, A. Seth et al. (eds.). New York: McGraw-Hill.

Hayden, C.S., et al. 1998. Air Volume Migration from Negative Pressure Isolation Rooms During Entry/Exit. *Applied Occupational and Environmental Hygiene* 13(7): 518–527.

Hayden, C.S., and P.A. Jensen. 1996. Isolation Rooms—Effective Economical Achievement and Maintenance of Negative Air Pressure. Report No. ECTB 212-05d. U.S. Department of Health and Human Services, Public Health Service, Centers for Disease Control and Prevention, National Institute for Occupational Safety and Health, Washington, D.C. (Also in *Health Care Facilities Management,* January 1997.)

Heirholzer, Jr., W.J. 1993. Workshop on Engineering Controls for Preventing Airborne Infections in Workers in Health Care and Related Facilities. DHHS Publication No. (NIOSH) 94-106. U.S. Department of Health and Human Services, Washington, D.C.

Hermans, R.D. 2000. Health care facility design manual—Room design. *ASHRAE Transactions* 106(2): 762-767.

Hermans, R.D., and A.J. Streifel. 1993. Ventilation Designs. In *Proceedings of the Workshop on Engineering Controls for Preventing Airborne Infections in Workers in Health Care and Related Facilities*, DHHS (NIOSH) Publication No. 94-106. Beirbaum, P.J., and M. Lippmann (eds.). U.S. Department of Health and Human Services, Washington, D.C.

Hospital Infection Control Practices Advisory Committee. 1996. Recommendations for isolation precautions in hospitals. *American Journal of Infection Control* 24: 24-52.

Howorth, F.H. 1985. Prevention of airborne infection during surgery. *ASHRAE Transactions* 91(1B): 291-304.

IEEE. 1992. Standard 519, *Recommended Practices and Requirements for Harmonic Control In Electric Power Systems.* New York: Institute of Electrical and Electronics Engineers, Inc.

ISO. 1994. EN 7730, *Moderate Thermal Environments—Determination of the PMV and PPD Indices and Specification of the Conditions for Thermal Comfort,* 2d ed. (Ref. No. ISO 7730:1994(E)). Geneva: International Standards Organization.

JCAHO. 2002. *Joint Commission Accreditation Manual for Hospitals.* Oakbrook Terrace, Ill.: Joint Commission on Accreditation of Healthcare Organizations.

JCAHO. 2000. *Comprehensive Accreditation Manual for Hospitals--The Official Handbook* (Standard EC.1.4. Intent—Item 1). Oakbrook Terrace, Ill.: Joint Commission on Accreditation of Healthcare Organizations.

JCAHO. 1997. *Hospital Accreditation Standards. Overview.* Oakbrook Terrace, Ill.: Joint Commission on Accreditation of Healthcare Organizations.

Klauss, A.K., et al. 1970. History of the changing concepts in ventilation requirements. *ASHRAE Journal* 12(6): 51-55.

Kowalski, W., and W. Bahnfleth. 1998. Airborne Respiratory Diseases and Mechanical Systems for Control of Microbes. *Heating/Piping/Air Conditioning* 70(7).

Kowalski, W.J., W.P. Bahnfleth, and T.S. Whittam. 1999. Filtration of airborne microorganisms: Modeling and prediction. *ASHRAE Transactions* 105(2): 4-17.

Kuehn, T.J., et al. 1996. Identification of contaminants, exposures, effects, and control options for construction renovation activities. *ASHRAE Transactions* 102(2): 89-101.

Kusuda, T. 1976. Control of ventilation to conserve energy while maintaining acceptable indoor air quality. *ASHRAE Transactions* 82(1): 1169-1181.

Laufman, H. 1999. Surgeons' requirements for OR air quality. Unreviewed paper presented to SP 91 by the author.

Laufman, H. 1994. Streamlining environmental safety in the operating room: A common bond between surgeons and hospital engineers. ASHE HealthCare Facility Management Series, December.

Laurel, V.L., et al. 1999. Pseudoepidemic of *Aspergillus nigeri* infections traced to specimen contamination in the microbiology laboratory. *Journal of Clinical Microbiology* 37(5): 1612–1616.

Levin, H. Commissioning: Life cycle design perspective. In *Proceedings of the Fifth National Conference on Building Commissioning* (Huntington Beach, Calif.). Portland, Ore.: Portland Energy Conservation, Inc.

Lewis, J.R. 1993. Operating room air distribution effectiveness. *ASHRAE Transactions* 99(2): 1191-1200.

Lewis, J.R. 1988. Application of VAV, DDC, and smoke management to hospital nursing wards. *ASHRAE Transactions* 94(1): 1193-1208.

Lieser, K.H. 1975. Sorption Mechanisms (pp. 91-145). In *Sorption and Filtration Methods for Gas and Water Purification*, Bonnevie-Svendsen, M. (ed.). NATO Advanced Study Institutes, Series E, Vol. 13. Leyden, Netherlands: Noordhoff International Publishing.

Martone, W.J., et al. 1998. Incidence and nature of endemic and epidemic nosocomial infections [referencing data from the U.S. National Center for Health Statistics]. In *Hospital Infections* (Chapter 30, 4th ed.), J.V. Bennett and P.S. Brachman (eds.). Philadelphia: Lippincott-Raven.

McCarthy, J.F., and M. Dykens. 2000. Commissioning programs for HVAC systems. In *Handbook of Facilities' Engineering and Management for Commercial, Institutional, and Industrial Buildings* (Section 6.2), A. Seth et al. (eds.). New York: McGraw-Hill.

McGraw-Hill Encyclopedia of Science and Technology. 1997. New York: McGraw-Hill.

Memarzadeh, F., and A.P. Manning. 2002. Comparison of operating room ventilation systems in the protection of the surgical site. *ASHRAE Transactions* 108(2): 3-15.

Memarzadeh, F., and A. Manning. 2000. Thermal comfort, uniformity, and ventilation effectiveness in patient rooms: Performance assessment using ventilation indices. *ASHRAE Transactions* 106(2): 748-761.

Memarzadeh, F., and J. Jiang. 2000. Methodology for minimizing risk from airborne organisms in hospital isolation rooms. *ASHRAE Transactions* 106(2): 731-747.

Memarzadeh, F. 2000. *Assessing the Efficacy of Ultraviolet Germicidal Irradiation and Ventilation in Removing Mycobacterium Tuberculosis.* Bethesda, Md.: National Institutes of Health.

Memarzadeh, F. 1998. *Ventilation Design Handbook on Animal Research Facilities Using Static Microisolators.* Washington, D.C.: National Institutes of Health.

Memarzadeh, F. 1996. *Methodology for Optimization of Laboratory Hood.* Washington, D.C.: National Institutes of Health.

Morrow, P.E. 1980. Physics of airborne particles and their deposition in the lung. *Annals of the New York Academy of Sciences* 353: 71-80.

Murray, W.A., A.J. Streifel, T.J. O'Dea, and F.S. Rahame. 1988. Ventilation for protection of immune compromised patients. *ASHRAE Transactions* 94(1): 1185-1192.

NADCA. 2002. *General Specifications for the Cleaning of Commercial Heating, Ventilating and Air Conditioning Systems.* Washington, D.C.: National Air Duct Cleaners Association.

Nevins, R.G. 1976. *Air Diffusion Dynamics: Theory, Design and Application.* Birmingham, Mich.: Business News Publishing Company.

NFEC. 1990. Design Policy Letter DPL-90-0004: Use of steam containing amines for food processing, humidification, and medical instrument sterilizers. Department of the Navy, Naval Facilities Engineering Command, Alexandria, Va.

NFPA. 2003. *Standard 101, Life Safety Code.* Quincy, Mass.: National Fire Protection Association, Inc.

NFPA. 2002a. *NFPA 70, National Electrical Code.* Quincy, Mass.: National Fire Protection Association.

NFPA. 2002b. *NFPA 99, Standard for Health Care Facilities.* Quincy, Mass.: National Fire Protection Association.

NFPA. 2002c. *NFPA 110, Standard for Emergency and Standby Power Systems.* Quincy, Mass.: National Fire Protection Association.

NFPA. 2000a. *NFPA 92A, Recommended Practice for Smoke-Control Systems.* Quincy, Mass.: National Fire Protection Association.

NFPA. 2000b. *NFPA 92B, Guide for Smoke Management Systems in Malls, Atria, and Large Areas.* Quincy, Mass.: National Fire Protection Association.

NFPA. 1999. *Standard 99, Health Care Facilities Standard.* Quincy, Mass: National Fire Protection Association.

NIOSH. 1999. International Chemical Safety Card, ICSC:0257, 2-Diethylaminoethanol. Washington, D.C.: National Institute for Occupational Safety and Health.

NIOSH. 1996. NEG and NIOSH Basis for an Occupational Health Standard: 2-Diethylaminoethanol (Publication No. 96-104). Washington, D.C.: National Institute for Occupational Safety and Health.

NIOSH. 1983. Health Hazard Evaluation Report, HETA 83-020-1351, Johnson Museum, Cornell University, Ithaca, New York. Washington, D.C.: National Institute for Occupational Safety and Health.

NIST. 2003. Building Economics Analysis Software (http://www.bfrl.nist.gov/oae/software.html). Gaithersburg, Md.: National Institute of Standards and Technology.

NIST. 2002. *Energy Price Indices and Discount Factors for LCC Analysis.* Gaithersburg, Md.: National Institute of Standards and Technology.

NIST. 1995. *Life-Cycle Costing Manual for the Federal Energy Management Program* (Handbook 135). Gaithersburg, Md.: National Institute of Standards and Technology.

NSC. 1988. *Fundamentals of Industrial Hygiene.* Chicago: National Safety Council.

Oglesby, S., Jr., and G.B. Nichols. 1977. Electrostatic Precipitation (pp. 189-256). In *Air Pollution*, 3d ed., Vol. IV, *Engineering Control of Air Pollution*, A.C. Stern (ed.). New York: Academic Press, Inc.

PECI. 1996. Summary Report. In *Proceedings of the Fourth National Conference on Building Commissioning* (St. Petersburg Beach, Fla.). Portland, Ore.: Portland Energy Conservation, Inc.

Piette, M., and B. Nordman. 1996. Cost and benefits from utility-funded commissioning of energy efficient measures in 16 buildings. *ASHRAE Transactions* 102(1): 482–491.

The Power of Prediction. *Industry Week* (July 4, 1994), pp. 45–47.

Rhame, F.S., A.J. Streifel, J.H. Kersey, and P.B. McGlave. 1984. Extrinsic risk factors for pneumonia in the patient at high risk of infection. *The American Journal of Medicine*, May 15: 42-52.

Ricks, R.C. 1984. *Hospital Emergency Department Management of Radiation Accidents.* Oak Ridge, Tenn.: Oak Ridge Associated Universities.

Riley, E.C. 1980. The role of ventilation in the spread of measles in an elementary school. In *Airborne Contagion: Annals of the New York Academy of Sciences* 353: 25-34.

Riley, E.C., G. Murphy, and R.L. Riley. 1978. Airborne spread of measles in a suburban elementary school. *American Journal of Epidemiology* 107: 421-432.

Riskowski, G.L., R.G. Maghirang, and W. Wang. 1996. Development of ventilation rates and design information for laboratory animal facilities: Part 2—Laboratory tests. *ASHRAE Transactions* 102(2): 195-209.

Rohles, F.H., Jr., J.E. Woods, and R.G. Nevins. 1974. The effects of air movement and temperature on the thermal sensations of sedentary man. *ASHRAE Transactions* 80(1): 101-119.

Ryan, K.J. (ed.) 1994. *Sherris Medical Microbiology*, 3d ed. Norwalk, Conn.: Appleton & Lange.

Simon, J.D. 1997. Biological terrorism. *Journal of the American Medical Association* 278: 428-430.

SMACNA. 1995. *IAQ Guidelines for Occupied Buildings Under Construction.* Chantilly, Va.: Sheet Metal and Air Conditioning Contractors' National Association, Inc.

SOCMA. 1991. News release (December 16): Alkyl Amines Council Announces Results for DEAE Studies. Washington, D.C.: Synthetic Organic Chemical Manufacturers Association.

SOCMA. 1988. News release (December 14): Alkyl Amines Council Announces Completion of Studies of the Effects of Amines in Steam Used for Humidification. Washington, D.C.: Synthetic Organic Chemical Manufacturers Association.

SOEC. 1996. Energy balance sheets. In: EUROSTAT, Statistical Document 4C, Energy and Industry, Accounts and Surveys. Belgium: Statistical Office of the European Commission.

Stedman's Medical Dictionary, 27th ed. 2000. Baltimore: Williams & Wilkins.

Streifel, A.J. 2000. Health-Care IAQ: Guidance for infection control. *Heating/Piping/AirConditioning (HPAC)* 72 (10 October): 28-30, 33-34, 36.

Streifel, A.J. 1997. Recognizing IAQ risk and implementing an IAQ program (Chapter 7). In *A Guide to Managing Indoor Air Quality in Health Care Organizations*, W. Hansen, ed. Oakbrook Terrace, Ill.: Joint Commission Press.

Streifel, A.J., and C. Hendrickson. 2002. Assessment of health risks: Related to construction. *Heating/Piping/Air Conditioning* 74(2): 27-28, 30, 32.

Streifel, A.J., et al. 1989. Control of airborne fungal spores in a university hospital. *Environment International* 15(1-6): 221-227.

Taber's Cyclopedic Medical Dictionary, 12th ed. 1970. Philadelphia: F.A. Davis Company.

Trane. 1982. Fans and their application in air conditioning. The Trane Company, La Crosse, Wisc.

Trane. 1996. Air Handling Unit Product Catalog (CLCH-DS-7). The Trane Company. La Crosse, Wisc.

University of Minnesota. 2001. Construction management for health care: Indoor air quality (course material for short course). Minneapolis: UM.

USDOE. 1978. Energy performance standards for new buildings. *Federal Register* 44:68218-68220 (U.S. Department of Energy and U.S. Department of Housing and Urban Development).

USDHS. 1992. *Managing Hazardous Materials Incidents, Volume II, Hospital Emergency Departments*. Washington, D.C.: U.S. Department of Human Services.

Verdicts and Settlements: Medical Malpractice. 1999. Infection at Surgical Site-Fungus. *Massachusetts Lawyers Weekly* 2674 (August 2, 1999): 27.

Wilk, S.M. 1985. Legal Issues. In *Freestanding Emergency Centers*, P.M. Friend and J.M. Shiver (eds.). Rockville, Md.: Aspen Systems Corp.

Woods, J.E., et al. 1986. Ventilation requirements in hospital operating rooms—Part I: Control of airborne particles. *ASHRAE Transactions* 92(2A): 396-426.

Yaglou, C.P., E.C. Riley, and D.I. Coggins. 1936. Ventilation requirements. *ASHVE Transactions* 42: 133-162.

BIBLIOGRAPHY

AGCC. 1996. *Natural Gas Cooling Equipment Guide.* Arlington, Va.: American Gas Cooling Center.

Air Infiltration and Ventilation Center (AIVC). *Technical Note 5* (An Air Infiltration Glossary). http://www.aivc.org/

Air Infiltration and Ventilation Center (AIVC). *Technical Note 28* (A Guide to Contaminant Removal Effectiveness). [http://www.aivc.org/].

AMA. 2000. Policy H-130.979: National Disaster Medical System. American Medical Association, Chicago.

ASHRAE. 2002. *2002 ASHRAE Handbook—Refrigeration.* Atlanta: American Society of Heating, Refrigerating and Air-Conditioning Engineers, Inc.

ASHRAE. 1997. *ANSI/ASHRAE Standard 129, Measuring Air Change Effectiveness.* Atlanta: American Society of Heating, Refrigerating and Air-Conditioning Engineers, Inc.

ASHRAE. 1993. *ASHRAE Guideline 4-1993, Preparation of Operating and Maintenance Documentation for Building Systems.* Atlanta: American Society of Heating, Refrigerating and Air-Conditioning Engineers, Inc.

ASHRAE. 1982. Climatic Data for Region X: Arizona, California, Hawaii, Nevada, 5th ed. Alhambra, Calif.: Golden Gate and Southern California Chapters, American Society of Heating, Refrigerating and Air-Conditioning Engineers, Inc.

Bloodborne Pathogen Exposure Control Program. 2000. University of Ohio, Athens.

BOMA. [Latest Edition]. *Model Mechanical Codes.* Washington, D.C.: Building Owners and Managers Association.

Carrier. 1983. *Centrifugal Refrigeration Equipment* (TDP Manual 791-329). Syracuse, N.Y.: Carrier Corporation.

Carrier. 1983. *Reciprocating Liquid Chilling Equipment Technical Development Manual* (TDP Manual 791-332). Syracuse, N.Y.: Carrier Corporation.

CDC (Centers for Disease Control and Prevention). 1995. Recommendations for civilian community weapons depots: guidelines for medical preparedness. *Federal Register* 60(123): June 27.

Chaddock, J.B. 1986. Ventilation and exhaust air requirements for hospitals—Part 1: Standards (RP-312). *ASHRAE Transactions* 92(2A): 350-371.

Cler, G.L. 1997. *Tech Update: Gas Chiller Buyer's Guide* (TU-97-11). Boulder, Colo.: E-Source.

Cole, E.C., and C.E. Cook. 1998. Characterization of infectious aerosols in health-care facilities: An aid to effective engineering controls and preventive strategies. *American Journal of Infection Control* 26: 453–464.

ECS. 1998. *EN 1886, Ventilation for Buildings — Air Handling Units —Mechanical Performance.* Brussels, Belgium: The European Committee for Standardisation.

ECS. 1992. *EN 14449, Guidelines for Ventilation Requirements in Buildings* (Report No. 11, European Concerted Action, Indoor Air Quality and Its Impact on Man). Prepared by Working

Group 6, Commission of the European Communities, The European Committee for Standardisation, Brussels, Belgium.

EPRI. 1996. *Advanced Motor Drive News* (Fall). Palo Alto, Calif.: Electric Power Research Institute.

EPRI. 1992. *Adjustable Speed Drives: Applications Guide* (TR-101140). Palo Alto, Calif.: Electric Power Research Institute.

EPRI. 1991. *Adjustable Speed Drives: Directory* (CU-7544, 3d ed.). Palo Alto, Calif.: Electric Power Research Institute.

Federal Standard 209-E, Clean Room Environment. 1988. Philadelphia: Naval Publications Center.

First, M.W., et al. 1999. Guidelines for the application of upper-room ultraviolet germicidal irradiation for preventing transmission of airborne contagion—Part I: Basic principles. *ASHRAE Transactions* 105(1): 869-876.

Fryer, L. 1995. *Tech Update: Electric Chiller Buyer's Guide* (TU-95-1). Boulder, Colo.: E-Source.

Gershon, R.M., et al. 1993. *TB Control in the Hospital Environment.* Chicago: American Society for Hospital Engineering, Health-Care Facilities Management Series.

Gill, K. 1993. Hospital retrofit: Dual-duct HVAC systems. *Heating/Piping/Air Conditioning* 65(11).

Hambraeus, A. 1988. Aerobiology in the operating room—A review. *Journal of Hospital Infection.*

Klote, J.H., and J.A. Milke. 1992. *Design of Smoke Management Systems.* Atlanta: American Society of Heating, Refrigerating and Air-Conditioning Engineers, Inc. Boston, Mass.: Society of Fire Protection Engineers.

Lawson, C. N. 1993. Commissioning hospitals for compliance. *ASHRAE Transactions* 99(2): 1183-1190.

Lawson, C.N. 1989. Commissioning—The construction phase. *ASHRAE Transactions* 95(1): 887-892.

Marley. 1982. *Cooling Tower Fundamentals.* Mission, Kans.: The Marley Cooling Tower Company.

NFPA. 1999. *NFPA 90A, Standard for the Installation of Air-conditioning and Ventilating Systems.* Quincy, Mass.: National Fire Protection Association.

Ninomura, P., and J. Bartley. 2001. New ventilation guidelines for health-care facilities. *ASHRAE Journal* 43(6): 29-30, 32-33.

NIOSH. 1973. *The Industrial Environment—Its Evaluation & Control.* Washington, D.C.: U.S. Department of Health and Human Services, Public Health Service, Centers for Disease Control and Prevention, National Institute for Occupational Safety and Health (DHHS – NIOSH Pub. No. 74-117).

NIST. CONTAM software series. Gaithersburg, Md.: National Institute of Standards and Technology.

NIST. 1999. *Energy Price Indices and Discount Factors for Life-Cycle Cost Analysis—April 1999* (NISTIR 85-3273-14r; Rev. 4/99). Gaithersburg, Md.: U.S. Department of Commerce, Technology Administration, National Institute of Standards and Technology.

PG&E. 1999. *Chilled Water Plant Design and Performance Specification Guide.* San Francisco: Pacific Gas and Electric Company.

Santoso, S., et al. 2003. *Electrical Power Systems Quality* (2d ed.). New York: McGraw-Hill.

Smit, K., et al. 1996. *Electric Chiller Handbook* (EPRI TR-105951). Palo Alto, Calif.: Electric Power Research Institute.

Stellman, J.M. (ed.). 1998. *Encyclopaedia of Occupational Health and Safety* (4th ed.). Geneva: International Labour Office.

Streifel, A.J., and J.W. Marshall. 1997. Parameters for ventilation controlled environments in hospitals. In *Design, Construction, and Operation of Healthy Buildings.* Atlanta: American Society of Heating, Refrigerating and Air-Conditioning Engineers, Inc.

Tamura, G.T. 1994. *Smoke Movement and Control in High-Rise Buildings.* Quincy, Mass.: National Fire Protection Association.

Theory and Rationale of Industrial Hygiene Practice. 1985. In *Patty's Industrial Hygiene and Toxicology: The Work Environment* (Vol. 3A). New York: John Wiley & Sons.

Trane. 1974. *Trane Air Conditioning Manual.* La Crosse, Wisc.: The Trane Company.

University of Wisconsin, Department of Engineering Professional Development, Madison, Wisc. [http://epdweb.engr.wisc.edu/].

USDHS. 1992. *Medical Management Guidelines for Acute Chemical Exposures.* Washington, D.C.: U.S. Department of Human Services, Public

Health Service, Agency for Toxic Substance and Disease Registry.

Waeckerle, J.F. 2000. Domestic preparedness for events involving weapons of mass destruction. *Journal of the American Medical Association* 283: 2.

Warden, D. 1996. Dual fan, dual duct systems. *ASHRAE Journal* 38(1): 36-41.

Zamuner, N. 1986. Operating room environment with turbulent air flow. *ASHRAE Transactions* 92(2A): 343-349.

A

abdominal endoscopic surgery 21
acoustical considerations 101
acute care hospital 11, 15, 37, 62, 241
administrative area 21, 47
age of air 5, 7, 129
AIA 2, 4, 6, 11, 12, 32, 37, 38, 40, 47, 58, 88, 94, 96, 105,
    107, 110, 131, 159, 181, 186, 189, 197, 201, 203, 205,
    207, 237-239, 241-244, 246
air
    exhaust 6, 9, 12, 30, 103, 104, 106-111, 113, 135, 145,
        187, 189, 214, 253, 254, 256-258, 260, 261
    makeup 6, 10, 30, 37, 40, 110, 120, 121, 125, 133, 180,
        186, 240
    outdoor 6, 7, 9, 11, 14, 33, 37, 39, 48, 51-53, 55, 63,
        77, 107-109, 174, 180, 181, 186, 187, 189, 234-
        238, 240, 258
    recirculated 6, 12, 87, 235
    supply 5, 6, 12, 13, 16, 38, 47, 51, 53, 54, 76, 77, 93,
        96, 98-101, 103, 107-109, 111-113, 120, 122,
        131, 133-135, 138, 139, 156, 168, 174, 181, 187,
        199, 253-262
    transfer 6, 13, 141
air and water induction units 53
air and water systems 47, 53
air balance 171, 201, 215
air change rate 4, 5, 14, 30, 40, 110, 145, 181, 183, 237,
    240, 241
air cleaning system 9
air diffusion criteria 237
air distribution pattern 133, 134, 136
air distribution system 42, 95, 98, 100, 108
air handling 6, 139
air irritant 6
air mixing 40, 41, 88, 89, 101, 134, 135, 138, 237
air movement 3, 27, 37, 97, 99, 100, 125, 127, 129, 134,
    137, 219, 241, 244
air pressure
    negative 16, 133, 134, 145
    positive 16, 136
air recirculated within room units 33, 239, 241
air volume migration 6, 134
airborne droplet nuclei 6
airborne infection isolation room 6, 7, 9, 12, 34, 38, 105,
    107, 238, 239, 242
airborne infectious agent 1, 6-8, 38, 241
airborne pathogen 6, 7, 30, 88, 131, 217
airborne respiratory diseases 4
airborne transmission 1, 6, 29, 217
air-conditioning general building supply 5
air-conditioning process 5, 61
air-conditioning system 5, 55, 132, 145, 232
air-cooled refrigerant condensers 66
airflow direction 38, 199, 242
airflow monitor 94

air-handling 3-5, 31, 38, 40, 43, 48, 50-53, 59, 76, 85, 87-
    97, 99, 101-103, 106, 112, 113, 117, 119, 125, 126,
    133, 138, 155-157, 165, 168, 174, 180, 181, 183, 186,
    187, 189, 192, 242, 248, 253-260, 262
air-handling system 3, 38, 48, 50-53, 59, 92, 94, 95, 101,
    106, 117, 119, 133, 138, 165, 174, 180, 181, 183, 186,
    187, 189, 192, 242, 248, 253, 255, 257, 258, 260
air-handling unit casing 85, 87, 90, 93
air-to-air heat recovery strategies 187
all-air system 47, 48
all-water system 47, 48, 54
ambulatory surgery center 143
anteroom 7, 9, 16, 34, 37, 38, 109, 110, 134-136, 218, 219,
    238, 239, 240, 242, 244
arthroscopy 21
asepsis 7, 37, 241
ASHRAE 1, 2, 4-11, 13, 14, 31, 32, 37-40, 47, 59, 61-66,
    72-74, 76-79, 88, 89, 96, 97, 100-102, 104, 105, 108,
    111, 124, 131, 132, 134, 135, 154, 159, 161, 181, 186,
    188, 199, 213, 232, 234-241, 243, 244, 263
aspergillosis 7, 136, 197, 198
assisted living 16
atria 27, 115, 121, 126, 157
autopsy 25, 29, 35, 58, 105, 107, 140, 182, 238, 239

B

bioaerosol 1, 7
bioterrorism 4, 203, 206, 207
birthing room 7, 8, 247
blood 19
blow-through 91, 95, 96, 157
boiler 40, 62, 71-76, 79, 80, 82, 84, 85, 88, 92, 150, 155,
    156, 165, 174, 192, 193, 195, 248
boiler codes 75
boiler controls 75
bone marrow transplant 17, 28, 136, 159, 160, 198, 200
bronchoscopy 13, 20, 33, 35, 38, 105, 107, 145, 238, 242
building air infiltration 7, 9, 10, 12
burn unit 137, 241
bypass terminal unit 99

C

capital investment planning 160
carbon dioxide 61, 80, 81, 84, 171, 237
cast room 137
central heating plant vs. distributed heating plant 193
central sterile services 18, 23
chemical fume hood 41
chilled water distribution system 67
chiller 48, 57, 61-67, 69, 70, 72, 106, 110, 147-149, 155,
    174, 180, 189, 192, 195, 231, 248
chiller performance 65
chiller plant controls 69
clean steam 7, 74, 77
climatic effects on building systems 127

clinical 19

clinics 1, 2-4, 14, 22, 39, 61, 70, 71, 79, 94, 97, 104, 111, 112, 120, 143-147, 153, 155, 248, 250

codes and standards 31, 39, 40, 42, 117, 120, 153, 233, 235, 236

    Europe 234

    United States 234

comfort 2-4, 9, 10, 27, 37, 40-43, 54, 61, 64, 76, 79, 87, 94, 99, 100, 106, 129, 130, 144, 145, 171-173, 181, 233, 235, 236, 239, 241, 244, 246

commissioning 2, 3, 40, 45, 57, 61, 70, 124, 157, 160-172, 195, 201

    construction process and commissioning interface 167

    costs, offsets, and benefits 170

    retro-commissioning 57, 168-170

    special health care facility considerations 168

commissioning documentation 166

commissioning process 61, 70, 160-163, 195, 201

communicable disease 133, 208

communication 2, 4, 5, 19, 22, 39, 42-44, 49, 83, 106, 147, 153, 160, 161, 197, 200, 201, 203, 205-209, 235

community acquired infection 7, 10, 11

comparison of operating room ventilation systems 4, 263

computational fluid dynamics (CFD) 237, 244-246

concept design 43, 44, 87

constant volume 2, 38, 47-49, 51, 55, 56, 94, 95, 98, 99, 107, 109-111, 174, 180, 183, 185, 187, 193, 215, 242

contaminant 4, 5, 7-10, 12, 14, 27, 28, 30, 31, 40, 41, 45, 53, 54, 80, 87, 88, 98, 100, 129-131, 134, 136, 139, 151, 152, 171, 237, 244

    airborne 2, 5, 7, 9, 10, 30, 131, 134, 237

contamination 3, 7, 8, 23, 29, 37, 40, 41, 43, 60, 78, 92, 98, 99, 104, 132, 133, 137, 138, 151, 152, 158, 159, 189, 203-205, 207, 208, 236, 241

continuity of services 153

control

    atrium smoke control 126

    DDC 109, 251, 255, 256, 258, 260, 262

    electrical 150

    electronic 106

    fan speed 108, 253, 256, 257, 259, 261

    HVAC&R 164, 165

    smoke 3, 14, 27, 112, 115-126, 157, 165, 204, 211, 260

    smoke exhaust 112

    supply air temperature 112

    variable speed 180, 189, 192

control method 105, 116

control of microbes 4, 217

control sequences 111, 121, 183

controllers

    specialized for isolation room 109

controls

    humidity in operating room 47, 110

    laboratory 111

    temperature in operating room 47, 110

controls and instrumentation 3, 69

cooling coil 29, 37, 43, 55, 61, 67, 68, 88-90, 94-96, 103, 110, 112, 113, 130, 138, 139, 156, 157, 160, 174, 180, 189, 192, 240, 258

cooling generator 40

cooling plants 47, 55

    for clinics 70

cooling tower 29, 40, 62, 63, 65-68, 88, 154-156, 165, 174, 175, 179, 180, 189, 192, 248

corridor 7, 8, 17, 25, 34, 37, 87, 103, 107, 109, 110, 115, 118, 123, 133-135, 138, 144, 153, 156, 182, 218, 219, 241, 242

    patient 8, 34, 238, 239

    public 8, 34, 238, 239

corrosion 3, 66, 76, 77, 79-82, 84, 87, 92, 157

corrosion control 81

crisis room 13, 139

criteria 1, 2, 12, 31, 37-40, 42, 44, 47, 48, 69, 72, 78, 79, 88, 92, 93, 95, 96, 100, 101, 106, 107, 109, 120, 121, 124, 133, 162, 163, 165, 166, 199, 213, 214, 234-237, 241, 244, 246, 247

    best practice 237

critical HVAC equipment 8

CT scan 7, 140, 198

CT scanning 140

cystoscopy 8, 20, 140

D

damper 52, 53, 95, 97-99, 102, 105-108, 111-113, 116-126, 156-158, 169, 183, 187, 253, 255-258, 260-262

    fire 53, 117-119, 123, 157

    location in fire-rated wall, floors, and ceilings 118

    location in smoke barriers 119

    maintenance 118, 119, 157

    other considerations 119

    smoke 97, 112, 113, 116, 118-120, 124, 126, 157, 254-256, 258, 260, 261

    special requirements 118, 119

DDC 69, 70, 89, 106, 108, 109, 113, 186, 187, 251, 254, 255-258, 260, 261

dedicated equipment connection 8

delivery room 7, 8, 17, 18, 33, 131, 144, 207, 238, 239, 243, 247

desiccant system 48, 103

design conditions 8, 27, 32, 39, 64, 65, 73, 89, 213, 242

design temperature 33, 39, 72, 93, 239, 243, 244, 248, 258

diagnosis 8, 10, 12, 14, 15, 19, 132, 173, 218

diagnostic and treatment 12, 17, 34, 35, 208, 238, 239

diagnostic clinic 8

dialysis 8, 19, 140, 145, 200

dietary department 23

differential pressure 12, 30, 38, 69, 89, 94, 106, 107, 109, 110, 113, 118, 136, 154, 187, 192, 193, 195, 241

diffuser types 3, 100, 129

dilution ventilation 9, 30, 40, 135

directional airflow 30, 31, 154

disaster

    biological 203, 205-207

chemical 205-207
    evacuation 205, 206
    isolation space 30, 41, 207
    nuclear 205-207
    trauma 203, 205, 206, 209
disaster classification 204
disaster management 4
diseases 4, 6, 9, 12, 15, 19, 28, 38, 63, 125, 133, 198, 205,
    207, 218, 240, 242
domestic water pump 40, 158
domestic water systems 78
draw-through 91, 95, 96, 103, 157
dual duct 48, 49, 51, 95
dual-fuel boiler 75
duct cleaning 97, 98, 158
duct static pressure safeties 113
ducts 5, 14, 41, 42, 51, 52, 57, 94, 95, 97-99, 111, 113, 117-
    119, 122, 124, 130, 158, 168, 187, 188, 254
ductwork 42-45, 48, 55, 57, 76, 79, 85, 92, 93, 96-98, 101,
    102, 113, 116-121, 123, 126, 140, 145, 148, 157, 158,
    167, 168, 183, 185, 188, 189, 193, 253, 256, 257, 259
dust and debris control 59
DX
    see *unitary*

E

economizer 32, 48, 49, 51-53, 55, 63, 76, 92, 93, 106-109,
    112, 120, 169, 180, 183, 189, 192, 193, 254, 258, 260,
    261
education department 22, 23
elevator 25, 63, 115, 116, 122, 123, 155, 157, 200, 205,
    206, 208
emergency 207
emergency room 37, 139, 174, 181, 182, 204, 206, 207,
    240, 242
emergency treatment areas 4, 203
emergency/trauma center 18, 139
endoscopy 8, 9, 20, 21, 33, 140, 145, 238, 239
endoscopy area 8, 182
energy
    electrical usage 175, 176
    primary cooling energy 174, 180
    thermal energy usage profile 177
    unoccupied period 181, 186, 187
energy conservation 2, 37, 49, 56, 73, 77, 110, 163, 170,
    171, 173, 189, 192, 193, 235, 241
energy costs 67, 95, 147, 149, 179-181, 189, 231, 232
energy recovery 165, 188
energy wheel 104
engineered smoke control 27, 112, 119
engineered smoke evacuation 3, 115
engineering and maintenance 24
environmental control 3, 25, 27, 28, 38, 41, 49, 129, 233,
    241
epidemiology 6, 9, 58

equipment
    medical 8, 9, 25, 39, 42, 43, 168, 213, 214
equipment heat gains 4, 144, 214
equipment interface 44
equipment load 39, 64, 133, 138, 213
equipment redundancy and service continuity 39
esophagoscopy 20
evaporative condensers 66
exam room 9, 13, 143, 144, 145, 182
exfiltration 6, 7, 9, 12, 37, 110, 134, 241, 242
exhaust air 12
exhaust of contaminants and odors 41
existing facilities 2, 38, 53, 57, 195, 241
exposure classifications 29

F

facility 2, 129
facility descriptions 3
fan coil unit 76, 102
fan tracking 111
fan-powered boxes 49
fan-powered terminal unit 99, 160
film processing area 141
filter 5, 8, 9, 16, 17, 29-31, 37, 38, 40, 43, 48, 51-55, 59, 60,
    79-81, 85, 88, 89, 91-94, 96, 103, 129-132, 136, 139,
    140, 148, 153, 155, 157, 159, 160, 189, 198-200, 208,
    211, 236, 237, 240-242, 249, 251, 255, 257, 258, 260,
    262
filtration 1, 2, 9, 30-32, 40, 41, 45, 47, 48, 51-53, 55-59, 79,
    87, 94, 130-132, 137, 138, 144, 145, 154, 157, 159,
    198, 199, 204, 209, 211
financing 195
fire alarm system 113, 116-120, 126, 154, 165
flexibility for future changes 43
flow diagram 164, 190, 191, 194
freestanding birthing center 144
freestanding emergency clinic 9
freestanding emergency facility 144
freeze considerations 89, 90
freeze protection 40, 76, 88, 90, 112, 117, 156, 254, 256,
    258, 260, 261
    cooling coil 112
fuel choices 64
fungi 6, 7, 10, 12, 29, 31, 97, 132, 198, 219

G

galvanic corrosion 81
gastrointestinal 19, 20, 133

H

hazard control 27, 30
health 10, 19, 27, 48, 88, 106, 121, 147, 168, 201, 205, 213
health and life safety 125
health care facility 1, 19, 28-30, 32, 92, 94, 95, 97, 98, 101,
    153, 154, 155, 158, 170, 173, 174, 180, 181, 186, 192,
    195, 214, 215

heat recovery 4, 32, 37, 48, 54, 75, 110, 145, 187-189, 240, 253, 255, 257

heat rejection device 61, 62

heating 1, 3-6, 13, 24, 32, 37, 38, 40, 47, 48, 51, 52, 54, 55, 61, 71-78, 80, 81, 85, 89, 90, 95, 96, 98-101, 104, 105, 108, 112, 130, 131, 133, 136-138, 156, 161, 165, 174, 179-181, 186, 188, 189, 192, 193, 199, 205, 213- 215, 232, 234, 240-242, 246-248, 253, 256-258, 262

 process heating system 3

heating and cooling coils 89

heating plant 72, 73, 192

hematology 9, 10, 19, 136, 141

HEPA 16

HEPA filter 5, 9, 17, 31, 37, 38, 136, 140, 159, 199, 200, 240-242

high-purity water aggressiveness 80

hospital (institution) 1-7, 9-13, 15, 17-25, 28, 32, 41, 47, 48, 53, 57, 58, 61, 62, 71-75, 77-79, 88, 94, 97, 98, 105- 112, 115-117, 120, 125-127, 131, 132, 137, 139, 140, 143-147, 149, 153, 158, 159, 164, 173-177, 179, 183, 189, 192, 197, 200, 201, 203-211, 234, 237, 239, 240, 241, 243, 247, 248, 250

hospital additional equipment
 on emergency power 248

hospital systems on emergency power 247

hot water 4, 40, 48, 49, 53-55, 71, 72, 74, 76-78, 89, 90, 98, 153, 189, 192-194, 209, 211, 248, 253, 255, 259

hot water demand 78, 79

humidifier 29, 43, 71, 74, 79, 82, 85, 88, 92, 93, 96, 97, 103, 111, 131, 138, 141, 254-258, 260- 262

HVAC 1-5, 8, 9, 27-32, 37- 40, 42-45, 47, 48, 57, 58, 65, 66, 74, 78, 79, 87-89, 97, 102, 104, 105, 111, 115-117, 119, 122, 123, 133, 134, 138, 139, 143, 148, 149, 155- 159, 162-164, 165, 171, 172, 174, 181, 195, 215, 217, 219, 231-233, 235, 239, 240, 241, 243, 247

HVAC systems 1-3, 13, 27, 32, 44, 47, 48, 57, 58, 76, 77, 94, 100, 104, 112, 121, 139, 159, 160, 172, 174, 180, 181, 188, 195, 247

hydronic heat exchangers 72, 74, 76

I

imaging 10, 12, 18, 19, 139

immunocompromised host 9, 11, 12

immunocompromised infectious host 7, 9

indoor air quality 2, 5, 6, 9, 37, 40, 47, 57, 154, 171, 172, 173, 186, 236, 237, 240, 241

induction unit 48, 53, 109, 241

industrial hygiene 8, 10

infection control 2-4, 6, 12, 27-30, 37, 41, 45, 54, 55, 58, 59, 105, 116, 125, 129, 133, 136, 144, 153, 155, 159, 172, 173, 197-201, 206, 217, 218, 240, 241

infection control issues 4

infection control monitoring checklist 200

infection control risk assessment (ICRA) 58, 60

infiltration 6, 7, 9, 10, 12, 37, 59, 64, 110, 134, 137, 163, 241, 242

installation 2, 3, 43, 45, 70, 75, 77, 78, 87, 90, 93, 97, 102, 108, 117-120, 124, 129, 133, 157, 163, 165, 168, 171, 188, 189, 195, 196, 236, 247, 251

integrated design 43

intensive care
 neonatal 11, 16, 17, 101, 137

intensive care room 10

Interim 153

invasive procedure 10-13, 29, 60, 130, 146

isolation 6

isolation room 6, 7, 9, 12, 16, 34, 37-39, 41, 94, 99, 105, 107, 109, 110, 130, 133-135, 145, 153, 154, 159, 164, 189, 218, 238-243, 247

J

JCAHO compliance 153

 first response 155
 interim life safety 154, 197
 pressure monitoring systems for isolation rooms 154
 prevention of Legionnaire's disease 154
 resolution of indoor air quality problems 154
 statement of conditions 153
 utilities management 154

L

laboratory 8-10, 19, 20, 28, 31, 34, 35, 49, 57, 78, 79, 84, 88, 91, 92, 111, 116, 145, 153, 174, 181, 198, 208, 238, 245-247

 acute care (emergency laboratory) 19
 biosafety 31, 111
 blood transfusion 19
 chemistry 19
 clinical immunology 19
 hematology 19
 microbiology 19
 special clotting section 19
 tissue typing 19

laboratory hoods 111, 198

layout 3, 44, 48, 54, 71, 115, 125, 129, 155, 158

LDR 7

LDRP 7, 34, 238, 239

life safety 2, 3, 27, 28, 58, 115-117, 120, 122, 124, 125, 127, 143, 146, 153, 154, 161, 163, 181, 197, 203

life safety approach 115

life-cycle cost analysis 4, 32, 63, 64, 67, 95, 213, 231, 232

lighting 3, 11, 21, 24, 64, 88, 106, 129, 163, 165, 174, 175, 179, 180, 213, 214, 233

linen services 24

load
 diversity factor 214
 lighting 129, 213
 medical equipment 39, 213
 occupancy 213
 ventilation 214

load calculations 4, 39, 64, 213, 215

local exhaust 10, 14, 25, 37, 139, 241

local ventilation exhaust 7, 10

location of outside air intakes 40, 41

lower gastrointestinal 20

M

machine room design 62

magnetic resonance imaging 10, 12

main lobby 22

maintenance 1-4, 15, 23-25, 28, 29, 32, 38, 39, 42-45, 47-
49, 52-58, 62-64, 66, 69, 71-73, 76-80, 82-85, 87-93,
95, 97, 102, 106, 108, 109, 112, 118-120, 122, 125,
129, 132, 133, 147-150, 153-160, 163-166, 169-174,
181, 182, 187, 195, 197, 198, 199, 203, 231, 232, 235,
241, 242, 258

    construction plan review 155

        balancing features 156

        central station air-handling units 157

        chemical treatment 156

        chillers and boilers 155

        cooling coils 156

        cooling towers 156

        domestic water pumps 158

        duct cleaning when existing ducts are used 158

        ductwork design considerations 157

        emergency generators 158

        emergency recovery plan 158

        filter replacement 159

        fire dampers 157

        fire protection systems 158

        freeze protection features 156

        general personnel access 156

        mechanical room layout 155, 158

        outside air intakes 158

        pumps 158

        redundancy 158

        roof-mounted equipment 155

        separate energy plants 156

        smoke dampers and smoke control dampers 157

        stainless steel drain pans 156

        valves 159

        water heaters 158

    fan-coil units 160

    fan-powered terminal units 160

    predictive 148, 149

    proactive 149

    reactive 147

    secondary air systems 160

maintenance tools

    dynamic balancing 152

    motor current analysis 148, 151

    oil analysis 148, 151

    refrigerant analysis 148, 152

    shaft alignment 152

    vibrational analysis 148, 149, 151

materials management 23, 24, 140

medical gas 8, 10, 44, 144, 164, 165, 168, 203, 205, 209

minimum 187

minimum air changes of outdoor air 33, 238

minimum total air changes per hour 33, 37, 238, 240

minor operating room 10, 11

minor surgery 10

modes of transmission

    direct contact and airborne 28

moisture carryover 89, 90, 96

morgue 25, 140, 198

MRI 10, 49, 139, 140, 145, 181

multiple parallel chiller 68

multiple series chiller 68

multizone 48, 49, 52, 94, 95, 180, 183, 185, 187

mycosis 10

N

nephroscopic 20

noise 3, 27, 42-44, 53, 54, 62, 77, 87, 91-93, 97, 101, 102,
152, 157, 197, 201, 249, 251

noncommunicable diseases 6

nosocomial infection 4, 7, 10, 11, 29, 42, 97, 98, 205

nosocomial infection costs 217

nursing

    24-hour care 10, 11

    acute medical/surgical patients 10

    critical patients 11, 13

    specialty care patients 11

nursing station 12, 133, 145

nursing unit

    psychiatric 137

O

obstetrical suite 18

occupancy patterns 182, 215

occupationally acquired infection 7, 10, 11

occupiable space 11

operating 242

operating cost 3, 32, 138, 147, 195, 231-233, 246

operating room 1, 4, 8-13, 18, 21, 31, 33, 37, 44, 47, 94, 99,
110, 111, 120, 125, 137, 138, 143, 144, 160, 166, 167,
182, 201, 207, 236-238, 240-243, 247, 255, 263

    cardiac transplant 11

    neurosurgery 11

operating room air 4, 138

operating room ventilation 4, 243, 263

operation and maintenance 2, 3, 62, 64, 73, 79, 91, 147,
163, 171

ophthalmology and optometry 145

opportunistic microorganism 11, 198

orthopedic 16, 17, 94, 139, 159, 160, 166, 218, 237

outdoor air intake 63

outpatient facilities 24

outpatient facility 15, 73, 153

outpatient surgery suite 21

outpatient surgical facility 11, 143

outside air economizer controls 106, 107

outside air quality 40

outside design conditions 39

oxidation 80, 151

P

packaged rooftop 55, 62, 104

packaged single-zone split system 55

packaged terminal air conditioners 48, 55
particle
    infectious 6, 29, 129, 130, 198
patient
    inpatient care unit 133
patient care areas 45, 47, 49, 54, 94, 132, 199, 241, 248
patient care units 11, 16
patient privacy 42, 102
patient rooms 8, 10, 12, 37, 38, 45, 53, 76, 112, 115, 130,
    133, 167, 182, 189, 240, 242, 247, 248
pharmacy 9, 24, 35, 141, 144, 145, 166, 181, 209, 210, 211,
    238, 239
physical therapy 17, 35, 137, 238, 239
piping 43-45, 48, 53, 54, 55, 57, 60-62, 66-68, 76-78, 80-
    82, 84, 87, 89, 95, 97, 117, 140, 145, 156, 158, 163,
    164, 168, 187, 189, 193, 248
piping system 48, 53, 54, 67, 76, 77, 80-82, 84, 95, 156,
    158, 168, 187, 189, 193
plant and equipment rooms 43, 44
plant configuration 73
plant redundancy 72, 73
plenums 40, 48, 97, 98
pneumonia 12, 132
pollutant 7, 8, 10, 12, 236
pollution 7, 9, 10, 12, 59, 236, 237
power quality issues 4
prefiltration 89
preheating coil 89
pressure relationship to adjacent areas 33
pressurization 1, 6, 12, 14, 27, 30, 32, 37, 45, 47, 48, 52, 53,
    56, 94, 95, 106-110, 112, 115, 117, 122-125, 127, 136,
    139, 163, 164, 181, 183, 186, 199, 205, 207, 211, 237
pressurization criteria 106, 107
primary care outpatient center 15, 143
procedure 7-13, 15, 16, 18-21, 23, 27, 29, 33, 38, 58-60, 72,
    78, 98, 116, 121, 126, 130, 137, 139, 140, 143-146,
    152-154, 163-165, 171, 187, 195, 197, 198, 201, 205-
    208, 213, 236- 239, 241, 242, 245
procedures 232
process cooling 3, 12, 129, 144, 145, 165
protective environment rooms 12, 17, 37, 136

R

radiant panel system 54
radiology 9, 12, 20, 22, 33, 34, 139-141, 143-145, 153, 166,
    174, 181, 182, 186, 198, 238, 239
radiology room 12
recovery 4, 7, 11, 17, 18, 21, 32-34, 37, 38, 48, 54, 74, 75,
    110, 136, 138, 143-146, 158, 159, 165, 173, 174, 181,
    182, 187-189, 215, 232, 238-240, 242, 243, 247, 253,
    255, 257
relative 111
relative humidity 5, 9, 27, 30-33, 37, 39, 41, 85, 92-94, 96,
    100, 103, 159, 237, 239, 243, 244, 254, 257, 259, 261
renal dialysis 19, 140
renovation 3, 4, 45, 53, 58, 59, 153-155, 160, 171, 197, 198,
    201

repair work 3
required services in emergency and disaster 207
    power 205, 207- 209
    sterilization 205, 207-209, 211
    transportation 205, 206, 208, 209
    ventilation 203-209, 211
    water 203-205, 207-209
retrofit 45, 173, 174, 180, 181, 183, 187-190, 192, 195
return fan 92, 94, 107, 108, 122, 254, 258, 260, 261
risk 3, 4, 7, 8, 12, 17, 28, 31, 42, 45, 58-60, 64, 75, 92, 98,
    99, 111, 126, 127, 131, 133, 137, 139, 150, 151, 153,
    154, 155, 158, 166, 195, 197-201, 237, 248
risk assessment 12, 58, 60, 155, 197, 199-201, 248
room air distribution 4, 12, 14, 95, 98-100, 136
room air distribution effectiveness 12, 14
room air exchange 38, 199, 242
room design 3, 38, 47, 62, 100, 242

S

sample control strategies 4, 181
sealed room 7, 9, 12
second filter bank 94
sensor location 106, 112
sequence of operation of 100% outside air-handling unit
    with exhaust fan and hot water run-around loop heat
    recovery system
        start-up mode 255
sequence of operation of 100% outside air-handling unit
    with face an bypass and exhaust fan 257
sequence of operation of 100% outside air-handling unit with
    two supply fans, a common exhaust fan, and a hot water
    run-around loop heat recovery system 253
sequence of operation of air-handling unit with return air
    fan and air-side economizer 258
sequence of operation of hot deck and cold deck air-han-
    dling unit with return air fan and air-side economizer
    (dehumidification and cooling of all supply air with
    reheat for hot stream) 260
service continuity 39
single chiller 67
siting the central plant 62
sizing 32, 39, 40, 48, 49, 52, 63, 67, 71, 78, 93, 96, 215
skilled nursing facility 13
skin squame 13
small primary outpatient facility 15
smoke compartment 115, 117, 119, 120, 124
smoke control
    active 115, 116, 117, 120, 121, 123
    energy management 124
    passive 120, 121
    testing and commissioning 124
smoke control mode of operation 120, 121
smoke control zones 121
smoke management 3, 119, 124, 157, 165
smoke spread 115, 116, 123, 126
smoke systems
    dedicated versus nondedicated 120

soiled utility 133, 141, 144

solid organ transplant 19, 139, 198

sources of infectious organisms 28

space temperature 31, 37, 48, 49, 51, 53, 56, 99, 100, 110, 186, 187, 237, 243

special exhaust connections 41

stairwell pressurization 122, 125

steam 7, 8, 13, 24, 40, 44, 48, 49, 53-55, 64, 71, 73, 74-85, 88-90, 92, 93, 98, 111, 138, 140, 156, 174, 192, 193, 205, 248, 255, 257, 258, 260, 262

steam autoclave 7, 13

steam classifications 79

steam for humidification 3, 7, 85

steam for sterilization 80, 84, 85

steam generation 40, 71, 81, 85, 208

steam system 71, 77, 80, 82, 84, 192, 193

steam trap 77

steam turbine generator 193

step-down units 11, 13, 16

sterile 7, 9, 13, 18, 20, 21, 23, 29, 36, 41, 49, 85, 92, 125, 132, 133, 136, 139, 140, 143, 144, 165, 166, 182, 238, 239

sterile field 13, 138, 139

sterilization and humidification 71, 79, 82, 83

subacute care units 17

supply 4-6, 8, 12, 13, 17, 24, 30, 31, 36-38, 40, 43, 49, 51, 53-56, 59, 62, 68, 70, 73, 76, 77, 79, 80, 82, 84, 85, 87, 91-101, 103, 106-113, 119, 122-124, 126, 127, 131, 133-135, 137-140, 145, 146, 154, 156, 157, 159, 165, 166, 174, 182, 183, 188, 189, 192, 199, 203, 205-207, 215, 237-242, 247-250, 253-258, 260-262

supply fan 4, 55, 56, 91, 92, 96, 107-109, 111, 113, 122, 123, 183, 253-258, 260, 261

supply outlet performance 100

support services 21, 23, 144

surgery

    cardiac 110, 138

    eye 138

    laser 9, 139

    neurosurgery 11

surgical site 4, 132, 138, 139, 263

surgical site infection 132

surgical suite 17, 18, 137, 140, 141, 143, 237

surgicenter 146

swing beds 13

system steam pressure requirements 74

T

terminal heating equipment 76

terminal reheat 48-51, 95

terminology 2, 5

terrorism 203, 204, 207, 209, 210

thermal surgical plume 13

total air changes 33, 37, 38, 187, 240, 242

training 2, 3, 22, 60, 73, 147, 158, 161, 163-165, 171, 172, 218, 245

trash and compactor area 25

trauma room 13, 33, 37, 137, 139, 144, 238, 239, 242, 243, 247

treatment 3, 4, 5, 8, 10-19, 22, 25, 27-31, 34, 35, 37, 66, 79-85, 88, 100, 111, 132, 140, 145, 154, 156, 173, 186, 187, 197, 198, 203-210, 219, 236, 240, 242

treatment chemicals (corrosion) 3, 79, 80-85

treatment clinic 9, 13, 144

treatment room 9, 13, 18, 20, 33, 35, 38, 144, 146, 181, 238, 239, 242, 243

triage 13, 18, 33, 205, 207- 211, 238, 239

triage space 206

trunk ducts 41

U

unitary (DX) 48

unitary refrigerant-based systems for air conditioning 55

unoccupied period 186

unplanned service interruptions 45

upper gastrointestinal 20

ureteroscopic 20

UV 14, 31, 204, 217

UVGI 14, 31, 130

V

variable air volume 37, 47, 48, 51-53, 55, 56, 94, 101, 107-111, 116, 180, 181, 183, 185, 241

variable air volume induction units 109

variable flow system 68, 69

variable frequency drives 248, 249

variable speed pumping 180, 193

VAV 47-49, 55, 56, 93-95, 99-102, 105, 107, 110, 111, 123, 124, 180, 181, 183, 186, 187

ventilation 2-10, 12-14, 16, 24, 30-32, 37-41, 47, 48, 51-56, 58, 59, 61, 62, 64, 75, 87, 94, 96, 98, 100, 106-109, 126, 129-135, 137, 139, 140, 143-145, 156, 158, 160, 165, 171, 173, 175, 179-181, 183, 186, 187, 197-199, 201, 203-209, 211, 214, 218, 219, 233-237, 240-244, 246, 247, 263

ventilation control 7, 55, 59, 129, 197, 199, 236

ventilation design 3, 8, 16, 40, 129, 130, 133, 135, 246

ventilation effectiveness 6, 10, 12, 14, 47, 100, 130, 135, 186

ventilation efficiency 7, 10, 14

ventilation rate 4, 11, 14, 37, 64, 95, 129, 130, 181, 186, 235-237, 240, 241, 243, 246

ventilation standards 4, 37, 145, 235, 237, 240

vertical fire spread 126

VFR pressurization 107

W

waiting rooms 5, 33, 35, 206, 213, 217, 238, 239

waiting spaces 22

wash area (decontamination) 206

waste anesthetic gas 14, 37, 236, 241

waste isolation 206, 209
water activity 14
water delivery temperature 79
water heater features 78
worker protection 60

X

X-ray 13, 20, 21, 28, 34, 41, 145, 181, 182, 207-211, 214, 238, 239